Hazardous Materials Response Handbook

THIRD EDITION

EDITED BY

L. Charles Smeby, Jr.
Senior Fire Service Specialist
NFPA Public Fire Protection Division

With the complete text of the 1997 editions of NFPA 471, *Recommended Practice for Responding to Hazardous Materials Incidents;* NFPA 472, *Standard for Professional Competence for Responders to Hazardous Materials Incidents;* and NFPA 473, *Standard for Competencies for EMS Personnel Responding to Hazardous Materials Incidents.*

NFPA® National Fire Protection Association

Product Manager: Lauren MacCarthy
Developmental Editor: Jennifer Falotico
Project Editor: Joyce Grandy
Copy Editor: Carrie Weber
Text Processing: Muriel McArdle and Lynn Lupo
Composition: Argosy
Art Coordinator: Nancy Maria
Illustrations: George Nichols and Todd Bowman
Interior Design Coordinator: Cathy Ray
Cover Design: Absolute Imagery and Greenwood Associates
Manufacturing Buyer: Ellen Glisker
Printer: Quebecor/Kingsport

Notice Concerning Liability: Publication of this handbook is for the purpose of circulating information and opinion among those concerned for fire and electrical safety and related subjects. While every effort has been made to achieve a work of high quality, neither the NFPA nor the contributors to this handbook guarantee the accuracy or completeness of or assume any liability in connection with the information and opinions contained in this handbook. The NFPA and the contributors shall in no event be liable for any personal injury, property, or other damages of any nature whatsoever, whether special, indirect, consequential, or compensatory, directly or indirectly resulting from the publication, use of, or reliance upon this handbook.

This handbook is published with the understanding that the NFPA and the contributors to this handbook are supplying information and opinion but are not attempting to render engineering or other professional services. If such services are required, the assistance of an appropriate professional should be sought.

Notice Concerning Code Interpretations: This third edition of *Hazardous Materials Response Handbook* is based on the 1997 editions of NFPA 471, *Recommended Practice for Responders to Hazardous Materials Incidents;* NFPA 472, *Standard for Professional Competence for Responders to Hazardous Materials Incidents;* and NFPA 473, *Standard for Competencies for EMS Personnel Responding to Hazardous Materials Incidents.* All NFPA codes, standards, recommended practices, and guides are developed in accordance with the published procedures of the NFPA technical committees comprised of volunteers drawn from a broad array of relevant interests. The handbook contains the complete text of NFPA 471, NFPA 472, and NFPA 473 and any applicable Formal Interpretations issued by the Association. These documents are accompanied by explanatory commentary and other supplementary materials.

The commentary and supplementary materials in this handbook are not a part of NFPA 471, NFPA 472, and NFPA 473 and do not constitute Formal Interpretations of the NFPA (which can be obtained only through requests processed by the responsible technical committees in accordance with the published procedures of the NFPA). The commentary and supplementary materials, therefore, solely reflect the personal opinions of the editor or other contributors and do not necessarily represent the official position of the NFPA or its technical committees.

NFPA No.: 472HB97
ISBN: 0-87765-412-1
Library of Congress Card Catalog No.: 97-061139

Printed in the United States of America
01 00 5 4 3

Contents

PART THREE

NFPA 473, *Standard for Competencies for EMS Personnel Responding to Hazardous Materials Incidents,* 1997 Edition, with Commentary 299

APPENDICES

PART FOUR

Supplements 353

Preface

Contrary to common belief, the issue of hazardous materials has been around for many years. In fact, the National Fire Protection Association has been developing standards that deal with various hazardous materials for decades. NFPA standards now cover flammable liquids, oxidizers, gases, pesticides, dangerous chemicals, chemical reactions, and explosives, and other NFPA documents pertain to the identification, classification, and handling of some of these materials.

During that time, the knowledge base has grown considerably, but new challenges are constantly arising. In my own experience, the changes have been enormous. For example, during my fire service career in 1981, my engine company was dispatched to an explosion at a university chemistry building. Our company was first due and, as the company officer, I quickly mentally reviewed my knowledge of hazardous materials incidents. Of course, I had not completed any formal classes, since there was no NFPA 472 at that time. I did read every fire service periodical faithfully, however, and during Officer Candidate School benefited from several lectures from chief fire officers who had completed a community college hazardous materials course taught by Ludwig Benner. At the time I asked myself, "Who is Ludwig Benner?" (See his classic work *A Textbook for Use in the Study of Hazardous Materials Emergencies,* 2nd edition, Lufred Industries, Inc., Oakton, VA, 1978.)

As we approached the chemistry building, I directed the driver to hook up to the fire department standpipe system and entered the building with the rest of the crew. We were all equipped with structural fire fighter protective clothing and SCBAs as we ascended the stairs to the third floor. Before opening the door on to the floor, I stopped and noticed a vision panel (wire glass) in the fire door, a fortunate finding, I thought, since we could observe the floor without actually entering the corridor. Through the glass I could see a university campus police officer in ordinary street uniform crossing the inside corridor from a classroom laboratory to the bathroom. I was convinced that it was safe to enter the corridor and proceed to find the victim of the blast—after all, we had seen the officer operating without any obvious symptoms of distress. We entered without even placing our SCBA facepieces on.

About five years later, the fire department instituted an official hazardous materials response team and formal training. It was a home brew program, again before NFPA 472, but it was very comprehensive and recognized nationally as being very progressive. I completed the hazardous materials response training and was assigned to a hazardous materials rescue squad. One summer afternoon in 1986, we were dispatched to a possible chlorine leak—not at your ordinary chlorine installation—at the central bulk storage for a major water theme park.

When we arrived at the haz mat scene, an engine and ladder company were already present. The fire fighters had evacuated all the water rides, had cordoned off a hot zone, and were awaiting our arrival in a safe location, upwind of the storage facility. They had not attempted an entry. This was real progress.

Hazardous materials responders today are very fortunate to have credible consensus standards—NFPA 471, 472, and 473—that can be used as the basis for their training and certification. These standards are the achievement of a select group of experts who comprise the NFPA Hazardous Materials Response Personnel Committee. They represent many different interests and views that form a synergistic consensus process that has produced the best hazardous materials response standards in the world.

Increased interest in the subject of hazardous materials over the past ten years has resulted in better regulation, improved training, and more effective mitigation techniques. In both the public and private (industrial) sectors, the U.S. Environmental Protection Agency, a major regulator of hazardous substances, is enforcing its regulations with increased efficiency. In addition, law enforcement, the military, and the fire service are forging new and expanded partnerships to combat the terrorist and criminal use of chemical and biological weapons. NFPA 472 and the recently issued Tentative Interim Amendment (TIA) on chemical/biological incidents are central tools of the Department of Defense and the National Fire Academy for newly developed training courses to address terrorist incidents. This training is being delivered to the fire service in major metropolitan cities and is funded by the federal government.

Another driving force in the increasing interest in hazardous materials has been the growing concern for worker safety and health. The Occupational Safety and Health Administration (OSHA) has developed rules that help focus attention on the needs of employees and on the obligations of their employers. Labor unions and litigation have helped bring about appropriate observance of the many and varied OSHA regulations.

Concern for worker safety has also resulted in the realization that emergency responders need, and are entitled to, adequate protection against the hazardous materials with which they come into contact at their jobs. In 1984 the International Society of Fire Service Instructors (ISFSI) and the International Fire Service Training Association (IFSTA) asked NFPA to develop standards for responders to hazardous materials incidents. NFPA sought public support for the project, and the response indicated that many thought there was indeed a need for a standard.

When NFPA began establishing the technical committee that would handle the project, the Association anticipated and received an eager response, not only from the fire service but from other key interest groups, including regulators, labor, manufacturers, and educators. The first NFPA staff liaison to the committee was Martin Henry, assistant vice president of NFPA's Public Fire Protection Division and editor of the first edition of this handbook. Henry's expertise was very helpful to the committee as it wrestled with the challenge of creating a comprehensive standard for emergency response to hazardous materials incidents. The editor of the second edition was Gary O. Tokle, assistant vice president. His work as a staff liaison was credited with verifying and expanding the editions of NFPA 471, 472, and 473 standards dealing with operating guidelines and with professional competencies of hazardous materials responders and EMS responders.

Acknowledgments

I would like to extend my thanks to all those who helped develop NFPA's hazardous materials standards. I also want to thank all the committee members who volunteer their time and expertise to maintain what I believe to be the best consensus standards in the world. The commitment of both the committee members and the nonmembers who have contributed has truly been outstanding and is clearly demonstrated in the quality of the documents they have produced.

I would also like to express my gratitude to the many people who helped me with this handbook. I can't begin to list them all individually, but I would particularly like to thank the following groups: the members present and past of the Hazardous Materials Response Committee; those experts, although not members of the committee, who have faithfully contributed their expertise; all those who submitted public proposals and comments for the committee's consideration; and, finally, the many people who sent needed material or reviewed various portions of the book.

I owe a special thank you to the following committee members for their commentary and review: Charles J. Wright, Union Pacific Railroad; M. Jo McMullen, M.D.; and Gregory G. Noll, Hildebrand & Noll Associates. In addition, NFPA Public Fire Protection Division staff members Gary Tokle, Stephen Foley, and Bruce Teele reviewed several sections of the commentary for consistency with other NFPA standards. I would like to acknowledge the work of Chairman Peter McMahon, who has been the guiding force behind the extensive review and revision of the 1997 editions of NFPA 471, 472, and 473. Special thanks go to Dana Gallant, whose help was vital to completing this manuscript.

Finally, I would like to thank the NFPA staff members who patiently worked with me during my introduction to the process of editing a handbook, especially Lauren MacCarthy, Product Manager. Thanks also to Jennifer Falotico, Carrie Weber, Joyce Grandy, and Sylvia Dovner, as well as others on the production staff, including Betty Carmichael, Debra Rose, Cathy Ray, Steve Dornbush, Nancy Maria, Muriel McArdle, and Lynn Lupo. Their help has been invaluable.

In closing, I would like to repeat a statement from the NFPA President, George D. Miller: "Our vision is for NFPA to be the premier source for the development and distribution of information about fire and related safety." It is my hope that this handbook will help make the hazardous materials response teams and personnel who use this book the best and safest they can be while performing the dangerous tasks of hazardous materials mitigation.

L. Charles Smeby, Jr., Editor
Senior Fire Service Specialist

PART ONE

NFPA 471

Recommended Practice for Responding to Hazardous Materials Incidents, 1997 Edition, with Commentary

This recommended practice and its commentary applies to all organizations that have responsibility at hazardous materials incidents and recommends standard operating guidelines for responding to such incidents. This new edition outlines the minimum requirements that should be considered and specifies operating guidelines for responding to hazardous materials incidents.

The text of the Standard itself and its accompanying figures appear in black. The expert commentary and its accompanying figures, photos, and tables are printed in an easy-to-read blue ink.

CHAPTER 1

Administration

1-1* Scope

This recommended practice applies to all organizations that have responsibilities when responding to hazardous materials incidents and recommends standard operating guidelines for responding to such incidents. Planning procedures, policies, and application of procedures for incident levels, personal protective equipment, decontamination, safety, and communications are specifically covered in this recommended practice.

NFPA's definition of a recommended practice is a document containing only advisory provisions (using the word *should* to indicate recommendations) in the body of the text. These practices are presented as minimum requirements recommended by the Technical Committee on Hazardous Materials Response Personnel. The committee members have many years of experience and knowledge, and their recommendations are based on safe, efficient, and effective operations.

The technical committee members come from diverse backgrounds and represent some of the largest fire departments in the United States and Canada, as well as the various smaller paid and volunteer hazardous materials response teams serving regional areas. Other committee members are drawn from industrial haz mat teams, national response organizations, other federal government officials, and major railroads.

This document applies to all hazardous materials response organizations, not just fire departments. The committee intends that the practices outlined here be suitable for use by, and be applicable to, all organizations that might respond to a hazardous materials incident.

A-1-1 Many of the recommendations in this document are based on U.S. federal laws and regulations that were in effect at the time of adoption. Users should carefully review laws and regulations that may have been added or amended or that may be required by other authorities. Users outside the jurisdiction of the United States should determine what requirements may be in force at the time of application of this document.

1-2 Purpose

The purpose of this document is to outline the minimum requirements that should be considered when dealing with responses to hazardous materials incidents and to specify operating guidelines for responding to hazardous materials incidents. It is not the intent of this recommended practice to restrict any jurisdiction from using more stringent guidelines.

Hazardous materials incidents will differ widely in terms of intensity, duration, and significance. Every incident brings a new set of variables. Deciding on the appropriate course of action for each incident requires that responders make judgments based on knowledge and experience plus minimum generally accepted guidelines.

The purpose of this recommended practice is to help a response organization safely achieve control of the hazardous materials incident by presenting suitable procedures and guidelines.

Other helpful guidelines suitable for all incidents are available from national response organizations and training/publishing associations.

1-3 Application

The recommendations contained in this document should be followed by organizations that respond to hazardous materials incidents and by incident commanders responsible for managing hazardous materials incidents.

Most incident commanders should already have identified the primary hazardous materials fixed sites in their communities and should have on hand blueprints or site plans, along with a preliminary operations strategy, in case of a hazardous materials incident at that site.

In situations where multiple agencies may need to cooperate, prior planning, often tested with drills or simulated incidents, can foster greater efficiency and smoother incident mitigation. Local emergency planning committees (LEPCs) are a great source of information for large-scale incidents. As part of their planning function, these committees will identify other organizations and resources that can be summoned to assist at hazardous materials incidents.

1-4 Definitions

Absorption. The process in which materials hold liquids through the process of wetting. Absorption is accompanied by an increase in the volume of the sorbate/sorbent system through the process of swelling. Some of the materials typically used as absorbents are sawdust, clays, charcoal, and polyolefin-type fibers. These materials can be used for confinement, but it should be noted that the sorbed liquid can be desorbed under mechanical or thermal stress. When absorbents become contaminated, they retain the properties of the absorbed liquid and are, therefore, considered to be hazardous materials and must be treated and disposed of accordingly. *(See ASTM F 716, Method of Testing Sorbent Performance of Absorbents, for further information.)*

Adsorption. The process in which a sorbate (hazardous liquid) interacts with a solid sorbent surface. See ASTM F 726, *Method of Testing Sorbent Performance of Adsorbents*, for further information. The principal characteristics are the following:

(a) The sorbent surface is rigid and no volume increase occurs as is the case with absorbents.
(b) The adsorption process is accompanied by heat of adsorption whereas absorption is not.
(c) Adsorption occurs only with activated surfaces, e.g., activated carbon, alumina, etc.

Authority Having Jurisdiction.* The organization, office, or individual responsible for approving equipment, an installation, or a procedure.

A-1-4 Authority Having Jurisdiction. The phrase "authority having jurisdiction" is used in NFPA documents in a broad manner, since jurisdictions and approval agencies vary, as do their responsibilities. Where public safety is primary, the authority having jurisdiction may be a federal, state, local, or other regional department or individual such as a fire chief; fire marshal; chief of a fire prevention bureau, labor department, or health department; building official; electrical inspector; or others having statutory authority. For insurance purposes, an insurance inspection department, rating bureau, or other insurance company representative may be the authority having jurisdiction. In many circumstances, the property owner or his or her designated agent assumes the role of the authority having jurisdiction; at government installations, the commanding officer or departmental official may be the authority having jurisdiction.

Confinement. Those procedures taken to keep a material, once released, in a defined or local area.

Containment. The actions taken to keep a material in its container (e.g., stop a release of the material or reduce the amount being released).

For clarity, a distinction is made between containment (keeping a material in its holding receptacle) and confinement (a means of limiting the spread or magnitude of contamination once a material is released). Thus, a large fuel oil tank can *contain* its stored product, while the dike surrounding the tank is designed to *confine* the fuel oil in the event of a spill. The use of plugging or patching techniques falls under containment, while improvising a dike to direct or limit a spill is confinement.

Most containment activities are considered to be "offensive" in nature and require a technician or a private sector specialist employee with Level A training. *(See Figure 1.1.)*

Contaminant. A hazardous material that physically remains on or in people, animals, the environment, or equipment, thereby creating a continuing risk of direct injury or a risk of exposure.

A contaminant possesses some property or characteristic that renders it threatening. Inherent in the definition of a contaminant are the concepts that the offending material is present where it should not be and does not belong, and that the offending material is somehow toxic or harmful.

The U.S. Department of Transportation (DOT) defines a hazardous material as any substance in any form (liquid, gas, solid, or a combination of any of these states) that poses an unreasonable risk to the health and safety of operating and emergency personnel, the public at large, and the environment if the substance is not properly controlled during handling, manufacture, storage, processing, packaging, transportation, use, and disposal.

Other government agencies that regulate hazardous materials include the Occupational Health and Safety Administration (OHSA), the U.S. Environmental Protection Agency (EPA), and Congress (under the

Figure 1.1 A technician or the private sector specialist employee with Level A training can enter the hot zone for assessment and initial rescue. The Level A specialist in this photograph is using a meter to identify the hazard class at hand. (Photo courtesy of MarMac Manufacturing, McBee, SC)

Comprehensive Environmental Response, Compensation, and Liability Act [CERCLA]). Federal, state, and local agencies may also have additional regulations for medical waste products and other human or environmental hazards.

Contamination. The process of transferring a hazardous material from its source to people, animals, the environment, or equipment, which may act as a carrier.

From a health and life safety standpoint, contamination is one of the more important considerations for emergency responders. The importance of determining whether personnel or equipment has become contaminated cannot be stressed too strongly. Because many initial response personnel are often unaware that contamination has occurred, it is imperative that procedures be established ahead of time to ensure that proper monitoring and decontamination take place in a timely fashion. In addition to rescue workers and first responders, civilians may also require decontamination at the scene. Decontamination procedures are fully described in Chapter 7 and Supplement 10.

Control. The defensive or offensive procedures, techniques, and methods used in the mitigation of a hazardous materials incident, including containment, extinguishment, and confinement.

Control Zones. The areas at a hazardous materials incident that are designated based upon safety and the degree of hazard. Many terms are used to describe the zones involved in a hazardous materials incident. For purposes of this document, these zones are defined as the hot, warm, and cold zones.

Control zones should be established at all hazardous materials incidents. The committee has used the terms *cold*, *warm*, and *hot* to describe these zones because they are easily understood and clearly suggest the nature of the situation one would expect to encounter within the zones. The relationship between these zones at the incident site is shown in Figure 1.2.

Decontamination (Contamination Reduction). The physical and/or chemical process of reducing and preventing the spread of contamination from persons and equipment used at a hazardous materials incident.

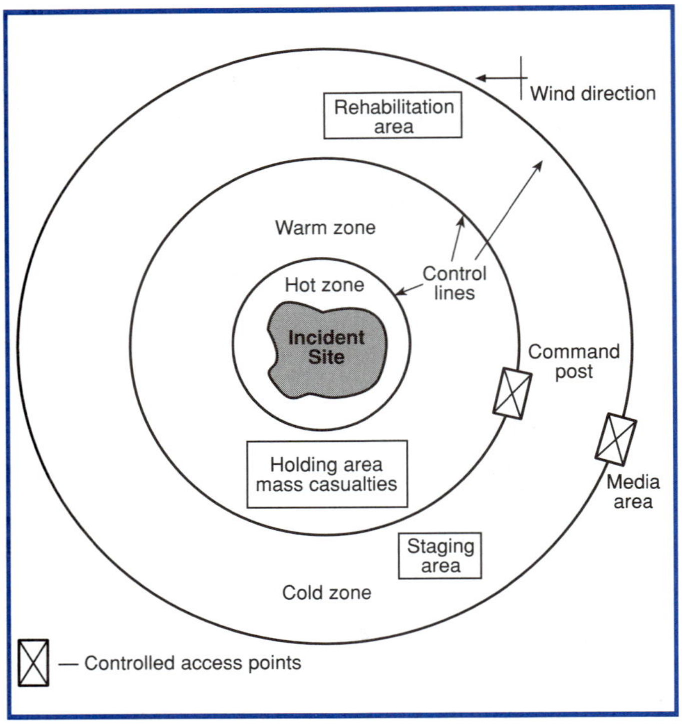

Figure 1. 2 *Control zones as they may appear in relation to the incident site.*

In the broadest sense, decontamination includes the preventive measures taken to protect against contamination wherever possible. In a narrower sense, decontamination involves the safe and effective physical removal of contaminants or the use of a chemical treatment (such as foam) that renders the contaminants less harmful.

Intelligent planning, the use of proper protective equipment, and the deployment of control zones are major factors to be considered in dealing with a contamination problem. The extent of decontamination needed is based largely on the degree of harm associated with the contaminant. Many standard hazardous materials reference sources contain information about decontamination procedures. However, the specific chemical must be positively identified first. Until this identification is accomplished, either *emergency decontamination* or *gross decontamination* may be appropriate (see definitions later in this section).

Decontamination Corridor. The area, usually located within the warm zone, where decontamination procedures take place. This area is also referred to as the "decontamination area" in other documents.

The purpose of the decontamination corridor is to prevent contamination from spreading to the uncontaminated cold zone. The decontamination corridor is usually located in the warm zone because that is the transition area between the uncontaminated cold zone and the contaminated hot zone.

Degradation.

(a) A chemical action involving the molecular breakdown of a protective clothing material or equipment due to contact with a chemical.

(b) The molecular breakdown of the spilled or released material to render it less hazardous during control operations.

Disinfection. The process used to destroy recognized pathogenic microorganisms. Proper disinfection results in a reduction in the number of viable organisms to some acceptable level. It may not totally destroy 100 percent of the microorganisms.

Emergency. A sudden and unexpected event calling for immediate action.

Implicit in this definition is the notion that the event requires urgent action for control or remediation in order to minimize the danger to people, the environment, or property.

In hazardous materials incidents, the emergency response plan is determined by the nature of the incident itself and the degree of mediation needed to control and limit the effects of the spill, leak, or other accidental or intentional release of hazardous materials into an uncontained area. For example, a gas release from a nuclear plant that could cause serious harm miles away from the actual incident would have an entirely different emergency plan than that required for a minor chemical spill resulting from a trucking accident or from a serious train accident such as the one shown in Figure 1.3.

Emergency Decontamination. The physical process of immediately reducing contamination of individuals in potentially life-threatening situations without the formal establishment of a contamination corridor.

Environmental Hazard. A condition capable of posing an unreasonable risk to air, water, or soil quality and to plants or wildlife.

An environmental hazard usually involves a release or potential release of a hazardous material that will endanger the environment. It should be treated as being no less significant than a fire or explosion, however. Environmental hazards are usually handled by more specialized workers rather than the HMRT teams and other first responders. The Valdez oil spill in early 1989 is an example of an environmentally hazardous incident that has had long-lasting and widespread adverse

Figure 1.3 A railroad freight train accident can be one of the most demanding hazardous materials incidents, both in magnitude and complexity. In this recent Montana accident, when chlorine gas leaked from five ruptured tank cars, two people were critically injured, and more than 1,000 area residents had to be evacuated from area homes and businesses. (Photo by Kurt Wilson/Missoulian/AP Worldwide)

effects despite the fact that the immediate danger to human life was minimal. Figures 1.4(a) and 1.4(b) depict another environmentally damaging oil spill off the coast of Rhode Island in 1996.

Exposure. The process by which people, animals, the environment, and equipment are subjected to or come in contact with a hazardous material. The magnitude of exposure is dependent primarily upon the duration of exposure and the concentration of the hazardous material. This term is also used to describe a person, animal, the environment, or a piece of equipment.

Gross Decontamination. The initial phase of the decontamination process during which the amount of surface contaminant is significantly reduced. This phase can include mechanical removal and initial rinsing.

Hazard/Hazardous. Capable of posing an unreasonable risk to health, safety, or the environment; capable of causing harm.

Hazard Sector. That function within an overall incident management system that deals with the mitigation of a hazardous materials incident. It is directed by a sector officer and deals principally with the technical aspects of the incident.

The hazard sector is now identified as the *hazardous materials branch,* a new term used in NFPA 472, *Standard for Professional Competence of Responders to Hazardous Materials Incidents.* The hazardous materials branch provides an organizational structure that allows for the necessary supervision and control of the technical operations related to a hazardous materials incident, including the following:

- Tactical objectives carried out in the hot zone
- Control of access to the site
- Decontamination

The term *hazardous materials branch* was selected to match the most common terminology used by response groups. *(See Figure 1.5.)* In some areas, the hazardous materials branch is referred to as the *hazard division, hazard group,* or *hazardous sector.*

Hazard Sector Officer. The person responsible for the management of the hazard sector.

The hazardous materials sector officer is now called the *hazardous materials branch officer,* a newly defined level in the 1997 edition of NFPA 472. The hazardous materials

Figure 1.4(a) *Oil spills at sea are environmentally hazardous incidents that have long-lasting and widespread adverse effects, even though the immediate danger to human life is minimal. Here, recovery crews remove an additional 1.2 million gallons from a tanker that ran aground off the coast of Rhode Island in 1996. (Photo by Matt York/AP Worldwide)*

Figure 1.4(b) *An oil slick resulting from a tanker accident off the coast of Rhode Island contaminated a 12-mile swath of ocean water, killing thousands of lobsters, shellfish, and birds at the site. Here, workers use absorbent rags to mop up the remains of the spill at a nearby salt pond also contaminated by the oil spill. (Photo by Susan Walsh/AP Worldwide)*

Figure 1.5 The hazardous materials branch, formerly called the hazard sector, team members review the tactical objectives to be carried out in the hot zone. Unlike other emergencies, hazardous materials incident management emphasizes careful assessment and planning prior to placing responders at risk. (Photo courtesy Jan Dunbar, Hazardous-Materials Division, Sacramento CA. FD.)

branch officer is responsible for managing the hazardous materials response team under the overall direction of the incident commander. This officer is a more highly skilled individual with technician level training plus the competencies described in Chapter 7 of NFPA 472. He or she is usually the director of rescue operations in the control zones. This position may also be known as the *hazardous materials division group officer* or *hazardous materials sector officer* in some areas.

Hazardous Material.* A substance (gas, liquid, or solid) capable of creating harm to people, the environment, and property. *(See specific regulatory definitions in Appendix A.)*

A-1-4 Hazardous Material. There are many definitions and descriptive names being used for the term hazardous material, each of which depends on the nature of the problem being addressed.

Unfortunately, there is no one list or definition that covers everything. The U.S. agencies involved, as well as state and local governments, have different purposes for regulating hazardous materials that, under certain circumstances, pose a risk to the public or the environment.

Hazardous Materials. The U.S. Department of Transportation (DOT) uses the term *hazardous materials* to cover 11 hazard classes, some of which have subcategories called divisions. DOT includes in its regulations hazardous substances and hazardous wastes as Class 9 (Miscellaneous Hazardous Materials) both of which are regulated by the U.S. Environmental Protection Agency (EPA), if their inherent properties would not otherwise be covered.

Hazardous Substances. EPA uses the term *hazardous substances* for the chemicals that, if released into the environment above a certain amount, must be reported, and, depending on the threat to the environment, federal involvement in handling the incident can be authorized. A list of the hazardous substances is published in Title 40, *Code of Federal Regulations,* Part 302, Table 302.4. The U.S. Occupational Safety and Health Administration (OSHA) uses the term *hazardous substance* in Title 29, *Code of Federal Regulations,* Part 1910.120, which resulted from Title I of Superfund Amendments and Reauthorization Act (SARA) and covers emergency response. OSHA uses the term differently than EPA. Hazardous substances, as used by OSHA, cover every chemical regulated by both DOT and EPA.

Extremely Hazardous Substances. EPA uses the term *extremely hazardous substances* for chemicals that must be reported to the appropriate authorities if released above the threshold reporting quantity. Each substance has a threshold reporting quantity. The list of extremely hazardous substances is identified in Title III of SARA of 1986 (Title 40, *Code of Federal Regulations,* Part 355).

Toxic Chemicals. EPA uses the term *toxic chemicals* for chemicals whose total emissions or releases must be reported annually by owners and operators of certain facilities that manufacture, process, or otherwise use a listed toxic chemical. The list of toxic chemicals is identified in Title III of SARA.

Hazardous Wastes. EPA uses the term *hazardous wastes* for chemicals that are regulated under the Resource, Conservation, and Recovery Act (Title 40, *Code of Federal Regulations,* Part 261.33). Hazardous wastes in transportation are regulated by DOT (Title 49, *Code of Federal Regulations,* Parts 170–179).

Hazardous Chemicals. OSHA uses the term *hazardous chemicals* to denote any chemical that would be a risk to employees if exposed in the workplace. Hazardous chemicals cover a broader group of chemicals than the other chemical lists.

Dangerous Goods. In Canadian transportation, hazardous materials are called dangerous goods.

Class 1 (Explosives)

An explosive is any substance or article, including a device, that is designed to function by explosion (i.e., an extremely rapid release of gas and heat) or that, by chemical reaction within itself, is able to function in a similar manner even if not designed to function by explosion. Explosives in Class 1 are divided into six divisions. Each division will have a letter designation.

Division 1.1 consists of explosives that have a mass explosion hazard. A mass explosion is one that affects almost the entire load instantaneously.

Examples of Division 1.1 explosives include black powder, dynamite, and TNT.

Division 1.2 consists of explosives that have a projection hazard but not a mass explosion hazard.

Examples of Division 1.2 explosives include aerial flares, detonating cord, and power device cartridges.

Division 1.3 consists of explosives that have a fire hazard and either a minor blast hazard or a minor projection hazard or both, but not a mass explosion hazard.

Examples of Division 1.3 explosives include liquid-fueled rocket motors and propellant explosives.

Division 1.4 consists of explosive devices that present a minor explosion hazard. No device in the division may contain more than 25 g (0.9 oz) of a detonating material. The explosive effects are largely confined to the package and no projection of fragments of appreciable size or range are expected. An external fire must not cause virtually instantaneous explosion of almost the entire contents of the package.

Examples of Division 1.4 explosives include line-throwing rockets, practice ammunition, and signal cartridges.

Division 1.5 consists of very insensitive explosives. This division is comprised of substances that have a mass explosion hazard but are so insensitive that there is very little probability of initiation or of transition from burning to detonation under normal conditions of transport.

Examples of Division 1.5 explosives include prilled ammonium nitrate fertilizer–fuel oil mixtures (blasting agents).

Division 1.6 consists of extremely insensitive articles that do not have a mass explosive hazard. This division is comprised of articles that contain only extremely insensitive detonating substances and that demonstrate a negligible probability of accidental initiation or propagation.

Class 2 (Gases)

Division 2.1 (flammable gas) consists of any material that is a gas at 20°C (68°F) or less and 101.3 kPa (14.7 psi) of pressure, a material that has a boiling point of 20°C (68°F) or less at 101.3 kPa (14.7 psi), and that

(a) Is ignitable at 101.3 kPa (14.7 psi) when in a mixture of 13 percent or less by volume with air
(b) Has a flammable range at 101.3 kPa (14.7 psi) with air of at least 12 percent regardless of the lower limit

Examples of Division 2.1 gases include inhibited butadienes, methyl chloride, and propane.

Division 2.2 (nonflammable, nonpoisonous compressed gas, including compressed gas, liquefied gas, pressurized cryogenic gas, and compressed gas in solution) consists of any material (or mixture) that exerts in the packaging an absolute pressure of 280 kPa (41 psia) at 20°C (68°F).

A cryogenic liquid is a refrigerated liquefied gas having a boiling point colder than –90°C (–130°F) at 101.3 kPa (14.7 psi) absolute.

Examples of Division 2.2 gases include anhydrous ammonia, cryogenic argon, carbon dioxide, and compressed nitrogen.

Division 2.3 (poisonous gas) consists of a material that is a gas at 20°C (68°F) or less and a pressure of 101.3 kPa (14.7 psi or 1 atm), a material that has a boiling point of 20°C (68°F) or less at 101.3 kPa (14.7 psi), and that

(a) Is known to be so toxic to humans as to pose a hazard to health during transportation
(b) In the absence of adequate data on human toxicity, is presumed to be toxic to humans because, when tested on laboratory animals, it has an LC50 value of not more than 5,000 ppm

Examples of Division 2.3 gases include anhydrous hydrogen fluoride, arsine, chlorine, and methyl bromide.

Hazard zones associated with Division 2.3 materials are the following:

Hazard zone A — LC50 less than or equal to 200 ppm

Hazard zone B — LC50 greater than 200 ppm and less than or equal to 1,000 ppm

Hazard zone C — LC50 greater than 1,000 ppm and less than or equal to 3,000 ppm

Hazard zone D — LC50 greater than 3,000 ppm and less than or equal to 5,000 ppm

Class 3 (Flammable Liquid)

Flammable liquid is any liquid having a flash point of not more than 60.5°C (141°F).

Examples of Class 3 liquids include acetone, amyl acetate, gasoline, methyl alcohol, and toluene.

Hazard zones associated with Class 3 materials are the following:

Hazard zone A — LC50 less than or equal to 200 ppm

Hazard zone B — LC50 greater than 200 ppm and less than or equal to 1,000 ppm

Combustible Liquid

Combustible liquid is any liquid that does not meet the definition of any other hazard class and has a flash point above 60°C (140°F) and below 93°C (200°F). Flammable liquids with a flash point above 38°C (100°F) may be reclassified as a combustible liquid.

Examples of combustible liquids include mineral oil, peanut oil, and No. 6 fuel oil.

Class 4 (Flammable Solids)

Division 4.1 (flammable solid) consists of any of the following three types of materials:

(a) Wetted explosives — explosives wetted with sufficient water, alcohol, or plasticizers to suppress explosive properties
(b) Self-reactive materials — materials that are liable to undergo, at normal or elevated temperatures, a strongly exothermic decomposition caused by excessively high transport temperatures or by contamination
(c) Readily combustible solids — solids that may cause a fire through friction and any metal powders that can be ignited

Examples of Division 4.1 materials include magnesium (pellets, turnings, or ribbons) and nitrocellulose.

Division 4.2 (spontaneously combustible material) consists of any of the following materials:

(a) Pyrophoric material — a liquid or solid that, even in small quantities and without an external ignition source, can ignite within 5 minutes after coming in contact with air
(b) Self-heating material — a material that, when in contact with air and without an energy supply, is liable to self-heat

Examples of Division 4.2 materials include aluminum alkyls, charcoal briquettes, magnesium alkyls, and phosphorus.

Division 4.3 (dangerous when wet material) consists of materials that, by contact with water, are liable to become spontaneously flammable or to give off flammable or toxic gas at a rate greater than 1 L/kg of the material per hour.

Examples of Division 4.3 materials include calcium carbide, magnesium powder, potassium metal alloys, and sodium hydride.

Class 5 (Oxidizers and Organic Peroxides)

Division 5.1 (oxidizer) consists of materials that can, generally by yielding oxygen, cause or enhance the combustion of other materials.

Examples of Division 5.1 materials include ammonium nitrate, bromine trifluoride, and calcium hypochlorite.

Division 5.2 (organic peroxide) consists of any organic compound containing oxygen (O) in the bivalent -O-O- structure that may be considered a derivative of hydrogen peroxide, where one or more of the hydrogen atoms have been replaced by organic radicals.

Division 5.2 (organic peroxide) materials are assigned to one of the following seven types:

Type A — organic peroxide that can detonate or deflagrate rapidly as packaged for transport. Transportation of Type A organic peroxides is forbidden.

Type B — organic peroxide that neither detonates nor deflagrates rapidly, but that can undergo a thermal explosion.

Type C — organic peroxide that neither detonates nor deflagrates rapidly and cannot undergo a thermal explosion.

Type D — organic peroxide that detonates only partially or deflagrates slowly, with medium to no effect when heated under confinement.

Type E — organic peroxide that neither detonates nor deflagrates and shows low, or no, effect when heated under confinement.

Type F — organic peroxide that will not detonate, does not deflagrate, shows only a low, or no, effect if heated when confined, and has low, or no, explosive power.

Type G — organic peroxide that will not detonate, does not deflagrate, shows no effect if heated when confined, and has no explosive power, is thermally stable, and is desensitized.

Examples of Division 5.2 materials include dibenzoyl peroxide, methyl, ethyl ketone peroxide, and peroxyacetic acid.

Class 6 (Poisonous Materials)

Division 6.1 (poisonous material) consists of materials, other than gases, that either are known to be so toxic to humans as to afford a hazard to health during transportation, or in the absence of adequate data on human toxicity, are presumed to be toxic to humans, including materials that cause irritation.

Examples of Division 6.1 materials include aniline, arsenic compounds, carbon tetrachloride, hydrocyanic acid, and tear gas.

Division 6.2 (infectious substance) consists of viable microorganisms, or their toxin, that cause or may cause disease in humans or animals. Infectious substance and etiologic agent are synonymous.

Examples of Division 6.2 materials include anthrax, botulism, rabies, and tetanus.

Class 7 (Radioactive Materials)

Radioactive material is any material having a specific activity greater than 0.002 microcuries per gram (μCi/g).

Examples of Class 7 materials include cobalt, uranium hexafluoride, and "yellow cake."

Class 8 (Corrosive Materials)

Corrosive material is a liquid or solid that causes visible destruction or irreversible alterations in human skin tissue at the site of contact, or a liquid that has a severe corrosion rate on steel or aluminum.

Examples of Class 8 materials include nitric acid, phosphorus trichloride, sodium hydroxide, and sulfuric acid.

Class 9 (Miscellaneous)

Miscellaneous hazardous material is a material that presents a hazard during transport, but that is not included in another hazard class, including the following:

(a) Any material that has an anesthetic, noxious, or other similar property that could cause extreme annoyance or discomfort to a flight crew member so as to prevent the correct performance of assigned duties
(b) Any material that is not included in any other hazard class, but is subject to the DOT requirements (a hazardous substance or a hazardous waste)

Examples of Class 9 materials include adipic acid, hazardous substances (e.g., PCBs), and molten sulfur.

ORM-D Material

An ORM-D material is a material that presents a limited hazard during transportation due to its form, quantity, and packaging.

Examples of ORM-D materials include consumer commodities and small arms ammunition.

Forbidden

Forbidden is defined as prohibited from being offered or accepted for transportation. Prohibition does not apply if these materials are diluted, stabilized, or incorporated in devices.

Incident. An emergency involving the release or potential release of a hazardous material, with or without fire.

Incident Commander. The person responsible for all decisions relating to the management of the incident. The incident commander is in charge of the incident site. This term is equivalent to the on-scene incident commander.

The incident commander is responsible for the overall control of operations at the scene. The actual command of a hazardous materials incident scene, however, can change from one person to another as the incident develops and becomes more complex. For example, the first responders to a chemical spill caused by a traffic collision may not be prepared to mitigate the spill and may not even be immediately aware that hazardous materials are involved. As the responders become aware that a hazardous incident has occurred, they may notify the regional haz mat response team. The initial command at this scene was held by the rescue, police, or responding fire department officers. The command control of the scene then shifts as haz mat experts arrive and the efforts of the response team become focused on containment or confinement.

Hazardous materials incidents are not limited to a small, easily controlled geographic area. Spills, leaks, or hazardous gases can cross jurisdictions, state lines, and national borders. For example, an oil spill enters a storm water system in a city and spreads oil for miles before finally entering a river. This incident will require a command structure that can cover several locations over a large geographic area. There may be several response "branches," each covering a separate location, under the command of a single incident commander. The overall incident commander may, in turn, assign subordinate incident commanders to different support branches and even to some of the separate locations if more complex operations are needed.

When multiple agencies are involved in an incident, the roles and responsibilities of the various agencies should be clarified ahead of time. The Local Emergency Planning Committee (LEPC) commonly identifies the various levels of response and coordinates the roles and responsibilities of the various response teams and their commanders.

Some incident management systems provide for a "unified command" when multiple agencies are involved. The exact structure of the response system is less important than the fact that there is a system for command and control, everyone involved is aware of their role, and training exercises have been conducted to work out any problems. Formal agreements between multiple responding agencies should be in writing and approved by the appropriate authorities or political bodies.

Incident Management System. An organized system of roles, responsibilities, and standard operating procedures used to manage and direct emergency operations. Such systems are sometimes referred to as incident command systems (ICS).

Mitigation. Actions taken to prevent or reduce product loss, human injury or death, environmental damage, and property damage due to the release or potential release of hazardous materials.

All actions taken to address a hazardous materials incident fall under the broad meaning of the term *mitigation*. The mitigation process serves to resolve or remediate the situation. *(See Figure 1.6.)*

Final mitigation can be a long-term process. For example, after the fire involving an overturned tanker is extinguished by being allowed to burn itself out (a common method of disposing of some chemical spills that are on fire at the scene), any runoff is controlled or contained. Once the scene is stabilized, specialized haz mat cleanup personnel take over the long-term response. This cleanup can take years to complete if an additional environmental contamination has occurred. If some of the gasoline has spilled into a small lake next to the road or extensively contaminated the soil, for example, a well may be constructed to pump out the gasoline that has soaked into the ground. These types of wells and pumps can operate unstaffed for years.

Figure 1.6 *Mitigating a hazardous materials spill at a tank car accident requires highly specialized training. In the 1997 Mississippi incident shown here, responders use explosives to vent off toxic gas from the chloroprene cargo of two of the tank cars. The gas forced the evacuation of a nearby town. Fires from other materials, including plastics also on the train, burned for several days. (Photo by Chris Todd/AP Worldwide for the Clarion-Ledger)*

Monitoring Equipment. Instruments and devices used to identify and quantify contaminants.

Monitoring equipment serves several important functions at an incident from helping to determine the scale of the emergency (through measurement of the quantity of the contamination) to identifying the material involved (which in turn helps to determine the entire response plan, from the type of protective clothing and personnel needed to the level of contamination of people and equipment at the scene). Some types of monitoring equipment may be very specific for a particular hazard found in a response team's normal area of responsibility. For example, in the area of a nuclear power plant, a hazardous materials team may need a radiological instrument for detecting neutrons while responders in another area would not need such a device since they might have no foreseeable risk of radioactive contamination in their area.

Several of the supplemental materials in this handbook offer guidance on the standard monitoring equipment that should be available for all teams as well as advice on selecting the personal protective equipment that will be needed for an incident, how to establish control zones, how to identify unknown contaminants, and how to determine the level of contamination or the effectiveness of decontamination.

National Contingency Plan.* Policies and procedures of the federal agency members of the National Oil and Hazardous Materials Response Team. This document provides guidance for responses, remedial action, enforcement, and funding mechanisms for hazardous materials incident responses.

A-1-4 National Contingency Plan. See Title 40, *Code of Federal Regulations*, Part 300, Subchapters A through J.

The National Contingency Plan (better known by its nickname "Superfund") came about as a result of Presidential Executive Order 12580 of January 23, 1987, shown in part in Figure 1.7. This federal program can provide the local responder with federal assistance to mitigate a large or significant hazardous materials incident and, in some cases, provide reimbursement for local expenditures to control the incident.

Additional sections of the Superfund Executive Order cover the following subjects:

- Response and related authorities
- Financial
- Cleanup schedules
- Employee protection
- Enforcement
- Management of the Hazardous Substance Superfund and claims
- Liability
- Litigation
- Federal facilities and general responsibility provisions

Neutralization. The process of applying acids or bases to a corrosive product to form a neutral salt.

Penetration. The movement of a material through a suit's closures, such as zippers, buttonholes, seams, flaps, or other design features of chemical-protective clothing, and through punctures, cuts, and tears.

Many haz mat workers have found ways to minimize penetration through zippers, buttonholes, and other design elements of protective clothing by using tape or other means that cover these small openings. Protection against penetration is vital. Proper storage, maintenance, and testing of protective clothing and equipment must be part of a response team's standard procedures. Following the manufacturer's recommendations helps to ensure that protective clothing will not degrade prematurely. Some manufacturers, for example, recommend hanging chemical protective clothing as opposed to storing it in a box or compartment. This is because some of the materials used to coat the protective clothing materials that make the clothing less permeable will degrade in the creases of the folds, reducing the degree of protection afforded by the garments at the fold lines.

Permeation. A chemical action involving the movement of chemicals, on a molecular level, through intact material.

Note the difference between penetration and permeation: The latter takes place at the molecular level through physically undamaged material. For example, if you use chemical-protective clothing (CPC) at the scene of an unidentified chemical incident, you may discover that the unknown chemical can permeate the clothing you are using. As a general precaution, responders should avoid any contact with, or splashing of, a material until the material is positively identified.

In addition, different fabrics have different levels of resistance to chemical permeation, and all fabrics will, over time, absorb chemicals. When purchasing CPC, it is important to be sure that the garments meet the appropriate standards and have been certified as meeting those standards. The following NFPA protective clothing standards contain criteria for testing and certification: NFPA 1991, *Standard on Vapor-Protective Suits for Hazardous Chemical Emergencies*[1]; NFPA 1992, *Standard on Liquid Splash-Protective Suits for Hazardous Chemical Emergencies*[2]; and NFPA 1993, *Standard on Support Function Protective Clothing for Hazardous Chemical Operations*.[3]

By the authority vested in me as President of the United States of America by Section 115 of the Comprehensive Environmental Response, Compensation, and Liability Act of 1980, as amended (42 U.S.C. 9615 et seq.) ("the Act"), and by Section 301 of Title 3 of the United States Code, it is hereby ordered as follows:

Section 1. National Contingency Plan.

(a) (1) The National Contingency Plan ("the NCP") shall provide for a National Response Team ("the NRT") composed of representatives of appropriate Federal departments and agencies for national planning and coordination of preparedness and response actions, and regional response teams as the regional counterpart to the NRT for planning and coordination of regional preparedness and response actions.

(2) The following agencies (in addition to other appropriate agencies) shall provide representatives to the National and Regional Response Teams to carry out their responsibilities under the NCP: Department of State, Department of Defense, Department of Justice, Department of the Interior, Department of Agriculture, Department of Commerce, Department of Labor, Department of Health and Human Services, Department of Transportation, Department of Energy, Environmental Protection Agency, Federal Emergency Management Agency, United States Coast Guard, and the Nuclear Regulatory Commission.

(3) Except for periods of activation because of a response action, the representative of the Environmental Protection Agency ("EPA") shall be the chairman and the representative of the United States Coast Guard shall be the vice chairman of the NRT and these agencies' representatives shall be co-chairs of the Regional Response Teams ("the RRTs"). When the NRT or an RRT is activated for a response action, the chairman shall be the EPA or United States Coast Guard representative, based on whether the release or threatened release occurs in the inland or coastal zone, unless otherwise agreed upon by the EPA and United States Coast Guard representatives.

(4) The RRTs may include representatives from State governments, local governments (as agreed upon by the States), and Indian tribunal governments. Subject to the functions and authorities delegated to executive departments and agencies in other sections of this Order, the NRT shall provide policy and program direction to the RRTs.

(b)(1) The responsibility for the revision of the NCP and all of the other functions vested in the President by Sections 105(a), (b), (c), and (g), 125, and 301(f) of the Act is delegated to the Administrator of the Environmental Protection Agency ("the Administrator").

(2) The function vested in the President by Section 118(p) of the Superfund Amendments and Reauthorization Act of 1986 (Public Law 99-499) ("SARA") is delegated to the Administrator.

(c) In accord with Section 107(f)(2)(A) of the Act and Section 311(f)(5) of the Federal Water Pollution Control Act, as amended [33 U.S.C.1321(f)(5)], the following shall be among those designated in the NCP as Federal trustees for natural resources:

(1) Secretary of Defense;
(2) Secretary of the Interior;
(3) Secretary of Agriculture;
(4) Secretary of Commerce;
(5) Secretary of Energy.

(d) Revisions to the NCP shall be made in consultation with members of the NRT prior to publication for notice and comment. Revisions shall also be made in consultation with the Director of the Federal Emergency Management Agency and the Nuclear Regulatory Commission in order to avoid inconsistent or duplicative requirements in the emergency planning responsibilities of those agencies.

(e) All revisions to the NCP, whether in proposed or final form, shall be subject to review and approval by the Director of the Office of Management and Budget ("OMB").

Figure 1.7 *Partial text of the presidential executive order creating the "Superfund" in 1987. (Source: Presidential Executive Order 12580, January 23, 1987, Code of Federal Regulations, Washington, DC)*

Protective Clothing. Equipment designed to protect the wearer's skin or eyes from heat and hazardous materials. Protective clothing is divided into the following three types.

(a) Chemical-protective clothing:

1. Liquid splash-protective clothing
2. Vapor-protective clothing

(b) High temperature-protective clothing
(c) Structural fire-fighting protective clothing

Response. That portion of incident management in which personnel are involved in controlling (defensively or offensively) a hazardous materials incident. The activities in the response portion of a hazardous materials incident include analyzing the incident, planning the response, implementing the planned response, and evaluating progress.

Sampling. The process of collecting a representative amount of gas, liquid, or solid for analytical purposes.

Sampling is essential for identification of hazardous materials at hazardous materials incidents. It must begin as early in the incident as possible, and it should continue periodically until the incident commander deems it no longer necessary. Initial sampling helps responders to determine what courses of emergency action are necessary. Some sampling methods allow for immediate identification at the scene. *(See Figure 1.8.)* Other sampling methods are more time consuming and can require sending the sampled material to a laboratory for accurate identification. In cases where terrorism or willful destruction is suspected, samples should be kept for evidence.

If the hazardous material involved in an incident cannot be identified, the most prudent action is to use Level A personnel protective equipment (PPE), which provides skin, respiratory, and eye protection. During a terrorist incident with numerous victims, however, the most expedient course of action may be to use

Level B PPE with self-contained breathing apparatus, which provides respiratory and skin protection but a lesser level of vapor protection, to reduce the time needed to start entry and rescue. In many incidents involving chemical or biological agents, the respiratory protection afforded by Level B PPE is sufficient by itself. In any case, a standard operating procedure should be developed after careful research and consultation with experts of chemical and biological agents.

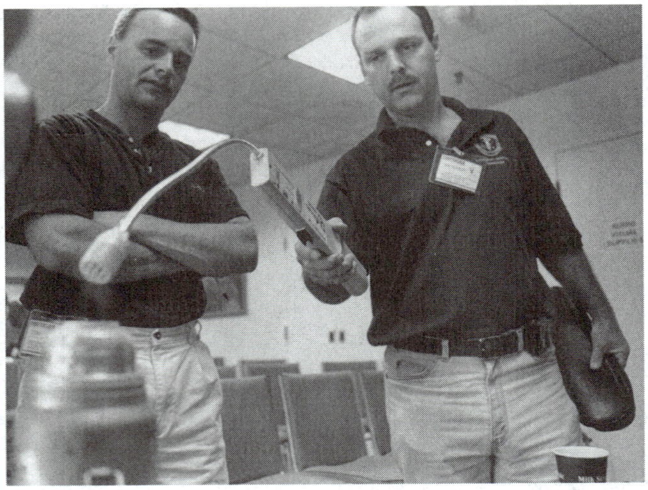

Figure 1.8 *Industry personnel may have instruments that can be used to identify a hazard. Here, during a training session, haz mat responders use a gas meter to identify liquefied natural gas in a container. (NFPA Photo by Rick Cinclair)*

Secondary Contamination. The process by which a contaminant is carried out of the hot zone and subsequently contaminates people, animals, the environment, or equipment.

Should. Indicates a recommendation or that which is advised but not required.

Solidification. The process whereby a hazardous liquid is treated chemically so that solid material results.

Stabilization. The point in an incident at which the adverse behavior of the hazardous material is controlled.

This can be considered an intermediate step in the mitigation process. An analogy may be made to a firefighting operation in which the fire is declared "under control" when the main body of fire has been extinguished. The situation will not worsen although, at this point, responding forces may be a long way from declaring the termination of the incident. In many cases, contractors are brought in to complete the long-term cleanup and only a few, if any, original responders remain on the scene.

Sterilization. The process of destroying all microorganisms in or on an object.

Waste Minimization. Treatment of hazardous spills by procedures or chemicals designed to reduce the hazardous nature of the material and to minimize the quantity of waste produced.

References Cited in Commentary

1. NFPA 1991, *Standard on Vapor-Protective Suits for Hazardous Chemical Emergencies,* National Fire Protection Association, Quincy, MA, 1994.
2. NFPA 1992, *Standard on Liquid Splash-Protective Suits for Hazardous Chemical Emergencies,* National Fire Protection Association, Quincy, MA, 1994.
3. NFPA 1993, *Standard on Support Function Protective Clothing for Hazardous Chemical Operations,* National Fire Protection Association, Quincy, MA, 1994.

CHAPTER 2

Incident Response Planning

2-1 Developing an Incident Response Plan

2-1.1

Planning is an essential part of emergency preparedness. The development of both facility response plans and community emergency plans is required by numerous state and federal laws, including Superfund Amendments and Reauthorization Act (SARA), Title III, "The Emergency Planning and Community Right to Know Act of 1986." Planning guides and reference materials are listed in Appendix C.

The purpose of planning is to be able to control a hazardous materials incident as effectively, safely, and efficiently as possible. Planning should be a continuing process, and periodically testing the plan is essential to its success.

To the greatest extent possible, representatives of everyone in the response community who may become involved in a hazardous materials incident should be included in the incident planning process. Typically, planning committees include representatives from the local police, fire, health, building, emergency preparedness, and environmental departments.

2-1.2

A planning team is necessary for developing the hazardous materials emergency plan. Local, state, and federal planning guidelines should be reviewed and consulted by the planning team when preparing plans for hazardous materials incidents.

As the *North American Emergency Planning Guide* points out, a team approach encourages the entire community to participate in the planning process. Regional teams comprised of local, county, and state authorities can combine to form a hazardous materials advisory council (HMAC). Larger metropolitan areas may require individual response teams to handle a larger number of local incidents than may be encountered in a less populated or less industrial area. In all cases, planning committees should consult federal and other planning guidelines and response regulations when initially creating their own hazardous materials response plans or revising existing plans.

Members of a hazardous materials response team should be selected on the basis of ability, commitment, authority, expertise, and compatibility. Members should represent all elements of the community and include all types of emergency responders to bring a range of experience and expertise to the response team. This team approach also enables communities and authorities to share the cost of equipment and staff.

2-2 Review and Training

2-2.1

As a minimum, an annual review and update of the hazardous materials emergency plan should be conducted.

It is important that someone on the planning committee be assigned the responsibility of keeping the effective haz mat response plans current in terms of equipment, decontamination techniques, and other areas of concern. The hundreds of details involved in haz mat response planning are all subject to changes in technology, changes in the community (such as the opening or closing of industrial sites, chemical storage facilities, and military bases), advances in assessment or measurement methods, and changes in legal requirements. That is why the Technical Committee on Hazardous Materials Response Personnel has recommended, at minimum, an annual review of each plan and its components to ensure that changes in any of the above areas have not rendered a plan less effective.

For communities with the available computer technology, the creation of a data base for storing and updating information can save valuable time when an incident occurs. For example, if the home phone numbers of heavy construction equipment contractors who have agreed to respond if needed to a hazardous materials incident change, a plan to update information in the data base or other records and plan materials can be in place to avoid needless delays in reaching these individuals. When a major change occurs, such as the opening of a new power plant or industrial site, the planning committee may choose to review the plans as a group at a special meeting to ensure that all contingencies are being met by the current plan.

2-2.2

As a minimum, a training exercise should be conducted annually to determine the adequacy and effectiveness of the hazardous materials emergency plan.

Training exercises serve different needs for different members of the hazardous materials response community. For the planning committee, an annual training exercise can be a full-scale simulation or a tabletop exercise followed by a review or critique by all agencies that are partners in the local planning. Problems or inconsistencies in the plans can be identified and corrected and new procedures tested.

For members of the hazardous materials response team itself, however, training exercises serve to keep skill levels high and should be conducted more frequently. Response teams should run smaller scale drills in addition to a major annual exercise. In addition, regional response teams can work closely on small-scale exercises with local first responders to coordinate interaction between the various response units or join drills with other regional teams. *(See Figure 2.1.)*

Each community plan should indicate how it will be tested and how often.

Figure 2.1 *Training exercises are vital to the efficiency of a haz mat response team. Here, team members tour a potential incident site with site safety officials to coordinate a response plan should the need arise.*

CHAPTER 3

Response Levels

3-1* Planning Guide

Table 3-1 is a planning guide intended to provide the user with assistance in determining incident levels for response and training. Potential applications to a jurisdiction's response activities can include development of standard operating procedures; implementation of a training program using the competency levels of NFPA 472, *Standard for Professional Competence of Responders to Hazardous Materials Incidents;* acquisition of necessary equipment; and development of community emergency response plans. When consulting this table, the user should refer to all of the incident condition criteria to determine the appropriate incident level.

A-3-1 These incidents can be considered as requiring either offensive operations or defensive operations.

Offensive operations include actions taken by a hazardous materials responder, in appropriate chemical-protective clothing, to handle an incident in such a manner that contact with the released material may result. These actions include patching or plugging to slow or stop a leak; containing a material in its own package or container; and cleanup operations that may require overpacking or transfer of a product to another container.

Defensive operations include actions taken during an incident where there is no intentional contact with the material involved. These actions include elimination of ignition sources, vapor suppression, and diking or diverting to keep a release in a confined area. Defensive operations require notification and possible evacuation, but does not involve plugging, patching, or cleanup of spilled or leaking materials.

Jurisdictions have the responsibility to develop standard operating procedures that equate levels of response to levels of training indicated in NFPA 472, *Standard for Professional Competence of Responders to Hazardous Materials Incidents*. Depending on the capabilities and training of personnel, the first responder operational level may equate to incident level one and the technician level may equate to incident level two.

Response personnel should operate only at that incident level that matches their knowledge, training, and equipment. If conditions indicate a need for a higher response level, then additional personnel, appropriate training, and equipment should be summoned.

Some response organizations have established a "tiered response plan" to match the response levels listed in Table 3-1. In many cases, the classification of an incident is the responsibility of the emergency call taker. Detailed training is necessary for call takers to make an accurate classification and human error is always a possibility.

The initial responders to the scene should be alert to signs that hazardous materials are involved. Some signs, such as truck placards, are obvious. Other indications of the presence of hazardous materials can be observed in the location of the incident. Is the incident taking place at an industrial site, a service station, or a licensed or unlicensed business location? Once the location has been established, it can then be determined what types of materials are normally associated with that type of occupancy and what substances may be present and in what quantities. For example, if the incident is at an unlicensed auto body shop, there are likely to be paints, solvents, and other flammable and combustible liquids present, but not in the same quantity as would be expected in a larger, licensed facility with the ability for bulk storage. Unlicensed or illegal businesses using hazardous materials will probably not be in compliance with any of the local regulations for equipment maintenance, hazardous materials storage, record keeping, or disposal.

First responders to any incident need to be aware of their limitations. For example, if a reported incident is classified as a Level 1 condition, initial responding units should be able to handle it or, after evaluation, call for additional resources. A Level 2 incident requires greater response capability and a Level 3 incident needs even more sophisticated equipment and highly trained personnel. Level 2 and Level 3 responses may be served by a regional or nearby mutual aid hazardous materials team. When planning for potential hazardous materials incidents, the planning body should address incidents at all levels to ensure a smooth response coordination.

Some of the terms and conditions in the table warrant explanation:

Placard Not Required. Refers to U.S. Department of Transportation regulations. However, the absence of a placard should not be taken as an assurance that the contents are harmless.

NFPA 0 or 1 in All Categories. A reference to NFPA 704, *Standard System for the Identification of the Hazards of Materials for Emergency Response.*[1] This standard deals with a labeling system that advises on three hazard conditions: health, flammability, and reactivity. There are five degrees of intensity, ranging from 0 through 4. A 0 or 1 in all three hazard conditions indicates relatively low hazard.

Class 9 (previously identified as ORM A, B, and C) and ORM-D. ORM means Other Regulated Materials.

Class 9 Miscellaneous includes *miscellaneous hazardous materials,* which refers to materials that present a hazard during transport, but that are not included in another hazard class, including:

(a) Any material that has an anesthetic, noxious, or similar property that could cause a flight crew such annoyance or discomfort as to prevent them from correctly performing their assigned duties
(b) Any material that is not included in any other hazard class but is subject to the DOT requirements (a hazardous substance or a hazardous waste)

Table 3-1 Planning Guide for Determining Incident Levels, Response, and Training

	Incident Level		
Incident Conditions	**One**	**Two**	**Three**
Product identifications	Placard not required, NFPA 0 or 1 all categories, all Class 9 and ORM-D	DOT placarded, NFPA 2 for any categories, PCBs without fire, EPA regulated waste	Class 2, Division 2.3—poisonous gases, Class 1, Division 1.1 and 1.2—explosives, organic peroxide, flammable solid, materials dangerous when wet, chlorine, fluorine, anhydrous ammonia, radioactive materials, NFPA 3 & 4 for any categories including special hazards, PCBs & fire, DOT inhalation hazard, EPA extremely hazardous substances, and cryogenics
Container size	Small (e.g., pail, drums, cylinders except 1-ton, packages, bags)	Medium (e.g., 1-ton cylinder, portable containers, nurse tanks, multiple small packages)	Large (e.g., tank cars, tank trucks, stationary tanks, hopper cars/trucks, multiple medium containers)
Fire/explosion potential	Low	Medium	High
Leak severity	No release or small release contained or confined with readily available resources	Release may not be controllable without special resources	Release may not be controllable even with special resources
Life safety	No life-threatening situation from materials involved	Localized area, limited evacuation area	Large area, mass evacuation area
Environmental impact (potential)	Minimal	Moderate	Severe
Container integrity	Not damaged	Damaged but able to contain the contents to allow handling or transfer of product	Damaged to such an extent that catastrophic rupture is possible

Examples of Class 9 materials include adipic acid, hazardous substances such as PCBs, and molten sulfur.

ORM-D Material. A material that presents a limited hazard during transportation due to its form, quantity, and packaging. Examples of ORM-D materials include consumer commodities and small arms ammunition.

PCBs Without Fire. Polychlorinated biphenyls (PCBs) present serious health threats to skin and the liver. Even without the added hazard of fire, they are sufficiently harmful to responders to warrant a Level 2 condition.

EPA Regulated Waste. These can be found in Title 40, *Code of Federal Regulations,* Part 261.

(a) *Class 2, Division 2.3—Poisonous Gases* (prior to 1991 classified as Poison A). Examples are arsine, hydrocyanic acid, and phosgene. These are extremely dangerous poisons.
(b) *Class 1, Division 1.1 and 1.2—Explosives* (prior to 1991 classified as Explosives A or B). Examples of Division 1.1 are dynamite and black powder. Examples of Division 1.2 are propellant explosives and rocket motors.

Organic Peroxide. Many organic peroxides are highly flammable, and most will decompose readily when heated. In some cases, the decomposition can be violent.

Flammable Solid. Examples are pyroxylin plastics, magnesium, and aluminum powder.

Materials Dangerous When Wet. Included in this category are sodium and potassium metals and calcium.

Chlorine. A greenish yellow gas that is highly toxic and irritating.

Fluorine. An extremely reactive and intensely poisonous yellow gas.

Anhydrous Ammonia. A very toxic and corrosive gas.

Radioactive Materials. Materials that spontaneously emit ionizing radiation having a specific activity greater than 0.002 microcurie per gram.

DOT Inhalation Hazard. Inhalation hazards are measured in terms of TLV/TWA (threshold limit value/time-weighted average). Shipping papers must indicate inhalation hazard and containers must be marked "Inhalation Hazard." Vehicles will be placarded "Poison" or "Poison Gas," in addition to the primary hazard listing requirements.

EPA Extremely Hazardous Substances. EPA has published a list of 366 such substances.

Cryogenics. Cryogenics are extremely cold liquefied gases [–200°F (–129°C)] that can cause severe damage to skin or other body parts.

Container Size. The larger the container, the greater the potential for risk, hence the increase in the level of incident condition. (*See Figure 3.1.*)

Fire/Explosion Potential. The assumption in each case is that the incident is not simply a fire, but that some hazardous material is involved. Where there is no fire, Level 1 may be appropriate, depending on other prevailing conditions. If a container is involved in fire, Level 3 may be more appropriate. It is conceivable that a fire involving a container can be handled safely by a responding fire department without the assistance of any hazardous materials response personnel. Nonetheless, appropriate authorities would have to be notified and alerted to the situation. It is also vitally important to keep in mind that containers involved in fire can overpressurize and explode. This is especially true of hazardous materials in liquid form stored in tanks and other larger and smaller containers. The explosion can spread hazardous material over a large geographic area, as well as spreading fire and chemical gases. Thus, every precaution must be taken when approaching containers that are exposed to fire. For the maximum protection of all individuals, the planning committee should address the possibility of fire in each of their hazardous materials response plans.

Leak Severity. The selection of levels obviously depends on the extent of the leak and the likelihood that it can be controlled.

Life Safety. The number of people potentially exposed is a major determining factor in selecting the appropriate level.

Figure 3.1 *Hazardous wastes may be found stored in containers, such as the barrels shown here, that have corroded or are unsecured, that lack appropriate marking information, and that are in generally poor condition. Poorly contained wastes may mix, forming new compounds that are more unstable and toxic than their original components and that require both time and expertise to identify and mitigate.*

Environmental Impact. The terms used are general. Judgment is required, and experts should be consulted. The environmental impacts of an incident may not be known at the start of the incident, and they are frequently more severe than anticipated.

Container Integrity. Extreme care must be taken with damaged containers before allowing them to be transferred. Once again, experts in this field should be consulted. If doubt exists, the incident should be considered as Level 3.

Reference Cited in Commentary

1. NFPA 704, *Standard System for the Identification of the Hazards of Materials for Emergency Response,* National Fire Protection Association, Quincy, MA, 1996.

CHAPTER 4

Site Safety

4-1 Emergency Incident Operations

4-1.1

Emergency incident operations should be conducted in compliance with Chapter 6 of NFPA 1500, *Standard on Fire Department Occupational Safety and Health Program*, or Title 29, *Code of Federal Regulations,* Part 1910.120 or EPA.

All fire fighters can be categorized as first responders at the operational level. Therefore, fire fighters should comply with Chapter 6, "Emergency Operations," of NFPA 1500 for a general safety program to be followed on all emergency incidents.[1] Chapter 6 of NFPA 1500 deals with emergency operations and covers organization, safety requirements, and incidents involving special hazards.

The first responder awareness category will apply to most police officers, public utility workers, emergency medical technicians, employees at hazardous waste facilities, and drivers of trucks carrying hazardous materials. In these cases, OSHA 1910.120 is applicable, and specified training in emergency operations and safety procedures will be required for these responders.

4-1.2*

An incident management system should be implemented at all hazardous materials incidents. Operations should be directed by a designated incident commander and follow established written standard operating procedures.

A-4-1.2 Although Title 29, *Code of Federal Regulations,* Part 1910.120 is cited in the text, it should be understood that some states will adopt these regulations under state OSHA plans and others will adopt these regulations through adoption of a similar regulation established by EPA and appropriate state agencies.

Various agencies involved in emergency response to hazardous materials incidents may use different types of the incident management system (IMS). The important point is that there is a system and that everyone who may respond to a hazardous materials incident be familiar with the way the IMS functions. NFPA 1561, *Standard on Fire Department Incident Management System*,[2] provides excellent guidance for developing an effective incident management system, clearly addressing the components that must be included in order to operate in as organized and safe a manner at an incident as possible.

4-1.2.1 Personnel Accountability. The incident management system should include a standard personnel identification system to maintain accountability for each member engaged in activities at an incident scene. This personnel identification system should have the ability to provide a rapid accounting of all members on the incident scene.

This new paragraph points out the importance of knowing where all personnel are at all times. A personnel identification system should include a "time keeper" to log entry into the hot zone and monitor the length of time each responder has been using his or her self-contained breathing apparatus. After a predetermined period of time, efforts to notify personnel that they are running low on air should be initiated or a stand-by team should be sent into the hot zone to evacuate personnel. A notification system to alert entry personnel to emergency messages should be predetermined and can consist of loud speakers, air horns, or portable radios.

Any accountability system should keep track of the exact location of each entry team. This will help locate the team if an immediate evacuation is necessary or if the team must be located quickly for a rescue attempt.

4-1.2.1.1 The personnel identification system should include a means to specifically identify and keep track of members entering and leaving the hot zone and any area where special protective equipment is required.

4-1.2.1.2 The incident management system should include a standard operating procedure to evacuate personnel from an area where an imminent hazard condition is found to exist and account for the safety of personnel. This system should include a method to immediately notify all personnel in the affected area of an imminent hazard condition by means of audible warning devices.

4-1.2.2 Rest and Rehabilitation. The incident commander should consider the circumstances of each incident and make suitable provisions for rest and rehabilitation for members operating at the scene. These considerations should include medical evaluation and treatment, food and fluid replenishment, and relief from extreme climatic conditions, according to the circumstances of the incident.

All incident commanders should maintain an awareness of the condition of members operating within their span of control and ensure that adequate steps are taken to provide for their safety and health. The command structure should be utilized to request relief and reassignment of fatigued members.

This new paragraph advises incident commanders to plan rest and rehabilitation for all personnel operating in chemical-protective clothing and respiratory protection. If an extended operation is expected, provisions should be made for additional personnel to operate on a rotating basis to allow for the rest and rehabilitation of personnel at the incident scene. It should be noted that requests for additional personnel can take a long time to be fulfilled. Incident commanders must request additional resources, such as personnel, food, and fluids, as soon as it becomes apparent that the incident will take more than a few minutes to mitigate.

The rest and rehabilitation (R & R) area should be set up in the cold zone where EMS staff can provide medical monitoring of response personnel. The R & R area should be cordoned off and an access control point created so that personnel do not leave without the proper medical consent. An appropriate level hazardous materials response team officer should act as the control person for the R & R area. All the resources for rehabilitation, such as fluids, shelter, toilets, and food, should be provided in the R & R area.

4-1.3

An emergency response plan describing the general safety procedures that are to be followed at an incident should be prepared in accordance with Title 29, *Code of Federal Regulations,* Part 1910.120. These procedures should be thoroughly reviewed and tested.

4-2 Ignition Sources

Ignition sources should be eliminated whenever possible at incidents involving releases, or probable releases, of ignitable materials. Whenever possible, electrical devices used within the hot zone should be certified as intrinsically safe by recognized organizations.

Most ignition sources, such as matches, smoking materials, and open flames, are well known and easily recognized. However, other ignition sources, such as pilot lights, engines of motor vehicles, incidental static discharges, and electrical sparks, often receive less attention. Whenever flammable vapor is present, all sources of ignition should be removed or eliminated.

4-3 Control Zones

Control zone names have not been consistently applied at incidents. The intent of this section is to show areas of responder control. The various zones or areas at a typical emergency response site are shown in Figure 4-3.

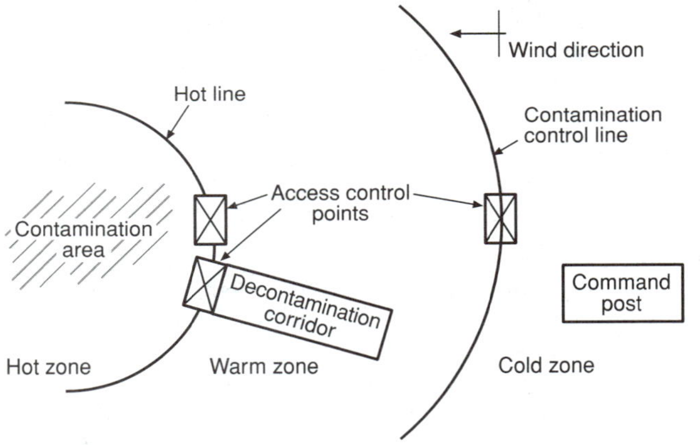

Figure 4-3 *Diagram of control zones.*

Control zones should be established at an incident as soon as possible to reduce contamination by controlling and directing the operations and movements of personnel at the incident. A site map that shows wind direction and topography will prove absolutely necessary for any incident where the hazardous materials can move via wind or flow across the ground. Also, construction plans for any manmade conduits, such as storm and sanitary sewers, will be needed to find any "hot zone" areas far from the original spill that will receive the contamination that flows into these pipes.

Boundaries for the various control zones are established using information gathered by monitoring the incident. Control zone areas should be cordoned off using some type of hazard tape or other method of marking by the response personnel first to arrive. Until the boundaries of the control zones have been established, a conservative estimate of the hot zone is necessary to ensure the safety of responding personnel. Once accurate monitoring of the incident has been finished, the hot zone can be resized if necessary.

Personnel should move only through the access control points of each control zone area in order to maintain control of the site and to prevent spread of contamination across zones. Each access control point will need a control officer to monitor the passage of personnel. This officer can double check appropriate personal protective equipment and log the entry time of each responder.

Control zones and access control points should be monitored to ensure that they are in the proper locations as the incident progresses. It may be necessary to expand or reduce the zones, and/or move the access control points.

4-3.1* Hot Zone.

The hot zone is the area immediately surrounding a hazardous materials incident, extending far enough to prevent adverse effects from hazardous materials releases to personnel outside the zone. This zone is also referred to as the exclusion zone or restricted zone in other documents.

A-4-3.1 Access into the hot zone is to be limited to those persons necessary to control the incident. A log is to be maintained at the access control point to record entry and exit time of all personnel in the hot zone.

Personnel may enter the hot zone, where contamination is likely to occur, for several reasons, including the need for sampling, cleanup, or spill control measures. The boundary lines should be clearly delineated by hazard tape, signs, or rope. It may be appropriate to have more than one access control point per zone so that there are separate entrance and exit points.

All personnel within the hot zone should wear the level of protective equipment the incident commander has determined to be appropriate. Differing levels of protection may be appropriate in the same area, depending on the specific task being performed.

4-3.2 Warm Zone.

The warm zone is the area where personnel and equipment decontamination and hot zone support take place. It includes control points for the access corridor and thus assists in reducing the spread of contamination. This zone is also referred to as the decontamination, contamination reduction, or limited access zone in other documents.

The severity of contamination should decrease as responders move from the hot zone toward the cold zone because of the effective decontamination procedures in the warm zone. Within the decontamination corridor, there should be one decontamination line for personnel and another for heavy equipment.

Personnel entering the warm zone from the cold zone should wear the level of protection required to operate in the warm zone. Personnel leaving the warm zone for the cold zone should remove the protective clothing they have worn in the warm zone.

The warm zone should be large enough to accommodate all the decontamination procedures that will take place in it.

4-3.3 Cold Zone.

The cold zone contains the command post and such other support functions as are deemed necessary to control the incident. This zone is also referred to as the clean zone or support zone in other documents.

Personnel in the cold zone may wear normal work clothes. The cold zone should be upwind of the hot zone and as far away from it as is practical. Support functions in the cold zone might include command post, site security, medical support, reserve equipment, and a field laboratory.

Many hazardous response teams have specially equipped support vehicles that can provide for command posts, research and planning areas, equipment donning and doffing areas, and even decontamination facilities. Some teams improvise and use fire command vehicles, tents and portable shelters, and even structures that may be in close proximity to the scene to create these areas. The weather can influence the selection of areas to serve as these facilities. For example, a decontamination corridor can be set up outside when the temperature is moderate, but not in cold weather. If the team is relying on makeshift facilities, standard operating procedures should be developed to guide the selection and/or acquisition of these facilities.

4-4 Communications

Effectively handling any emergency depends on establishing and implementing a coordinated communications program. Hazardous materials incidents, however, are often more complicated than routine emergencies. Many emergency scenes are spread out geographically and portable two-way radios are essential for communications. At most incidents, contact with several data and information sources is required before any plan for mitigation can be formulated. Contact with other agencies, such as police, environmental protection agencies, the health department, and EMS responders, is also often necessary. Many of these agencies will be on different radio channels and a coordinated communications plan is essential. *(See Figure 4.1.)*

4-4.1

When personal protective clothing or remote operations inhibit communications, an effective means of communication, such as radios, should be established.

Radio equipment has improved substantially in recent years. Every consideration should be given to equipping workers with two-way radio equipment, particularly where protective clothing isolates the individual. There are now effective methods, such as specially designed two-way radios, for communicating with personnel in totally encapsulating suits.

4-4.2

The frequencies employed in these radios should be "dedicated" and not used or shared with other local agencies.

Where multichannel radios are available to personnel, the incident commander can designate a particular channel for all on-scene communications. This radio channel should be a non-repeated channel (simplex) used only for emergency on-scene communications. Another channel (not a dispatch channel) should be reserved for the incident commander to communicate with the central alarm office. Any request for additional resources and information can be handled expediently if this radio channel can be dedicated to this vital link.

4-4.3

Communication should be supplemented by a prearranged set of hand signals and hand-light signals to be used when primary communication methods fail. Hand-lights employed for this purpose should be in accordance with NFPA 70, *National Electrical Code*®, for use in hazardous environments.

Where hand signals are to be employed, they should be simple to use and understand, and they should be lim-

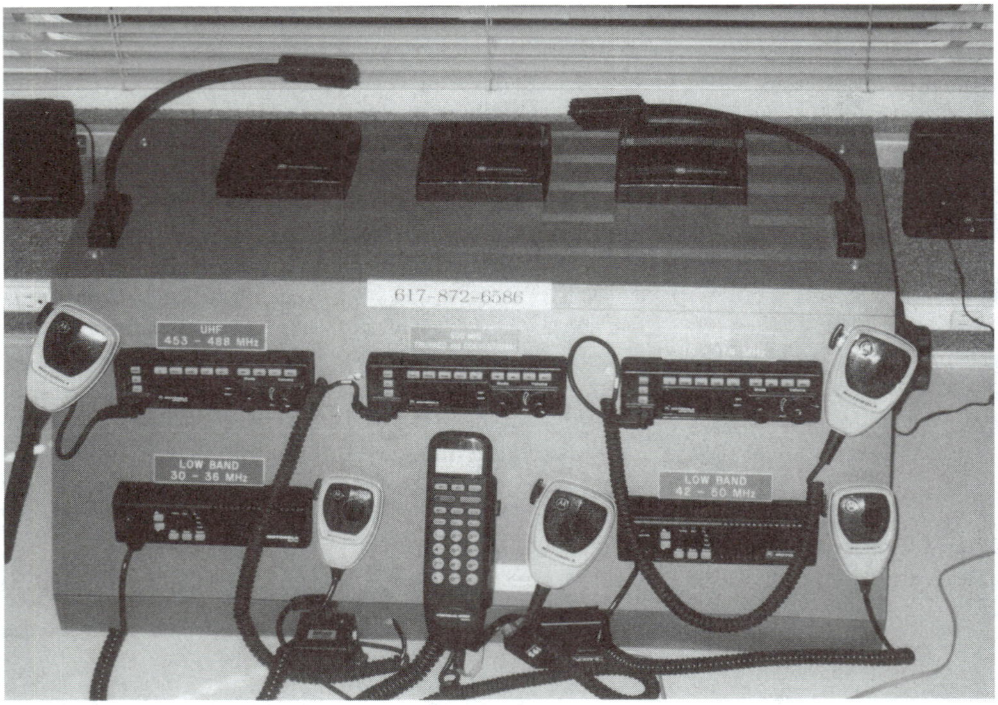

Figure 4.1 *Maintaining effective communications is a top priority at hazardous materials incidents. This state-of-the-art mobile command station features cellular phone hookups and more traditional walkie talkies. (NFPA photo by Rick Cinclair)*

ited to commands that are essential. Since an operation may well involve personnel from different disciplines and agencies, it is important that everyone involved in the operation understand and be able to use the appropriate hand or hand-light signals.

4-5 Monitoring Equipment

4-5.1

Monitoring equipment operates on several different principles and measures different aspects of hazardous materials releases. Examples of this equipment include the following:

(a) Oxygen meters

Normal atmospheric air contains 21 percent oxygen by volume. Sixteen percent is needed to support human life. Atmospheres that contain less than 19.5 percent oxygen are generally considered to be deficient and can cause reduced mental capability and dizziness.

Several instruments can be used to determine the oxygen level, many of which are small and easy to use. For example, if responders are working in a confined space, oxygen levels must be constantly monitored.

(b) Combustible gas indicator (explosimeter)
(c) Carbon monoxide meter
(d) pH meter
(e) Radiation detection instruments
(f) Colorimetric detector tubes
(g) Organic vapor analyzer
(h) Photoionization meter
(i) Air sampling devices
(j) Other meters to measure specific products such as chlorine, hydrogen sulfide, or ethylene oxide
(k) pH paper or strips
(l) Organic vapor badge or film strip
(m) Mercury badge
(n) Formaldehyde badge or strip

4-5.2

All monitoring equipment should be operationally checked prior to use and periodically calibrated in accordance with manufacturers' specifications.

References Cited in Commentary

1. NFPA 1500, *Standard on Fire Department Occupational Safety and Health Program,* National Fire Protection Association, Quincy, MA, 1997.
2. NFPA 1561, *Standard on Fire Department Incident Management System,* National Fire Protection Association, Quincy, MA, 1995.

CHAPTER 5

Personal Protective Equipment

5-1 General

It is essential that personal protective equipment meeting appropriate NFPA and OSHA standards be provided, maintained, and used. Protection against physical, chemical, and thermal hazards should be considered when selecting personal protective equipment.

Personal protective equipment includes structural fire-fighting clothing, chemical-protective clothing, and high temperature-protective clothing. The hazardous materials incident responder, however, does not need to be equipped with all three types. For example, many hazardous materials incidents do not involve fire, so structural fire-fighting clothing may not be needed. Even at a scene involving fire, the first responders at the awareness or operational levels may include police officers, emergency medical service personnel, and fixed site workers who are not expected to be equipped with structural fire-fighting clothing since they are not trained fire fighters.

Whatever personal protective equipment is used must meet the relevant governmental and NFPA standards. It must also be used carefully, since there are hazards associated with its use. Among other things, personal protective equipment can provide the wearer with a false sense of security. The protected internal environment of a totally encapsulating suit can also induce rapid fatigue and heat stress, limit vision, and impair communications. Avoiding underprotection is a vital concern for the haz mat responder, but overprotection can cause its own needless hardship affecting a responder's stamina and effectiveness. *(See Figure 5.1.)*

Additional information about protective clothing can be found in NFPA 472 and the supplements included in this handbook.

Figure 5.1 *Level A protective clothing, shown left, offers the highest level of protection and is essential when the chemical hazard at hand is unknown or unidentified. In this ensemble, all skin surfaces are protected. The less restrictive Level B protection can be used when appropriate or when an initial hazard is sufficiently mitigated and permeation of the suit material is not an issue. (Drawings courtesy of Trelleborg)*

5-1.1

A written personal protective equipment program should be established in accordance with Title 29, *Code of Federal Regulations,* Part 1910.120. Elements of the program should include personal protective equipment selection and use; storage, maintenance, and inspection procedures; and training considerations. The selection of personal protective clothing should be based on the hazardous materials and conditions present and should be appropriate for the hazards encountered.

Providing a complete range of protective equipment is not enough. Responders also need an intensive training program that covers how to select the appropriate equipment to use and how to use that equipment correctly. A thorough training program will also include guidance on maintenance, storage, and inspection of equipment. A regular periodic inspection program to ensure that the equipment is serviceable should also be a part of every hazardous materials response team's duties.

Whatever personal protective equipment program is established, the instructions regarding the program and its use must be clear, concise, and easy to follow. Personnel should never operate beyond the capabilities of their training and/or equipment. To do so puts both the responders and the community they serve in danger.

5-1.2

Protective clothing and equipment used to perform fire suppression operations, beyond the incipient stage, should meet the requirements of Chapter 5 of NFPA 1500, *Standard on Fire Department Occupational Safety and Health Program.* Structural fire-fighting protective clothing is not intended to provide chemical protection to the user.

The following excerpts from NFPA 1500 are worth citing:

> **5-1.1*** The fire department shall provide each member with the appropriate protective clothing and protective equipment to provide protection from the hazards to which the member is or is likely to be exposed. Such protective clothing and protective equipment shall be suitable for the tasks that the member is expected to perform.
>
> **5-1.2** Protective clothing and protective equipment shall be used whenever the member is exposed or potentially exposed to the hazards for which it is provided.
>
> **5-1.3** Members shall be fully trained in the care, use, inspection, maintenance, and limitations of the protective clothing and protective equipment assigned to them or available for their use.
>
> **5-1.5*** Cleaning processes for protective clothing ensembles shall be appropriate for the types of contaminants and for the materials that are to be cleaned.[1]

The limitations of protective clothing and equipment are important to consider. For example, structural fire-fighting clothing is not designed to offer the user chemical protection. Every fire department and every fire fighter is generally considered to have at least first responder operational capability; their structural fire-fighting equipment is governed by OSHA regulations and by NFPA 1500. Yet this equipment is not appropriate protection from exposure to chemical spills, even though it may provide some protection in some cases. In other words, structural fire-fighting equipment and chemical-protective clothing constitute two different categories of personal protective clothing, even though self-contained breathing apparatus may be common to each.

In some cases, of course, chemical-protective clothing rather than structural fire-fighting clothing may be appropriate (e.g., a structural fire in a chemical facility), even where the situation is clearly a structural fire. This is a judgment call, and the decision falls to the officer in charge of the incident.

5-2 Respiratory Protective Equipment

5-2.1

Self-contained breathing apparatus (SCBA) should meet the requirements of NFPA 1981, *Standard on Open-Circuit Self-Contained Breathing Apparatus for Fire Fighters.*

Standard operating procedure is to assume that an inhalation hazard is present or potentially present during an emergency response until the material can be positively identified and evaluated. Positive-pressure self-contained breathing apparatus (SCBA) is the minimum type of respiratory protection that responders must wear. Once it has been determined through monitoring that a decreased level of protection is appropriate, the incident commander can allow the use of other types of respiratory protection.

Open-circuit SCBA provides air to the mask from a cylinder, and the wearer exhales directly to the atmosphere. When wearing closed-circuit SCBA, on the other hand, responders rebreathe the exhaled, recycled gases, which have been chemically scrubbed and supplemented with oxygen from a supply source. The latter type of apparatus has a longer operating time. *(See Figure 5.2.)*

5-2.2

Personal alert safety systems should meet the requirements of NFPA 1982, *Standard on Personal Alert Safety Systems (PASS) for Fire Fighters.*

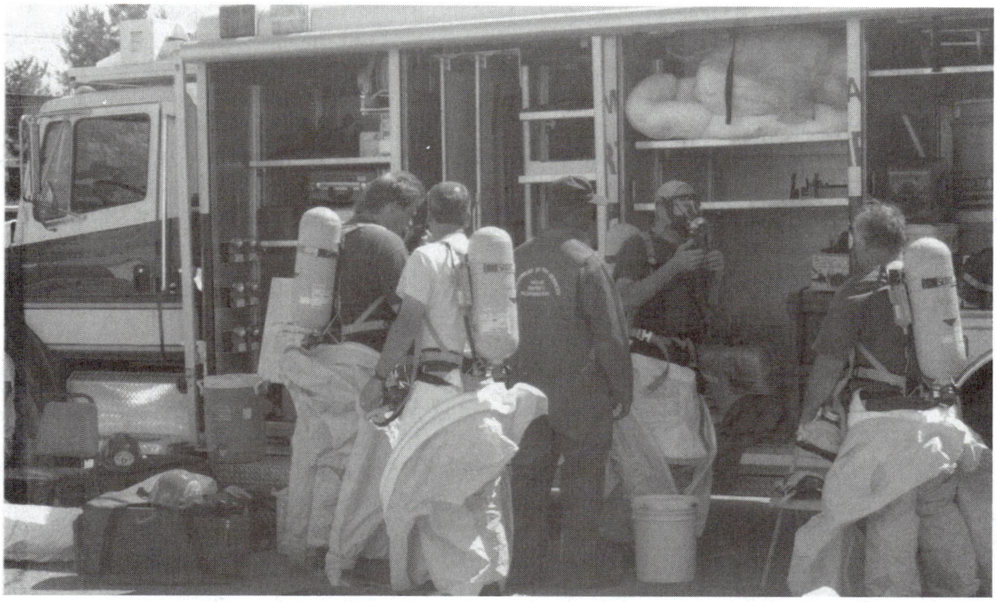

Figure 5.2 Respiratory protection must be the primary concern in nonencapsulated protective clothing ensembles. Positive-pressure self-contained breathing apparatus provides the highest level of respiratory protection. Here, responders donning Level A protection put on their breathing apparatus and are checked by the safety officer before closing themselves into the suit hood. (Photo courtesy Lt. David Hansen, Bedford MA Fire Department)

NFPA 1500, *Standard on Fire Department Occupational Safety and Health Program*,[2] requires fire service members involved in rescue, fire fighting, or other hazardous duty to use a Personal Alert Safety System (PASS) device that sounds an alarm if the wearer does not move after 30 (±5) seconds. The standard also recommends that the device be worn on the protective clothing and used whether SCBA is being used or not.

5-2.3 Air Purifying Respirators.

These devices are worn to filter particulates and contaminants from the air. They should be worn only in atmospheres where the type and quantity of the contaminants are known and sufficient oxygen is known to be present.

Air purifying respirators do not have an air source, so their use is very limited. These devices rely on filters designed to purify the ambient air in which they are used. Air purifying respirators cannot be used in atmospheres that contain less than 19.5 percent oxygen or in atmospheres that contain contaminants immediately dangerous to life or health. When air purifying respirators are used, the oxygen level and the contaminated atmosphere must be monitored.

5-3 Chemical-Protective Clothing

5-3.1

Chemical-protective clothing (CPC) is made from special materials and is designed to prevent the contact of chemicals with the body. Chemical-protective clothing is of two types: totally encapsulating and nonencapsulating.

Selecting the appropriate chemical-protective clothing is extremely important. It is essential that the wearer be adequately trained in its use and limitations and that the manufacturer's instructions be followed. Totally encapsulating suits are generally one-piece suits designed to protect the wearer against gases and vapors. Nonencapsulating suits usually come in component parts and will not protect against gases and vapors, since they are not gastight.

Factors to consider when acquiring protective clothing include its cost, the ease with which it can be decontaminated, and the anticipated life of the garment. Many disposable garments are now available and are becoming popular with busy hazardous materials teams. Since these garments are never reused, there is no need to decontaminate them or perform any time-consuming maintenance, such as checking for any residual contamination or looking for breaches in the garment's material or closures.

See NFPA 472 and Supplement 3 in this handbook for more information on protective clothing.

5-3.2

A variety of materials are used to make the fabric from which chemical-protective clothing is manufactured. Each material provides protection against certain specified chemicals or mixtures of chemicals but might afford little or no protection against certain other chemicals. It is most important to note that there is no material that provides satisfactory protection from all chemicals. Protective clothing material needs to be compatible with the chemical substances involved, consistent with manufacturers' instructions.

Knowing the limitations of a particular protective garment is essential to safe operation at a hazardous materials incident. Awareness of the material from which the suit is made and the manufacturer's instructions regarding the garment's performance when exposed to chemicals for specified exposure times is essential for an accurate understanding of the garment's protection and limitations.

5-3.3*

Performance requirements need to be considered in selecting the appropriate chemical-protective material. These requirements would include chemical resistance, permeation, penetration, flexibility, abrasion, temperature resistance, shelf life, and sizing criteria.

The purpose of chemical-protective clothing is to protect the wearer from exposure. Performance expectations for chemical-protective clothing have been established by the standardized testing of third-party testing labs. No single material can protect against every chemical, however, and different types of materials are more effective than others in protecting against specific chemicals. In addition, the potential combinations of chemicals can further complicate protection from chemical exposure. It is vital that the manufacturer's literature be reviewed for a detailed listing of chemicals that the garment will and will not protect against. There are some chemicals for which there is no effective protective material. When dealing with these chemicals, any mitigation options should not include actions where the chemical can contact the garment.

A-5-3.3 Chemical resistance is the ability of the material from which the protective garment is made to prevent or reduce degradation and permeation of the fabric by the attack chemical. Degradation is a chemical action involving the molecular breakdown of the material due to contact with a chemical. The action may cause the fabric to swell, shrink, blister, or discolor; become brittle, sticky, or soft; or deteriorate. These changes permit chemicals to penetrate the suit more rapidly or increase the probability of permeation.

Permeation is a chemical action involving the movement of chemicals, on a molecular level, through intact material. There is usually no indication that this process is occurring. Permeation is defined by two terms, permeation rate and breakthrough time. Permeation rate is the quantity of chemical that will move through an area of protective garment in a given period of time, usually expressed as micrograms of chemical per square centimeter per minute. Breakthrough time is the time required for the chemical to be measured on the inside surface of the fabric. The most desirable protective fabric is one that has the longest breakthrough time and a very low permeation rate. Breakthrough times and permeation rates are not available for all the common suit materials and the variety of chemicals that exist. Manufacturers' data and reference sources should be consulted. Generally, if a material degrades rapidly, permeation will occur rapidly.

Penetration is the movement of material through a suit's closures, such as zippers, buttonholes, seams, flaps, or other design features. Torn or ripped suits will also allow penetration.

5-4 Thermal Protection

5-4.1 Proximity Suits.

These suits provide short duration and close proximity protection at radiant heat temperatures as high as 2000°F (1093°C) and can withstand some exposure to water and steam. Respiratory protection needs to be provided with proximity suits.

Proximity suits *(see Figure 5.3)* are not designed for fire entry. These two-piece or three-piece ensembles are made of a heat-reflective material with layers of insulating linings. In addition to the suit itself, the wearer must also use special heat-reflective mittens and boots. Proximity suits are often worn over other protective clothing. NFPA 1500,[3] Section 5-4, provides guidelines on the use of clothing for proximity fire fighting. NFPA 1976, *Standard on Protective Clothing for Proximity Fire Fighting,*[4] provides criteria for the design of proximity clothing.

5-4.2 Fire Entry Suits.

These suits provide protection for brief entry into a total flame environment at temperatures as high as 2000°F (1093°C). They are not effective or meant to be used for rescue operations. Respiratory protection needs to be provided with fire entry suits.

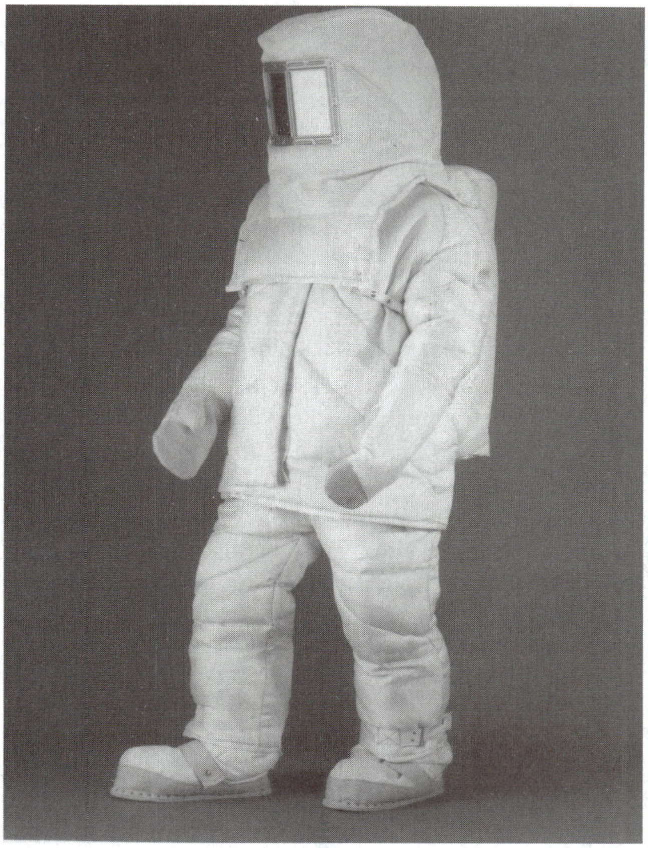

Figure 5.3 Proximity suits are primarily used for close-proximity, short-duration exposures to both flame and radiant heat temperatures as high as 2000°F (1093°C). They will withstand exposures to steam, liquids, and weak corrosive chemicals. (Photo courtesy of Fyrepel Industries, Decatur, AL)

This suit is composed of a coat, pants, boots, gloves, and a hood, each made up of many layers of flame-retardant materials. The outer layer is usually aluminized to reflect radiant heat. NFPA 403, *Standard for Aircraft Rescue and Fire Fighting Services at Airports*, cautions that "Fire entry suits are not recommended for civil airport application. Rapid fire control afforded by present fire-fighting equipment and short times for survival without fire control make the fire entry suit unnecessary and inappropriate."[5]

5-4.3 Overprotection Garments.

These garments are worn in conjunction with chemical-protective encapsulating suits.

5-4.3.1 Flash Cover Protective Suits. Flash cover suits are neither proximity nor fire entry suits. They provide limited overprotection against flashback only. They are worn outside of other protective suits and are used only when the risks require them.

5-4.3.2 Low Temperature Suits. Low temperature suits provide some degree of protection of the encapsulating chemical-protective clothing from contact with low temperature gases and liquids. They are worn outside of the encapsulating chemical-protective clothing and are used only when the risks require them.

5-5 Levels of Protection

Personal protective equipment is divided into four categories based on the degree of protection afforded.

Those who have not been adequately trained to select and use personal protective equipment should not be permitted to wear such equipment at a hazardous materials incident. Training in the selection and use of personal protective equipment should be thorough and frequent enough for the responder to become intimately familiar with the equipment's limitations. Responders should be trained to select, don, operate, test, clean, maintain, and care for the clothing that they may need to use at an incident.

During an incident, responders may have to change the level of protection they are wearing, from a high level of protection to a lower one or vice versa. This decision will be made by the incident commander, based on evaluation of the hazards to personnel present at the scene.

5-5.1 Level A.

A Level A equipment is to be selected when the greatest level of skin, respiratory, and eye protection is required. The following constitute Level A equipment and should be used as appropriate:

(a) Pressure-demand, full facepiece, self-contained breathing apparatus (SCBA), or pressure-demand air line respirator with escape SCBA, approved by the National Institute of Occupational Safety and Health (NIOSH)

(b) Vapor-protective suits: totally encapsulating chemical-protective suits (TECP suits) constructed of protective clothing materials that meet the following criteria:

1. Cover the wearer's torso, head, arms, and legs
2. Include boots and gloves that may either be an integral part of the suit or separate and tightly attached
3. Completely enclose the wearer by itself or in combination with the wearer's respiratory equipment, gloves, and boots

(All components of a TECP suit, such as relief valves, seams, and closure assemblies, should provide equivalent chemical resistance protection. Vapor-protective suits should meet the requirements in NFPA 1991, *Standard on Vapor-Protective Suits for Hazardous Chemical Emergencies*.)

(c) Coveralls (optional)
(d) Long underwear (optional)
(e) Gloves, outer, chemical-resistant
(f) Gloves, inner, chemical-resistant
(g) Boots, chemical-resistant, steel toe and shank
(h) Hard hat (under suit) (optional)
(i) Disposable protective suit, gloves, and boots (depending on suit construction, can be worn over totally encapsulating suit)
(j) Two-way radios (worn inside encapsulating suit)

5-5.2 Level B.

Level B personal protective equipment should be used when the highest level of respiratory protection is necessary but a lesser level of skin protection is needed. The following constitute Level B equipment and should be used as appropriate:

(a) Pressure-demand, full facepiece, self-contained breathing apparatus (SCBA), or pressure-demand air line respirator with escape SCBA, NIOSH approved
(b) Hooded chemical-resistant clothing that meets the requirements of NFPA 1992, *Standard on Liquid Splash-Protective Suits for Hazardous Chemical Emergencies* (overalls and long-sleeved jacket, coveralls, one- or two-piece chemical-splash suit, disposable chemical-resistant overalls)
(c) Coveralls (optional)
(d) Gloves, outer, chemical-resistant
(e) Gloves, inner, chemical-resistant
(f) Boots, outer, chemical-resistant, steel toe and shank
(g) Boot covers, outer, chemical-resistant (disposable) (optional)
(h) Hard hat
(i) Two-way radios (worn inside encapsulating suit)
(j) Face shield (optional)

5-5.3* Level C.

Level C personal protective equipment should be used when the concentration(s) and type(s) of airborne substance(s) are known and the criteria for using air purifying respirators are met. The following constitute Level C equipment and should be used as appropriate:

(a) Full-face or half-mask, air purifying respirators, self-contained positive pressure breathing apparatus, NIOSH approved
(b) Hooded chemical-resistant clothing that meets the requirements of NFPA 1993, *Standard on Support Function Protective Clothing for Hazardous Chemical Operations* (overalls, two-piece chemical-splash suit, disposable chemical-resistant overalls)
(c) Coveralls (optional)
(d) Gloves, outer, chemical-resistant
(e) Gloves, inner, chemical-resistant
(f) Boots, outer, chemical-resistant, steel toe and shank
(g) Boot covers, outer, chemical-resistant (disposable) (optional)
(h) Hard hat
(i) Escape mask (optional)
(j) Two-way radios (worn under outside protective clothing)
(k) Face shield (optional)

A-5-5.3 Refer to OSHA Title 29, *Code of Federal Regulations*, Part 1910.134.

5-5.4 Level D.

A work uniform affording minimal protection, Level D personal protective equipment should be used for nuisance contamination only. The following constitute Level D equipment and should be used as appropriate:

(a) Coveralls
(b) Gloves (optional)
(c) Boots/shoes, chemical-resistant, steel toe and shank
(d) Boots, outer, chemical-resistant (disposable) (optional)
(e) Safety glasses or chemical-splash goggles
(f) Hard hat
(g) Escape mask (optional)
(h) Face shield (optional)

5-6 Types of Hazards

The types of hazards for which Levels A, B, C, and D protection are appropriate are described in this section.

5-6.1

Level A protection should be used under any of the following conditions:

(a) When the hazardous material has been identified and requires the highest level of protection for skin, eyes, and the respiratory system based on either the measured (or potential for) high concentration of atmospheric vapors, gases, or particulates; or the site operations and work functions involve a high potential for splash, immersion, or exposure to unexpected vapors, gases, or particulates of material that are harmful to skin or capable of being absorbed through the intact skin
(b) When substances with a high degree of hazard to the skin are known or suspected to be present, and skin contact is possible
(c) When operations need to be conducted in confined, poorly ventilated areas, and the absence of conditions requiring Level A has not yet been determined

The totally encapsulating protective clothing provides the greatest protection and should be used when the hazardous material has not been identified. Table 5.1 lists EPA/OSHA recommended levels of protection.

*Table 5.1 EPA/OSHA Protection Levels**

Level of Protection	Equipment	Protection Provided	Should Be Used When	Limiting Criteria
A	RECOMMENDED • Pressure-demand, full-facepiece SCBA or pressure-demand, supplied-air respirator with escape SCBA. • Fully encapsulating chemical-resistant suit. • Inner chemical-resistant gloves. • Chemical-resistant safety boots/shoes. • Two-way radio communications. OPTIONAL • Cooling unit. • Coveralls. • Long cotton underwear. • Hard hat. • Disposable gloves and boot covers.	The highest available level of respiratory, skin, and eye protection.	• The chemical substance has been identified and requires the highest level of protection for skin, eyes, and the respiratory system based on either: — measured (or potential for) high concentration of atmospheric vapors, gases, or particulates, or — site operations and work functions involving a high potential for splash, immersion, or exposure to unexpected vapors, gases, or particulates of materials that are harmful to skin or capable of being absorbed through the intact skin. • Substances with a high degree of hazard to the skin are known or suspected to be present, and skin contact is possible. • Operations must be conducted in confined, poorly ventilated areas until the absence of conditions requiring Level A protection is determined.	Fully encapsulating suit material must be compatible with the substances involved.
B	RECOMMENDED • Pressure-demand, full face-piece SCBA or pressure-demand supplied-air respirator with escape SCBA. • Chemical-resistant clothing (overalls and long-sleeved jacket; hooded, one- or two-piece chemical splash suit; disposable chemical-resistant one-piece suit). • Inner and outer chemical-resistant gloves. • Chemical-resistant safety boots/shoes. • Hard hat. • Two-way radio communications. OPTIONAL • Coveralls. • Disposable boot covers. • Face shield. • Long cotton underwear.	The same level of respiratory protection but less skin protection than Level A. It is the minimum level recommended for initial site entries until the hazards have been further identified.	• The type and atmospheric concentration of substances have been identified and require a high level of respiratory protection, but less skin protection. This involves atmospheres: — with IDLH concentrations of specific substances that do not represent a severe skin hazard; or — that do not meet the criteria for use of air purifying respirators. • Atmosphere contains less than 19.5 percent oxygen. • Presence of incompletely identified vapors or gases is indicated by direct-reading organic vapor detection instrument, but vapors and gases are not suspected of containing high levels of chemicals harmful to skin or capable of being absorbed through the intact skin. Use only when the vapor or gases present are not suspected of containing high concentrations of chemicals that are harmful to skin or capable of being absorbed through the intact skin.	• Use only when the vapor or gases present are not suspected of containing high concentrations of chemicals that are harmful to skin or capable of being absorbed through the intact skin. • Use only when it is highly unlikely that the work being done will generate either high concentrations of vapors, gases, or particulates or splashes of material that will affect exposed skin.

(continues)

Table 5.1 (Continued)

Level of Protection	Equipment	Protection Provided	Should Be Used When	Limiting Criteria
C	RECOMMENDED • Full facepiece, air purifying, canister-equipped respirator. • Chemical-resistant clothing (overalls and long-sleeved jacket; hooded, one- or two-piece chemical splash suit; disposable chemical-resistant one-piece suit). • Inner and outer chemical-resistant gloves. • Chemical-resistant safety boots/shoes. • Hard hat. • Two-way radio communications. OPTIONAL • Coveralls. • Disposable boot covers. • Face shield. • Escape mask. • Long cotton underwear.	The same level of skin protection as Level B, but a lower level of respiratory protection.	• The atmospheric contaminants, liquid splashes, or other direct contact will not adversely affect any exposed skin. • The types of air contaminants have been identified, concentrations measured, and a canister is available that can remove the contaminant. • All criteria for the use of air purifying respirators are met.	• Atmospheric concentration of chemicals must not exceed IDLH levels. • The atmosphere must contain at least 19.5 percent oxygen.
D	RECOMMENDED • Coveralls. • Safety boots/shoes. • Safety glasses or chemical splash goggles. • Hard hat. OPTIONAL • Gloves. • Escape mask. • Face shield.	No respiratory protection. Minimal skin protection.	• The atmosphere contains no known hazard. • Work functions preclude splashes, immersion, or the potential for unexpected inhalation of, or contact with, hazardous levels of any chemicals.	• This level should not be worn in the Exclusion Zone. • The atmosphere must contain at least 19.5 percent oxygen.

Source: *Standard Operating Safety Guides,* Environmental Response Branch, Office of Emergency and Remedial Response, Environmental Protection Agency, Washington, DC, 1992, pp. 49, 50.

*Based on EPA protective ensembles.

5-6.2

Level B protection should be used under any of the following conditions:

(a)* When the type and atmospheric concentration of substances have been identified and require a high level of respiratory protection, but less skin protection

A-5-6.2(a) This situation involves atmospheres with IDLH (immediately dangerous to life and health) concentrations of specific substances that do not represent a severe skin hazard or that do not meet the criteria for use of air purifying respirators.

(b) When the atmosphere contains less than 19.5 percent oxygen

(c) When the presence of incompletely identified vapors or gases is indicated by a direct-reading organic vapor detection instrument, but the vapors and gases are known not to contain high levels of chemicals harmful to skin or capable of being absorbed through the intact skin

Level B protection cannot keep out vapors or gases that contain high concentrations of chemicals that may harm the skin or that may be absorbed through the skin. Level B should not be used when the work being performed is likely to generate high concentrations of gases or splashes of material that will affect exposed skin.

(d) When the presence of liquids or particulates is indicated, but they are known not to contain high levels of chemicals harmful to skin or capable of being absorbed through the intact skin

5-6.3

Level C protection should be used under any of the following conditions:

(a) When the atmospheric contaminants, liquid splashes, or other direct contact will not adversely affect or be absorbed through any exposed skin
(b) When the types of air contaminants have been identified, concentrations have been measured, and an air purifying respirator is available that can remove the contaminants
(c) When all criteria for the use of air purifying respirators are met

Level C protection is not appropriate where atmospheric concentrations of chemicals exceed IDLH levels, nor where the atmosphere contains less than 19.5 percent oxygen.

(d)* Atmospheric concentration of chemicals must not exceed IDLH levels. The atmosphere must contain at least 19.5 percent oxygen.

A-5-6.3(d) Refer to OSHA Title 29, *Code of Federal Regulations*, Part 1910.134.

5-6.4

Level D protection should be used when both of the following conditions exist:

(a) The atmosphere contains no known hazard
(b)* Work functions preclude splashes, immersion, or the potential for unexpected inhalation of or contact with hazardous levels of any chemicals

A-5-6.4(b) Combinations of personal protective equipment other than those described for Levels A, B, C, and D protection may be more appropriate and may be used to provide the proper level of protection.

Level D protection is not appropriate for personnel operating in the warm zone. The atmosphere where Level D protection is used must contain at least 19.5 percent oxygen.

References Cited in Commentary

1. NFPA 1500, *Standard on Fire Department Occupational Safety and Health Program,* National Fire Protection Association, Quincy, MA, 1997.
2. Ibid.
3. Ibid.
4. NFPA 1976, *Standard on Protective Clothing for Proximity Fire Fighting,* National Fire Protection Association, Quincy, MA, 1992.
5. NFPA 403, *Standard for Aircraft Rescue and Fire Fighting Services at Airports,* National Fire Protection Association, Quincy, MA, 1993.

CHAPTER 6

Incident Mitigation

6-1 Control

This chapter addresses those actions necessary to ensure confinement and containment (the first line of defense) in a manner that will minimize risk to both life and the environment in the early, critical stages of a spill or leak. Both natural and synthetic methods can be employed to limit the releases of hazardous materials so that effective recovery and treatment can be accomplished with minimum additional risk to the environment or to life.

The well-respected hazardous materials expert, Ludwig Benner, Jr., offers a popular definition of hazardous materials:

> Something that jumps out of its container at you when something goes wrong and hurts or harms the thing it touches.[1]

An important element of that definition is that the harmful "something" is normally controlled or contained. Only when it is outside its normal controlling element does a hazardous materials incident occur.

It is only reasonable, then, that mitigating an incident must involve controlling the material that is presenting the problem. Control methods are divided into confinement and containment, and the methods of mitigation are either physical or chemical. This approach presents some order to the process and simplifies it for better understanding.

6-2 Types of Hazardous Materials

All hazardous materials can be subdivided into the following three general categories, based on the principal characteristic that makes them harmful or dangerous:

(a) Chemical
(b) Biological
(c) Radioactive

Of course, there are other safety hazards that exist at all emergencies. NFPA 1500, *Standard on Fire Department Occupational Safety and Health Program,* is a complete standard devoted to the elimination or reduction of risks associated with fire fighting and other emergencies.

6-2.1 Chemical Materials.

Chemical materials are those materials that pose a hazard based upon their chemical and physical properties.

Examining the U.S. Department of Transportation (DOT) list of hazard classes reveals that most of the classes would fall under the chemical hazard type of material. The effect of exposure to chemical hazards can be either acute or chronic. An acute exposure occurs in a relatively short period of time. Hazardous materials responders need to consider acute exposure limits when choosing their personal protective equipment (PPE), treating the victims, and selecting the methods to mitigate an incident. A worker who was exposed for up to 40 hours per week would run the risk of chronic exposure.

6-2.2 Biological Materials.

Biological materials are those organisms that have a pathogenic effect to life and the environment and can exist in normal ambient environments.

Examples of biological materials that are hazardous are those whose packaging requires an "Etiologic Agents" label. Biological hazards include toxins or microorganisms that cause diseases such as cholera, typhus, anthrax, and botulism. Disease-causing organisms are also likely to be found in waste from hospitals, laboratories, and research institutions. Medical waste, such as used needles, hospital dressing gauze, and bandages, should be disposed of in red bags with medical waste and biohazard warnings printed on the plastic bag.

Biological warfare and terrorist devices and the illegal disposal of medical waste are all biological hazards. Such materials are often not labeled and may be packaged in unmarked containers or not packaged at all.

6-2.3 Radioactive Materials.

Radioactive materials are those materials that emit ionizing radiation.

DOT lists three classes of radioactive materials. Of these, Class I is the least harmful. Packaging requirements for radioactive materials vary depending on the potential hazards the material itself presents. Radioactive materials emit the following three types of harmful radiation: alpha, beta, and gamma, each with its own specific characteristics. For more information about these characteristics and their relative hazards, see 4-2.5.2.2 of NFPA 472 in this handbook.

6-3 Physical States of Hazardous Materials

Hazardous materials can be classified into three states, namely gases, solids, and liquids. They can be stored or contained at a high or low pressure. All three states can be affected by the environment in which the incident occurs. The emergency responder needs to take into account such conditions as heat, cold, rain, or wind, which can have a significant effect on the methods used to accomplish a safe operation.

All matter exists as a gas, a solid, or a liquid. Each state has specific properties that have a bearing on how a specific material appears or behaves in the environment. For example, a liquid with a boiling point below 100°F (37.8°C) tends to give off vapor at ambient temperatures. Similarly, a gas with a vapor density that is substantially heavier than the surrounding air may collect in ditches and other low points at the scene and migrate along the ground as it mixes with air. Although in many cases you cannot actually see the gas, it acts like water that has been poured on the ground. If the gas is a flammable gas such as propane, a fire or explosion will occur if it finds an ignition source at ground level.

6-4 Methods of Mitigation

There are two basic methods for mitigation of hazardous materials incidents: physical and chemical. Table 6-4.1 lists many physical methods and Table 6-4.2 lists many chemical methods that are acceptable for mitigation of hazardous materials incidents. Recommended practices should be implemented only by personnel appropriately prepared by training, education, or experience.

Many of the methods listed for mitigating an incident require a high degree of specialized training and the use of sophisticated technical equipment, while others might be carried out by personnel at the first responder operational level. For example, diking or blanketing a liquid spill of diesel fuel can often be accomplished easily by the first responder operations. Plugging a hole in a damaged tank truck to stop a leak, however, would require specialized training and equipment that only a technician would possess. Other operations, such as vent and burn techniques, should only be attempted by technicians with a tank car specialty *(see Chapter 9 in NFPA 472 of this handbook for details on this competency)*. In every case, the incident commander should be the primary decision maker on which personnel are assigned to deal with each specific incident.

6-4.1* Physical Methods.

Physical methods of control involve any of several processes or procedures to reduce the area of the spill, leak, or other release mechanism. In all cases, methods used should be acceptable to the incident commander. The selection of personal protective clothing should be based on the hazardous materials and/or conditions present and should be appropriate for the hazards encountered. Refer to Table 6-4.1.

A-6-4.1 Procedures described in 6-4.1.1 through 6-4.1.11 should be completed only by personnel trained in those procedures.

6-4.1.1* Absorption. Absorption is the process in which materials hold liquids through the process of wetting. Absorption is accompanied by an increase in the volume of the sorbate/sorbent system through the process of swelling. Some of the materials typically used as absorbents are sawdust, clays, charcoal, and polyolefin-type fibers. These materials can be used for confinement, but it should be noted that the sorbed liquid can be desorbed under mechanical or thermal stress. When absorbents become contaminated, they retain the properties of the absorbed hazardous liquid and are, therefore, considered to be hazardous materials and must be treated and disposed of accordingly. *(See ASTM F716, Method of Testing Sorbent Performance of Absorbents, for further information.)*

Many commercially available products are suitable for use as absorbents. Different types of absorbents are designed for different types of spilled materials so labels should be carefully checked prior to each use. Absor-

Table 6-4.1 Physical Methods of Mitigation of Hazardous Materials

	Chemical				Biological				Radiological			
	Gases				Gases				Gases			
Method	LVP*	HVP**	Liq.	Sol.	LVP	HVP	Liq.	Sol.	LVP	HVP	Liq.	Sol.
Absorption	yes	yes	yes	no	no	no	yes[4]	no	no	no	yes	no
Covering	no	no	yes	yes	no	no	yes	yes	no	no	yes[3]	yes[3]
Dikes, dams, diversions, and retention	yes	yes[5]	yes	yes	no	no	yes	yes	no	no	yes	yes
Dilution	yes	yes	yes	yes	no	no	no	no	yes	no	yes	yes
Overpack	yes	no	yes	yes	yes	no	yes	yes	yes	no	yes	yes
Plug/patch	yes	yes	yes	yes	yes	yes	yes	yes	yes	yes	yes	yes
Transfer	yes	no	yes	yes	yes	no	yes	yes	yes	no	yes	yes
Vapor suppression (blanketing)	no	no	yes	yes	no	no	yes	yes	no	no	no	no
Vacuuming	no	no	yes	yes	no	no	yes	yes	no	no	yes	yes
Venting[1]	yes	yes	yes	no	yes	no	no	no	yes[2]	no	no	no

NOTE: For substances involving more than one type, the most restrictive control measure should be used.

* Low Vapor Pressure ** High Vapor Pressure

1. Venting of low-vapor-pressure gases is recommended only when an understanding of the biological system is known. Venting is allowed when the bacteriological system is known to be nonpathogenic, or if methods can be employed to make the environment hostile to pathogenic bacteria.
2. Venting of low-vapor-pressure radiological gases is allowed when the gas(es) is/are known to be alpha or beta emitters with short half-lives. Further, this venting is only to be allowed after careful consultation with a certified health physicist.
3. Covering should be done only after consultation with appropriate experts.
4. Absorption of liquids containing bacteria is permitted where the absorption bacteria or environment is hostile to the bacteria.
5. Water dispersion on certain vapors and gases only.

bents can help reduce vapor generation and can facilitate cleanup procedures.

A-6-4.1.1 Absorbents saturated with volatile liquid chemicals can create a more severe vapor hazard than the spill alone because of severely enlarged surface area for vapor release.

6-4.1.2 Covering. Covering is a temporary form of mitigation for radioactive, biological, and some chemical substances such as magnesium. It should be done after consultation with a certified health physicist (in the case of radioactive materials) or other appropriate experts.

6-4.1.3 Dikes, Dams, Diversions, and Retention. These terms refer to the use of physical barriers to prevent or reduce the quantity of liquid flowing into the environment. Dikes or dams usually refer to concrete, earth, and other barriers temporarily or permanently constructed to hold back the spill or leak. Diversion refers to the methods used to physically change the direction of flow of the liquid. Vapors from certain materials, such as liquefied petroleum gas (LPG), can be dispersed by means of a water spray.

These techniques are the most commonly employed methods of controlling releases because responders can always improvise and simple methods of confinement can be devised with a little ingenuity. On the other hand, substantial liquid spills of hazardous materials can pose significant challenges and, in some rare cases, insurmountable problems for the hazardous materials response team first to arrive on the scene.

In addition to the techniques listed, trenches can be used to collect spilled liquids, and pumps can transfer materials to containers or to a containment system. Earthen dikes or dams can be erected quickly under favorable conditions, and even sand bags can be used in the damming effort. Commercial booms, such as the one shown in Figure 6.1, are available and are widely used to control spills, especially spills on waterways.

Figure 6.1 Commercial booms can be placed across a waterway to collect hazardous materials spilled into the waterway.

6-4.1.4 Dilution. Dilution is the application of water to water-miscible hazardous materials. The goal is to reduce the hazard to safe levels.

Responders should not use water indiscriminately or without knowing what effect it will have on the hazardous material involved in a hazardous materials incident. Even if a material is water-soluble, the amount of water necessary to achieve a safe level could well render dilution an impractical approach. Adding water to a liquid spill can also increase confinement problems. Unconfined diluted hazardous materials have the potential to cause widespread, long-lasting environmental problems. Many hazardous materials can also react with water, thus increasing the intensity of the incident. Water is nonetheless a viable option for mitigation in many instances and should be considered when appropriate.

6-4.1.5 Overpacking. The most common form of overpacking is accomplished by the use of an oversized container. Overpack containers should be compatible with the hazards of the materials involved. If the material is to be shipped, DOT specification overpack containers need to be used. (The spilled materials still should be treated or properly disposed of.)

If it is possible to do so, a leaking drum or container should be temporarily repaired to reduce spillage before the container is placed in an overpack container. Reducing a leak can sometimes be accomplished simply by repositioning the original container. Holes can be covered, and temporary patches applied. Overpack containers typically have a form-fitting gasket in a lid that can be tightly secured with a ring-type closure. *(See Figure 6.2.)*

A leaking container can be put into an overpack drum or container by placing the overpack on its side and sliding the smaller container into it; by lowering the overpack over the leaking container and then tipping it upright; or by using mechanical equipment to raise and lower the leaking container into the overpack container. *(See Figure 6.3.)*

The overpack container must be labeled in accordance with DOT regulations for the particular product it is carrying.

Responders should make sure that other containers without visible leaks or punctures that may be weakened by deterioration or impact do not fail. Responders should also try to avoid physical injury when lifting or moving large or heavy containers. Based on the hazards that are present, personnel should wear the appropriate chemical-protective clothing and respiratory protection.

Figure 6.2 Overpack containers typically have a form-fitting gasket in a lid that can be tightly secured with a ring-type closure. (Photo courtesy of UPRIGHT, St. Louis, MO)

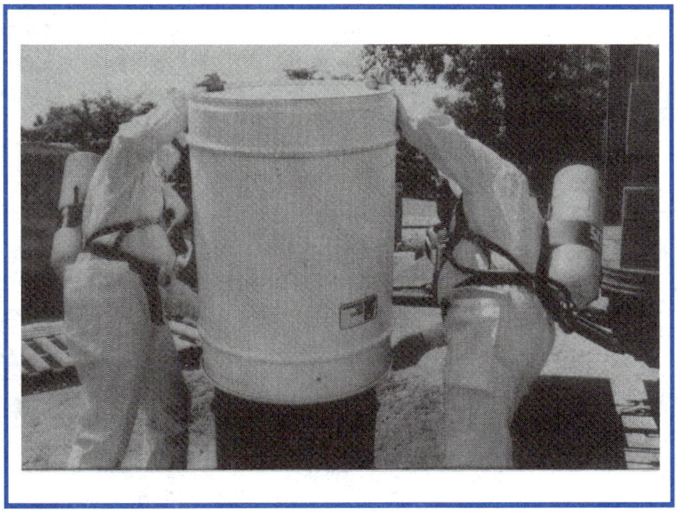

Figure 6.3 One method of overpacking involves lowering the overpack over the leaking container, then tipping it upright.

6-4.1.6 Plug and Patch. Plugging and patching is the use of compatible plugs and patches to reduce or temporarily stop the flow of materials from small holes, rips, tears, or gashes in containers. The repaired container should not be reused without proper inspection and certification.

Plugging involves putting something into a container hole to reduce both the size of the hole and the flow from the hole. Tapered wooden plugs are often used. *(See Figure 6.4.)* No matter what material the plug is made of, however, it must be compatible with both the product and the container. For example, soft pine may not be appropriate for plugging a strong acid leak. Again, responders must wear the appropriate chemical-protective clothing and respiratory protection before attempting any plugging activity.

Patching involves placing something over a hole to keep the material inside the container from leaking out. Patches are generally secured with clamps or adhesives. Patches designed to repair leaks in pipes of various sizes are commercially available. *(See Figure 6.5.)*

Limiting or restricting a leak is an important condition of the mitigation process, so it is essential that responders master this skill. At all times, however, the safety of the responder must be paramount.

6-4.1.7 Transfer. Transfer is the process of moving a liquid, gas, or some forms of solids, either manually, by pump, or by pressure, from a leaking or damaged container or tank. Care needs to be taken to ensure the pump, transfer hoses and fittings, and container selected are compatible with the hazardous material. When a product transfer presents fire or explosion hazard, proper concern for electrical continuity (such as bonding/grounding) needs to be observed.

Materials should be transferred from one tank truck to another by personnel who are skilled and practiced in the procedure, such as technicians with a tank car, cargo tank, or intermodal tank specialty *(see Chapters 9, 10, and 11 of NFPA 472 in this handbook)*. The incident commander will be in charge of the transferring operation and is responsible for seeing that proper precautions are taken. However, responders must also rely on the experience of industry personnel or specialty technicians who are appropriately trained and equipped to perform the transfer operation.

It is essential that all electrical equipment used to transfer flammable liquids be grounded or bonded and that it be approved for such usage. See Supplement 13.

6-4.1.8 Vacuuming. Many hazardous materials may be placed in containment simply by vacuuming them up. This has the advantage of not causing an increase in volume. Care needs to be taken to ensure compatibility of materials. The exhaust air can be filtered, scrubbed, or treated as needed. The method of vacuuming will depend on the nature of the hazardous material.

6-4.1.9 Vapor Dispersion. Vapors from certain materials can be dispersed or moved by means of a water spray. With other products, such as liquefied petroleum gas (LPG), the gas concentration may be reduced below the lower flammable limit through rapid mixing of the gas with air, using the

Figure 6.4 *Plugs and wedges are commercially available to fill holes in containers and stop leaks. (Photo courtesy of Mike Callan)*

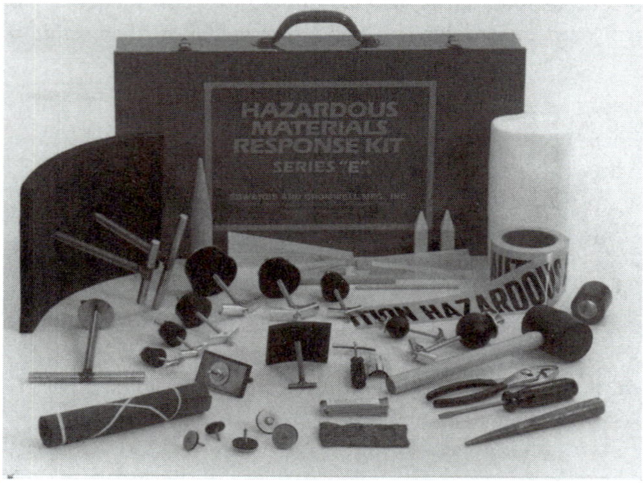

Figure 6.5 *Commercially available patching kits provide a variety of tools and patching materials to stop leaks in pipes and containers. (Photo courtesy of Edward Cronwall, Mfg., Inc.)*

turbulence created by a fine water spray. Reducing the concentration of the material through the use of water spray may bring the material into its flammable range.

See Figure 6.6.

6-4.1.10* Vapor Suppression (Blanketing). Vapor suppression is the reduction or elimination of vapors emanating

Figure 6.6 *A fine water spray can be used to disperse some hazardous vapors.*

from a spilled or released material through the most efficient method or application of specially designed agents. A recommended vapor suppression agent is an aqueous foam blanket.

A-6-4.1.10 One technique available for handling a spill of a hazardous liquid is the application of foams to suppress the vapor emanating from the liquid. This technique is ideally suited for liquid spills that are contained, i.e., diked. It can also be used where the spill is not confined. In all cases this technique should be undertaken only by personnel who have been trained in the use of foam concentrate for vapor suppression. Training in the use of foam as a fire extinguishing agent is not sufficient to qualify an individual for applying foam application as a vapor-suppressing agent.

Vapor-suppressing foam concentrates vary in their effectiveness depending on a number of factors. These factors can include the type of foam, the 25 percent drainage time of the foam, the rate of application of the foam, and the depth of the foam blanket. These variables serve to emphasize the need for training of the person selecting this technique for applying foam as a vapor-suppressing medium.

Foams are produced by mechanically mixing a dilute solution of the foam concentrate and water with air, producing an expanded foam. Foams have been developed basically as fire extinguishing agents. Data have also been developed on their capability to suppress vapor release from water-immiscible flammable or combustible hydrocarbon liquids.

Foam and specific foam concentrates for each category, along with the definitions of appropriate terms, can be obtained by consulting NFPA 11, *Standard for Low-Expansion Foam;* NFPA 11A, *Standard for Medium- and High-Expansion Foam Systems;* NFPA 16, *Standard for the Installation of Deluge Foam-Water Sprinkler and Foam-*

Water Spray Systems; and ASTM Standard Guide F 1129, *Using Aqueous Foams to Control the Vapor Hazard from Immiscible Volatile Liquids.*

The use of fire-fighting foam as a vapor suppressant involves some considerations that are different from those required for fire-extinguishing agents. It should be noted that fire-fighting foams are predominantly restricted to use on water-immiscible hydrocarbon liquids or polar compounds. They are not usually effective on inorganic acids or bases, nor on liquefied gases, including the hydrocarbon gases such as methane and propane, in controlling vapor release. One of the obvious issues of concern is the stability of the foam blanket as a function of time. This can be approached by looking at what is referred to as the foam quality.

Foam quality is generally measured in terms of foam expansion ratio and foam 25 percent drainage time. Foam expansion ratio refers to the volume of foam solution. AFFF is often used in nonaspirating equipment such as water fog nozzles. Nonaspirated AFFF solutions have significantly limited effectiveness in comparison with aspirated foam solutions in vapor suppression.

The 25 percent drainage time is that time which is required for 25 percent of the foam solution to drain from the foam. This is the property that is generally used to measure the stability of the foam. The slower the drainage of any expanded foam, regardless of expansion, the more effective and longer lasting is the foam blanket. This formula assumes weather conditions are ideal.

An important factor is the vapor pressure of the liquid that is being suppressed. Liquid vapor pressures can vary widely. The higher the vapor pressure, the slower the control time. The key to effective use of foam as a vapor-suppressing agent is to have a continuous foam blanket on the fuel surface. Films from AFFF/FFFP are no guarantee of effective vapor control.

It is important to recognize that there are some limitations in the use of foam fire extinguishing agents in vapor suppression. As indicated, these materials are basically designed for flammable hydrocarbon liquids. They have severe shortcomings for inorganic acids or bases or liquefied gases. They should not be used for vapor suppression of these categories of volatile hazardous chemicals without consultation with the manufacturer of the specific foam agent being considered.

Most fire-fighting foam concentrates have a limited range of pH tolerance. The pH is a measure of the acidity or alkalinity of inorganic acids or bases. The pH tolerance is the level that the bubble wall of the foam can tolerate before collapsing catastrophically. A few surfactant foams and the polar compound-type foams have good pH tolerance. Most of the protein, fluoroprotein, AFFFs, and high-expansion foams are not suitable for inorganic acids or bases.

Liquefied gas spills may be controlled by the application of high-expansion foam blankets. Low-expansion foams are not effective for liquefied gas spill control. Because of the large temperature differential between the liquefied gas and the foam, the drainage from the foam initially exaggerates boiloff from the spill. The higher the expansion, the lesser the effect of the drainage. For liquefied gases and all water-reactive inorganic materials, the foam should exhibit the best chemical resistance and expansion ratios to ensure maximum water retention consistent with the condition of the spill site. Since each spilled material can have unique properties, the manufacturer of the foam concentrate should be consulted for directions.

The great differences in the chemistry of flammable hydrocarbon liquids and the water-reactive inorganic materials have resulted in the development of foam concentrates specifically applicable to the inorganic chemicals. Few fire-fighting foams have capabilities of vapor suppression of the inorganic acids and bases. For effective control, special foam concentrates should be employed.

Some special foam concentrates are specific for either acids or alkalis but not both. Further, they are not applicable to all inorganic materials, nor are they effective in fire suppression. In many cases, their effectiveness is limited, and intermittent foam make-up may be required to maintain the foam blanket. Others, usually containing a polymer modification, can cover a wide range of materials, both acids and bases, and may possess some degree of fire resistance. This is important for those inorganic materials that may also pose a fire hazard.

At present, there is no single foam concentrate that is truly effective against all categories of volatile hazardous chemicals. A few possess limited capabilities in most categories, but they are compromise materials, sacrificing in one category to provide some capability in other categories. These may, however, be the best choice for first responders where an overall capability is essential.

In all cases, however, the foam manufacturer or the manufacturer's literature should be consulted to provide specific guidance for the chemical to be treated.

Vapor suppression can also be considered a chemical method of mitigation.

While vapor suppression or blanketing does not change the nature of a hazardous material, it can greatly reduce the immediate hazard and danger associated with the presence of uncontrolled vapor. In addition, it buys additional time to use other measures that can control and resolve the incident under safer circumstances. *(See Figure 6.7.)*

6-4.1.11 Venting. Venting is a process that is used to deal with liquids or liquefied compressed gases where a danger, such as an explosion or mechanical rupture of the container or vessel, is considered likely. The method of venting will depend on the nature of the hazardous material. In general, it involves the controlled release of the material to reduce

Figure 6.7 Chemical methods of hazardous materials mitigation include the use of foam, available in free-standing foam extinguishers, as shown here, or in specialized compartments on other vehicles. Haz mat response training should include information on how to identify when to use foam and which type of foam is the most appropriate to use.

and contain the pressure and diminish the probability of an explosion.

6-4.2* Chemical Methods.

Chemical methods of control involve the application of chemicals to treat spills of hazardous materials. Chemical methods may involve any one of several actions to reduce the involved area affected by the release of a hazardous material. *(See Table 6-4.2.)* In all cases, methods used should be acceptable to the incident commander. The selection of personal protective clothing should be based on the hazardous materials and/or conditions present and should be appropriate for the hazards encountered.

A-6-4.2 The procedures described in 6-4.2.1 through 6-4.2.10 should be used only by personnel trained in those procedures.

6-4.2.1* Adsorption. Adsorption is the process in which a sorbate (hazardous liquid) interacts with a solid sorbent surface. See ASTM F 726, *Method of Testing Sorbent Performance of Adsorbents*, for further information. The principal characteristics of this interaction are the following:

(a) The sorbent surface, unlike absorbents, is rigid and no volume increase occurs.
(b) The adsorption process is accompanied by heat of adsorption whereas absorption is not.
(c) Adsorption occurs only with activated surfaces, e.g., activated carbon, alumina, etc.

A-6-4.2.1 Spontaneous ignition can occur through the heat of adsorption of flammable materials and caution should be exercised.

Adsorbents saturated with volatile liquid chemicals can create a more severe vapor hazard than the spill alone because of the severely enlarged surface area for vapor release.

The term *sorbents* encompasses both absorbents and adsorbents. Adsorbents act in such a way that the internal structure of the material is not penetrated. They can be natural or synthetic materials and can be used on liquid spills on land and, to some degree, in water. Adsorbents should be nonreactive to the spilled material. Porous clay and sand are two commonly used adsorbents.

6-4.2.2 Controlled Burning. For purposes of this practice, controlled combustion is considered a chemical method of control. However, it should be used only by qualified personnel trained specifically in this procedure.

In some emergency situations where extinguishing a fire will result in large, uncontained volumes of contaminated water, or threaten the safety of responders or the public, controlled burning is used as a technique. It is recommended

Table 6-4.2 Chemical Methods of Mitigation of Hazardous Materials

	Chemical				Biological				Radiological			
	Gases				Gases				Gases			
Method	**LVP***	**HVP****	**Liq.**	**Sol.**	**LVP**	**HVP**	**Liq.**	**Sol.**	**LVP**	**HVP**	**Liq.**	**Sol**
Adsorption	yes	yes	yes	no	yes[3]	yes	yes[3]	no	no	no	no	no
Burn	yes	yes	yes	yes	yes	yes	yes	yes	no	no	no	no
Dispersion/ emulsification	no	no	yes	yes	no	no	yes[3]	no	no	no	no	no
Flare	yes	yes	yes	no	yes	yes	yes	no	no	no	no	no
Gelatin	yes	no	yes	yes	yes[3]	no	yes[3]	yes[3]	no	no	no	no
Neutralization	yes[1]	yes[4]	yes	yes[2]	no	no	no	no	no	no	no	no
Polymerization	yes	no	yes	yes	no	no	no	no	no	no	no	no
Solidification	no	no	yes	no	no	no	yes[3]	no	no	no	yes	no
Vapor suppression	yes	yes	yes	yes	yes	yes	yes	yes	yes	yes	yes	yes
Vent/Burn	yes	yes	yes	no	yes	yes	yes	no	no	no	no	no

*Low Vapor Pressure **High Vapor Pressure

1. Technique may be possible as a liquid or solid neutralizing agent, and water can be applied.
2. When solid neutralizing agents are used, they must be used simultaneously with water.
3. Technique is permitted only if resulting material is hostile to the bacteria.
4. The use of this procedure requires special expertise and technique.

that consultation be made with the appropriate environmental authorities when this method is used.

The deliberate burning of a hazardous material should only be attempted by personnel at a technician level with appropriate specialty training *(see NFPA 472, Chapters 9, 10, and 11 of this handbook, for more information on the competencies required for this work)* or by a private sector specialist employee A *(see NFPA 472, Chapter 6).*

There are some occasions when extinguishing a fire is not the proper approach because of the large amount of contaminated runoff that is generated by fire fighting. A Swiss pharmaceutical company fire, for example, was responsible for years of pollution to the Rhine River caused by the water runoff from the extinguishment of that fire. However, a similar fire in a paint factory in the United States was allowed to burn out without applying the large quantity of water that would have been necessary to extinguish the fire. The environment and area water supply were protected from pollution.

Controlled burning may also be used to incinerate the spilled hazardous material. Transportable incinerators are designed to promote combustion of spilled materials, especially oil.

6-4.2.3 Dispersants, Surface Active Agents, and Biological Additives. Certain chemical and biological agents can be used to disperse or break up the materials involved in liquid spills. The use of these agents results in a lack of containment and generally results in spreading the liquid over a much larger area. Dispersants are most often applied to spills of liquids on water. The dispersant breaks down a liquid spill into many fine droplets, thereby diluting the material to acceptable levels. Use of this method may require the prior approval of the appropriate environmental authority. See ASTM STP 659, *Chemical Dispersants for the Control of Oil Spills*, and ASTM STP 840, *Oil Spill Chemical Dispersants: Research, Experience, and Recommendations*, for further information.

Dispersants generally result in oil-in-water emulsions because chemicals are used to reduce the surface tension of water so it can mix with oil. Chemical dispersants should not be used in situations where they might produce increased biological damage. It is essential that environmental authorities be consulted prior to the use of these agents. Surface-active agents also increase emulsification and dispersion of a spill.

Surface cleaning equipment is available for soil surface cleaning, too. This equipment agitates the soil's surface with water to form a slurry. The contamination

Figure 6.8 *Venting, shown here, and burning techniques are often used in train accidents involving hazardous chemicals. These are highly skilled operations that should only be attempted by specially trained personnel such as technicians with a tank car specialty. (See Chapter 10 of NFPA 472 in this handbook for more information.) (Photo by Tony Campbell/AP Worldwide for the Effingham Daily News)*

is then removed through a separation process that takes place in a specially designed sand separator.

Biological additives can be used to degrade a hazardous material by biochemical oxidation. Biochemical accelerators are useful for mitigation of certain hazardous materials spilled on land or in water.

6-4.2.4 Flaring. Flaring is a process that is used with high-vapor-pressure liquids or liquefied compressed gases for the safe disposal of the product. Flaring is the controlled burning of material in order to reduce or control pressure and/or dispose of a product.

6-4.2.5 Gelation. Gelation is the process of forming a gel. A gel is a colloidal system consisting of two phases, a solid and a liquid. The resulting gel is considered to be a hazardous material and needs to be disposed of properly.

Gelling agents used on hazardous chemicals produce a gel that is more easily cleaned up, either by mechanical or physical methods, although the gel itself is a hazardous material. Gelling agents can be used on liquids spilled in water and, to a lesser degree, on land.

6-4.2.6 Neutralization. Neutralization is the process of applying acids or bases to a spill to form a neutral salt. The application of solids for neutralizing can often result in confinement of the spilled material. Special formulations are available that do not result in violent reactions or local heat generation during the neutralization process. In cases where special neutralizing formulations are not available, special considerations should be given to protecting persons applying the neutralizing agent, as heat is generated and violent reactions can occur. One of the advantages of neutralization is that a hazardous material can be rendered nonhazardous.

The pH scale is used to categorize compounds as acids or bases. A value of 7 on the scale is neutral, while descending values denote increasing acidity. Levels 8 to 14 denote bases, with the higher values indicating increasingly stronger bases. It is possible to neutralize acidic or base spills by mixing the spilled material with a neutralizing agent.

6-4.2.7 Polymerization. Polymerization is a process in which a hazardous material is reacted in the presence of a catalyst, in the presence of heat or light, or with itself or another material to form a polymeric system.

6-4.2.8 Solidification. Solidification is the process whereby a hazardous liquid is treated chemically so that a solid material results. Adsorbents can be considered an example of a solidification process. There are other materials that can be used to convert hazardous liquids into nonhazardous solids. Examples are applications of special formulations designed to form a neutral salt in the case of spills of acids or caustics. The advantage of the solidification process is that a spill of small scale can be confined relatively quickly and treatment effected immediately.

Commercially available adsorbents can be used to solidify oily wastes that are water insoluble. The spilled liquids are adsorbed into granules to form a solid, nonflowing mixture. The resulting product is safer than the spilled material in its liquid form and is more easily transported to an appropriate disposal facility.

6-4.2.9 Vapor Suppression. Vapor suppression is the use of solid activated materials to treat hazardous materials so as to effect suppression of the vapor off-gasing from the materials. This process results in the formation of a solid that affords easier handling but that may result in a hazardous solid that must be disposed of properly.

6-4.2.10 Venting and Burning. This process involves the use of shaped charges to vent the high vapor pressure at the top of the container and then the use of additional charges to release and burn the remaining liquid in the container in a controlled fashion.

In a train derailment in the early 1980s, shaped explosive charges were used to "vent and burn" tank cars that were too badly damaged to attempt transfer of the hazardous materials to another container. This was eight days into the incident response. Vent and burn is a highly sophisticated technique that should be attempted only under very controlled conditions by trained specialists such as technicians with a tank car, cargo car, or intermodal tank specialty. *(See Figure 6.8 and Chapters 9, 10, and 11, of NFPA 472.)*

Reference Cited in Commentary

1. Ludwig Benner, Jr., *A Textbook for Use in the Study of Hazardous Materials Emergencies,* 2nd edition, Lufred Industries Inc., Oakton, VA, 1978.

CHAPTER 7

Decontamination

7-1 Decontamination Plan

At every incident involving hazardous materials, there is a possibility that personnel, their equipment, and members of the general public will become contaminated. The contaminant poses a threat, not only to the persons contaminated, but to other personnel who may subsequently come into contact with the contaminated personnel and equipment. The entire process of decontamination should be directed toward confinement of the contaminant within the hot zone and the decontamination corridor to maintain the safety and health of response personnel, the general public, and the environment. Sound judgment should be exercised and the potential effects of the decontamination process upon personnel should be considered when developing the decontamination plan.

Most of this chapter has been completely rewritten for the 1997 edition. Material was added to expand on, and to provide a greater understanding of, decontamination.

Personnel and their equipment can be decontaminated by removing or neutralizing the contaminants that have accumulated on them, or by disposing of their protective clothing. Decontamination requires an organized and well-ordered procedure, hence the need for a plan in order to carry it out successfully. The plan must take into account measures that will minimize contamination as a line of first defense.

The decontamination plan should address such factors as the following:

(a) Site layout
(b) Decontamination methods to be used and equipment needed
(c) Number of personnel needed
(d) Level of protective clothing and equipment that will have to be processed
(e) Disposal methods
(f) Run-off control
(g) Emergency medical requirements
(h) Methods for collecting and disposing of contaminated clothing and equipment

The ultimate responsibility for implementing a decontamination plan falls to the incident commander. The hazardous materials branch officer will normally formulate and implement the decontamination procedures. *(See Figure 7.1.)*

Figure 7.1 *Dilution is one common method of decontamination. It reduces the concentration of the contaminant to a level at which it is no longer harmful. Water is used, except when the potential exists for a chemical reaction.*

7-1.1

Although decontamination is typically performed following site entry, the determination of proper decontamination methods and procedures needs to be considered before the incident as part of the overall pre-incident planning and hazard and risk evaluation process. No entry into the hot zone should be permitted until appropriate decontamination methods are determined and established based on the hazards present, except in those situations where a rescue may be possible and emergency decontamination is available.

Good operating practices can reduce the extent of contamination to clothing and equipment. For example, sampling and monitoring equipment can be bagged for protection, leaving a limited number of openings as needed for operation. Disposable outer garments also help, and covering the source of the contamination where possible can greatly reduce the need for extensive decontamination procedures. *(See Figure 7.2.)*

Figure 7.2 *For some types of contaminants, protective clothing can never be adequately decontaminated and so it must be disposed. However, sufficient decontamination must take place in order to allow workers to remove their protective clothing safely.*

7-1.2

Emergency response personnel should be familiar with the definitions of the following terminology:

(a) Contaminant
(b) Contamination
(c) Decontamination (contamination reduction)
(d) Decontamination corridor
(e) Emergency decontamination
(f) Exposure
(g) Gross decontamination
(h) Secondary contamination

7-2 Decontamination

Decontamination consists of reducing and preventing the spread of contamination from persons and equipment used at a hazardous materials incident by physical and/or chemical processes. Emergency response personnel should implement a thorough, technically sound decontamination procedure until it is determined or judged to be no longer necessary.

There are established methods for testing the effectiveness of decontamination procedures, and they should be used. If the decontamination procedure is not working effectively, the process may have to be revised or repeated.

Test methods include visual examination in both natural and ultraviolet light, laboratory analysis of a wipe sample, analysis of the cleaning solution used, and laboratory analysis of a segment of protective clothing.

7-2.1

Emergency response personnel should have an established procedure to minimize contamination or contact, to limit migration of contaminants, and to properly dispose of contaminated materials. The primary objective of decontamination is to avoid becoming contaminated or contaminating other personnel or equipment outside of the hot zone. If contamination is suspected, decontamination of personnel, equipment, and apparatus should be performed.

7-2.2

Procedures for all phases of decontamination need to be developed and implemented to reduce the possibility of contamination to personnel and equipment. Initial procedures should be upgraded or downgraded as additional information is obtained concerning the type of hazardous materials involved, the degree of hazard, and the probability of exposure of response personnel. Reference guides for the development of decontamination procedures can be found in Appendix C. Assuming protective equipment is grossly contaminated, appropriate decontamination methods should be used for the chemicals encountered.

Some decontamination procedures may actually present additional hazards. For example, the decontamination solution may react with the chemical to which the clothing was exposed, it may permeate or degrade some protective clothing, or it may emit harmful vapors. Compatibility should be determined before use.

7-2.3

The decision to implement all or part of a decontamination procedure should be based upon a field analysis of the hazards and risks involved. This analysis generally consists of referring to technical reference sources to determine the general hazards, such as flammability and toxicity, and then evaluating the relative risks. Decontamination procedures should be implemented upon arrival at the scene, should provide an adequate number of decontamination stations and personnel, and should continue until the incident commander determines that decontamination procedures are no longer required.

7-2.4 Precautionary Decontamination.

There are occasions when an apparently normal alarm response turns into a hazardous materials incident. Frequently, most of the initial assignment crews will have already gone into the incident area and exposed themselves to the contamination threat.

It is essential that all members so involved remove themselves from the area at once, call for decontamination capability, and stay together in one location. They must not wander around, climb on and off apparatus, and mix with other personnel since there is a potential for them to be contaminated.

Fire fighters so exposed should be given gross decontamination as a precautionary measure. Knowledgeable hazardous materials personnel, such as the decontamination sector officer, in conjunction with the incident commander, should determine whether more definitive decontamination is necessary.

Remember, the primary objective of decontamination is to avoid contaminating anyone or anything beyond the hot zone. When in doubt about contamination, decontaminate all involved personnel, equipment, and apparatus.

7-3 Decontamination Methods

7-3.1 Physical Methods.

Physical methods generally involve the physical removal of the contaminant from the contaminated person or object and containment of the contaminant for appropriate disposal. While these methods can reduce the contaminant's concentration, generally the contaminant remains chemically unchanged. Examples of physical decontamination methods include the following:

(a) Absorption
(b) Brushing and scraping
(c) Isolation and disposal
(d) Vacuuming
(e) Washing

Placing contaminated outer clothing on a plastic drop cloth within the decontamination area of the warm zone is a common and useful procedure. Contaminated clothing and equipment should be packed in hazardous waste containers. It is also helpful to have lined containers on hand in which to pack the contaminated clothing and equipment. *(See Figure 7.3.)*

If time is not an overriding factor, and if technicians are not on site or immediately available, the detergent-water solution method of preliminary decontamination is the safest and most appropriate approach. Metal or plastic drums are effective for storing washing or rinsing solutions used in decontamination work. The detergent-water solution method is described in Supplement 10 of this handbook. See the commentary on 7-2.1 regarding hazards associated with the use of chemical solutions.

7-3.2 Chemical Methods.

Chemical methods are used on equipment, not people, and generally involve decontamination by changing the contaminant through some type of chemical reaction in an effort to render the contaminant less harmful. In the case of etiologic contaminants, chemical methods are actually biologically "killing" the organism. Examples of chemical methods include the following:

(a) Adsorption
(b) Chemical degradation
(c) Disinfection or sterilization
(d) Neutralization
(e) Solidification

7-3.3 Prevention Methods.

If contact with a contaminant can be controlled, the risk of exposure is reduced and the need for decontamination can be minimized. The following points should be considered to prevent contamination:

(a) Stress work practices that minimize contact with hazardous substances.
(b) Wear limited-use or disposable protective clothing and equipment, where appropriate.

7-4 Decontaminating Personal Protective Equipment (PPE)

During doffing of personal protective equipment, the clothing should be removed in a manner such that the outside surfaces do not touch or make contact with the wearer. A log of personal protective equipment used during the incident should be maintained. Personnel wearing disposable personal protective equipment should proceed through the

Figure 7.3 Decontamination gear can include plastic sheeting, hazardous waste containers, and even inflatable wading pools, shown on the left. These pools are inexpensive, portable when uninflated, and catch contaminated runoff water effectively. (Photo courtesy of Lt. David Hansen, Bedford, MA Fire Department)

decontamination process setup in the decontamination area, and the disposable protective equipment should be containerized and identified for disposal in accordance with established procedures.

Some heavy contamination of PPE can be removed physically by wiping off, wetting down, and allowing to dry. Chemical means can also be used to deactivate a contaminant, as can a combination of physical and chemical means. The hazards of using chemical solutions are described in detail in 7-2.2 of this chapter.

The log of personal protective equipment used during an incident should record the type of equipment used, the duration of use of the equipment and exposure to the chemicals, the decontamination procedures used, and the types of chemicals to which the equipment was exposed. It should also record the name of the person using the equipment.

Disposable protective equipment should be placed in plastic bags or plastic trash cans pending final disposal.

7-4.1

The physical and chemical compatibility of decontamination solutions needs to be determined before they are used. Any decontamination method that permeates, degrades, damages, or otherwise impairs the safe function of PPE should not be used unless there are plans to isolate and dispose of the PPE.

7-4.2

Water or other solutions for washing or rinsing may have to be confined, collected, containerized, and analyzed for proper treatment and disposal. Consult with environmental and public health agencies or other appropriate reference sources and guidelines to determine the need for confinement and the appropriate disposal methods for collected decontamination fluids and personal protective equipment.

7-4.3

Decontamination methods vary in their effectiveness for removing different substances. The effectiveness of any decontamination method should be assessed throughout the decontamination operation. If decontamination does not appear to be effective, a different method should be selected and implemented. Before initiating decontamination, the following questions should be considered:

(a) Can decontamination be conducted safely?
(b) Are existing resources adequate and immediately available to perform decontamination of personnel and equipment? If not, where can they be obtained, and how long will it take to get them?

If the decontamination method being used is not effectively removing contaminants, different and additional measures must be taken to prevent further contamination. If necessary, specialists should be consulted.

The decontamination plan may have to be changed whenever the type of protective clothing and equipment changes, when site conditions change, or when new information is received. If necessary, protective clothing and equipment manufacturers should be consulted.

7-4.4

Criteria that can be used for evaluating decontamination effectiveness during field operations include the following:

(a) Contamination levels are reduced as personnel move through the decontamination corridor.
(b) Contamination is confined to the hot zone and decontamination corridor.
(c) Contamination is reduced to a level that is as low as reasonably achievable.

7-4.5*

Methods that may be useful in assessing the effectiveness of decontamination include the following:

A-7-4.5 It should be noted that for etiologic hazards and many chemical hazards, there is no real-time way to determine the effectiveness of decontamination in the field.

(a) Visual observation (stains, discolorations, corrosive effects, etc.)
(b) Monitoring devices (Devices such as photoionization detectors (PIDs), detector tubes, radiation monitors, and pH paper strips/meters can show that contamination levels are at least below the device's detection limit.)
(c) Wipe sampling (Such sampling provides for after-the-fact information on the effectiveness of decontamination. Once a wipe swab is taken, it is analyzed by chemical means, usually in a laboratory. Both protective clothing, equipment, and skin may be tested using wipe samples.)

7-4.6*

Large items of equipment, such as vehicles and trucks, should be subjected to decontamination by washes, high-pressure washes, steam, or special solutions. Water or other solutions used for washing or rinsing may have to be confined, collected, containerized, analyzed, and treated prior to disposal. Consult with environmental and public health agencies to determine the appropriate disposition.

Apparatus can become contaminated in several ways. These include placing the apparatus downwind where vapors or smoke may contaminate it, placing the apparatus too close to the isolation area where it can be splashed or sprayed by hazardous materials, driving it through a spill, and placing contaminated equipment back on the apparatus. Tools should be inspected frequently at the scene to determine how contaminated they are and to establish the best method of decontaminating them.

To decontaminate large equipment, responders will have to have different supplies on hand. These might include adequately sized storage tanks or collection systems, pumps or drains, long-handled brushes, and wash booths or containers. *(See Figure 7.4.)*

Figure 7.4 *In some cases, fire fighting equipment and apparatus may require decontamination, which is generally done with water.*

A-7-4.6 Additional information can be found in NFPA 472, *Standard for Professional Competence of Responders to Hazardous Materials Incidents,* A-15-2.3.4.5

If a large number of vehicles need to be decontaminated, the following recommendations should be considered:

(a) Establish a decontamination pad as a primary wash station. The pad may be a coarse gravel pad, concrete slab, or a pool liner. It may be necessary to collect these decontamination fluids, and the decontamination pad may be bermed or diked with a sump or some form of water recovery system.

(b) Completely wash and rinse vehicles several times with detergent. Pay particular attention to wheel wells, radiators, engines, and chassis. Depending on the nature of the contaminant, it may be necessary to collect all runoff water from the initial gross rinse, particularly if there is contaminated mud and dirt on the underside of the chassis.

(c) Vehicles should be inspected thoroughly by qualified personnel for possible mechanical or electrical damage. Areas of concern include air intakes, filters, cooling systems, and air-operated systems.

(d) Empty completely and thoroughly wash any outside compartments that were opened. The equipment should be washed and rinsed prior to being replaced.

(e) Equipment sprayed with acids should be flushed or washed as soon as possible with a neutralizing agent such as baking soda and then flushed again with rinse water.

(f) If vehicles have been exposed to minimal contaminants such as smoke and vapors, they may be decontaminated on-site and then driven to an off-site car wash for a second, more thorough washing. Car washes may be suitable if the drainage area is fully contained and all runoff drains into a holding tank.

(g) Verification of adequacy of decontamination, where necessary, may consist of samples collected from the cab and exterior surfaces that are analyzed in an off-site laboratory.

7-4.7

Personnel assigned to the decontamination team should wear an appropriate level of personal protective equipment (PPE) and may require decontamination themselves. Personal protective equipment can be upgraded or downgraded as additional information is obtained concerning the type of hazardous materials involved, the degree of hazard, and the probability of exposure of response personnel.

The members of the decontamination team closest to the hot zone may require a higher level of protective clothing than those closest to the cold zone. The level of protection required varies with the decontamination equipment in use. Protective clothing should be selected by the hazardous materials technician under the direction of the hazardous materials branch officer. The selection should be approved by the incident commander.

7-4.8

If personnel display any symptoms of heat exhaustion or possible exposure, appropriate emergency measures need to be implemented to doff PPE, while protecting the individual from contaminants and preventing the spread of any contaminants. These individuals should be transferred to the care of emergency medical services personnel who have completed training in accordance with applicable standards (e.g., NFPA 473, *Standard for Competencies for EMS Personnel Responding to Hazardous Materials Incidents*).

The responder in PPE must be aware of the signs and symptoms of heat exhaustion and be able to request assistance at the first indication of a problem *(see Figure 7.5)*. For the wearer to doff the PPE quickly and be decontaminated properly, sufficient time must be allowed for the process. See Section 8-4 of NFPA 471 for those medical symptoms that indicate that actions need to be taken to avoid heat exhaustion.

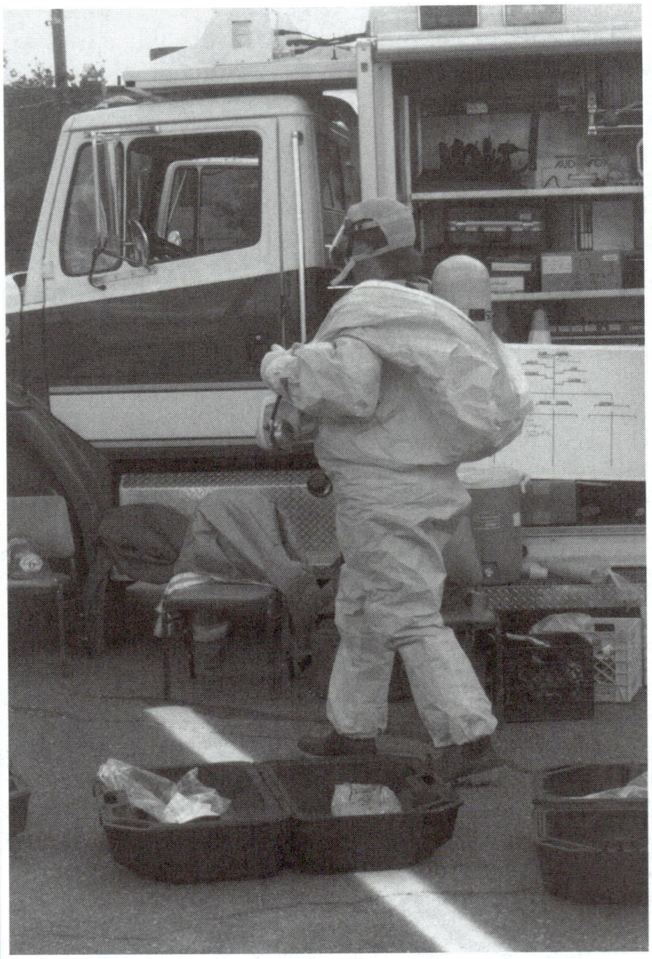

Figure 7.5 *Wearing the Level A PPE shown here is another skill requiring special training and practice. Because the suit is totally encapsulating, it traps body heat and increases the stress on its wearer. Responders in PPE must be aware of the signs and symptoms of heat exhaustion and be able to request assistance at the first indication of a problem. (Photo courtesy of Lt. David Hansen, Bedford, MA Fire Department)*

7-4.9

A debriefing should be held for those involved in decontamination as soon as practical. Exposed persons should be provided with as much information as possible about the delayed health effects of the hazardous materials involved in the incident. If necessary, follow-up examinations should be scheduled with medical personnel.

7-4.10

Exposure records should be maintained for future reference by the individual's personal physician and employer.

CHAPTER 8

Medical Monitoring

8-1 Introduction

This entire chapter is new to the 1997 edition. These guidelines are the recommendations of medical professionals who have participated in hazardous materials responses. Alterations to the guidelines in this recommended practice should only be undertaken with the advice of a medical authority that has expertise and knowledge of the physical demands of operating at a hazardous materials incident.

Written procedures should not allow any variance from these medical monitoring benchmarks by the incident commander.

8-1.1 Purpose.

The purpose of this chapter is to provide guidelines for local jurisdictions to perform medical monitoring for hazardous materials response personnel. It is not the intent of this recommended practice to restrict any jurisdiction's medical authority from using different or modified guidelines. Locally established guidelines for medical monitoring should not be negated by a decision of command personnel.

8-1.2 Definition.

Medical monitoring is the ongoing, systematic evaluation of response personnel who are at risk of suffering adverse effects of heat/cold exposure, stress, or hazardous materials exposure. This monitoring is done for the purpose of achieving early recognition and prevention of these effects in order to maintain the optimal health and safety of on-scene personnel.

8-1.3 Objectives.

Medical monitoring is performed at the site of a hazardous materials incident for the following reasons:

(a) To obtain baseline vital signs and physical assessment

(b) To identify and preclude from participation in the hot zone and warm zone activities individuals at increased risk for sustaining injury and illness as a result of on-scene activities

(c) To provide early recognition and treatment of personnel with adverse physiological responses as a result of on-scene activities

Working at a hazardous materials incident is demanding enough without the worry that a fellow responder will need emergency medical attention. What would happen if a coworker had a heart attack and needed CPR while you both were in Level A personal protection in the hot zone?

Personnel in poor physical condition will use their air supply faster than a fit person. This difference can be substantial. A fit individual may be able to work for 25 minutes, while an unfit worker may have to leave after 10 to 15 minutes. Since personnel work in teams, both would have to leave at an earlier time.

The medical monitoring criteria listed in Section 8-3 and Section 8-6 will not ensure that a person is physically fit, but only that it is unlikely that he or she will experience a life threatening medical emergency. If your departmental goal is to have personnel perform at a pre-determined physical level, a sports physician should be consulted to create a physical fitness and wellness program for your hazardous materials response members.

8-1.4

Pre-entry medical monitoring should be completed on all individuals wearing chemical liquid splash- and vapor-protective clothing and performing hazardous materials operations. It should be completed within one hour prior to entry.

8-2 Components of Pre-Entrance Medical Monitoring

If an individual makes more than one entry into the hot zone, this medical monitoring must be done for each re-entry in addition to the initial entry and exit. In situations where the person meets or exceeds the exclusion criteria in Section 8-3 for the first entry but then fails to meet the criteria before a second or later entry, dehydration or not enough rest between entries may be to blame. High ambient temperature can also increase an individual's need for more hydration and rest.

8-2.1 Vital Signs.

Pre-entrance medical monitoring should include the evaluation of the following vital signs:

(a) Blood pressure
(b) Pulse
(c) Respiratory rate
(d) Temperature
(e) EKG rhythm strip (10 seconds), if available

8-2.2 Skin Evaluation.

Pre-entrance medical monitoring should include an examination of the individual's skin for the following:

(a) Rashes
(b) Open sores/wounds

8-2.3 Mental Status.

The individual should be alert and oriented to time and place, have clear speech and a normal gait, and be able to respond appropriately to the situation.

8-2.4 Medical History.

A recent medical history should be obtained that includes the following:

(a) Medications, including over the counter, taken within the past 72 hours
(b) Alcohol consumption within the past 24 hours
(c) Any new medical treatment or diagnosis made within the past two weeks
(d) Symptoms of fever, nausea, vomiting, diarrhea, or cough within the past 72 hours

8-2.5 Weight.

The individual's weight should be recorded.

8-2.6 Hydration.

It should be determined whether the individual has consumed 8–16 ounces of water or diluted activity drink.

8-3 Exclusion Criteria

8-3.1

The following exclusion criteria should be applied to findings of all medical monitoring completed on hazardous materials response personnel. These criteria provide the EMS Control Officer and the Hazardous Materials Branch Officer with guidelines to determine medical/physical fitness for entry.

(a) Blood pressure—diastolic greater than 105 mm Hg
(b) Pulse—greater than 70 percent maximum heart rate (220–age)

Table 8-3.1(b) Age-Predicted Heart Rates

Age	70 Percent
20–25	140
25–30	136
30–35	132
35–40	128
40–45	125
45–50	122

(c) Respiratory rate—greater than 24 per minute
(d) Temperature—greater than 99.5°F (oral) or greater than 100.5°F (core) or less than 97.0°F (oral) or less than 98.0°F (core)
(e) Weight—no pre-entry exclusion
(f) EKG—dysrhythmia not previously detected (must be cleared by medical control)
(g) Skin evaluation—open sores, large area of rash or significant sunburn
(h) Mental status—altered mental status (i.e., slurred speech, clumsiness, weakness)
(i) Recent medical history:

1. Presence of nausea, vomiting, diarrhea, fever, upper respiratory infection, heat illness, or heavy alcohol intake within past 72 hours, all of which contribute to dehydration
2. New prescription medications taken within past two weeks or over the counter medications such as cold, flu, or allergy medicines, taken within past 72 hours (must be cleared through local medical control or hazardous materials medical director)
3. Any alcohol within past six hours
4. Pregnancy

It is vital that these guidelines be placed in a department's SOPs and not be deviated from. Any changes should be made only with the advice of a qualified medical professional and then added to the SOPs for consistency and reference. Adhering to these established SOPs on scene provides a measure of safety for the team members at risk. *(See Figure 8.1.)*

8-4 Components of Medical Monitoring During Entry

8-4.1

Changes in gait, speech, or behavior that require entry personnel to undergo immediate decontamination, doffing of protective clothing, and assessment should be monitored.

8-4.2

If entry personnel complain of chest pain, dizziness, shortness of breath, weakness, nausea, or headache, they should undergo immediate decontamination, doffing of protective clothing, and assessment.

8-5 Post-Entry Medical Monitoring

8-5.1 Objectives.

Post-entry medical monitoring is performed to determine the following:

(a) Whether an individual has suffered any immediate effects from exposure to a hazardous material or the environment

(b) An individual's health status for future assignment during or following incident (This assessment should include both physiological and psychological considerations.)

8-5.2

Components of post-entry medical monitoring should include the following:

(a) History—any symptom of hazardous material exposure, environmental exposure, or cardiovascular collapse

(b) Vital signs:

1. Blood pressure
2. Pulse
3. Respiratory rate
4. Temperature
5. EKG (if available)

(c) Weight

(d) Skin evaluation

(e) Mental status

The EPA offers a guide to appropriate medical monitoring after exposure to these common toxicants. See Table 8.1 for a breakdown of these toxicants, their effects, and EPA recommendations for treatment.

8-6 Post-Medical Monitoring Follow-Up

8-6.1

Post-medical monitoring follow-up should include the following:

(a) Repeat monitoring of vital signs every 5–10 minutes until they return to less than 85 percent of maximum pulse rate. If at 10 minutes the signs have not returned to within 10 percent of baseline, perform orthostatic vital signs.

(b) Determine from medical control what information regarding latent reactions/symptoms should be communicated to response personnel.

(c) If any of the following symptoms are present, contact medical control for direction and preparation for possible transport to a medical facility:

1. Body weight loss of greater than 3 percent or positive orthostatic (pulse increase by 20 beats per minute or systolic blood pressure decrease by 20 mm of Hg at two minutes standing)
2. Greater than 85 percent maximum pulse at 10 minutes
3. Temperature greater than 101°F (oral) or 102°F (core)
4. Nausea, vomiting, diarrhea, altered mental status, or respiratory, cardiac, or dermatologic complaints

8-7 Treatment Protocol for Hazardous Materials Team Members

8-7.1

Rest time for all personnel should equal at least minimum suit time. Individuals may require additional time for oral rehydration. All personnel should be informed of signs and symptoms to watch for.

8-7.2

If the team member is not within 10 percent of baseline within 10 minutes, orthostatic vital signs should be taken.

8-7.3

If personnel experience greater than 3 percent body weight loss (4 ½ pounds in a 150-pound person); positive orthostatic (pulse increases by 20 beats per minute or systolic blood pressure decreases by 20 mm of Hg at two minutes

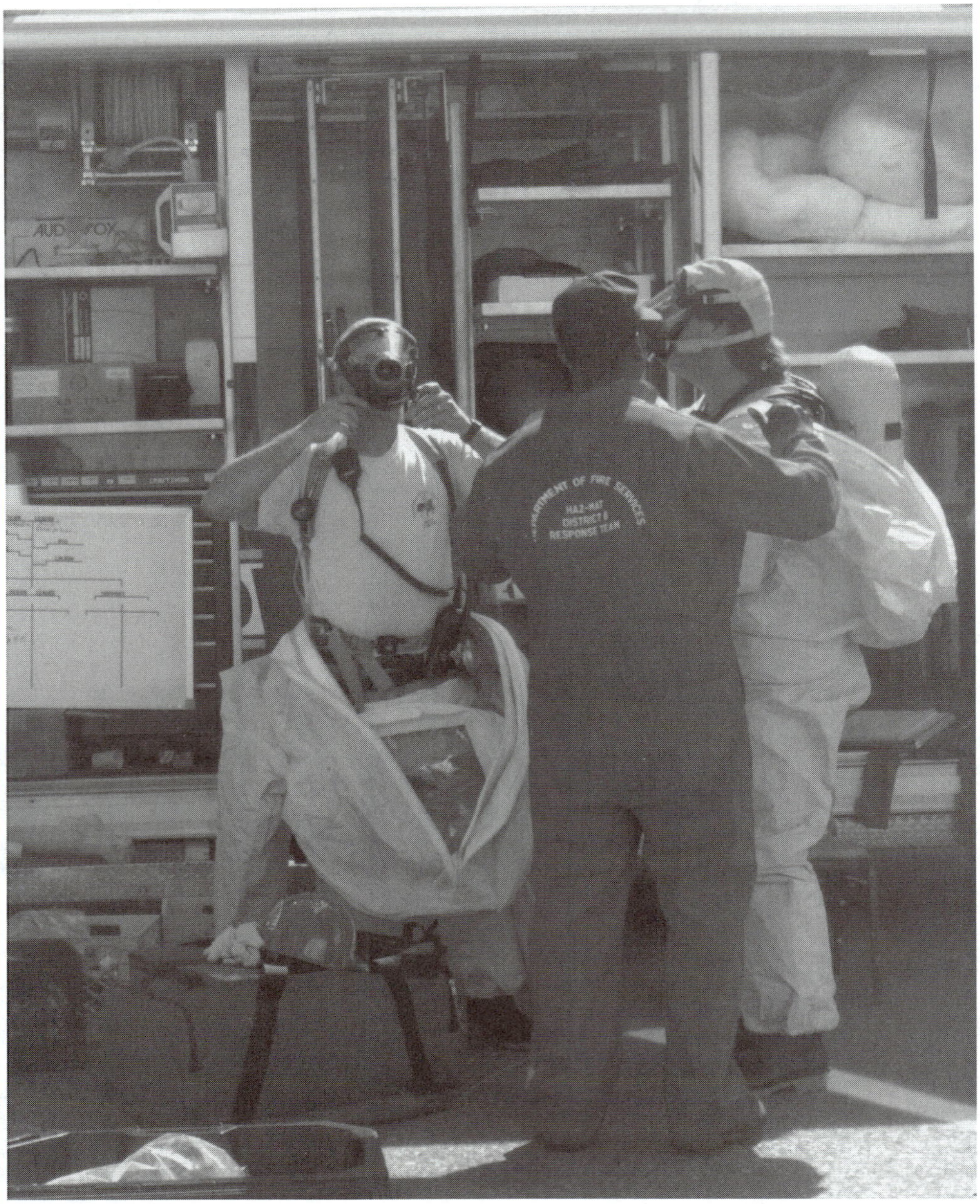

Figure 8.1 The pre-entry assessment is important. These responders are being evaluated by a safety officer prior to donning Level A protective gear. (Photo courtesy of Lt. David Hansen, Bedford, MA Fire Department)

standing); greater than 85 percent of maximum pulse at 10 minutes; temperature greater than 101˚F oral (102˚F core); nausea, altered mental status, or any other symptoms, the following treatment should be performed:

(a) Intravenous fluids hydration with Ringers Lactate or Normal Saline at rate (usually wide open) to get pulse less than 100 beats per minute, systolic blood pressure greater than 110 mm of Hg

(b) Administration of oxygen 4 L to 6 L per minute via nasal cannula, may increase as needed

(c) Consultation of reference protocols or medical control for treatment of specific symptoms/types of exposure

Table 8.1 EPA List of Common Chemical Toxicants Found at Hazardous Waste Sites, Health Effects, and Medical Monitoring

Hazardous Substance or Chemical Group	Compounds	Uses	Target Organs	Potential Health Effects	Medical Monitoring
Aromatic Hydrocarbons	Benzene Ethyl benzene Toluene Xylene	Commercial solvents and intermediates for synthesis in the chemical and pharmaceutical industries.	Blood Bone marrow CNS[a] Eyes Respiratory system Skin Liver Kidney	All cause: CNS[a] depression: decreased alertness, headache, sleepiness, loss of consciousness. Defatting dermatitis. Benzene suppresses bone-marrow function, causing blood changes. Chronic exposure can cause leukemia. Note: Because other aromatic hydrocarbons may be contaminated with benzene during distillation, benzene-related health effects should be considered when exposure to any of these agents is suspected.	Occupational/general medical history emphasizing prior exposure to these or other toxic agents. Medical examination with focus on liver, kidney, nervous system, and skin. Laboratory testing: CBC[b] Platelet count Measurement of kidney and liver function.
Asbestos (or asbestiform particles)		A variety of industrial uses, including Building construction Cement work Insulation Fireproofing Pipes and ducts for water, air, and chemicals. Automobile brake pads and linings	Lungs Gastrointestinal system	Chronic effects: Lung cancer Mesothelioma Asbestosis Gastrointestinal malignancies Asbestos exposure coupled with cigarette smoking has been shown to have a synergistic effect in the development of lung cancer.	History and physical examination should focus on the lungs and gastrointestinal system. Laboratory tests should include a stool test for occult blood evaluation as a check for possible hidden gastrointestinal malignancy. A high-quality chest X-ray and pulmonary function test may help to identify long-term changes associated with asbestos diseases; however, early identification of low-dose exposure is unlikely.

(continues)

Table 8.1 (Continued)

Hazardous Substance or Chemical Group	Compounds	Uses	Target Organs	Potential Health Effects	Medical Monitoring
Dioxin (see Herbicides)					
Halogenated Allphatic Hydrocarbons	Carbon tetrachloride Chloroform Ethyl bromide Ethyl chloride Ethylene dibromide Ethylene dichloride Methyl chloride Methylene chloride Methyl chloroform Tetrachloroethane Tetrachloroethylene (perchloroethylene) Trichloroethylene Vinyl chloride	Commercial solvents and intermediates in organic synthesis.	CNS[a] Kidney Liver Skin	All cause: CNS[a] depression: decreased alertness, headaches, sleepiness, loss of consciousness. Kidney changes: deceased urine flow, swelling (especially around eyes), anemia. Liver changes: fatigue, malaise, dark urine, liver enlargement, jaundice. Vinyl chloride is a known carcinogen: several others in this group are potential carcinogens.	Occupational/general medical history emphasizing prior exposure to these or other toxic agents. Medical examination with focus on liver, kidney, nervous system, and skin. Laboratory testing for liver and kidney function; carboxyhemoglobin where relevant.
Heavy Metals	Arsenic Beryllium Cadmium Chromium Lead Mercury	Wide variety of industrial and commercial uses.	Multiple organs and systems including Blood Cardiopulmonary Gastrointestinal Kidney Liver Lung CNS[a] Skin.	All are toxic to the kidneys. Each heavy metal has its own characteristic symptom cluster. For example, lead causes decreased mental ability, weakness (especially in hands), headache, abdominal cramps, diarrhea, and anemia. Lead can also affect the blood-forming mechanism, kidneys, and the peripheral nervous system. Long-term effects[c] also vary. Lead toxicity can cause permanent kidney and brain damage; cadmium can cause kidney or lung disease. Chromium, beryllium, arsenic, and cadmium have been implicated as human carcinogens.	History-taking and physical exam: search for symptom clusters associated with specific metal exposure, e.g., for lead look for neurological deficit, anemia, and gastrointestinal symptoms. Laboratory testing: Measurements of metallic content in blood, urine, and tissues (e.g., blood lead level; urine screen for arsenic, mercury, chromium, and cadmium). CBC[b] Measurement of kidney function, and liver function where relevant. Chest X-ray or pulmonary function testing where relevant.

Table 8.1 (Continued)

Hazardous Substance or Chemical Group	Compounds	Uses	Target Organs	Potential Health Effects	Medical Monitoring
Herbicides	Chlorophenoxy compounds: 2,4-dichloro-phenosyacetic acid (2,4-D) 2,4,5-trichloro-phenosyacetic acid (2,4,5-T) Dioxin (tetachloro-dibenzo-p-dioxin, TCDD), which occurs as a trace contaminant in these compounds, poses the most serious health risk.	Vegetation control.	Kidney Liver CNS[a] Skin	Chlorophenoxy compounds can cause chloracne, weakness or numbness of the arms and legs, and may result in long-term nerve damage. Dioxin causes chloracne and may aggravate pre-existing liver and kidney diseases.	History and physical exam should focus on the skin and nervous system. Laboratory tests include: Measurement of liver and kidney function, where relevant. Urinalysis.
Organochlorine Insecticides	Chlorinated ethanes: DDT Cyclodienes: Aldrin Chlordane Dieldrin Endrin Chlorocyclohexanes: Lindane	Pest control.	Kidney Liver CNS[a]	All cause acute symptoms of apprehension, irritability, dizziness, disturbed equilibrium, tremor, and convulsions. Cyclodienes may cause convulsions without any other initial symptoms. Chlorocyclohexanes can cause anemia. Cyclodienes and chlorocyclohexanes cause liver toxicity and can cause permanent kidney damage.	History and physical exam should focus on the nervous system. Laboratory tests include: Measurement of kidney and liver function. CBC[b] for exposure to chlorocyclohexanes.

(continues)

Table 8.1 (Continued)

Hazardous Substance or Chemical Group	Compounds	Uses	Target Organs	Potential Health Effects	Medical Monitoring
Organophosphate and Carbamate Insecticides	Organophosphate: Diazinon, Dichlorovos, Dimethoate, Trichlofon, Malathion, Methyl parathion, Parathion Carbamate: Aldicarb, Baygon, Zectran	Pest control.	CNS[a] Liver Kidney	All cause a chain of internal reactions leading to neuromuscular blockage. Depending on the extent of poisoning, acute symptoms range from headaches, fatigue, dizziness, increased salivation and crying, profuse sweating, nausea, vomiting, cramps, and diarrhea to tightness in the chest, muscle twitching, and slowing of the heartbeat. Severe cases may result in rapid onset of unconsciousness and seizures. A delayed effect may be weakness and numbness in the feet and hands. Long-term, permanent nerve damage is possible.	Physical exam should focus on the nervous system. Laboratory tests should include: RBC[d] cholinesterase levels for recent exposure (plasma cholinesterase for acute exposures). Measurement of delayed neurotoxicity and other effects.
Polychlorinated Biphenyls (PCBs)		Wide variety of industrial uses.	Liver CNS[a] (speculative) Respiratory system (speculative) Skin	Various skin ailments, including chloracne; may cause liver toxicity; carcinogenic to animals.	Physical exam should focus on the skin and liver. Laboratory tests include: Serum PCB levels. Triglycerides and cholesterol. Measurement of liver function.

Source: *Occupational Safety and Health Guidance Manual for Hazardous Waste Site Activities*, NIOSH/OSHA/USCG/EPA, U.S. Department of Human Services, NIOSH, 1985.

[a] CNS = Central nervous system.

[b] CBC = Complete blood count.

[c] Long-term effects generally manifest in 10 to 30 years.

[d] RBC = Red blood count.

CHAPTER 9

Referenced Publications

9-1

The following documents or portions thereof are referenced within this recommended practice and should be considered as part of its recommendations. The edition indicated for each referenced document is the current edition as of the date of the NFPA issuance of this recommended practice. Some of these documents might also be referenced in this recommended practice for specific informational purposes and, therefore, are also listed in Appendix B.

9-1.1 NFPA Publications.

National Fire Protection Association, 1 Batterymarch Park, P.O. Box 9101, Quincy, MA 02269-9101.

NFPA 70, *National Electrical Code®*, 1996 edition.

NFPA 472, *Standard for Professional Competence of Responders to Hazardous Materials Incidents,* 1997 edition.

NFPA 473, *Standard for Competencies for EMS Personnel Responding to Hazardous Materials Incidents*, 1997 edition.

NFPA 1500, *Standard on Fire Department Occupational Safety and Health Program,* 1997 edition.

NFPA 1981, *Standard on Open-Circuit Self-Contained Breathing Apparatus for Fire Fighters,* 1997 edition.

NFPA 1982, *Standard on Personal Alert Safety Systems (PASS) for Fire Fighters,* 1993 edition.

NFPA 1991, *Standard on Vapor-Protective Suits for Hazardous Chemical Emergencies,* 1994 edition.

NFPA 1992, *Standard on Liquid Splash-Protective Suits for Hazardous Chemical Emergencies,* 1994 edition.

NFPA 1993, *Standard on Support Function Protective Clothing for Hazardous Chemical Operations,* 1994 edition.

9-1.2 Other Publications.

9-1.2.1 ASTM Publications. American Society for Testing and Materials, 100 Barr Harbor Drive, West Conshohocken, PA 19428-2959.

ASTM F 716, *Method of Testing Sorbent Performance of Absorbents,* 1982.

ASTM F 726, *Method of Testing Sorbent Performance of Adsorbents,* 1981.

ASTM STP 659, *Chemical Dispersants for the Control of Oil Spills.*

ASTM STP 840, *Oil Spill Chemical Dispersants: Research, Experience, and Recommendations.*

9-1.2.2 U.S. Government Publication. U.S. Government Printing Office, Superintendent of Documents, Washington, DC 20402.

Title 29, *Code of Federal Regulations,* Part 1910.120, 1995.

APPENDIX A

The material contained in Appendix A of this standard is not part of the requirements of the *Code* but is included with the *Code* for informational purposes only. For the convenience of readers, in this handbook the Appendix A material is interspersed among the verbiage of Chapters 1 through 8 and, therefore, is not repeated here.

APPENDIX B

Referenced Publications

B-1

The following documents or portions thereof are referenced within this recommended practice for informational purposes only and are thus not considered part of its recommendations. The edition indicated here for each reference is the current edition as of the date of the NFPA issuance of this recommended practice.

B-1.1 NFPA Publications.

National Fire Protection Association, 1 Batterymarch Park, P.O. Box 9101, Quincy, MA 02269-9101.

NFPA 11, *Standard for Low-Expansion Foam,* 1998 edition.

NFPA 11A, *Standard for Medium- and High-Expansion Foam Systems*, 1994 edition.

NFPA 16, *Standard for the Installation of Deluge Foam-Water Sprinkler and Foam-Water Spray Systems*, 1995 edition.

NFPA 472, *Standard for Professional Competence of Responders to Hazardous Materials Incidents*, 1997 edition.

B-1.2 Other Publications.

B-1.2.1 ASTM Publication. American Society for Testing and Materials, 100 Barr Harbor Drive, West Conshohocken, PA 19428-2959.

ASTM F 1129, *Using Aqueous Foams to Control the Vapor Hazard from Immiscible Volatile Liquids*, 1988.

B-1.2.2 U.S. Government Publications. U.S. Government Printing Office, Superintendent of Documents, Washington, DC 20402.

Title 29, *Code of Federal Regulations,* Parts 1910.120 and 1910.134, 1995.

Title 40, *Code of Federal Regulations,* Parts 261.33, 300, 302, and 355, 1994.

Title 49, *Code of Federal Regulations,* Parts 170–179, 1995.

APPENDIX C

Suggested Reading List

This appendix is not a part of the recommendations of this NFPA document but is included for informational purposes only.

C-1 Introduction

This list provides the titles of references and organizations that may be of value to those responding to hazardous materials incidents. This list can be expanded based on personal preferences and requirements.

The references are categorized by subject. The title, author, publisher, and place of publication are given for each. The year of publication is not always given because many are revised annually. The user should attempt to obtain the most recent edition.

The last section lists sources of these references as well as other information that might be useful. Usually, these agencies or associations will provide a catalog on request. Where available, phone numbers are also listed.

C-2 References

C-2.1 Industrial Hygiene (Air Sampling and Monitoring, Respiratory Protection, Toxicology).

Air Sampling Instruments for Evaluation of Atmospheric Contaminants, American Conference of Governmental Industrial Hygienists, Cincinnati, OH, 8th edition, 1995.

Fundamentals of Industrial Hygiene, National Safety Council, Chicago, IL, 4th edition, 1996.

Patty's Industrial Hygiene and Toxicology, John Wiley and Sons, Inc., New York, NY, 4th edition, 1995.

NIOSH Pocket Guide to Chemical Hazards, DHHS No. 85-114, NIOSH, Department of Health and Human Services, Cincinnati, OH, 1995.

Occupational Health Guidelines for Chemical Hazards, DHHS No. 81-123, NIOSH, Department of Health and Human Services, Cincinnati, OH.

Occupational Safety and Health Standards, Title 29, *Code of Federal Regulations,* Part 1910.120, "Hazardous Waste Operations and Emergency Response Final Rule," U.S. Government Printing Office, Washington, DC, 1995.

Documentation of Threshold Limit Values and Biological Exposure Indices, American Conference of Governmental Industrial Hygienists, Cincinnati, OH, 6th edition, 1991.

C-2.2 Chemical Data.

Chemical Hazard Response Information System (CHRIS), U.S. Coast Guard, Washington, DC, Commandant Instruction M.16565.12A.

CHRIS — A Condensed Guide to Chemical Hazards, U.S. Coast Guard, Commandant Instruction M.16565.11a.

Hawley Condensed Chemical Dictionary, Van Nostrand Reinhold Co., New York, NY, 12th edition, 1993.

Dangerous Properties of Industrial Materials, N. Irving Sax, Van Nostrand Reinhold Co., New York, NY, 9th edition, 1996.

Effects of Exposure to Toxic Gases, Matheson, 3rd edition, 1988.

Emergency Handling of Hazardous Materials in Surface Transportation, Association of American Railroads, Washington, DC, 1992.

Farm Chemicals Handbook, Farm Chemicals Magazine, Willoughby, OH.

Firefighter's Handbook of Hazardous Materials, Baker, Charles J., Maltese Enterprises, Indianapolis, IN, 5th edition, 1990.

Fire Protection Guide to Hazardous Materials, National Fire Protection Association, Quincy, MA, 11th edition, 1996.

The Merck Index, Merck, Whitehouse Station, NJ, 1996.

C-2.3 Safety and Personnel Protection.

A Guide to the Safe Handling of Hazardous Materials Accidents, ASTM STP 825, American Society for Testing and Materials, Philadelphia, PA, 2nd edition, 1990.

Fire Protection Handbook, National Fire Protection Association, Quincy, MA, 18th edition, 1997.

Guidelines for Decontamination of Firefighters and Their Equipment Following Hazardous Materials Incidents, Canadian Association of Fire Chiefs, Ottawa (May 1987).

Guidelines for the Selection of Chemical Protective Clothing. Volume 1: Field Guide, A. D. Schwope, P. P. Costas, J. O. Jackson, D. J. Weitzman; Arthur D. Little, Inc., Cambridge, MA (March 1983).

Guidelines for the Selection of Chemical Protective Clothing. Volume 2: Technical and Reference Manual, A. D. Schwope, P. P. Costas, J. O. Jackson, D. J. Weitzman, J. O. Stull; Arthur D. Little, Inc., Cambridge, MA, 3rd edition (February 1987).

Hazardous Materials Emergencies Response and Control, John R. Cashman, Technomic Publishing Company, Lancaster, PA (June 1983).

Hazardous Materials for the First Responder, International Fire Service Training Association, Stillwater, OK (1988).

Hazardous Materials: Managing the Incident, Gregory Noll, Michael Hildebrand, and James Yvorra, Fire Service Publications, Stillwater, OK (1995).

Handling Radiation Emergencies, Purington and Patterson, National Fire Protection Association, Quincy, MA, 1997.

National Safety Council Safety Sheets, National Safety Council, Chicago, IL.

Radiological Health — Preparedness and Response in Radiation Accidents, U.S. Department of Health and Human Services, Washington, DC.

C-2.4 Planning Guides.

Federal Motor Carrier Safety Regulations Pocketbook, U.S. Department of Transportation, J. J. Keller and Associates, Inc., 1993.

Occupational Safety and Health Guidance Manual for Hazardous Waste Site Activities, NIOSH/OSHA/USCG/EPA, U.S. Department of Health and Human Services, NIOSH, 1985.

Hazardous Materials Emergency Planning Guide (March 1987), National Response Team.

Standard Operating Safety Guides, Environmental Response Branch, Office of Emergency and Remedial Response, U.S. Environmental Protection Agency, 1992.

C-3 Agencies and Associations

Agency for Toxic Substances Disease Registry
1600 Clifton Road, NE
Centers for Disease Control
Atlanta, GA 30333
(800) 447-4784 dial 329-1175

American Conference of Governmental Industrial Hygienists
6500 Glenway Avenue — Building D-5
Cincinnati, OH 45211
(513) 661-7881

American Industrial Hygiene Association
2700 Prosperity Avenue, Suite 250
Fairfax, VA 22031
(703) 849-8888

American National Standards Institute, Inc.
11 W. 42nd Street, 13th Floor
New York, NY 10018
(212) 642-4900

American Petroleum Institute (API)
1220 L Street N.W., 9th Floor
Washington, DC 20005
(202) 682-8100

Association of American Railroads
50 F Street N.W.
Washington, DC 20001
(202) 639-2100

Chemical Manufacturers' Association
2501 M Street N.W.
Washington, DC 20037
(202) 877-1100

CHEMTREC
Washington, DC
(800) 424-9300

The Chlorine Institute
2001 L Street N.W.
Washington, DC 20036
(202) 775-2790

Compressed Gas Association
1725 Jefferson Davis Highway
Arlington, VA 22202
(703) 412-0900

The Fertilizer Institute (TFI)
501 2nd Street N.E.
Washington, DC 20002
(202) 675-8250

International Society of Fire Service Instructors
P.O. Box 2320
Stafford, VA 22555
(800) 435-0005

National Fire Protection Association
1 Batterymarch Park, P.O. Box 9101
Quincy, MA 02269-9101
(617) 770-3000

Spill Control Association of America
Suite 1900
400 Renaissance Center
Detroit, MI 48243
(313) 567-0500

U.S. Department of Transportation
Research and Special Programs Administrator
Washington, DC 20590
(202) 366-4555

U.S. EPA Office of Research & Development
Publications — CERI
Cincinnati, OH 45268
(513) 684-7562

U.S. EPA Office of Solid Waste (WH-562)
Superfund Hotline
401 M Street S.W.
Washington, DC 20460
(800) 424-9346

U.S. Mine Safety and Health Administration
Department of Labor
4015 Wilson Boulevard, Room 600
Arlington, VA 22203
(703) 235-1452

U.S. National Oceanic and Atmospheric Administration
Hazardous Materials Response Branch N/CMS 34
7600 Sand Point Way NE
Seattle, WA 98115

C-4 Computer Data Base Systems

Hazardous Materials Information Exchange (HMIX)
Federal Emergency Management Agency
State and Local Programs Support Directory
Technological Hazards Division
500 C Street S.W.
Washington, DC 20472

PART TWO

NFPA 472

Standard for Professional Competence of Responders to Hazardous Materials Incidents, 1997 Edition, with Commentary

This Standard identifies the levels of competence required of responders to hazardous materials incidents. It specifically covers the competencies for first responders at the awareness and operational levels, hazardous materials technicians, incident commanders, hazardous materials branch officers, hazardous materials branch safety officers, and other specialist employees.

In this 1997 edition of the Standard, the Committee has created two new levels, the Hazardous Materials Branch Officer and the Safety Officer, based on the work of two task groups formed in 1992. In addition, three new specialty levels—for tank cars, cargo tanks, and intermodal tanks—are now included in the Standard. The Committee also clarified the existing requirements, especially those for the technician-level responder.

For ease of reading, the text of the Standard appears in black, while the commentary and its accompanying art captions, tables, and charts are printed in blue.

NOTICE

The Hazardous Materials Response Personnel Committee has issued a Tentative Interim Amendment addressing the issue of hazardous materials incidents due to acts of terrorism or other criminal activity. (See page 293.)

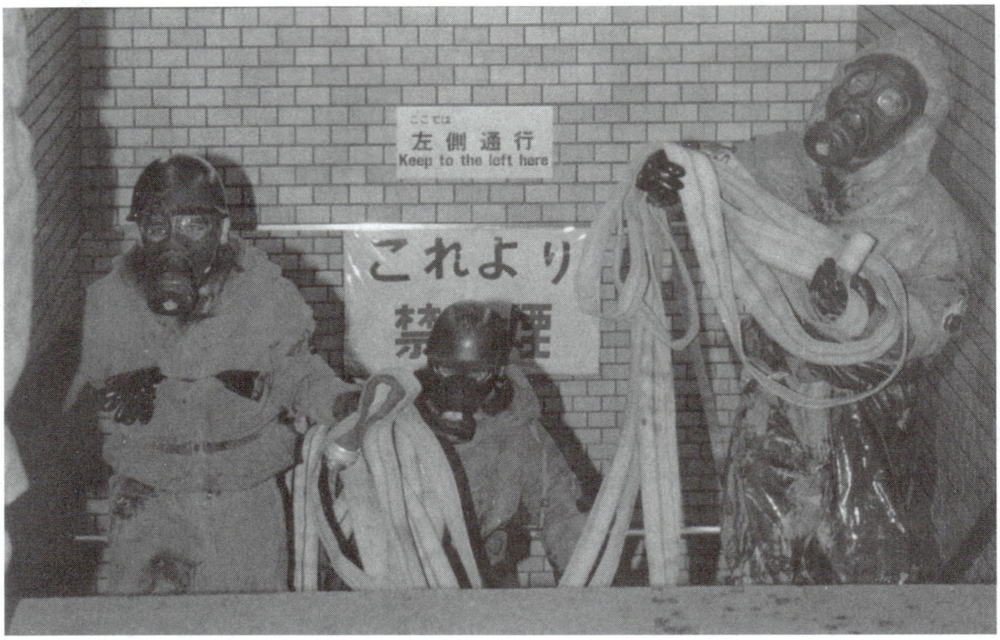

The concept of terrorist/criminal use of hazardous materials was frighteningly illustrated by the Sarin release in the Tokyo subway, the anthrax terrorism scare in Washington, DC, and the Oklahoma City bombing. Many of the techniques for creating terrorist weapons of mass destruction are easily available on the Internet, creating an increased likelihood that hazardous materials may even be used on the public by those without an underlying political or other agenda. (Tokyo and Washington, DC, photos shown here courtesy of Associated Press.)

CHAPTER 1

Administration

This document applies to all personnel whose normal duties may require them to be first on the scene. This includes responders from fire service, emergency medical service, law enforcement, and other public sector agencies as well as responders from private industry, including industrial fire brigades and workers engaged in both transportation and fixed hazardous materials handling and disposal operations.

For those organizations that must comply with either OSHA or EPA hazardous materials emergency response regulations, Table 1.1 compares these federal regulations to the specific competency levels outlined in NFPA 472.

1-1 General

1-1.1 Scope.

This standard identifies the levels of competence required of responders to hazardous materials incidents. It specifically covers the competencies for first responders at the awareness level, first responders at the operational level, hazardous materials technicians, incident commanders, hazardous materials branch officers, hazardous materials branch safety officers, and other specialist employees.

The key to achieving a given level of competence is training and testing. Because NFPA 472 is a performance-based standard, no training hour requirements are given. Instead, NFPA 472 deals with the objectives and abilities that a responder must attain in order to be considered competent. The performance-based approach was chosen by committee members because they believed that hazardous materials identification and mitigation was a constantly changing field of knowledge, skills, and control methods, based on constantly developing technology, chemicals, and needs. The knowledge and skills required for competency will change as technology develops.

Competencies can identify the minimum job performance requirements for specific hazardous materials responder levels. This standard can be used for designing training and evaluation programs, certification, measuring and critiquing on-the-job performance, defining hiring practices, and setting organizational policies, procedures, and goals.

Those familiar with the 1992 edition of NFPA 472 will notice that some changes have been made in this 1997 edition. For example, the technician with a specialty designation has been introduced for the following three specific areas of expertise: tank cars (Chapter 9), cargo tanks (Chapter 10), and intermodal tanks (Chapter 11).

The creation of these new specialty levels does not limit the technician level in the performance of those tasks that have always been assigned at that level. Instead, the committee has added specific language to explain that the capabilities and operations performed by the technician level may still be performed by technicians in hazardous materials incidents involving tank cars, cargo tanks, and intermodal tanks. The new specialty levels describe the "infrequent responders that are qualified to remove or transfer products from damaged containers."

In addition, NFPA 472 now includes the following two new levels of competencies: hazardous materials branch officer (Chapter 7) and hazardous materials branch safety officer (Chapter 8).

The hazardous materials branch officer is the "officer-in-charge" of the hazardous materials team. The hazardous materials branch officer can be a part of the entry team or can closely supervise the operation from the warm zone. This officer reports to and takes direction from the incident commander. At some larger incidents, there may be more than one hazardous materials

Table 1.1 NFPA and OSHA Comparison

NFPA 472, 1997 edition	OSHA 1910.120
Chapter 2, First Responder Awareness	1910.120 (q)(6)(i), First Responder Awareness
Chapter 3, First Responder Operations	1910.120 (q)(6)(ii), First Responder Operations
Chapter 4, Hazardous Materials Technician	1910.120 (q)(6)(iii), Hazardous Materials Technician
Chapter 5, Incident Commander	1910.120 (q)(6)(v), On-Scene Incident Commander
Chapter 6, Private Sector Specialist Employee B and C	1910.120 (q)(5), Specialist Employee
Chapter 6, Private Sector Specialist Employee A	1910.120 (q)(6)(iv), Specialist
Chapter 7, Hazardous Materials Branch Officer	No OSHA equivalent
Chapter 8, Hazardous Materials Branch Safety Officer	No OSHA equivalent
Chapter 9, Technician with a Tank Car Specialty	No OSHA equivalent
Chapter 10, Technician with a Cargo Tank Specialty	No OSHA equivalent
Chapter 11, Technician with an Intermodal Tank Specialty	No OSHA equivalent

branch officer needed for each separate team working at the incident.

A response team may be composed of members at several different levels. For example, a team may have personnel at the operations level and at the technician level, or it may be made up of personnel at private sector specialist employee A and B levels. The levels of competence in this standard apply to individuals rather than to response teams.

1-1.2* Purpose.

The purpose of this standard is to specify minimum competencies for those who will respond to hazardous materials incidents. It is not the intent of this standard to restrict any jurisdiction from exceeding these minimum requirements.

One purpose of the competencies contained herein is to reduce the numbers of accidents, injuries, and illnesses during response to hazardous materials incidents and to help prevent exposure to hazardous materials to reduce the possibility of fatalities, illness, and disabilities affecting emergency response personnel.

Hazardous materials are an integral part of the industrial society in which we live, and incidents involving such materials are inevitable. Many responders will experience a complex hazardous materials incident only once in their careers. However, those dedicated to providing emergency services must be prepared to manage such an incident effectively and safely. It is also important that those involved in manufacturing, using, storing, and transporting hazardous materials be trained to safely undertake initial protective actions when an unplanned release occurs and to assist emergency responders who are called upon to minimize and control the hazard.

Protecting the responders and ensuring their safety at the scene of an incident is one of the principal purposes of this document. Adhering to the provisions of this standard at each level of competency should provide a high degree of safety, despite the hazards encountered.

The committee has used a standard system to organize the approach and mitigation of a hazardous materials incident. That system is represented in Figure 1.1.

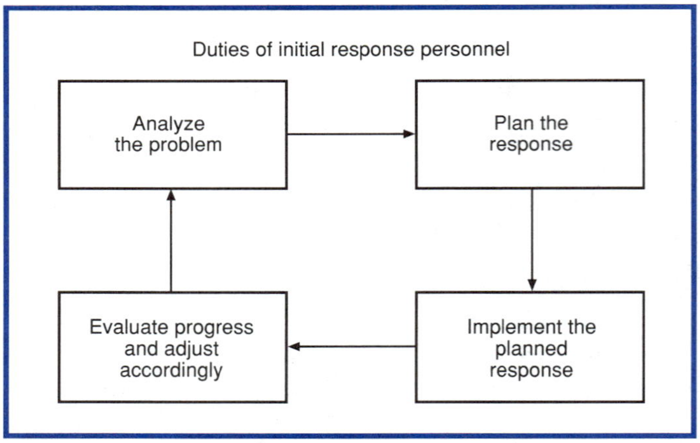

Figure 1.1 *The successful mitigation of a hazardous materials incident depends on organization and planning. This flow diagram shows the response duties associated with emergencies involving hazardous materials. (Source: Fire Protection Handbook, 18th edition, Fig. 10-9A)*

Each duty involves a series of tasks and steps that must be considered and resolved by decisions and actions. These duties, when supported by the response community, are the framework for an appropriate, survival-oriented response to hazardous material incidents. Reasoned decisions based on this approach will minimize harm resulting from a hazardous materials incident while reducing the risk to the responders.[1]

A-1-1.2 Definitions of Responder Levels.

Various responder levels may all work at the same incident but in very different capacities, based on the responder level involved. These include the awareness, level, the operational level, the technician level, and the command level. *(See Figure 1.2.)*

Figure 1.2 At every incident, responders of different levels must work together. Here, the safety officer (on the left, in vest and hard hat) and the incident commander (in center, with SCBA gear) confer with a technician in Level B protective gear while an awareness level responder and a second operations level responder look on. (Photo courtesy of Henrik G. de Gyor)

Awareness Level. First responders at the awareness level are those persons who, in the course of their normal duties, can be the first on the scene of an emergency involving hazardous materials. First responders at the awareness level are expected to recognize the presence of hazardous materials, protect themselves, call for trained personnel, and secure the area.

Operational Level. First responders at the operational level are those persons who respond to releases or potential releases of hazardous materials as part of the initial response to the incident for the purpose of protecting nearby persons, the environment, or property from the effects of the release. They should be trained to respond in a defensive fashion to control the release from a safe distance and keep it from spreading.

Technician Level. Hazardous materials technicians are those persons who respond to releases or potential releases of hazardous materials for the purpose of controlling the release. Hazardous materials technicians are expected to use specialized chemical-protective clothing and specialized control equipment.

Command Level. The incident commander is that person who is responsible for all decisions relating to the management of the incident. The incident commander is in charge of the incident site.

List of Tasks by Responder Level Analysis Tasks

(a) *Awareness Level.* The first responder at the awareness level should analyze an incident to determine both the hazardous materials present and the basic hazard and response information for each hazardous material by completing the following tasks:

1. Detect the presence of the hazardous materials
2. Survey a hazardous materials incident from a safe location to identify the name, UN/NA identification number, or type placard applied for any hazardous materials involved
3. Collect hazard and response information from the current edition of the *North American Emergency Response Guidebook*

(b) *Operational Level.* The first responder at the operational level should be competent at the awareness level and be able to analyze a hazardous materials incident to determine the magnitude of the problem in terms of outcomes by completing the following tasks:

1. Survey the hazardous materials incident to identify the containers and materials involved, determine whether hazardous materials have been released, and evaluate the surrounding conditions
2. Collect hazard and response information from material safety data sheets (MSDS), CHEMTREC/CANUTEC/SETIQ, and shipper/manufacturer contacts
3. Predict the likely behavior of a material and its container
4. Estimate the potential harm at a hazardous materials incident

(c) *Technician Level.* The hazardous materials technician should be competent at the awareness and operational level and be able to analyze a hazardous materials incident to determine the magnitude of the problem in terms of outcomes by completing the following tasks:

1. Survey the hazardous materials incident to identify special containers involved, to identify or classify unknown materials, and to verify the presence and concentrations of hazardous materials through the use of monitoring equipment
2. Collect and interpret hazard and response information from printed resources, technical resources, computer data bases, and monitoring equipment
3. Determine the extent of damage to containers
4. Predict the likely behavior of released materials and their containers when multiple materials are involved
5. Estimate the size of an endangered area using computer modeling, monitoring equipment, or specialists in this area

(d) *Command Level.* The incident commander should be competent to analyze a hazardous materials incident to determine the magnitude of the problem in terms of outcomes by completing the following tasks:

1. Collect and interpret hazard and response information from printed resources, technical resources, computer data bases, and monitoring equipment
2. Estimate the potential outcomes within the endangered area at a hazardous materials incident

Planning Tasks

(a) *Awareness Level.* No requirements.

(b) *Operational Level.* The first responder at the operational level should be competent at the first responder awareness level and be able to plan an initial response within the capabilities and competencies of available personnel, personal protective equipment, and control equipment by completing the following tasks:

1. Describe the response objectives for hazardous materials incidents
2. Describe the defensive options available by response objective
3. Determine if the personal protective equipment provided is appropriate for implementing each action option
4. Identify the emergency decontamination procedures

(c) *Technician Level.* The hazardous materials technician should be competent at both the first responder awareness and operational levels and be able to plan a response within the capabilities of available personnel, personal protective equipment, and control equipment by completing the following tasks:

1. Identify the response objectives for hazardous materials incidents
2. Identify the potential action options available by response objective
3. Select the personal protective equipment required for a given action option
4. Select the appropriate decontamination procedures
5. Develop a plan of action, including safety considerations, consistent with the local emergency response plan and the organization's standard operating procedures and within the capability of the available personnel, personal protective equipment, and control equipment

(d) *Command Level.* The incident commander should be competent to plan response operations within the capabilities and competencies of available personnel, personal protective equipment, and control equipment by completing the following tasks:

1. Identify the response objectives for hazardous materials incidents
2. Identify the potential action options (defensive, offensive, and nonintervention) available by response objective
3. Approve the level of personal protective equipment required for a given action option
4. Develop a plan of action, including safety considerations, consistent with the local emergency response plan and the organization's standard operating procedures and within the capability of available personnel, personal protective equipment, and control equipment

Implementation Tasks

(a) *Awareness Level.* The first responder at the awareness level should be able to implement actions consistent with the local emergency response plan, the organization's standard operating procedures, and the current edition of the *North American Emergency Response Guidebook* by completing the following tasks:

1. Initiate protective actions
2. Initiate the notification process

(b) *Operational Level.* The first responder at the operational level should be competent at the awareness level and be able to implement the planned response to favorably change the outcomes consistent with the local emergency response plan and the organization's standard operating procedures by completing the following tasks:

1. Establish and enforce scene control procedures, including control zones, decontamination, and communications
2. Initiate an incident management system (IMS)
3. Don, work in, and doff personal protective equipment provided by the authority having jurisdiction
4. Perform the defensive control actions identified in the plan of action

(c) *Technician Level.* The hazardous materials technician should be competent at both the first responder awareness and operational levels and be able to implement the planned response to favorably change the outcomes consistent with the organization's standard operating procedures or safety considerations by completing the following tasks:

1. Perform the duties of an assigned position within the local incident management system (IMS)
2. Don, work in, and doff appropriate personal protective clothing, including, but not limited to, both liquid splash- and vapor-protective clothing with appropriate respiratory protection
3. Perform the control functions identified in the plan of action

(d) *Command Level.* The incident commander should be competent at the operational level and be able to implement a response to favorably change the outcomes consistent with the local emergency response plan and the organization's standard operating procedures by completing the following tasks:

1. Implement the incident management system, including the specified procedures for notification and utilization of nonlocal resources (including private, state, and federal government personnel)
2. Direct resources (private, governmental, and others) with expected task assignments and on-scene activities, provide management overview, technical review, and logistical support to private and governmental sector personnel
3. Provide a focal point for information transfer to media and local elected officials through the IMS structures

Evaluation Tasks

(a) *Awareness Level.* No requirements.

(b) *Operational Level.* The first responder at the operational level should be competent at the awareness level and be able to evaluate the progress of the actions taken to ensure that the response objectives are being met safely, effectively, and efficiently by completing the following tasks:

1. Evaluate the status of the defensive actions taken in accomplishing the response objectives
2. Communicate the status of the planned response

(c) *Technician Level.* The hazardous materials technician should be competent in evaluating the progress of the planned response by evaluating the effectiveness of the control functions.

(d) *Command Level.* The incident commander should be competent at the operational level and be able to evaluate the progress of the planned response to ensure the response objectives are being met safely, effectively, and efficiently and adjust the plan of action accordingly by evaluating the effectiveness of the control functions.

Termination Tasks

(a) *Awareness Level.* No requirements.

(b) *Operational Level.* No requirements.

(c) *Technician Level:* The hazardous materials technician should be competent to terminate an incident by completing the following tasks:

1. Assist in the incident debriefing
2. Assist in the incident critique
3. Provide reports and documentation of the incident

(d) *Command Level:* The incident commander should be competent to terminate an incident by completing the following tasks:

1. Transfer of command (control) when appropriate
2. Conduct an incident debriefing
3. Conduct a multi-agency critique
4. Report and document the hazardous materials incident and submit the reports to the proper entity

1-2 Definitions

Approved.* Acceptable to the authority having jurisdiction.

A-1-2 Approved. The National Fire Protection Association does not approve, inspect, or certify any installations, procedures, equipment, or materials; nor does it approve or evaluate testing laboratories. In determining the acceptability of installations, procedures, equipment, or materials, the authority having jurisdiction may base acceptance on compliance with NFPA or other appropriate standards. In the absence of such standards, said authority may require evidence of proper installation, procedure, or use. The authority having jurisdiction may also refer to the listings or labeling practices of an organization that is concerned with product evaluations and is thus in a position to determine compliance with appropriate standards for the current production of listed items.

Authority Having Jurisdiction.* The organization, office, or individual responsible for approving equipment, an installation, or a procedure.

In a document dealing with the very broad concept of hazardous materials response, the authorities will include officials at all levels of government, from federal to local.

A-1-2 Authority Having Jurisdiction. The phrase "authority having jurisdiction" is used in NFPA documents in a broad manner, since jurisdictions and approval agencies

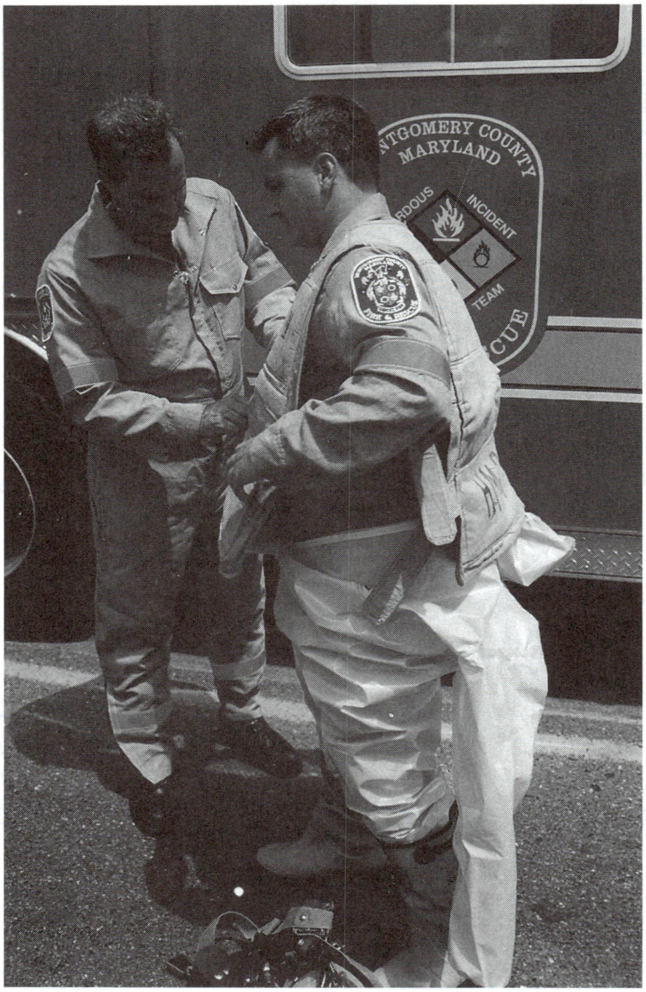

Figure 1.3 Different levels of protective clothing may be required at each incident, depending on the hazards involved. Here, a Level A technician is donning his totally encapsulating chemical-protective clothing. The vest shown is filled with cooling packets to reduce heat stress. Any gaps or seams will be taped shut to ensure no penetration to the skin. (Photo courtesy of Henrik G. de Gyor)

vary, as do their responsibilities. Where public safety is primary, the authority having jurisdiction may be a federal, state, local, or other regional department or individual such as a fire chief; fire marshal; chief of a fire prevention bureau, labor department, or health department; building official; electrical inspector; or others having statutory authority. For insurance purposes, an insurance inspection department, rating bureau, or other insurance company representative may be the authority having jurisdiction. In many circumstances, the property owner or his or her designated agent assumes the role of the authority having jurisdiction; at government installations, the commanding officer or departmental official may be the authority having jurisdiction.

CANUTEC. The Canadian Transport Emergency Center operated by Transport Canada. CANUTEC provides emergency response information and assistance on a 24-hour basis for responders to hazardous materials incidents.

Chemical. Regulated and nonregulated hazardous materials (solids, liquids, and gases, whether natural or man-made, including petroleum products) with the potential for creating harm to people, the environment, and property when released.

Chemical-Protective Clothing. Items made from chemical-resistive materials, such as clothing, hood, boots, and gloves, that are designed and configured to protect the wearer's torso, head, arms, legs, hands, and feet from hazardous materials. Chemical-protective clothing (garments) can be constructed as a single- or multipiece garment. The garment can completely enclose the wearer either by itself or in combination with the wearer's respiratory protection, attached or detachable hood, gloves, and boots.

Chemical-protective clothing (CPC) allows responders to work for a specified length of time in or near an area contaminated by hazardous materials by isolating their bodies from the chemical or physical hazards. Figure 1.3 shows the Level A responder donning his CPC. The type of CPC needed will vary depending on the type of hazardous materials and conditions present. Each CPC comes with a list of specific chemicals that the manufacturer has tested on the garments. At this time, no single type of CPC is suitable for all types of incidents. For more information on protective clothing, including selection and care, see Chapter 5 of NFPA 471.

CHEMTREC. The Chemical Transportation Emergency Center, a public service of the Chemical Manufacturers Association. CHEMTREC provides emergency response information and assistance on a 24-hour basis for responders to hazardous materials incidents.

Cold Zone. The control zone of a hazardous materials incident that contains the command post and such other support functions as are deemed necessary to control the incident. This zone is also referred to as the clean zone or support zone in other documents.

It might appear that the cold zone has no outer boundary, but this is not the case. One can equate the outer boundary at a hazardous materials incident with the fire lines drawn at a major fire or some other emergency that is controlled by local law enforcement officers. The public does not have access to the cold zone under most circumstances. However, the cold zone is an important and active area during incident mitigation. Medical evaluation and treatment; transportation of victims; incident command; media, food, water, and toilet facilities are all usually located within the cold zone.

Competence. Possessing knowledge, skills, and judgment needed to perform indicated objectives satisfactorily.

Knowledge and skills can be measured, but judgment is not as easily evaluated—and judgment and decision-making skills can vary substantially with the circumstances. Nonetheless, training and experience can effectively improve a responder's emergency decision-making process. The various competencies outlined in this performance-based standard focus on the skills necessary rather than the hours of training needed to achieve that skill. Necessary training hours may vary from individual to individual and jurisdiction to jurisdiction, depending on prior individual training and experience and on the requirements of the authority having jurisdiction. In addition to training, experience and practice through drills, table top exercises, and other hands-on practice and training exercises is invaluable.

Confined Space. A space that by design has limited openings for entry and exit, that has unfavorable natural ventilation that could contain or produce dangerous concentrations of air contaminants, and that is not intended for continuous occupancy. Examples of confined spaces include, but are not limited to, storage tanks, compartments of ships, process vessels, pits, silos, vats, degreasers, reaction vessels, boilers, ventilation and exhaust ducts, sewers, tunnels, underground utility vaults, and pipelines.

The U.S. Occupational Safety and Health Administration (OSHA) has promulgated new regulations relating to worker safety in confined spaces. These regulations introduced a system of working in such spaces that includes hazard recognition and risk assessment; testing, evaluation, and monitoring; and permits for entry, work, and rescue.

Confinement. Those procedures taken to keep a material, once released, in a defined or local area.

Container. Any vessel or receptacle that holds material, including storage vessels, pipelines, and packaging (*see definition of "Packaging"*). Containers include the following:

(a) Nonbulk packaging, such as bags, bottles, boxes, carboys, cylinders, drums, jerricans, multicell packages, and wooden barrels
(b) Bulk packaging, such as bulk bags, bulk boxes, cargo tanks, covered hopper cars, freight containers, gondolas, pneumatic hopper trailers, portable tanks and bins, protective overpacks for radioactive materials, tank cars, ton containers, and van trailers
(c) Fixed containers, such as piping, reactors, storage bins, tanks, and storage vessels

Although some regulations and codes define a container by placing size limitations on its capacity, this document does not. NFPA 472 says, in effect, that a container is anything designed or intended to hold a hazardous material.

Containment. The actions taken to keep a material in its container (e.g., stop a release of the material or reduce the amount being released).

Containment will often involve plugging or patching a container to stop a leak. Committing personnel to this type of operation must be carefully considered, and must take into account the level of training they have received. Many, if not most, containment activities can be considered to be "offensive" in nature and require training to the technician or the private sector specialist employee A level.

Contaminant. A hazardous material that physically remains on or in people, animals, the environment, or equipment, thereby creating a continuing risk of direct injury or a risk of exposure.

Inherent in the definition of a contaminant is the concept that the offending material is present where it does not belong and that it is somehow toxic or harmful to persons, animals, or the environment. Contaminants may be in any form, i.e., solid, gas, liquid, or vapor, and dealing with each hazard type requires a different set of skills and operations.

Contamination. The process of transferring a hazardous material from its source to people, animals, the environment, and/or equipment, which may act as a carrier.

Contamination is one of the more important considerations for emergency responders from a health and safety standpoint. The importance of determining whether personnel or equipment has been contaminated cannot be stressed too strongly. Because personnel are often unaware that contamination has occurred, it is imperative that procedures be established ahead of time to ensure proper monitoring and decontamination procedures are established and followed at each incident scene.

Control. The procedures, techniques, and methods used in the mitigation of a hazardous materials incident, including containment, extinguishment, and confinement.

The word *control* can be used interchangeably with the word *mitigation*. Every measure taken to control a hazardous materials incident is part of the mitigation process. Limiting the degree of contamination by whatever means is available is also part of the control or mitigation process.

Control Zones. The areas at hazardous materials incidents that are designated based upon the degree of hazard. Many terms are used to describe these control zones; however, for the purposes of this standard, these zones are defined as the hot, warm, and cold zones.

The committee's choice of basic terms such as *hot, warm,* and *cold* is based on the fact that the words are simple and easily understood and that they clearly suggest the nature of the situation one would expect to encounter in any area with such a designation. *(See also the definitions of Cold Zone, Hot Zone, and Warm Zone.)*

Coordination. The process used to get people, who might represent different agencies, to work together integrally and harmoniously in a common action or effort.

Determining the specific individual who is in charge of a major hazardous materials incident can be one of the more difficult problems responders encounter. It can be solved by good local emergency planning prior to any potential incident. At most incidents, the command is passed from one specific individual to another as the incident develops. For example, a responding fire department suppression incident commander may have initial command of a scene until a hazardous materials incident is recognized. That commander may then turn the incident command over to the individual named in the specific hazardous materials incident plan for that situation.

Decontamination. The physical or chemical process of reducing and preventing the spread of contaminants from persons and equipment used at a hazardous materials incident.

The broad concept of decontamination includes all actions taken at an incident that serve to reduce or prevent contamination. The narrower meaning suggests those steps taken to remove contaminants that may have accumulated on equipment or personnel at an incident. Good decontamination practices should incorporate and emphasize the notion of prevention as the first step in the process. Additional information on decontamination can be found in Chapter 7 of NFPA 471 and in Supplement 11 of this handbook.

Decontamination Corridor. The area usually located within the warm zone where decontamination procedures take place. This area is also referred to as the decontamination area in other documents.

The purpose of the decontamination corridor is to keep contamination from spreading to the cold, or uncontaminated, zone. It is usually located in the warm zone because that is the transition area between the uncontaminated cold zone and the contaminated area of the hot zone. *(See Figure 4-3 in Part I of this handbook.)*

Degradation

(a) A chemical action involving the molecular breakdown of a protective clothing material or equipment due to contact with a chemical.

(b) The molecular breakdown of the spilled or released material to render it less hazardous during control operations.

Demonstrate. To show by actual performance. This performance can be supplemented by simulation, explanation, illustration, or a combination of these.

Describe. To explain verbally or in writing using standard terms recognized in the hazardous materials response community.

Emergency Decontamination. The physical process of immediately reducing contamination of individuals in potentially life-threatening situations with or without the formal establishment of a decontamination corridor.

Emergency decontamination is needed when a sudden, unexpected release of a life-threatening material occurs or when the responders are not aware of the nature of the materials involved in an incident and are inadvertently exposed. In such instances, immediate measures, such as applying large amounts of water, must be taken. Once initial emergency decontamination is completed, responders can proceed with normal decontamination procedures as described in Supplement 10.

Emergency Response Plan. A plan that establishes guidelines for handling hazardous materials incidents as required by relevant legislation such as Title 29, *Code of Federal Regulations*, Part 1910.120 (q) (1).

The law regarding hazardous materials response is very clear. In addition to emergency responders and governmental authorities, employers whose workers could potentially be exposed to hazardous materials while on the job are required to develop emergency response plans. To avoid duplication, the private sector employers may use the appropriate plan developed by the local authorities, the plan developed by the state, or both as part of their own emergency response plan. Supplement 9 offers an example of a fire department emergency response plan.

Endangered Area. The actual or potential area of exposure from a hazardous material. This area is sometimes referred to as the engulfed area.

The size of the endangered area is a key element in determining the magnitude of a hazardous materials incident. Obviously, a hazardous material that poses a threat to a 500 ft^2 area will be much easier to manage than one that affects 1 mi^2. The Table of Initial Isolation and Protective Action Distances found in the *1996 North American Emergency Response Guidebook*[2] will provide guidance in determining the size of the endangered area based on the contaminants involved.

Exposure. The process by which people, animals, the environment, and equipment are subjected to or come in contact with a hazardous material. The magnitude of exposure is dependent primarily upon the duration of exposure and the concentration of the hazardous material. This term is also used to describe a person, animal, the environment, or a piece of equipment.

Gross Decontamination. The initial phase of the decontamination process during which the amount of surface contaminant is significantly reduced. This phase can include mechanical removal or initial rinsing.

Hazard/Hazardous. Capable of posing an unreasonable risk to health, safety, or the environment; capable of causing harm.

Hazardous Material.* A substance (solid, liquid, or gas) that when released is capable of creating harm to people, the environment, and property.

A-1-2 Hazardous Material. There are many definitions and descriptive names being used for the term hazardous material, each of which depends on the nature of the problem being addressed.

Unfortunately, there is no one list or definition that covers everything. The U.S. agencies involved, as well as state and local governments, have different purposes for regulating hazardous materials that, under certain circumstances, pose a risk to the public or the environment.

Hazardous Materials. The U.S. Department of Transportation (DOT) uses the term *hazardous materials* to cover 11 hazard classes, some of which have subcategories called divisions. DOT includes in its regulations hazardous substances and hazardous wastes as Class 9 (Miscellaneous Hazardous Materials), both of which are regulated by the U.S. Environmental Protection Agency (EPA), if their inherent properties would not otherwise be covered.

Hazardous Substances. EPA uses the term *hazardous substances* for chemicals that, if released into the environment above a certain amount, must be reported, and, depending on the threat to the environment, federal involvement in handling the incident can be authorized. A list of the hazardous substances is published in Title 40, *Code of Federal Regulations,* Part 302, Table 302.4. The U.S. Occupational Safety and Health Administration (OSHA) uses the term *hazardous substance* in Title 29, *Code of Federal Regulations,* Part 1910.120, which resulted from Title I of Superfund Amendments and Reauthorization Act (SARA) and covers emergency response. OSHA uses the term differently than EPA. Hazardous substances, as used by OSHA, cover every chemical regulated by both DOT and EPA.

Extremely Hazardous Substances. EPA uses the term *extremely hazardous substances* for chemicals that must be reported to the appropriate authorities if released above the threshold reporting quantity. Each substance has a threshold reporting quantity. The list of extremely hazardous substances is identified in Title III of SARA of 1986 (Title 40, *Code of Federal Regulations*, Part 355).

Toxic Chemicals. EPA uses the term *toxic chemicals* for chemicals whose total emissions or releases must be reported annually by owners and operators of certain facilities that manufacture, process, or otherwise use a listed toxic chemical. The list of toxic chemicals is identified in Title III of SARA.

Hazardous Wastes. EPA uses the term *hazardous wastes* for chemicals that are regulated under the Resource, Conservation, and Recovery Act (Title 40, *Code of Federal Regulations*, Part 261.33). Hazardous wastes in transportation are regulated by DOT (Title 49, *Code of Federal Regulations*, Parts 170–179).

Hazardous Chemicals. OSHA uses the term *hazardous chemicals* to denote any chemical that would be a risk to employees if exposed in the workplace. Hazardous chemicals cover a broader group of chemicals than the other chemical lists.

Dangerous Goods. In Canadian transportation, hazardous materials are called *dangerous goods.*

Highly Hazardous Chemicals. OSHA uses the term *highly hazardous chemicals* for those chemicals that fall under the requirements of Title 29, *Code of Federal Regulations*, Part 1910.119, "Process Safety Management of Highly Hazardous Chemicals." *Highly hazardous chemicals* are those chemicals that possess toxic, reactive, flammable, or explosive properties. A list of covered substances is published in Appendix A of the OSHA rule.

Hazardous Materials Branch. That function within an overall incident management system that deals with the mitigation of the hazardous materials portion of a hazardous materials incident. It is directed by a hazardous materials branch officer and deals principally with the technical aspects of the incident.

The hazardous materials branch provides an organizational structure that allows the necessary supervision and control of the operations that are essential at a hazardous materials incident. These include the tactical objectives carried out in the hot zone, control of access to the site, and decontamination.

In some areas, the hazardous materials branch is referred to as the *hazard division, hazard group,* or *hazard sector.*

Hazardous Materials Branch Officer. The person responsible for the management of the hazardous materials branch.

The person holding this position is responsible for managing the hazardous materials response team under the overall direction of the incident commander. Rescue operations in the control zones also come under the direction of this position.

This position is also known as the *hazardous materials division officer, hazardous materials group officer,* or *hazardous materials sector officer* in some areas.

Hazardous Materials Response Team. An organized group of trained response personnel operating under an emergency response plan and appropriate standard operating procedures who handle and control actual or potential leaks or spills of hazardous materials requiring possible close approach to the material. The team members respond to releases or potential releases of hazardous materials for the purpose of control or stabilization of the incident.

A hazardous materials response team may be made up of various personnel. In some cases, these responders may all come from the same agency. In others, they may be drawn from various agencies and/or disciplines. However, all members of a hazardous materials response team must operate under one set of operating procedures, have an organizational structure, and all train together on a regular basis. *(See Figure 1.4.)*

As stated earlier, the personnel on the team need not all be trained to the same level. It is important, however, that the duties and responsibilities of each member be commensurate with their level of training. For example, if the incident calls for operations to control the release and for work in specialized chemical-protective clothing, these functions should only be attempted by certified hazardous materials technicians or private sector specialist employees A.

High-Temperature-Protective Clothing. Protective clothing designed to protect the wearer for short-term high temperature exposures. This type of clothing is usually of limited use in dealing with chemical commodities.

Specialized high-temperature clothing is designed to provide brief protection against radiant heat exposure to temperatures as high as 2000°F (1093°C). NFPA 1976, *Standard on Protective Clothing for Proximity Fire Fighting,*[3] provides performance criteria for proximity suits. These suits consist of a one- or two-piece overgarment with hood, gloves, and, often, boot covers of an aluminized or cotton fabric. Fire entry suits are another type of specialized high-temperature ensemble designed to protect the wearer against abnormally high temperatures. Fire entry suits offer the least protection, having only a brief exposure limit of two or three minutes.

Figure 1.4 *Frequent hands-on drills and realistic training exercises help to build experience for all team members. Here responders in Level A and Level B protective clothing are taking part in a full-scale drill that will include decontamination procedures. The safety officer, front center, is checking the decontamination equipment laid out in the decontamination corridor, marked with red cones. (Photo courtesy of Henrik G. de Gyor)*

Hot Zone. The control zone immediately surrounding a hazardous materials incident, which extends far enough to prevent adverse effects from hazardous materials releases to personnel outside the zone. This zone is also referred to as the exclusion zone or the restricted zone in other documents.

The hot zone is the area where the hazardous materials release has occurred or could take place. It is also the area where cleanup operations occur. The boundary between the hot zone and warm zone should be clearly indicated by some physical means, such as barrier tape, barricades, or some other type of obvious demarcation. Movement of personnel from one zone to another must be strictly regulated and supervised to keep contamination from being carried across zones. Regulating movement between zones will also limit the number of personnel exposed to the most hazardous conditions.

Identify. To select or indicate verbally or in writing using standard terms to establish the identity of; the fact of being the same as the one described.

Incident. An emergency involving the release or potential release of a hazardous material, with or without fire.

Incident Commander. The person responsible for all decisions relating to the management of the incident. The incident commander is in charge of the incident site. This is equivalent to the on-scene incident commander.

The incident commander is responsible for the overall control of operations. Where multiple agencies are likely to be involved (which is generally the case when hazardous materials are involved), the roles and responsibilities of the various agencies should be clarified ahead of time. The actual command may change from one person to another as the incident develops and becomes more complex. Some incident management systems provide for a "unified command" when multiple agencies are involved. How the system is structured is less important than the fact that there is a system for command and control, that everyone involved is aware of his or her role, and that training exercises have been conducted to work out any problems.

Incident Management System.* An organized system of roles, responsibilities, and standard operating procedures used to manage and direct emergency operations. Such systems are sometimes referred to as incident command systems (ICS).

A-1-2 Incident Management System. For more information, see NFPA 1561, *Standard on Fire Department Incident Management System.*

An effective incident management system is one of the most important aspects of operating safely during an emergency. NFPA 1561, *Standard on Fire Department Incident Management Systems,*[4] provides an excellent guide for developing an effective incident management system and clearly addresses the components that must be included for personnel to operate at an incident in an organized and safe manner.

Individual Area of Specialization. The qualifications or functions of a specific job(s) associated with chemicals and/or containers used within an organization.

This definition applies to those who have expertise in a specific product or container. These individuals are typically from industry and, because of their work, have acquired an in-depth knowledge of such products or containers. They may be part of the initial incident response plan or they may arrive later as part of a more specialized clean-up contracting crew.

Liquid Splash-Protective Clothing. The garment portion of a chemical-protective clothing ensemble that is designed and configured to protect the wearer against chemical liquid splashes but not against chemical vapors or gases. Liquid splash-protective clothing must meet the requirements of NFPA 1992, *Standard on Liquid Splash-Protective Suits for Hazardous Chemical Emergencies.* This type of protective clothing is a component of EPA Level B chemical protection.

This type of clothing consists of chemical-resistant coveralls or one- or two-piece splash suits. It is used only in situations where the products and hazards have been accurately identified and when the likelihood of contamination is minimal. These garments are often worn by medical personnel operating in the cold zone medical area who are treating patients that have already been decontaminated in the warm zone.

Listed.* Equipment, materials, or services included in a list published by an organization that is acceptable to the authority having jurisdiction and concerned with evaluation of products or services, that maintains periodic inspection of production of listed equipment or materials or periodic evaluation of services, and whose listing states that either the equipment, material, or service meets identified standards or has been tested and found suitable for a specified purpose.

A-1-2 Listed. The means for identifying listed equipment may vary for each organization concerned with product evaluation; some organizations do not recognize equipment as listed unless it is also labeled. The authority having jurisdiction should utilize the system employed by the listing organization to identify a listed product.

Local Emergency Response Plan. The plan promulgated by the authority having jurisdiction, such as the local emergency planning committee for the community or a facility.

Whether it is developed for a community, county, state, or industrial facility, the local emergency response plan must identify the hazards that are present within given sites in a community or region and establish written procedures for handling such incidents. The development of a community plan is described in Supplement 5.

Match. To provide with a counterpart.

Material Safety Data Sheet (MSDS). A form, provided by manufacturers and compounders (blenders) of chemicals, containing information about chemical composition, physical and chemical properties, health and safety hazards, emergency response, and waste disposal of the material.

Monitoring Equipment. Instruments and devices used to identify and quantify contaminants.

Monitoring equipment is extremely useful for several reasons. It can help determine the personal protective equipment that can be used safely, it can help establish control zones, it can identify unknowns, and it can determine the level of contamination or decontamination. *(See Figure 1.5.)*

Figure 1.5 *Special meters, like the gas detector shown here, are an essential tool for hazardous materials responders because they provide warning to responders and help to identify the nature of the hazardous material. In many cases, very specialized meters may be borrowed from the private companies that routinely handle specific kinds of hazardous materials.*

North American Emergency Response Guidebook (NAERG). A reference book, written in plain language, to guide emergency responders in their initial actions at the incident scene.

This book is the most widely used reference material available to emergency responders in the United States, Canada, and Mexico. The guidebook, written in plain language, provides basic guidelines for initially identifying hazardous materials and the hazards present at an incident scene, as well as some general recommendations for dealing with an incident involving the identified materials.

Objective. A goal that is achieved through the attainment of a skill, knowledge, or both, that can be observed or measured.

Organization's Area of Specialization. Any chemicals and containers used by the private sector specialist employee's employer.

This refers to the specific products or containers with which an individual has intimate knowledge as part of his or her regular job duties. Even though a company may manufacture, use, or transport a wide variety of products, specific individuals may only have knowledge of a few of these products.

Packaging. Any container that holds a material (hazardous and nonhazardous). Packaging for hazardous materials includes bulk and nonbulk packaging.

Bulk Packaging. Any packaging, including transport vehicles, having a capacity meeting one of the criteria listed below. Bulk packaging can be either placed on or in a transport vehicle or vessel or constructed as an integral part of the transport vehicle.

(a) Liquid — internal volume of more than 119 gal (450 L)
(b) Solid — capacity of more than 882 lb (400 kg)
(c) Compressed gas — water capacity of more than 1,001 lb (454 kg)

Nonbulk Packaging. Any packaging having a capacity meeting one of the following criteria:

(a) Liquid — internal volume of 119 gal (450 L) or less
(b) Solid — capacity of 882 lb (400 kg) or less
(c) Compressed gas — water capacity of 1,001 lb (454 kg) or less

Penetration. The movement of a material through a suit's closures, such as zippers, buttonholes, seams, flaps, or other design features of chemical-protective clothing, and through punctures, cuts, and tears.

Figure 1.6 illustrates how hazardous materials can penetrate chemical-protective clothing even where made of approved fabrics. A regular program of inspection and the practice of inspections after each use can help uncover conditions that may allow penetration.

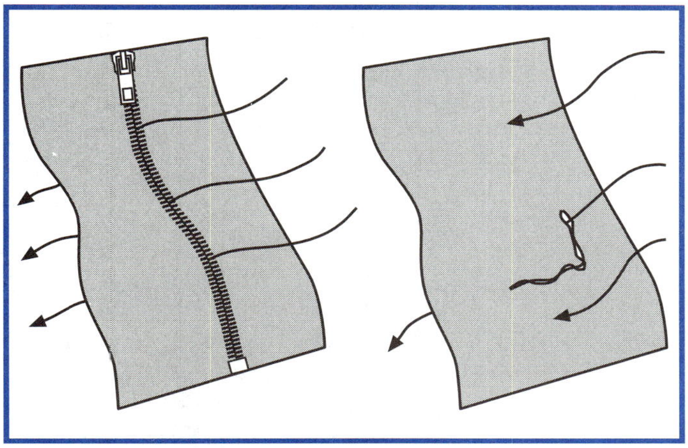

Figure 1.6 Penetration involves the movement of a material through a suit's closures, such as zippers, buttonholes, and seams, or through rips, tears, or flaws in the fabric.

Permeation. A chemical action involving the movement of a chemical, on a molecular level, through intact material.

As illustrated in Figure 1.7, different fabrics have different levels of resistance to chemical permeation, and all fabrics will absorb chemicals over a period of time. NFPA 1991, *Standard on Vapor-Protective Suits for Hazardous Chemical Emergencies,*[5] NFPA 1992, *Standard on Liquid Splash-Protective Suits for Hazardous Chemical Emergencies,*[6] and NFPA 1993, *Standard on Support Function Protective Clothing for Hazardous Chemical Operations,*[7] provide guidelines for manufacturer permeation testing and certification of chemical-protective clothing (CPC). When purchasing CPC, it is important to be sure the garments meet the appropriate standard and have been certified as meeting that standard. In any event, the user should exercise extreme caution that the garments selected are appropriate for the hazardous material at the incident.

Proper care of CPC, including appropriate decontamination and storage procedures, should be emphasized in all training programs and standard operating procedures. Proper care, or the lack of it, can significantly affect the protection afforded by chemical-protective clothing.

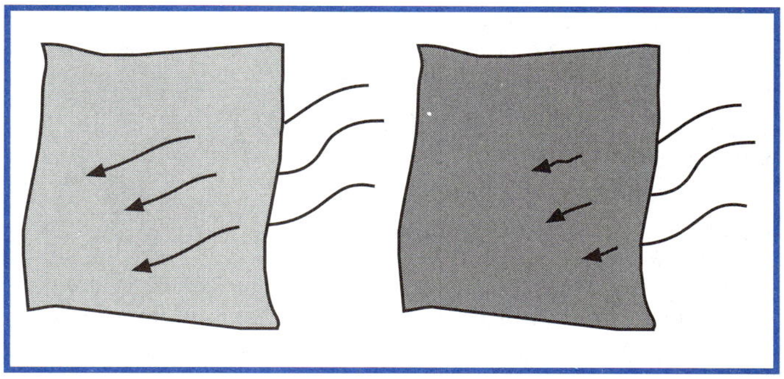

Figure 1.7 Permeation involves chemical movement, on a molecular level, through intact material. Different fabrics allow different levels of permeation.

Personal Protective Equipment. The equipment provided to shield or isolate a person from the chemical, physical, and thermal hazards that can be encountered at a hazardous materials incident. Personal protective equipment includes both personal protective clothing and respiratory protection. Adequate personal protective equipment should protect the respiratory system, skin, eyes, face, hands, feet, head, body, and hearing.

Personal protective equipment is designed to protect the individual responder against any anticipated hazard. Although protective equipment has been improved substantially in recent years, hazards have also become much more complex. It is imperative for responders to be adequately trained to use, care for, and select appropriate personal protective equipment. Protective equipment will not prevent injuries or illness if improperly used.

Planned Response.* The plan of action, with safety considerations, consistent with the local emergency response plan and an organization's standard operating procedures for a specific hazardous materials incident.

Appropriate control actions are identified based on the magnitude of the problem. This process considers available resources and training levels of responders, then determines the direction the response effort must take to influence the events and to favorably change the outcome. The material in A-1-2 "Planned Response" also describes the various areas of concern that should be included in any complete incident plan.

A-1-2 Planned Response. The following site safety plan considerations are referenced from the Standard Operating Safety Guides, EPA, June 1992:

(a) Site description
(b) Entry objectives

(c) On-site organization
(d) On-site control
(e) Hazard evaluations
(f) Personal protective equipment
(g) On-site work plans
(h) Communication procedures
(i) Decontamination procedures
(j) Site safety and health plan

Protective Clothing. Equipment designed to protect the wearer from heat and/or hazardous materials contacting the skin or eyes. Protective clothing is divided into three types:

(a) Structural fire-fighting protective clothing

Structural fire-fighting protective clothing, as defined here, includes appropriate footwear, trousers, a coat, gloves, a helmet, a hood, and PASS (Personal Alert Safety Systems) device. When properly worn, this ensemble provides protection from the hazards normally encountered in structural fire fighting. In most cases, this clothing does not offer adequate protection from hazardous materials.

(b) Chemical-protective clothing

1. Liquid splash-protective clothing

NFPA 1992, *Standard on Liquid Splash-Protective Clothing for Hazardous Chemical Emergencies,* provides criteria for this type of protective clothing. This clothing protects against splash or spill hazards. It does not protect against hazardous vapors or gases.

2. Vapor-protective clothing

NFPA 1991, *Standard on Vapor-Protective Suits for Hazardous Chemical Emergencies,* provides criteria for this type of protective clothing. Used with the proper respiratory protection, it provides the highest level of protection. However, this protection is not without a price. Responders who must wear these suits require special training and on-scene medical evaluation. See Chapter 8 of NFPA 471 and Supplements 3 and 11 in this handbook.

(c) High-temperature-protective clothing

NFPA 1976, *Standard on Protective Clothing for Proximity Fire Fighting,* provides criteria for the type of high-temperature-protective clothing normally used in aircraft fire fighting and rescue, bulk flammable liquids fire fighting, flammable gas fire fighting, and similar situations in which high levels of radiant heat are released.

Qualified. Having satisfactorily completed the learning objectives.

Radioactive Material. Any material that spontaneously emits ionizing radiation.

Respiratory Protection. Equipment designed to protect the wearer from the inhalation of contaminants. Respiratory protection is divided into three types:

Since inhalation of toxins is one of the principal causes of serious injury to responders, respiratory protection is of the utmost importance. Guidance on selection of appropriate respiratory protection is offered in 3-3.3 of NFPA 472.

(a) Positive pressure self-contained breathing apparatus

This is the type of breathing apparatus fire fighters normally use. It does not restrict the wearer's mobility except for the physical limitation of its size, and it provides the highest level of respiratory protection. The most commonly used units are rated at 30 to 60 minutes of protection. However, units are available that provide longer periods of use. NFPA 1981, *Standard on Open-Circuit Self-Contained Breathing Apparatus for the Fire Service,*[8] provides performance criteria for self-contained breathing apparatus (SCBA). The actual time protection provided by SCBA will be substantially reduced for persons not at their best level of physical fitness and for those performing exhausting and demanding work. On-scene medical evaluation and careful timekeeping will help to prevent reliance on SCBA beyond the optimal time limits established for each worker and their unit.

(b) Positive pressure airline respirators

Positive pressure airline respirators give the user an unlimited supply of air and are lighter than SCBA. However, these respirators restrict the travel distance of the user to a maximum of 300 ft (91 m). In addition, the path of travel must be kept clear of obstructions while the user is negotiating the incident scene. Nonetheless, these respirators are an ideal method of supplying air to the emergency worker under certain conditions.

(c) Air purifying respirators

Air purifying respirators (APR) use a filter or a sorbent to remove airborne contaminants. They should not be used by the initial responders to an incident involving hazardous materials. They should be used only when the hazard and the concentration of the hazardous material are known and the ambient atmosphere at the scene has been verified to contain more than 19.5 percent oxygen.

Response. That portion of incident management in which personnel are involved in controlling a hazardous materials incident. The activities in the response portion of a hazardous materials incident include analyzing the incident, planning the response, implementing the planned response, evaluating progress, and terminating the emergency phase of the incident.

Safely. To perform the assigned tasks without injury to self or others, to the environment, or to property.

From the inception of this document, it has been the committee's intent to outline the *minimum* competencies responders need to increase their level of safety. Throughout the document, the committee has stressed conducting operations safely.

Secondary Contamination. The process by which a contaminant is carried out of the hot zone and contaminates people, animals, the environment, or equipment.

Controlling secondary contamination is a key factor in establishing control zones and decontamination areas. It is important not only to the health and safety of the on-scene responder, but also to the health and safety of the public at large. Contaminants can be carried far from the immediate incident site and have serious health consequences beyond the scene of the emergency. For example, ambulances, hospital emergency rooms, and fire stations can become contaminated. And contaminants carried home by responders may be hazardous to members of their families.

SETIQ. The Emergency Transportation System for the Chemical Industry in Mexico.

This is the Mexican equivalent to CHEMTREC.

Shall. Indicates a mandatory requirement.

Should. Indicates a recommendation or that which is advised but not required.

The term *should* is not used in the main body of an NFPA standard, but it can be found in the appendices where the committee wants to make a recommendation.

Stabilization. The point in an incident at which the adverse behavior of the hazardous material is controlled.

Stabilization does not mean that the incident is over, but rather that the hazardous conditions are not likely to escalate or intensify further. It could well be that the clean-up operations following stabilization are prolonged and that specialized types of equipment and expertise will be needed before the operations are completed.

State. Any outlying U.S. areas where this standard is in effect. Use of the noun "state" shall also imply "provinces and territories" in Canada.

The committee does not intend to restrict the use of this document to the United States. In countries where other terminology is used, references made to "state" regulations should be understood to mean whatever type of governmental authority is appropriate.

Structural Fire-Fighting Protective Clothing. Often called turnout or bunker gear, the protective clothing normally worn by fire fighters during structural fire-fighting operations. It includes a helmet, coat, pants, boots, gloves, PASS device, and a hood to cover parts of the head not protected by the helmet and facepiece. Structural fire fighters' protective clothing provides limited protection from heat but might not provide adequate protection from the harmful gases, vapors, liquids, or dusts that are encountered during hazardous materials incidents.

With or without respiratory protection, this type of protective clothing provides the lowest level of protection, Level D, which is equivalent to that of an ordinary work uniform.

Termination. That portion of incident management in which personnel are involved in documenting safety procedures, site operations, hazards faced, and lessons learned from the incident. Termination is divided into three phases: debriefing the incident, post-incident analysis, and critiquing the incident.

Debriefing can be done on a formal or informal basis. However, the closer the process is to the incident, the more effective it will be. *(See Figure 1.8.)*

***Figure 1.8** Debriefing, critiquing, and lessons learned are important elements of post-incident analysis. Here a command level responder confers with the haz mat branch officer as others close down the response scene. The more immediately the incident is reviewed, the fresher the details recalled will be.*

UN/NA Identification Number. Four-digit numbers assigned to a hazardous material. The number is used to identify and cross-reference products in the transportation mode.

Vapor-Protective Clothing. The garment portion of a chemical-protective clothing ensemble that is designed and configured to protect the wearer against chemical vapors or gases. Vapor-protective clothing must meet the requirements of NFPA 1991, *Standard on Vapor-Protective Suits for Hazardous Chemical Emergencies.* This type of protective clothing is a component of EPA Level A chemical protection.

This type of clothing must be worn when the greatest level of skin, respiratory, and eye protection is needed. It should be worn when the hazard cannot be identified or is identified as immediately dangerous to life and health.

Warm Zone. The control zone at a hazardous materials incident site where personnel and equipment decontamination and hot zone support takes place. It includes control points for the decontamination corridor, thus helping to reduce the spread of contamination. This zone is also referred to as the decontamination zone or limited access zone in other documents.

One function of the warm zone is to contain contamination and to prevent a contaminant's spread to the cold zone and beyond. To some extent, the warm zone serves as a buffer between the hot zone and cold zone. The intensity of contamination in the warm zone should decrease the closer one gets to the cold zone, not only because decontamination is taking place, but also because of the intervening space the warm zone affords between the hot zone and the cold zone.

A decontamination corridor is a defined path between the hot zone and cold zone where personnel and equipment are decontaminated. Several decontamination corridors may be needed at very large incidents. The corridors must be tightly controlled and supervised to regulate movement between the zones. A site access control leader should be assigned to ensure that all people and equipment use the appropriate access routes and that records of entry are maintained for tracking purposes. Individuals entering the warm zone from the cold zone must wear the appropriate personal protective equipment.

References Cited in Commentary

1. *Fire Protection Handbook,* 18th edition, National Fire Protection Association, Quincy, MA, 1997, pp. 10–104.
2. *North American Emergency Response Guidebook,* U.S. Department of Transportation, Washington, DC, 1996.
3. NFPA 1976, *Standard on Protective Clothing for Proximity Fire Fighting,* National Fire Protection Association, Quincy, MA, 1992.
4. NFPA 1561, *Standard on Fire Department Incident Management Systems,* National Fire Protection Association, Quincy, MA, 1995.
5. NFPA 1991, *Standard on Vapor-Protective Suits for Hazardous Chemical Emergencies,* National Fire Protection Association, Quincy, MA, 1994.
6. NFPA 1992, *Standard on Liquid Splash-Protective Suits for Hazardous Chemical Emergencies,* National Fire Protection Association, Quincy, MA, 1994.
7. NFPA 1993, *Standard on Support Function Protective Clothing for Hazardous Chemical Operations,* National Fire Protection Association, Quincy, MA, 1994.
8. NFPA 1981, *Standard on Open-Circuit Self-Contained Breathing Apparatus for the Fire Service,* National Fire Protection Association, Quincy, MA, 1997.

CHAPTER 2

Competencies for the First Responder at the Awareness Level

2-1 General

2-1.1 Introduction.

First responders at the awareness level shall be trained to meet all competencies of this chapter. They also shall receive any additional training to meet applicable United States Department of Transportation (DOT), United States Environmental Protection Agency (EPA), Occupational Safety and Health Administration (OSHA), and other appropriate state, local, or provincial occupational health and safety regulatory requirements.

2-1.2 Definition.

First responders at the awareness level are those persons who, in the course of their normal duties, could be the first on the scene of an emergency involving hazardous materials. First responders at the awareness level are expected to recognize the presence of hazardous materials, protect themselves, call for trained personnel, and secure the area.

Individuals at this level are those who are likely to witness or discover a hazardous materials release during their normal job activities and who would be expected, as part of their responsibilities, to begin emergency response procedures. Awareness level responders include truck drivers, train crew members, industrial or chemical plant workers, law enforcement officers, and others whose duties require them to work in facilities where hazardous materials are transported, stored, or used. Responders at the awareness level are not expected to take any action that would require a great deal of training and experience. Rather, their actions will be basic, defensive, and limited as outlined in this chapter.

2-1.3 Goal.

The goal of the competencies at the awareness level shall be to provide first responders with the knowledge and skills to perform the following tasks safely. Therefore, when first on the scene of an emergency involving hazardous materials, the first responder at the awareness level shall be able to:

(a) Analyze the incident to determine both the hazardous materials present and the basic hazard and response information for each hazardous material by completing the following tasks:

The first step in analyzing the problem is to determine whether hazardous materials are present. A few typical indicators that an awareness level responder should immediately recognize include operators or witnesses who report the presence of a hazard or a breach of a container; individuals who exhibit signs of exposure; placards; the type of containers involved; and the presence of fires or explosions. This standard clearly indicates that training in recognizing and identifying a hazardous material is a given and that the employer, whether in the public or private sector, is responsible for seeing that employees likely to be first on the scene receive such training. *(See Figure 2.1.)*

1. Detect the presence of hazardous materials
2. Survey a hazardous materials incident from a safe location to identify the name, UN/NA identification number, or type placard applied for any hazardous materials involved
3. Collect hazard information from the current edition of the *North American Emergency Response Guidebook*

(b) Implement actions consistent with the local emergency response plan, the organization's standard operating procedures, and the current edition of the *North American Emergency Response Guidebook* by completing the following tasks:

All actions must be taken with appropriate safety precautions. The responder at this level will not have any

Figure 2.1 First responders, whether in the public or private sector like these shown at a railroad yard, run the greatest risk for contamination at a hazardous materials incident because they are usually first on the scene. The training for all first responders must focus on awareness and safety.

specialized protective clothing or equipment and must therefore exercise extreme caution when confirming the presence of hazardous materials.

The responder also must be trained in the appropriate community response procedures and know how to initiate them. Responders should be familiar with their own organization's response plan and with their role in it. In many cases, these actions will consist of notifying the local emergency responders, such as the fire department, and securing the immediate area to prevent exposure to others.

1. Initiate protective actions
2. Initiate the notification process

2-2 Competencies — Analyzing the Incident

2-2.1 Detecting the Presence of Hazardous Materials.

Given various facility or transportation situations, or both, with and without hazardous materials present, the first responder at the awareness level shall identify those situations where hazardous materials are present. The first responder at the awareness level shall be able to:

2-2.1.1* Identify the definition of hazardous materials (or dangerous goods, in Canada).

A-2-2.1.1 See A-1-2 Hazardous Material.

2-2.1.2* Identify the DOT hazard classes and divisions of hazardous materials and identify common examples of materials in each hazard class or division.

Because proper identification of hazardous materials is extremely important, the actions of the awareness level responder can be critical to a successful emergency response. By being able to identify the hazard classes, the responder will have a better understanding of potential problems that may arise.

A-2-2.1.2, A-2-2.1.3 Definitions of Department of Transportation Hazard Classes and Divisions. Title 49, *Code of Federal Regulations*, Parts 170–180.

Class 1 (Explosives)

An explosive is any substance or article, including a device, that is designed to function by explosion (i.e., an extremely rapid release of gas and heat) or that, by chemical reaction within itself, is able to function in a similar manner even if not designed to function by explosion. Explosives in Class 1 are divided into six divisions. Each division will have a letter designation.

Division 1.1 consists of explosives that have a mass explosion hazard. A mass explosion is one that affects almost the entire load instantaneously.

Examples of Division 1.1 explosives include black powder, dynamite, and TNT.

Division 1.2 consists of explosives that have a projection hazard but not a mass explosion hazard.

Examples of Division 1.2 explosives include aerial flares, detonating cord, and power device cartridges.

Division 1.3 consists of explosives that have a fire hazard and either a minor blast hazard or a minor projection hazard, or both, but not a mass explosion hazard.

Examples of Division 1.3 explosives include liquid-fueled rocket motors and propellant explosives.

Division 1.4 consists of explosive devices that present a minor explosion hazard. No device in the division may contain more than 25 g (0.9 oz) of a detonating material. The explosive effects are largely confined to the package and no projection of fragments of appreciable size or range is expected. An external fire must not cause virtually instantaneous explosion of almost the entire contents of the package.

Examples of Division 1.4 explosives include line-throwing rockets, practice ammunition, and signal cartridges.

Division 1.5 consists of very insensitive explosives. This division is comprised of substances that have a mass explosion hazard but are so insensitive that there is very little probability of initiation or of transition from burning to detonation under normal conditions of transport.

Examples of Division 1.5 explosives include pilled ammonium nitrate fertilizer–fuel oil mixtures (blasting agents).

Division 1.6 consists of extremely insensitive articles that do not have a mass explosive hazard. This division is comprised of articles that contain only extremely insensitive detonating substances and that demonstrate a negligible probability of accidental initiation or propagation.

Class 2 (Gases)

Division 2.1 (flammable gas) consists of any material that is a gas at 20°C (68°F) or less and 101.3 kPa (14.7 psi) of pressure, a material that has a boiling point of 20°C (68°F) or less at 101.3 kPa (14.7 psi), and that:

(a) Is ignitable at 101.3 kPa (14.7 psi) when in a mixture of 13 percent or less by volume with air
(b) Has a flammable range at 101.3 kPa (14.7 psi) with air of at least 12 percent regardless of the lower limit

Examples of Division 2.1 gases include inhibited butadienes, methyl chloride, and propane.

Division 2.2 (nonflammable, nonpoisonous compressed gas, including compressed gas, liquefied gas, pressurized cryogenic gas, and compressed gas in solution) consists of any material (or mixture) that exerts in the packaging an absolute pressure of 280 kPa (41 psia) at 20°C (68°F).

A cryogenic liquid is a refrigerated liquefied gas having a boiling point colder than –90°C (–130°F) at 101.3 kPa (14.7 psi) absolute.

Examples of Division 2.2 gases include anhydrous ammonia, cryogenic argon, carbon dioxide, and compressed nitrogen.

Division 2.3 (poisonous gas) consists of a material that is a gas at 20°C (68°F) or less and a pressure of 101.3 kPa (14.7 psi or 1 atm), a material that has a boiling point of 20°C (68°F) or less at 101.3 kPa (14.7 psi), and that:

(a) Is known to be so toxic to humans as to pose a hazard to health during transportation
(b) In the absence of adequate data on human toxicity, is presumed to be toxic to humans because, when tested on laboratory animals, it has an LC_{50} value of not more than 5,000 ppm

Examples of Division 2.3 gases include anhydrous hydrogen fluoride, arsine, chlorine, and methyl bromide.

Hazard zones associated with Division 2.3 materials are the following:

(a) Hazard zone A – LC_{50} less than or equal to 200 ppm
(b) Hazard zone B – LC_{50} greater than 200 ppm and less than or equal to 1,000 ppm
(c) Hazard zone C – LC_{50} greater than 1,000 ppm and less than or equal to 3,000 ppm
(d) Hazard zone D – LC_{50} greater than 3,000 ppm and less than or equal to 5,000 ppm

Class 3 (Flammable Liquid)

Flammable liquid is any liquid having a flash point of not more than 60.5°C (141°F).

Examples of Class 3 liquids include acetone, amyl acetate, gasoline, methyl alcohol, and toluene.

Combustible Liquid

Combustible liquid is any liquid that does not meet the definition of any other hazard class and has a flash point above 60°C (140°F) and below 93°C (200°F). Flammable liquids with a flash point above 38°C (100°F) can be reclassified as a combustible liquid.

Examples of combustible liquids include mineral oil, peanut oil, and No. 6 fuel oil.

Class 4 (Flammable Solids)

Division 4.1 (flammable solid) consists of any of the following three types of materials:

(a) Wetted explosives – explosives wetted with sufficient water, alcohol, or plasticizers to suppress explosive properties
(b) Self-reactive materials – materials that are liable to undergo, at normal or elevated temperatures, a strongly exothermic decomposition caused by excessively high transport temperatures or by contamination
(c) Readily combustible solids – solids that can cause a fire through friction and any metal powders that can be ignited

Examples of Division 4.1 materials include magnesium (pellets, turnings, or ribbons) and nitrocellulose.

Division 4.2 (spontaneously combustible material) consists of any of the following materials:

(a) Pyrophoric material – a liquid or solid that, even in small quantities and without an external ignition source, can ignite within five minutes after coming in contact with air
(b) Self-heating material – a material that, when in contact with air and without an energy supply, is liable to self-heat

Examples of Division 4.2 materials include aluminum alkyls, charcoal briquettes, magnesium alkyls, and phosphorus.

Division 4.3 (dangerous when wet material) consists of materials that, by contact with water, are liable to become spontaneously flammable or to give off flammable or toxic gas at a rate greater than 1 L/kg of the material per hour.

Examples of Division 4.3 materials include calcium carbide, magnesium powder, potassium metal alloys, and sodium hydride.

Class 5 (Oxidizers and Organic Peroxides)

Division 5.1 (oxidizer) consists of materials that can, generally by yielding oxygen, cause or enhance the combustion of other materials.

Examples of Division 5.1 materials include ammonium nitrate, bromine trifluoride, and calcium hypochlorite.

Division 5.2 (organic peroxide) consists of any organic compound containing oxygen (O) in the bivalent -O-O- structure that can be considered a derivative of hydrogen peroxide, where one or more of the hydrogen atoms have been replaced by organic radicals.

Division 5.2 (organic peroxide) materials are assigned to one of seven types:

Type A – organic peroxide that can detonate or deflagrate rapidly as packaged for transport. Transportation of Type A organic peroxides is forbidden.

Type B – organic peroxide that neither detonates nor deflagrates rapidly, but that can undergo a thermal explosion.

Type C – organic peroxide that neither detonates nor deflagrates rapidly and cannot undergo a thermal explosion.

Type D – organic peroxide that detonates only partially or deflagrates slowly, with medium to no effect when heated under confinement.

Type E – organic peroxide that neither detonates nor deflagrates and shows low, or no, effect when heated under confinement.

Type F – organic peroxide that will not detonate, does not deflagrate, shows only a low, or no, effect if heated when confined, and has low, or no, explosive power.

Type G – organic peroxide that will not detonate, does not deflagrate, shows no effect if heated when confined, and has no explosive power, is thermally stable, and is desensitized.

Examples of Division 5.2 materials include dibenzoyl peroxide, methyl ethyl ketone peroxide, and peroxyacetic acid.

Class 6 (Poisonous Materials)

Division 6.1 (poisonous material) consists of materials, other than gases, that either are known to be so toxic to humans as to afford a hazard to health during transportation, or in the absence of adequate data on human toxicity, are presumed to be toxic to humans, including materials that cause irritation.

Examples of Division 6.1 materials include aniline, arsenic compounds, carbon tetrachloride, hydrocyanic acid, and tear gas.

Division 6.2 (infectious substance) consists of viable microorganisms, or their toxin, that cause or can cause disease in humans or animals. Infectious substance and etiologic agent are synonymous.

Examples of Division 6.2 materials include anthrax, botulism, rabies, and tetanus.

Hazard zones associated with Class 6 materials are the following:

(a) Hazard zone A- LC_{50} less than or equal to 200 ppm
(b) Hazard zone B- LC_{50} greater than 200 ppm and less than or equal to 1,000 ppm

Class 7 (Radioactive Materials)

Radioactive material is any material having a specific activity greater than 0.002 microcuries per gram (mCi/g).

Examples of Class 7 materials include cobalt, uranium hexafluoride, and "yellow cake."

Class 8 (Corrosive Materials)

Corrosive material is a liquid or solid that causes visible destruction or irreversible alterations in human skin tissue at the site of contact or a liquid that has a severe corrosion rate on steel or aluminum.

Examples of Class 8 materials include nitric acid, phosphorus trichloride, sodium hydroxide, and sulfuric acid.

Class 9 (Miscellaneous Hazardous Materials)

Miscellaneous hazardous material is a material that presents a hazard during transport, but that is not included in another hazard class, including the following:

(a) Any material that has an anesthetic, noxious, or other similar property that could cause extreme annoyance or discomfort to a flight crew member so as to prevent the correct performance of assigned duties
(b) Any material that is not included in any other hazard class, but is subject to the DOT requirements (a hazardous substance or a hazardous waste)

Examples of Class 9 materials include adipic acid, hazardous substances (e.g., PCBs), and molten sulfur.

ORM-D Material

An ORM-D material is a material that presents a limited hazard during transportation due to its form, quantity, and packaging.

Examples of ORM-D materials include consumer commodities and small arms ammunition.

Forbidden

Forbidden means prohibited from being offered or accepted for transportation. Prohibition does not apply if these materials are diluted, stabilized, or incorporated in devices.

Marine Pollutant

A marine pollutant is a material that has an adverse effect on aquatic life.

Elevated Temperature Material

An elevated temperature material is a material that, when offered for transportation in a bulk packaging, meets one of the following conditions:

(a) Liquid at or above 100°C (212°F)
(b) Liquid with a flash point at or above 37.8°C (100°F) that is intentionally heated and is transported at or above its flash point
(c) Solid at a temperature at or above 240°C (464°F)

2-2.1.3* Identify the primary hazards associated with each of the DOT hazard classes and divisions of hazardous materials by hazard class or division.

By being able to accurately identify the type of hazardous materials present and the primary hazards they involve, the awareness level responder can begin to take the correct defensive protective actions early, if it is safe to do so. In addition, he or she can give this information to the hazardous materials response team members, who will then understand the type of incident they are responding to and be able to request any specialized equipment or additional resources they might need. For example, a responder would initiate considerably different actions dealing with a Class 1, Division 1.1 material (mass detonating explosives) than dealing with a Class 2, Division 2.2 (nonflammable gases) material. *(See Table 2.1.)*

2-2.1.4 Identify the difference between hazardous materials incidents and other emergencies.

The adverse consequences of exposure to a hazardous material can be far-reaching and severe. *(See Figure 2.2.)* Hazardous materials emergencies thus stand apart from other types of emergencies because they present such a large potential for doing great harm and because responders must be specifically trained and equipped to deal with them properly. This standard also notes that responders must take care to avoid making the situation worse than it is.

2-2.1.5 Identify typical occupancies and locations in the community where hazardous materials are manufactured, transported, stored, used, or disposed of.

Individuals involved with hazardous materials response planning and at the first responder awareness level should know where in a given community or industrial or manufacturing location hazardous materials are most likely to be found. This will help select appropriate emergency actions that can be planned and coordinated as necessary with other responders from the public and private sectors. Local planning for response should be based, in part, on the knowledge that particular hazardous materials may be present at certain fixed sites within a specified area or community. For example, an area fire chief should know where the auto body painting businesses in his community are located and what chemicals and solvents these sites are likely to contain. Similarly, the plant manager of a pharmaceutical company should be aware of what chemicals and chemical compounds are on-site at any given time. The manager should be able to advise responders what chemicals are present, where and how they are stored, and what, if any, built-in precautions have been taken.

2-2.1.6 Identify typical container shapes that can indicate hazardous materials.

The configuration of some containers is so unusual that it signals the presence of some hazardous materials. Containers that provide clues include those used for radioactive materials, pressurized products, cryogenics, and corrosives.

2-2.1.7 Identify facility and transportation markings and colors that indicate hazardous materials, including the following:

(a) UN/NA identification numbers

Several numbers are used on placards. The first, which denotes the class and/or division number, would be displayed at the bottom of the placard (for example, 6). In addition, the four-digit product identification number, such as 2020, may be used. In some cases, both numbers are used on the same placard. *(See Figure 2.3.)*

The colors of the placards also indicate the hazard class. For example, yellow is used for Class 5, Oxidizing Substances, and black-and-white is used to denote Class 8, Corrosives.

(b) NFPA 704 markings
(c) Military hazardous materials markings

The military uses different types of markings for shipments on military facilities. The military marking system establishes the following four hazard classes:

(a) Class 1—Materials that present a mass detonation hazard
(b) Class 2—Materials that present an explosive with fragmentation hazard
(c) Class 3—Materials with a mass fire hazard
(d) Class 4—Materials that present a moderate fire hazard

In addition, there are three special warnings that are indicated separately. These include the following:

(a) Chemical hazard
    Highly toxic
    Harassing agents
    White phosphorus munitions
(b) Apply no water

Table 2.1 DOT Hazard Classes

Class	Division with Explanation	Examples of Materials (by Hazard Class or Division)	General Hazard Properties (Not All-Inclusive)
Class 1	Division 1.1—explosive with mass explosion hazard	Dynamite, TNT, black powder	Explosive; exposure to heat, shock, or contamination could result in thermal and mechanical hazards.
	Division 1.2—explosive with projection hazard	Projectiles with bursting charges	
	Division 1.3—explosive with fire, minor blast, or minor projection hazard	Propellant explosives, rocket motors, special fireworks	
	Division 1.4—explosive device with minor explosion hazard	Common fireworks, small arms ammunition	
	Division 1.5—very insensitive explosive	Ammonium nitrate-fuel oil mixtures	
	Division 1.6—extremely insensitive explosive		
Class 2	Division 2.1—flammable gas	Propane, butadiene (inhibited) acetylene, methyl chloride	Under pressure; container may rupture violently (fire and nonfire); may be a flammable, poisonous, a corrosive, an dasphyxiant and/or thermally unstable.
	Division 2.2—nonflammable, nonpoisonous gases	Carbon dioxide, anhydrous ammonia	
	Division 2.3—poisonous (toxic) gas	Arsine, phosgene, chlorine, methyl bromide	
	Division 2.4—corrosive gas (Canada)	Anhydrous Ammonia (Canada only)	
Class 3	Flammable Liquids Division 3.1—flash point <0˚F (17.7˚C) Division 3.2—flash point ≥0˚F (17.7˚C) to <73˚F (22.7˚C) Division 3.3—flash point ≥73˚ (22.7˚C) to <141˚F (60.5˚C)	Acetone, amyl acetate, gasoline, methyl alcohol, toluene	Flammable; container may rupture violently from heat/fire; may be corrosive, toxic, and/or thermally unstable.
	Combustible liquids	Fuel oils	
Class 4	Division 4.1—flammable solids	Nitrocellulose, matches	Flammable, some spontaneously; may be water reactive, toxic, and/or corrosive; may be extremely difficult to extinguish.
	Division 4.2—spontaneously combustible material	Phosphorus, pyrophoric liquids and solids	
	Division 4.3—Dangerous when wet material	Calcium carbide, potassium, sodium, magnesium	
Class 5	Division 5.1—oxidizer	Ammonium nitrate fertilizer	Supplies oxygen to support combustion; sensitive to heat, shock, friction, and/or contamination.
	Division 5.2—organic peroxides	Dibenzoyl peroxide	
Class 6	Division 6.1—poisonous (toxic) material	Aniline, arsenic, tear gas, carbon tetrachloride	Toxic by inhalation, ingestion, and skin and eye contact; may be flammable.
	Division 6.2—infectious substances	Anthrax, botulism, rabies, tetanus	
Class 7	Radioactive material	Cobalt, uranium hexafluoride	May cause burns and biologic effects; energy and matter.
Class 8	Corrosive Material	Hydrochloric acid, sulfuric acid, sodium hydroxide, nitric acid	Disintegration of contacted tissues; may be fuming, water-reactive.
Class 9	Miscellaneous hazardous materials	Dry ice, molten sulfur, adipic acid, PCBs	
ORM-D		Consumer commodities	

Source: *Fire Protection Handbook*, 18th edition.[1]

Figure 2.2 In a large-scale emergency, responders of all levels can be at risk simply because a complex incident, such as this train wreck, involves so many factors. At this accident in California, fires from the wreck ignited chemicals transported on board, creating thick black smoke. One person died in the incident. (Photo by William Wilson Lewis III/AP Worldwide)

(c) Wear protective breathing apparatus
(d) Special hazard communication markings

These may be found in some facilities and identify hazardous materials. The U.S. military uses both special hazard symbols and detonation hazard symbols. *(See Figure 2.4.)*

(e) Pipeline markings

Pipeline marker signs are usually metal signs placed adjacent and above a hazardous materials pipeline. They contain information about the location and ownership of the line.

(f) Container markings

Often, markings on a container will provide some indication as to the type of product it holds. These markings may include product names such as "chlorine."

2-2.1.8 Given an NFPA 704 marking, describe the significance of the colors, numbers, and special symbols.

The NFPA 704[2] marking system is based on the "704 diamond" (*see Figure 2.5*), which visually presents information on three categories of hazard: health, flammability, and instability, as well as the degree of severity of each hazard. It also indicates two special hazards: reactivity with water and oxidizing ability. The NFPA 704 diamond symbol is intended to provide immediate general information to the emergency responder.

The five degrees of hazard, in descending order, have these general meanings to fire fighters:

4—Fire is too dangerous to approach with standard fire-fighting equipment and procedures. Withdraw and obtain expert advice on how to handle.

3—Fire can be fought using methods intended for extremely hazardous situations, such as remote-control monitors or personal protective equipment that prevents all bodily contact.

2—Fire can be fought with standard procedures, but hazards are present that can be handled safely only with certain special equipment or procedures.

1—Nuisance hazards are present that require some care, but standard fire-fighting procedures can be used.

0—No special hazards are present; therefore, no special measures are needed.

Figure 2.3 *Several numbers are used on placards. The first, which denotes the class or division number, may be displayed at the bottom of the placard (for example, 6). In addition, the four-digit product identification number, such as 2020, may be used. In some cases, both numbers are used on the same placard. (Source: Fire Protection Handbook, 18th edition)*

NFPA 704 describes the hazard categories and the security levels that the various numbers indicate for the three hazards. The following, adapted from Appendix B of NFPA 704, summarizes the hazard information and recommends protective actions.[3]

The numbers from 0 through 4 are placed in the three upper squares of the diamond to show the degree of hazard present for each of the three hazard categories. The 0 indicates the lowest degree of hazard, and 4 indicates the highest. The fourth square, at the bottom, is used for special information. Two symbols for this bottom space are recognized by NFPA 704. Either symbols, or both, may appear in this square, or it may be blank. The recognized symbols are:

(a) A letter W with a bar through it (~~W~~) to indicate that a material is unusually reactive with water.

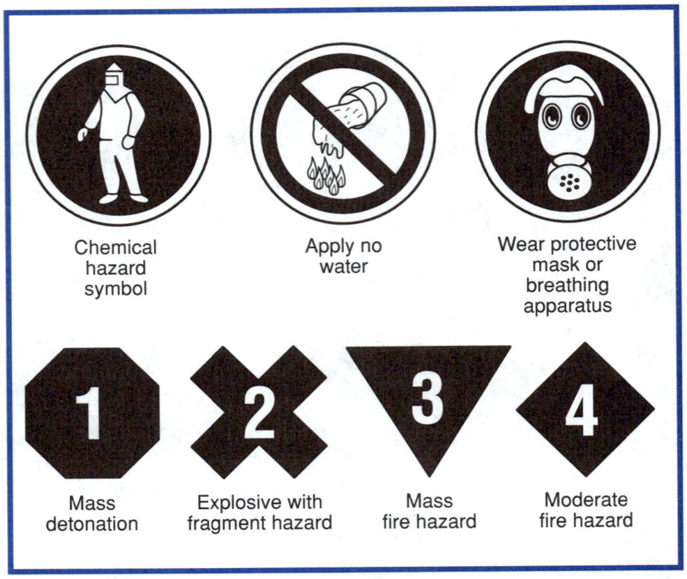

Figure 2.4 *The U.S. military uses special hazard symbols (top), as well as detonation hazard symbols (bottom).*

This does not mean "do not use water," since some forms of water, such as fog or spray, may be used in some cases. What it does say is: "Water may cause a hazard, so use it very cautiously until you have proper information."

(b) The letters OX to indicate an oxidizer.

Although not recognized by NFPA 704, some users will insert the letters ALK for alkaline materials and ACID for acidic materials in this square.

Health Hazards

In general, the health hazard in fire fighting is that of a single exposure, the duration of which may vary from a few seconds up to an hour. The physical exertion demanded in fire fighting or other emergencies may be expected to intensify the effects of any exposure. In assigning degrees of danger, local conditions must be considered. The following explanation is based on use of the protective equipment normally worn by fire fighters. *(See Figure 2.5.)*

4—Materials that under emergency conditions can be lethal. A few whiffs of the vapor could cause death, or the vapor or liquid could be fatal on penetrating the fire fighter's normal full-protective clothing. The normal full-protective clothing and breathing apparatus available to the average fire department will not provide adequate protection against inhalation or skin contact with these materials.

3—Materials that under emergency conditions can cause serious or permanent injury. Full-protective

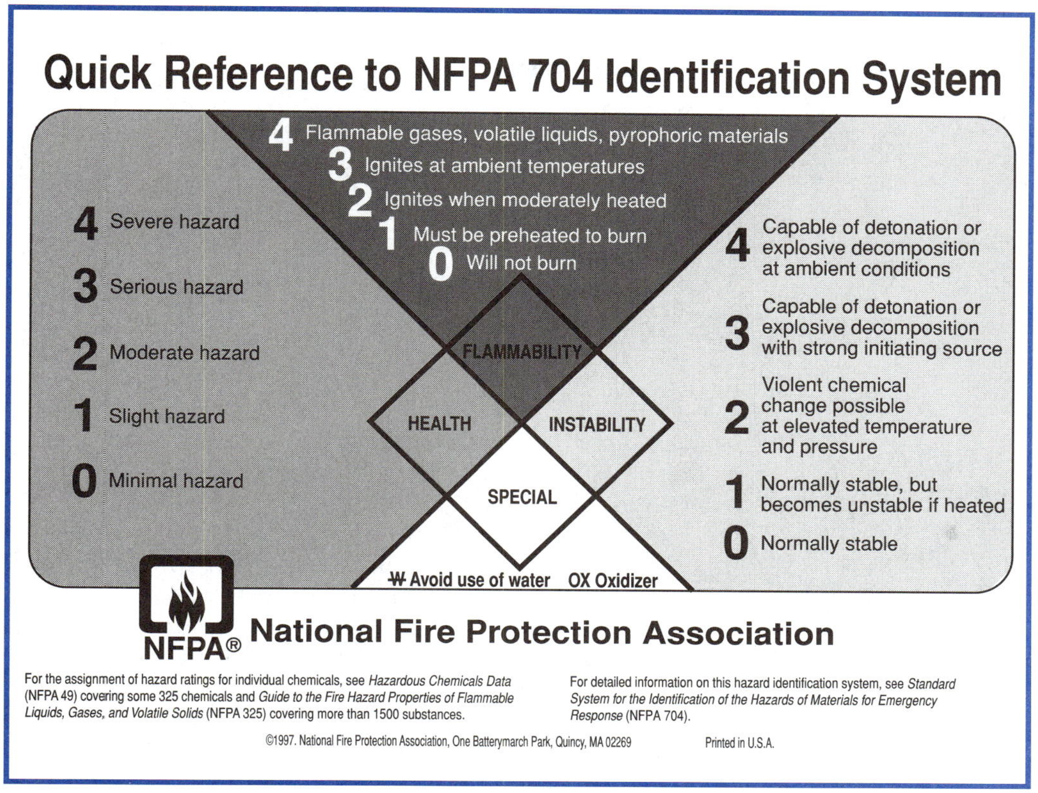

Figure 2.5 *The system is based on the "704 diamond," which visually presents information on three categories of hazard—health, flammability, and instability—as well as the degree of severity of each hazard. It also indicates two special hazards: reactivity with water and oxidizing ability. The NFPA 704 diamond symbol is intended to provide immediate general information to the emergency responder. (Source: Fire Protection Handbook, 18th edition)*

clothing, self-contained breathing apparatus (SCBA), gloves, boots, and bands around legs, arms, and waist should be provided. No skin surfaces should be exposed.

2—Materials that under emergency conditions can cause temporary incapacitation or residual injury. Full-face mask self-contained breathing apparatus that provides eye protection should be provided.

1—Materials that under emergency conditions can cause significant irritation. It may be desirable to wear self-contained breathing apparatus.

0—Materials that, under emergency conditions, would offer no health hazard beyond that of ordinary combustible materials.

Flammability Hazards

Susceptibility to burning is the basis for assigning degrees within this category (*see Figure 2.5*). The method of attacking the fire is influenced by this susceptibility factor.

4—Flammable gases, flammable cryogenic materials, very volatile flammable liquids, Class IA liquids, or materials that ignite spontaneously in air (pyrophoric). If possible, shut on/off flow and keep cooling water streams on exposed tanks or containers. Withdrawal may be necessary.

3—Materials that can be ignited under almost all normal temperature conditions (Class IB). Water may be ineffective because of the low flash point.

2—Materials that must be moderately heated or exposed to relatively high ambient temperatures before ignition will occur (Class II and Class IIIA liquids). Water spray may be used to extinguish the fire because the material can be cooled below its flash point.

1—Materials that must be preheated before ignition can occur (Class IIIB liquids). Water may cause frothing if it gets below the surface of the liquid and turns to steam. If this is the case, water fog gently applied to the surface will cause a frothing that will extinguish the fire.

0—Materials that will not burn.

Instability Hazards

The assignment of relative degrees of hazard in the reactivity category is based on the susceptibility of materials to release energy either by themselves or in combination with other materials (*see Figure 2.5*). Fire exposure was one of the factors considered along with conditions of shock and pressure.

4—Materials that are readily capable of detonation or explosive decomposition at normal temperatures and pressures. Includes materials that are sensitive to localized thermal or mechanical shock. If they are involved in a massive fire, vacate the area.

3—Materials that are capable of detonation, explosive decomposition, or explosive reaction, but require a strong initiating source, or that must be heated under confinement before initiation. Includes materials that are sensitive to thermal or mechanical shock at elevated temperatures and pressures or that may react explosively with water without requiring heat or confinement. Fire fighting should be conducted from behind explosion-resistant locations.

2—Materials that readily undergo a violent chemical change at elevated temperature and pressures. Includes materials that react violently with water or that may form potentially explosive mixtures with water. Use portable monitors, hose holders, or straight hose streams from a distance to cool the tanks and the material in them. Use caution.

1—Materials that are normally stable but may become unstable at elevated temperatures and pressures or that react vigorously with water, but not violently. Includes materials that change or decompose on exposure to air, light, or moisture. Use normal precautions as in approaching any fire.

0—Materials that are normally stable and therefore do not present any reactivity hazard to fire fighters.

Special Information

When ~~W~~ appears at the bottom in the fourth space *(see Figure 2.5)*:

4—~~W~~ is not used with reactivity hazard 4.

3—In addition to hazards above, these materials can react explosively with water. Explosion protection is essential if water is to be used.

2—In addition to hazards above, these materials may react with water or form potentially explosive mixtures with water.

1—In addition to hazards above, these materials may react vigorously but not violently with water.

0—W is not used with reactivity hazard 0.

Methods of Presentation

Several methods for presentation of the ratings are shown in Figure 2.5. A basic requirement is that numbers be spaced as though they were in the diamond outline. Chapter 6 of NFPA 704 presents recommended layout and sizes for the symbol, a distance-legibility table, and several examples using the symbol.

Assigning Degrees of Hazard

Numbers (degrees of hazard) for use in the diamond are assigned on the basis of the worst hazard expected in the area, whether it be from hazards of the original material or of its combustion or breakdown products. The effects of local conditions must be considered. For instance, a drum of carbon tetrachloride sitting in a well-ventilated storage shed presents a different hazard than a drum sitting in an unventilated basement.

Advantages of the NFPA 704 System

The NFPA 704 system can warn against hazards under fire conditions of materials that other information systems class as non-hazardous. For example, edible tallow produces toxic and irritating combustion products. It would be given a "2" degree of health hazard, indicating the need for air-supplied respiratory equipment.

NFPA 704 also can warn against overall fire hazards in an area. On the door of a laboratory or storage room, it can warn of the worst hazards likely in a fire situation. Such information is useful both in preplanning and in actual fires.

NFPA 704 also can be used without a supplementary manual. Because of its simplicity, the general meanings of the numbers are easily understood and the whole symbol is read and interpreted quickly on the spot, in poor light, and at a distance.

Disadvantages of the NFPA 704 System

The NFPA 704 system supplies only minimum information on the hazards themselves. Since the system informs on protective measures, the same number may be used for various types of hazards so that, for instance, a health hazard "3" means "serious hazard" without saying whether the hazard is corrosive to the skin or toxic by absorption through the skin. Thus, the symbol is most useful to trained or informed persons.

2-2.1.9 Identify U.S. and Canadian placards and labels that indicate hazardous materials.

2-2.1.10 Identify the basic information on material safety data sheets (MSDS) and shipping papers that indicates hazardous materials.

An MSDS contains information on the following major categories: the manufacturer's name and location; the name and family of the chemical; the hazardous ingredients; physical data; fire and explosion hazard data; health hazard data; spill or leak procedures; special protection information; and special precautions that must be taken when dealing with the material. *(See Figures 2.6 and 2.7.)*

2-2.1.10.1 Identify where to find material safety data sheets (MSDS).

Employers are required to maintain material safety data sheets for all hazardous chemicals used at their facilities. This is part of the Hazard Communication Standard Title 29, *Code of Federal Regulations,* Part 1910.1200.[4]

2-2.1.10.2 Identify entries on a material safety data sheet that indicate the presence of hazardous materials.

The major categories on an MSDS that indicate the presence of hazardous materials include hazardous ingredients, fire and explosion hazard data, health hazard data, reactivity data, spill or leak procedures, special protection information, and special precautions.

2-2.1.10.3 Identify the entries on shipping papers that indicate the presence of hazardous materials.

Shipping papers may contain several pieces of information that indicate the presence of a hazardous material. These include the material's proper shipping name, its hazard class or division, and its product identification number.

2-2.1.10.4 Match the name of the shipping papers found in transportation (air, highway, rail, and water) with the mode of transportation.

2-2.1.10.5 Identify the person responsible for having the shipping papers in each mode of transportation.

Table 2.2 offers a listing by transit route of the likely location of shipping papers and the person responsible.

2-2.1.10.6 Identify where the shipping papers are found in each mode of transportation.

See Table 2.2.

2-2.1.10.7 Identify where the papers can be found in an emergency in each mode of transportation.

See Table 2.2.

2-2.1.11* Identify examples of clues (other than occupancy/location, container shape, markings/color, placards/labels, MSDS, and shipping papers) that use the senses of sight, sound, and odor to indicate hazardous materials.

A-2-2.1.11 These clues would include odors, gas leaks, fire or vapor cloud, visible corrosive actions or chemical reactions, pooled liquids, hissing of pressure releases, condensation lines on pressure tanks, injured victims, or casualties.

2-2.1.12 Describe the limitations of using the senses in determining the presence or absence of hazardous materials.

One problem in using your senses to evaluate the presence of hazardous materials is the fact that, if you are close enough to use them, you may already have endangered yourself. In addition, many gases are odorless, tasteless, and colorless.

See the Tentative Interim Amendment on p. 294 for new paragraphs 2-2.1.13, A-2-2.1.13, 2-2.1.14, and A-2-2.1.14.

2-2.2 Surveying the Hazardous Materials Incident from a Safe Location.

Given examples of facility and transportation situations involving hazardous materials, the first responder at the awareness level shall identify the hazardous material(s) in each situation by name, UN/NA identification number, or type placard applied. The first responder at the awareness level shall be able to:

2-2.2.1 Identify difficulties encountered in determining the specific names of hazardous materials in both facilities and transportation.

Even if the awareness level responder knows placarding and labeling systems, and is also familiar with other methods of identifying the presence of hazardous materials, the responder may still have difficulty determining which materials are involved in a specific incident. The responder may not be able to get close enough to make accurate identification and, in some cases, the labels or placards will be missing; the placards or labels will list only the class or division, not the specific product identifier; shipments may contain mixed loads of hazardous materials and require only the "dangerous" placard; the shipper may err in the labeling and placarding; or the shipping papers may be inaccessible.

2-2.2.2 Identify sources for obtaining the names of, UN/NA identification numbers for, or types of placard associated with hazardous materials in transportation.

One of the best ways to identify products or types of placards is to use the *North American Emergency Response Guidebook* (NAERG).[5] The shipping papers, if available,

Hazardous Material Data Sheet	Containment System ID.

Material Name ______________________ DOT ID № ________ STCC № ____________

Synonyms ____

Hazard Class ________________________

NFPA 704 Marking: Health ______ Flammability ______ Reactivity ______ Other ____________

Physical Properties

Form	Color	Odor	Chemical Formula	Molecular Wt.
☐ Solid ☐ Liquid ☐ Gas				

Chemical Properties

Actual Temp.	Boiling Point	Melting Point	Vapor Pressure	Expansion Ratio	Specific Gravity	Vapor Density	Soluble?	Degree of Solubility
							☐ Yes	

Physical Hazards

	Actual Temperature	Flash Point	Ignition Temperature
Flammable (heat/fire) ☐ Yes Cryogenic (cold) ☐ Yes Oxidizer (supports combustion) ☐ Yes Explosive ☐ Yes Reactive ☐ Yes To What? ________			
	Actual Concentration	**Flammable Range**	**Toxic Products of Combustion**

Health Hazards

	Actual Concentration	Non-life Threatening Exposure Limits		
Acute Health Hazards: Poisonous ☐ Yes Corrosive ☐ Yes To What? ____________ Asphyxiation ☐ Yes Etiologic ☐ Yes Radiation ☐ Yes Type: alpha beta gamma		**TLV-TWA(PEL)**	**TLV-C**	**TLV-STEL**
	Odor Threshold	**Life Threatening Exposure Limits**		
		IDLH	**LC_{50}**	**LD_{50}**

	Route of Entry ☒ = YES		Toxicity Rating	Notes
Chronic Health Hazards: Carcinogen ☐ Yes Mutagen ☐ Yes Teratogen ☐ Yes Aquatic Hazard ☐ Yes	Inhalation	☐	1 2 3 4 5 6	
	Dermal	☐	1 2 3 4 5 6	
	Ingestion	☐	1 2 3 4 5 6	

Response Information

Evacuation Distances ____

First Aid ____

____

Personal Protective Equipment ____

Decontamination ____

Extinguishing Agents ____

Neutralizing Agents ____

Figure 2.6 *Hazardous material data sheet for recording information obtained during the task of collecting and interpreting hazard and response information. (Source: Fire Protection Handbook, 18th edition)*

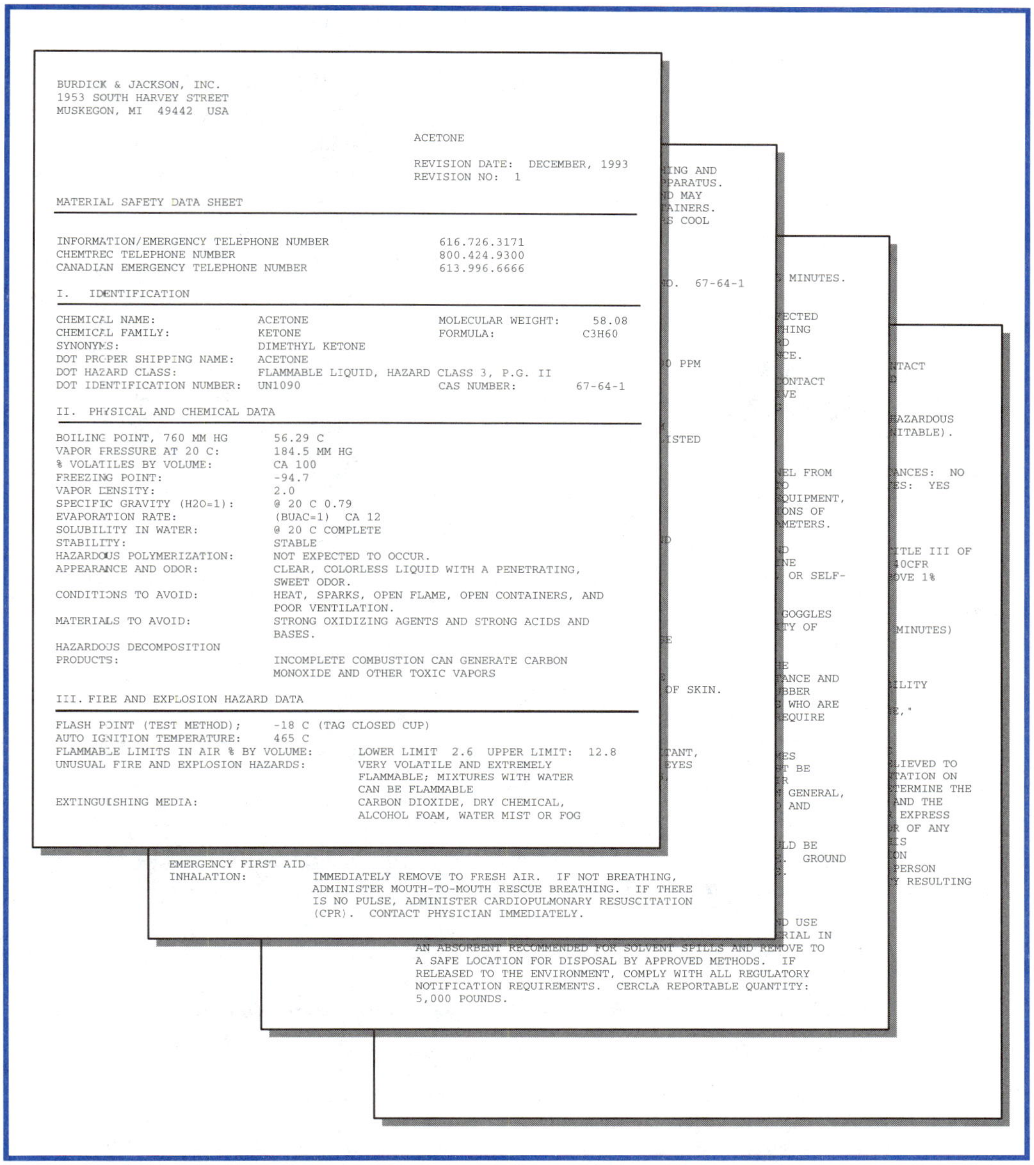

BURDICK & JACKSON, INC.
1953 SOUTH HARVEY STREET
MUSKEGON, MI 49442 USA

ACETONE

REVISION DATE: DECEMBER, 1993
REVISION NO: 1

MATERIAL SAFETY DATA SHEET

INFORMATION/EMERGENCY TELEPHONE NUMBER	616.726.3171
CHEMTREC TELEPHONE NUMBER	800.424.9300
CANADIAN EMERGENCY TELEPHONE NUMBER	613.996.6666

I. IDENTIFICATION

CHEMICAL NAME:	ACETONE	MOLECULAR WEIGHT:	58.08
CHEMICAL FAMILY:	KETONE	FORMULA:	C3H6O
SYNONYMS:	DIMETHYL KETONE		
DOT PROPER SHIPPING NAME:	ACETONE		
DOT HAZARD CLASS:	FLAMMABLE LIQUID, HAZARD CLASS 3, P.G. II		
DOT IDENTIFICATION NUMBER:	UN1090	CAS NUMBER:	67-64-1

II. PHYSICAL AND CHEMICAL DATA

BOILING POINT, 760 MM HG	56.29 C
VAPOR PRESSURE AT 20 C:	184.5 MM HG
% VOLATILES BY VOLUME:	CA 100
FREEZING POINT:	-94.7
VAPOR DENSITY:	2.0
SPECIFIC GRAVITY (H2O=1):	@ 20 C 0.79
EVAPORATION RATE:	(BUAC=1) CA 12
SOLUBILITY IN WATER:	@ 20 C COMPLETE
STABILITY:	STABLE
HAZARDOUS POLYMERIZATION:	NOT EXPECTED TO OCCUR.
APPEARANCE AND ODOR:	CLEAR, COLORLESS LIQUID WITH A PENETRATING, SWEET ODOR.
CONDITIONS TO AVOID:	HEAT, SPARKS, OPEN FLAME, OPEN CONTAINERS, AND POOR VENTILATION.
MATERIALS TO AVOID:	STRONG OXIDIZING AGENTS AND STRONG ACIDS AND BASES.
HAZARDOUS DECOMPOSITION PRODUCTS:	INCOMPLETE COMBUSTION CAN GENERATE CARBON MONOXIDE AND OTHER TOXIC VAPORS

III. FIRE AND EXPLOSION HAZARD DATA

FLASH POINT (TEST METHOD);	-18 C (TAG CLOSED CUP)
AUTO IGNITION TEMPERATURE:	465 C
FLAMMABLE LIMITS IN AIR % BY VOLUME:	LOWER LIMIT 2.6 UPPER LIMIT: 12.8
UNUSUAL FIRE AND EXPLOSION HAZARDS:	VERY VOLATILE AND EXTREMELY FLAMMABLE; MIXTURES WITH WATER CAN BE FLAMMABLE
EXTINGUISHING MEDIA:	CARBON DIOXIDE, DRY CHEMICAL, ALCOHOL FOAM, WATER MIST OR FOG

EMERGENCY FIRST AID
INHALATION: IMMEDIATELY REMOVE TO FRESH AIR. IF NOT BREATHING, ADMINISTER MOUTH-TO-MOUTH RESCUE BREATHING. IF THERE IS NO PULSE, ADMINISTER CARDIOPULMONARY RESUSCITATION (CPR). CONTACT PHYSICIAN IMMEDIATELY.

A SAFE LOCATION FOR DISPOSAL BY APPROVED METHODS. IF RELEASED TO THE ENVIRONMENT, COMPLY WITH ALL REGULATORY NOTIFICATION REQUIREMENTS. CERCLA REPORTABLE QUANTITY: 5,000 POUNDS.

Figure 2.7 *Alternative examples of presenting the information gathered for the MSDS. (Source: Fire Protection Handbook, 18th edition)*

Table 2.2 A List of the Shipping Papers by Route of Transportation, Title of Shipping Paper, Location, and Responsible Person

Transport Route	Title of Shipping Paper	Location of Shipping Papers	Responsible Person
Highway	Bill of lading or freight bill	Cab or vehicle	Driver
Rail	Waybill and/or consist	With member of train crew (conductor or engineer)	Conductor
Water	Dangerous cargo manifest	Wheelhouse or pipe-like container or barge	Captain or master
Air	Air bill with shippers' certification for restricted articles	Cockpit (may also be found attached to the outside of packages)	Pilot

Source: *Fire Protection Handbook,* 18th edition.[6]

should also contain both the four-digit identification number and the proper shipping name of the material.

2-2.2.3 Identify sources for obtaining the names of hazardous materials in a facility.

At fixed facilities, the names of hazardous materials are found on the MSDS and in the emergency planning documents, and there may be signs or other markings on storage containers.

2-2.3* Collecting Hazard Information.

Given the identity of various hazardous materials (name, UN/NA identification number, or type placard), the first responder at the awareness level shall identify the fire, explosion, and health hazard information for each material by using the current edition of the *North American Emergency Response Guidebook.* The first responder at the awareness level shall be able to:

A-2-2.3 It is the intent of this standard that the first responder at the awareness level be taught the noted competency to a specific task level. This task level would be to have knowledge of the contents of the current edition of the *North American Emergency Response Guidebook* or other reference material provided. Awareness level responders should be familiar with the information provided in those documents so that they can use it to assist with accurate notification of an incident and take protective actions.

If other sources of response information [including the material safety data sheet (MSDS)] are provided to the hazardous materials responder at the awareness level in lieu of the current edition of the *North American Emergency Response Guidebook*, the responder should identify hazard information similar to that found in the current edition of the *North American Emergency Response Guidebook.*

The information responders at the awareness level can use to identify products is generally limited. The most likely sources of this information are the *North American Emergency Response Guidebook* (NAERG). It is therefore important that the awareness level responder be familiar with this book and be able to look up information quickly.

If the responders use other types of documents, such as the MSDS, to identify products and locate information about handling a spill, leak, fire, or explosion, they must be able to find the information quickly. Speed is important when dealing with an emergency.

2-2.3.1* Identify the three methods for determining the appropriate guide page for a hazardous material.

To find this information in the *North American Emergency Response Guidebook*, the responder must:

(a) Identify the material by finding the four-digit UN/NA identification number on a placard or orange panel, in a shipping paper, or on the package, then locate the number in the yellow-bordered pages and determine the appropriate guide page; or

(b) Locate the name of the material in the shipping papers or on the placard or package, then locate the material in the alphabetical listing of products on the blue-bordered pages and determine the appropriate guide page; or

(c) If a name or identification number is not available but the responder can see the placard, the responder should locate a matching placard in the table of placards and consult the three-digit guide number found next to the look-alike placard. If the material is an explosive, the responder should consult one of the four guides listed inside the front cover of the *North American Emergency Response Guidebook.*

A-2-2.3.1 Three methods for determining the appropriate guide page include the following:

(a) Using the numerical index for UN/NA identification numbers
(b) Using the alphabetical index for chemical names
(c) Using the "Table of Placards and Initial Response Guides"

2-2.3.2 Identify the two general types of hazards found on each guide page.

Each guide page of the *North American Emergency Response Guidebook* contains information on the fire and explosion hazard and on the health hazard of the specific hazardous material or material class.

2-3 Competencies — Planning the Response

(No competencies currently required at this level.)

The committee felt that the responder at this level would *not* be involved in planning for an emergency response but would apply standard operating procedures established by the organization or found in the local emergency response plan. At this level, the responder's sole responsibilities are to identify a hazardous material, notify the authorities, and isolate the material if possible.

2-4 Competencies — Implementing the Planned Response

2-4.1* Initiating Protective Actions.

Given examples of facility and transportation hazardous materials incidents, the local emergency response plan, the organization's standard operating procedures, and the current edition of the *North American Emergency Response Guidebook*, first responders at the awareness level shall be able to identify the actions to be taken to protect themselves and others and to control access to the scene. The first responder at the awareness level shall be able to:

The competencies in this section are designed to ensure that the awareness level responder can implement the appropriate protective actions based on the knowledge they have acquired while analyzing the incident. Emergency response plans should establish the methods and procedures that facility owners and operators, as well as local emergency and medical response personnel, are to follow. Responders at all levels must understand their role and its importance. If a response is to be handled effectively, the first responder on the scene must accurately assess the situation and initiate the appropriate measures.

A-2-4.1 Those jurisdictions that have not developed an emergency response plan can refer to the document NRT-1, *Hazardous Materials Emergency Planning Guide*, developed by the National Response Team.

The National Response Team, composed of 14 federal agencies having major responsibilities in environmental, transportation, emergency management, worker safety, and public health areas, is the national body responsible for coordinating federal planning, preparedness, and response actions related to oil discharges and hazardous substance releases. Under the Superfund Amendments and Reauthorization Act of 1986, the NRT is responsible for publishing guidance documents for the preparation and implementation of hazardous substance emergency plans.

NRT-1 was first published and distributed in March 1987. It discusses the elements required to develop an effective hazardous materials emergency response plan and addresses the planning process.

2-4.1.1 Identify the location of both the local emergency response plan and the organization's standard operating procedures.

2-4.1.2 Identify the role of the first responder at the awareness level during a hazardous materials incident.

2-4.1.3 Identify the basic precautions to be taken to protect themselves and others in a hazardous materials incident.

2-4.1.3.1 Identify the precautions necessary when providing emergency medical care to victims of hazardous materials incidents.

2-4.1.3.2 Identify typical ignition sources found at the scenes of hazardous materials incidents.

Sources of ignition may include open flames; smoking materials; cutting and welding operations; heated surfaces; frictional heat; radiant heat; static, electrical, and mechanical sparks; and spontaneous ignition, such as occurs during heat-producing chemical reactions or is produced by pyrophoric materials.

Without approaching too closely, the responder may be able to control or eliminate some, but not all, ignition sources. If flammable vapors are present, responders should take safe measures to reduce or eliminate them or to disperse them into the atmosphere if possible using limited defensive actions.

2-4.1.3.3* Identify the ways hazardous materials are harmful to people, the environment, and property at hazardous materials incidents.

A-2-4.1.3.3 This would include thermal, mechanical, poisonous, corrosive, asphyxiation, radiation, and etiologic. This can also include psychological harm.

2-4.1.3.4* Identify the general routes of entry for human exposure to hazardous materials.

A-2-4.1.3.4 General routes of human exposure are contact, absorption, inhalation, and ingestion. Absorption includes entry through the eyes and through punctures.

Contact: A corrosive material will damage skin or body tissue on contact. Acids and alkalis can cause severe burns. If the skin is broken or the responder has an open wound, another entry route exists.

Absorption: In this process, one substance penetrates the inner structure of another. Hydrogen cyanide, for example, can be absorbed through the skin with fatal results.

Inhalation: Many substances cause severe damage if inhaled. Chlorine is an example of such a substance.

Ingestion: Toxic substances can be present in drinking water and in food.

Obviously, proper personal protective equipment is important, and the responder must fully understand both the potential hazards and the appropriate safeguards.

2-4.1.4* Given the identity of various hazardous materials (name, UN/NA identification number, or type placard), identify the following response information:

(a) Emergency action (fire, spill, or leak and first aid)
(b) Personal protective equipment necessary
(c) Initial isolation and protective action distances

At the awareness level, responders are generally expected to take protective actions to isolate the hazard and to evacuate or direct threatened persons out of the "hot zone" without ever entering the "hot zone" themselves. In some cases, sheltering-in-place protection may be all that is required. The NAERG recommends that persons sheltered "in place" be warned to stay far away from windows with a direct line of sight of the scene because windows may explode during a fire or explosion and shower them with glass or metal fragments.

A-2-4.1.4 If other sources of response information [including the material safety data sheet (MSDS)] are provided to the hazardous materials responder at the awareness level in lieu of the current edition of the *North American Emergency Response Guidebook*, the responder should identify response information similar to that found in the current edition of the *North American Emergency Response Guidebook.*

Again, it is important that responders demonstrate their proficiency in using the various emergency response guides and other sources of information they may be required to consult. The NAERG provides general information about the potential hazards of a number of products and outlines the emergency procedures to be used in handling incidents involving these products. Responders should be given several exercises that will allow them to demonstrate their skill at locating and interpreting the appropriate information both from the NAERG and other documents.

2-4.1.4.1 Given the name of a hazardous material, identify the recommended personal protective equipment from the following list:

(a) Street clothing and work uniforms
(b) Structural fire-fighting protective clothing
(c) Positive pressure self-contained breathing apparatus
(d) Chemical-protective clothing and equipment

2-4.1.4.2 Identify the definitions for each of the following protective actions:

Protective actions are those steps taken to preserve the health and safety of emergency responders and the public during an incident involving the release of hazardous materials.

(a) Isolation of the hazard area and denial of entry

Everybody not directly involved in the emergency response operations should be kept away from the affected area, and unprotected emergency responders should not be allowed within the isolation area.

(b) Evacuation

Evacuation is the movement of everyone from a threatened area to a safer place. To perform an evacuation, there must be enough time to warn people, to get them ready to go, and to leave the area. If there is enough time for evacuation, it is likely to be the best protective action.

Begin evacuating people who are nearby and those outdoors in direct view of the scene. Send evacuees upwind by a specific route to a definite place far enough away from the contaminated area that they will not have to be moved again if the wind shifts. As you acquire additional help, expand the area to be evacuated downwind and crosswind at least to the extent recommended in Table 2.3, Initial Isolation and Protective Action Distances. Even after people move to the distances recommended, they are not completely safe from harm and may have to be decontaminated.

(c)* Sheltering in-place protection

Sheltering-in-place protection is used when an evacuation cannot be performed or when evacuating the public would put them at greater risk than directing them to stay where they are. When using in-place protection, the responder directs people to go quickly inside a building and remain there until the danger has passed. The people inside the building should be told to close all doors and windows and to shut off all ventilating, heating, and cooling systems.

In-place protection may not be the best option if there are explosive vapors present, if it will take a long time to clear the area of gas, or if the building cannot be tightly closed. Vehicles are not as effective as buildings for sheltering-in-place protection, but can offer some protection for a short period if the vehicle windows are closed and the ventilating system is shut off.

A-2-4.1.4.2(c) "In-place protection," "sheltering in-place," and "protection in-place" all mean the same thing.

2-4.1.4.3 Identify the shapes of recommended initial isolation and protective action zones.

The NAERG provides initial isolation zones and protective action distances for hazardous materials whose vapors may produce poisonous effects. The shapes of those areas are shown in Figure 2.8.

These distances are provided in the Table of Initial Isolation and Protective Action Distances on the green-bordered pages in the NAERG.

2-4.1.4.4 Describe the difference between small and large spills as found in the table of Initial Isolation and Protective Action Distances.

The NAERG defines a small spill as one that involves a single, small package, up to the size of a 55-gal (208-L) drum, or a small cylinder. A small spill may also be a small leak from a large package. A large spill involves a big spill from an opening in a large package or spills from many small packages. A large spill would come from a 1-ton cylinder, a tank truck, or a railcar.

In determining the isolation and protective action distances, the NAERG assumed that the maximum pool size for a small spill that formed a liquid pool was

Table 2.3 Sample of Table of Initial Isolation and Protective Action Distances from the North American 1996 Emergency Response Guidebook

		Small Spills (From a small package or small leak from a large package.)						Large Spills (From a large package or from many small packages.)					
		First ISOLATE in All Directions		Then, PROTECT Persons Downwind during—				First, ISOLATE in All Directions		Then, PROTECT Persons Downwind during—			
				Day		Night				Day		Night	
ID No.	Name of Material	m	(ft)	km	(mi)	km	(mi)	m	(ft)	km	(mi)	km	(mi)
1005	Ammonia, anhydrous	30 m	(100 ft)	0.2 km	(0.1 m)	0.3 km	(0.2 mi)	95 m	(300 ft)	0.3 km	(0.2 m)	0.8 km	(0.5 mi)
1005	Ammonia, anhydrous, liquefied												
1005	Ammonia solution with more than 50% ammonia	30 m	(100 ft)	0.2 km	(0.1 m)	0.2 km	(0.1 mi)	60 m	(200 ft)	0.2 km	(0.1 m)	0.3 km	(0.2 mi)
1005	Anhydrous ammonia	30 m	(100 ft)	0.2 km	(0.1 m)	0.3 km	(0.2 mi)	95 m	(300 ft)	0.3 km	(0.2 m)	0.8 km	(0.5 mi)
1005	Ammonia, anhydrous, liquefied												
1008	Boron trifluoride	60 m	(200 ft)	0.2 km	(0.1 m)	0.36 km	(0.4 mi)	185 m	(600 ft)	0.6 km	(0.4 m)	2.4 km	(1.5 mi)
1008	Boron trifluoride compressed									0.8			
1016	Carbon monoxide	30 m	(100 ft)	0.2 km	(0.1 m)	0.2 km	(0.1 mi)	95 m	(300 ft)	0.2 km	(0.1 m)	0.6 km	(0.4 mi)
1016	Carbon monoxide, compressed												
1017	Chlorine	60 m	(200 ft)	0.3 km	(0.1 m)	0.8 km	(0.5 mi)	185 m	(600 ft)	0.8 km	(0.5 m)	3.1 km	(1.9 m)
1023	Coal gas	30 m	(100 ft)	0.2 km	(0.1 m)	0.2 km	(0.1 mi)	30 m	(100 ft)	0.3 km	(0.2 m)	0.8 km	(0.5 mi)
1023	Coal gas, compressed												
1026	Cyanogen	60 m	(200 ft)	0.3 km	(0.1 m)	1.0 km	(0.6 mi)	215 m	(700 ft)	0.8 km	(0.5 m)	3.5 km	(2.2 m)
1026	Cyanogen, liquefied												
1026	Cyanogen gas												
1040	Ethylene oxide	60 m	(200 ft)	0.2 km	(0.1 m)	0.3 km	(0.2 mi)	125 m	(400 ft)	0.3 km	(0.2 m)	1.0 km	(0.6 mi)
1040	Ethylene oxide with nitrogen												
1045	Fluorine	60 m	(200 ft)	0.2 km	(0.1 m)	0.8 km	(0.5 mi)	185 m	(600 ft)	0.6 km	(0.4 m)	2.7 km	(1.7 m)
1045	Fluorine, compressed												
1048	Hydrogen bromide, anhydrous	60 m	(200 ft)	0.2 km	(0.1 m)	0.3 km	(0.2 mi)	125 m	(400 ft)	0.3 km	(0.2 m)	1.1 km	(0.7 mi)
1050	Hydrogen chloride, anhydrous	60 m	(200 ft)	0.2 km	(0.1 m)	0.5 km	(0.3 mi)	155 m	(500 ft)	0.5 km	(0.3 m)	1.8 km	(1.1 mi)

Source: *North American Emergency Response Guidebook.*[7]

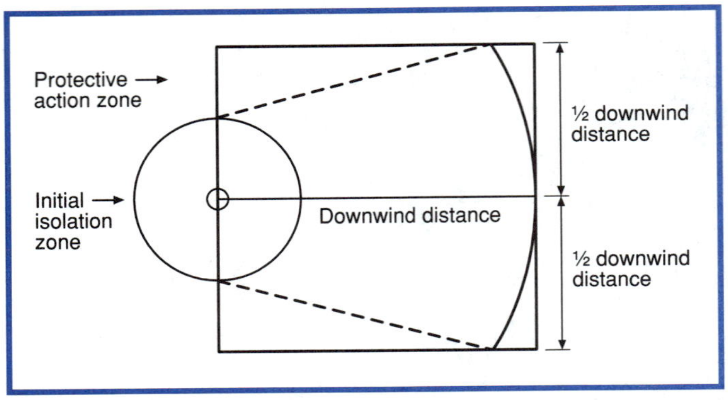

Figure 2.8 *Initial isolation zone and protective action zone.*

48 ft (15 m) in diameter. A large spill pool was assumed to be a maximum of 60 ft (18 m) in diameter. The distances were calculated following a 30-minute period from the start of the release. This is the reason the NAERG cautions that the distances are valid only for the 30-minute period following a spill.

2-4.1.4.5 Identify the circumstances under which the following distances are used at a hazardous materials incident:

(a) Table of initial isolation and protective action distances

These distances are used only for products whose vapors present an inhalation hazard, where the release does not involve a fire, and *where no more than 30 minutes have elapsed* between the spill and the response.

(b) Isolation distances in the numbered guides

The isolation distances in the guide pages are to be used when a hazardous material or its container is exposed to fire or when the product's vapors have potentially poisonous effects.

2-4.1.4.6 Describe the difference between the isolation distances in the orange-bordered guide pages and the protective action distances in the green-bordered pages in the document.

The orange-bordered, or emergency action guide, pages in the "Emergency Action Section" of the NAERG provide isolation distances for selected materials that are involved in a fire. These distances may extend up to 1 mile (1600 m) in all directions. The protective action distances listed in the green-bordered pages (that is, in the Table of Initial Isolation and Protective Action Distances) in the guide are to be used only if the material is *not involved* in a fire. The distances found in this table are the recommended downwind protective action distances for materials whose poisonous vapors present inhalation hazards.

For example, ethylene oxide has an isolation distance, as found in the orange-bordered pages, of 1 mile (1600 m) when involved in a fire. When it is not involved in a fire, this same material has a recommended isolation distance of 200 ft (60 m) for a small spill and 400 ft (125 m) for a large spill.

The distances recommended in the Table of Initial Isolation and Protective Action Distances are to be used only during the first 30 minutes of an incident.

This competency points out how important it is that responders understand how to use the *North American Emergency Response Guidebook* (NAERG) or similar guidebooks.

2-4.1.5 Identify the techniques used to isolate the hazard area and deny entry to unauthorized persons at hazardous materials incidents.

At this level, responders do not have many resources available to them. However, there are several steps they may be able to take. They could use a vehicle to block a road or driveway, or they might place a rope or some other type of barricade across the entrance to the area to block access. They may also notify law enforcement officials to begin diverting traffic from the scene. In a fixed facility, responders may close a door or gate, use the public address system to announce the problem to the facility's occupants, or notify security.

See the Tentative Interim Amendment on p. 294 for new paragraphs 2-4.1.6 and A-2-4.1.6.

2-4.2 Initiating the Notification Process.

Given either a facility or transportation scenario involving hazardous materials, the first responder at the awareness level shall identify the appropriate initial notifications to be made and how to make them, consistent with the local emergency response plan or the organization's standard operating procedures.

See the Tentative Interim Amendment on p. 296 for revised wording for paragraph 2-4.2.

Awareness level responders must be familiar with the notification process they must follow to begin an effective response to a hazardous materials incident. This may only involve notifying the local fire or police department. In some fixed facilities, internal notification procedures may be used to initiate the response of private sector specialists, the plant fire brigade, or security personnel. Whatever the procedures, the responder must rapidly set the proper notification process in motion.

2-5 Competencies — Evaluating Progress

(No competencies currently required at this level.)

2-6 Competencies — Terminating the Incident

(No competencies currently required at this level.)

References Cited in Commentary

1. *Fire Protection Handbook,* National Fire Protection Association, Quincy, MA, 1997, p. 10–105.
2. NFPA 704, *Standard System for the Identification of the Hazards of Materials for Emergency Response,* National Fire Protection Association, Quincy, MA, 1996.
3. Ibid.
4. Hazard Communication Standard, Title 29, *Code of Federal Regulations,* Part 1910.1200, U.S. Government Printing Office, Washington, DC.
5. *North American Emergency Response Guidebook,* Department of Transportation, Washington, DC, 1996.
6. *Fire Protection Handbook,* p. 10-110.
7. *North American Emergency Response Guidebook.*

CHAPTER 3

Competencies for the First Responder at the Operational Level

3-1 General

3-1.1 Introduction.

First responders at the operational level shall be trained to meet all competencies at the first responder awareness levels and the competencies of this chapter. First responders at the operational level also shall receive any additional training to meet applicable United States Department of Transportation (DOT), United States Environmental Protection Agency (EPA), Occupational Safety and Health Administration (OSHA), and other appropriate state, local, or provincial occupational health and safety regulatory requirements.

It is important to note here that the competencies for the operational level responder build on those for the awareness level responder. Therefore, the responder at this level is assumed to have first successfully demonstrated competency at the awareness level.

3-1.2 Definition.

First responders at the operational level are those persons who respond to releases or potential releases of hazardous materials as part of the initial response to the incident for the purpose of protecting nearby persons, the environment, or property from the effects of the release. First responders at the operational level are expected to respond in a defensive fashion to control the release from a safe distance and keep it from spreading.

The wording clearly indicates that the responder at this level belongs to some public or private emergency response service or organization. Generally, these organizations include the fire service, emergency medical services, law enforcement, special chemical response teams, industrial fire brigades, and regional response teams. First responders at the operational level are assumed to have a considerable level of experience and skill in dealing with hazardous materials emergencies. Hazardous materials technicians, who make up the majority of hazardous materials response teams, have an even higher level of training than the operational level responder.

Operational level responders are expected to take defensive control measures to protect people, the environment, or property from the effects of an unplanned hazardous materials release. Their function is to contain the release from a safe distance, while limiting exposure to other structures, people, and environmentally sensitive areas such as rivers and lakes. These responders will not ordinarily come in direct contact with the hazardous material in the normal course of their work.

3-1.3 Goal.

The goal of the competencies at the operational level shall be to provide first responders with the knowledge and skills to perform the following tasks safely. Therefore, in addition to being competent at the awareness level, the first responder at the operational level shall be able to:

Safety must be considered in every action taken at an incident scene because risks will always be present. By demonstrating the knowledge and skills that follow, a responder should be able to reduce the risk inherent in a hazardous materials incident.

(a) Analyze a hazardous materials incident to determine the magnitude of the problem in terms of outcomes by completing the following tasks:

Charles Wright notes in Section 9, Chapter 14 of the 18th edition of the *Fire Protection Handbook:* "The analysis process begins when a responder receives notification of a problem and continues throughout the incident, typically at the scene threatened by any hazardous materials involved."[1]

Outcomes are the direct and indirect results or consequences associated with an emergency. Direct outcomes are considered in terms of people, property, and/or the environment. *(See Figure 3.1.)*

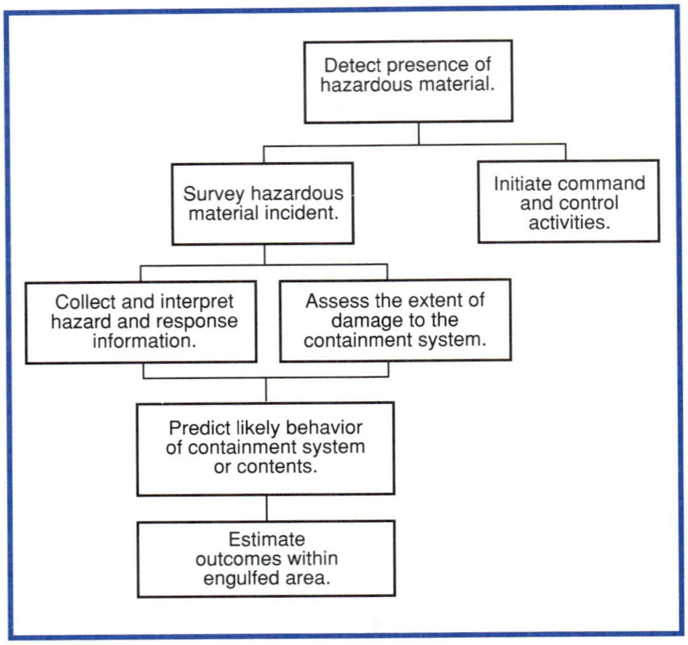

Figure 3.1 *A flow diagram of the tasks associated with analyzing a hazardous material problem. (Source: Fire Protection Handbook, 18th edition)*

1. Survey the hazardous materials incident to identify the containers and materials involved, determine whether hazardous materials have been released, and evaluate the surrounding conditions

According to Charles Wright, the incident survey should be done from a safe distance so that the responder is not exposed to any released materials:[2]

The following steps should be completed during the survey of a hazardous material incident.

1. *Identify each containment system by type, identifier, and size.* Containment systems fit into one of three types: (1) nonbulk, (2) bulk, or (3) facility containment systems. *(See Table 3.1.)* The containment system identifier (e.g., facility or carrier name and number) is used to differentiate one containment system from another and to allow tracking of that container throughout the incident. The quantity within, or capacity of, the containment system can be obtained from markings on the container or entries on the shipping papers or facility documents. The quantity information will help indicate the magnitude of the problem.

2. *Identify the name, DOT identification number, or placard applied to each hazardous material containment system.* This information provides a means of accessing various sources of hazard and response information.

Table 3.1 A Listing of the Various Types of Nonbulk, Bulk, and Facility Containment Systems

Transportation		
Nonbulk	**Bulk**	**Facility Containment Systems**
Bags	Bulk Bags	Buildings
Bottles	Bulk Boxes	Machinery
Boxes	Cargo Tanks	Open Piles (outdoors and indoors)
Carboys	Covered Hopper Cars	Piping
Cylinders	Freight Containers	Reactors (chemical and nuclear)
Drums	Gondolas	Storage Bins, Cabinets, or Shelves
Jerricans	Pneumatic Hopper Trailers	
Multicell	Portable Tanks and Bins	
Tanks and Storage	Protective Overpacks or Radioactive Materials	
Vessels Packages		
Wooden Barrels	Tank Cars	
	Ton Containers	
	Van Trailers	

Source: *Fire Protection Handbook,* 18th edition.[3]

For facilities: Sources for identifying the material include pre-emergency planning document, markings and color, contact with the facility manager, and review of appropriate MSDS.

In transportation: The identity of the hazardous material can be determined from the DOT identification number, commodity stencil, type of placard or label applied, shipping paper entries, and manufacturer, shipper, or consignee contacts using the 24-hr emergency telephone number on the shipping papers. Pipeline markers provide the name of the commodity or at least the name and telephone number of the pipeline company.

3. *Identify leaking containment systems.* Clues indicating leakage include material on the outside of the containment system, taste or smell, presence of vapor clouds, or the operation of a safety relief valve. If possible during the survey, note the form of the released material (solid, liquid, or gas) and the location of the release. *(See Figure 3.2.)*

Figure 3.2 *Leaking containers, smells, vapor clouds (such as the one shown here indicating a leak), fires, or explosions help a responder establish whether there has been a hazardous materials release at the site.*

4. *Identify the surrounding conditions.* Surrounding conditions should be noted when surveying hazardous material incidents. These conditions include topography, land use (including utilities and fiber optic cables), accessibility, weather conditions, bodies of water (including recharging ponds), public exposure potential, and the nature and extent of injuries. If a facility is involved, look for information about floor drains, ventilation ducts, air returns, etc., as appropriate.

For ease of collection, recording, and interpretation of information obtained during the survey of an incident, a hazardous material incident survey form is used. *(See Figure 3.3.)*

Finally, the information collected in the incident survey should be reviewed to verify its accuracy. For example, if the shipping paper identifies the material as a gas and a solid is being released, some of the information obtained may not be correct. An understanding of the characteristics of various containment systems will help to verify information on the contents.

2. Collect hazard and response information from material safety data sheets (MSDS), CHEMTREC/CANUTEC/SETIQ, and shipper/manufacturer contacts

It is very important for the responder to know what resources are available for providing technical assistance during hazardous materials emergencies and to know how to use those resources.

3. Predict the likely behavior of a material as well as its container

The responder must be able to assess the potential behavior of a hazardous material and its container. Is it likely to explode? Is it nonflammable? Is it corrosive? Will the container rupture violently?

4. Estimate the potential harm at a hazardous materials incident

As the responder collects the information necessary to predict the behavior of the material and its container, he or she can begin to estimate the potential harm it presents. Generally, initial assessments should be very conservative and should look at the worst possible event that could occur. As more information becomes available, these predictions can be modified.

(b) Plan an initial response within the capabilities and competencies of available personnel, personal protective equipment, and control equipment by completing the following tasks:

A plan of action must be developed by using the information gathered and the estimates of potential harm. This plan will establish the responders' objectives in controlling the incident. Control operations include containment, extinguishment, and confinement. Keep in mind that the responder at the operational level is expected to only carry out defensive control actions. Any plan of action must be formulated based on the resources that can be brought to bear on the mitigation process.

Responders at this level could completely control an incident if it were relatively minor. At more severe

Hazardous Material Incident Survey Form

Location ______________________________

Date ____ - ____ - ____ Time: ____ : ____ ____ Weather Conditions ______________________________

Terrain ______________________________

Closest Populated Buildings ______________________________

Closest Bodies of Water ______________________________

Closest Other Buildings ______________________________

No. Deaths ______ No. Injuries ______ Remedial Actions Taken ______________________________

Containment System			Material Identification			Release		
Container Type	**Container ID No.**	**Qty**	**DOT ID No.**	**Placard**	**Name of Material**	**Yes**	**Form**	**Location**
						☒	☐ Solid ☐ Liquid ☐ Gas	
						☒	☐ Solid ☐ Liquid ☐ Gas	
						☒	☐ Solid ☐ Liquid ☐ Gas	
						☒	☐ Solid ☐ Liquid ☐ Gas	
						☒	☐ Solid ☐ Liquid ☐ Gas	
						☒	☐ Solid ☐ Liquid ☐ Gas	

Sketch of scene

N

Figure 3.3 *This worksheet is used for recording information collected during the task of surveying a hazardous materials incident. (Source: Fire Protection Handbook, 18th edition)* incidents, responders at the operational level would perform to the extent their training and equipment allowed and would be required to summon appropriate help.

1. Describe the response objectives for hazardous materials incidents

The response objectives for a hazardous materials incident focus on controlling events as they occur or keeping even more severe events from occurring.

2. Describe the defensive options available for a given response objective

Defensive options are those actions the responders can take safely without coming in direct contact with the hazardous material involved in the incident. These options may include constructing a dike to contain a material, placing hose streams to protect exposures, even placing a pail under a leaking valve. These actions can be done safely with the protective clothing and equipment available to the responder at this level.

3. Determine whether the personal protective equipment provided is appropriate for implementing each defensive option

Individuals involved in emergency response must understand their limitations, particularly where personal protective clothing and equipment are concerned. Responders must also understand that clothing and equipment requirements vary depending on the material involved in an incident. Fire fighters responding to structural fires generally use the same type of protective clothing each time. In hazardous materials incidents, however, what is appropriate for one material may be totally unacceptable for another, so the defensive tactics responders use may be very different.

4. Identify the emergency decontamination procedures

Emergency decontamination may be necessary if a life-threatening exposure has occurred and the individual needs immediate medical treatment. Normal decontamination will not be available until the hazardous materials response team arrives with the technicians and equipment necessary to set up the decontamination corridor in the warm zone.

(c) Implement the planned response to favorably change the outcomes consistent with the local emergency response plan and the organization's standard operating procedures by completing the following tasks:

Once responders have analyzed the incident and planned the initial response, they must implement that response. Although some might expect that this is a lengthy process, it frequently takes only a few minutes. For example, a responder may be able to analyze, plan, and implement the response to a small spill of home heating fuel in a non-threatening location within minutes. However, if the incident involved an 8000 gal (30,280 L) gasoline tank truck overturned on a congested highway interchange, the process would take a little longer. No matter how severe the incident, the responder should go through the same planning process to ensure that nothing has been overlooked.

1. Establish and enforce scene control procedures including control zones, emergency decontamination, and communications

Scene control is critical in keeping both responders and the public safe, so it should be established immediately. Responders can do this by establishing control zones and an exclusion perimeter to keep the public away from the emergency responder's working areas.

2. Initiate an incident management system (IMS) for hazardous materials incidents

When arriving on the scene, operational level responders must begin implementing the incident management system developed in the local emergency response plan. An incident management plan identifies the roles and responsibilities that will help personnel control the incident safely and effectively.

3. Don, work in, and doff personal protective equipment provided by the authority having jurisdiction

Response personnel must be able to correctly use protective clothing and equipment that is provided. An effective training program will give them the opportunity to demonstrate this ability during various training exercises.

4. Perform defensive control functions identified in the plan of action

The responder at the operational level must be able to select and use the equipment as necessary and to implement the defensive control functions chosen.

(d) Evaluate the progress of the actions taken to ensure that the response objectives are being met safely, effectively, and efficiently by completing the following tasks:

Part of an effective response is the ongoing evaluation of the actions that have been undertaken and their effectiveness. Responders must not base their actions solely on their initial assessment of conditions at the site because these conditions can, and do, change; for example, the wind may shift, it may begin to rain, or resources may become unavailable.

1. Evaluate the status of the defensive actions taken in accomplishing the response objectives

Are the defensive actions being taken having the desired results? Is the incident stabilizing, or is it intensifying? Responders may find that the actions they chose initially are no longer correct because they no longer suit the circumstances. The weather may have changed, for example, or the arrival of additional personnel may have been delayed.

2. Communicate the status of the planned response

The incident commander must be kept informed of the effectiveness of the defensive actions being taken. An effective response cannot be carried out without frequent status reports. Everyone must be aware of this and provide the necessary information through the appropriate channels.

3-2 Competencies — Analyzing the Incident

3-2.1* Surveying the Hazardous Materials Incident.

Given examples of both facility and transportation scenarios involving hazardous materials, the first responder at the operational level shall survey the incident to identify the containers and materials involved, determine whether hazardous materials have been released, and evaluate the surrounding conditions. The first responder at the operational level shall be able to:

A-3-2.1 The survey of the incident should include an inventory of the type of containers involved, identification markings on containers, quantity in or capacity of containers, materials involved, release information, and surrounding conditions. The accuracy of the data should be verified.

As Charles Wright notes in the *Fire Protection Handbook*, 18th edition:

> After detecting the presence of hazardous materials in an emergency, and while initiating command and control activities, the next task is to survey the hazardous materials incident. Completion of this task provides an inventory of the containment systems and materials involved, materials released, and surrounding conditions. This incident survey should be conducted from a safe distance, using aided vision, without exposure to the released materials.[4]

3-2.1.1* Given three (3) examples each of liquid, gas, and solid hazardous materials, identify the general shapes of containers in which the hazardous materials are typically found.

A-3-2.1.1 Examples should include all containers, including nonbulk packaging, bulk packaging, vessels, and facility containers such as piping, open piles, reactors, and storage bins. Refer to the Chemical Manufacturers Association/ Association of American Railroads Hazardous Materials Technical Bulletin *Packaging for Transporting Hazardous and Non-hazardous Materials*, issued June 1989.

Recognizing the shapes of various containers and knowing what each normally holds helps the responder verify the presence of hazardous materials and could help him or her identify the particular materials involved in an incident. *(See Supplement 7 and Figure 3.4.)*

Figure 3.4 The responder should be able to identify various containers and have a general idea of the products they contain. The containers shown all hold liquified natural gas, maintained under cryogenic conditions.

3-2.1.1.1 Given examples of the following tank cars, identify each tank car by type:

Roger Fitch and Charles Wright note in Section 9, Chapter 35, "Rail Transportation Systems," of the *Fire Protection Handbook* that "Tank cars are classed according to their construction, features, and fittings. The tank's specification determines the product it may transport."[5] *(See Figure 3.5.)*

(a) Nonpressure tank cars with and without expansion domes

Fitch and Wright note in Section 9, Chapter 35, "Rail Transportation Systems," of the *Fire Protection Handbook* that

> Nonpressure tank cars, also known as general-service or low-pressure tank cars, transport a wide variety of hazardous and nonhazardous materials at low pressures.
>
> Nonpressure tank cars transport hazardous materials, such as flammable and combustible

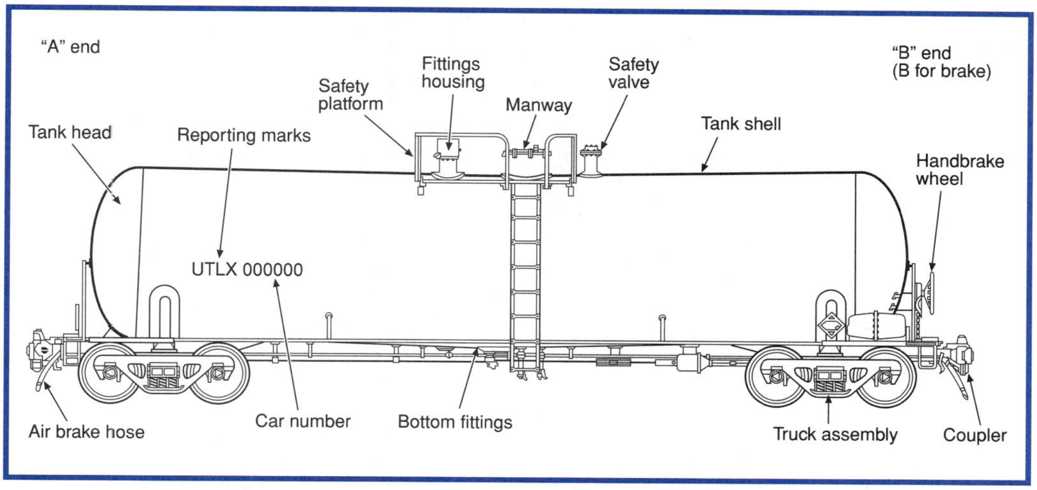

Figure 3.5 *Diagram of tank car with basic features identified. (Source: Union Tank Car Company)*

liquids, flammable solids, oxidizers, organic peroxides, poison B materials, corrosive materials, molten solids, and certain flammable and nonflammable gases. They also transport nonhazardous materials, such as tallow, fruit and vegetable juices, tomato paste, and caramel.

Tank test pressures for nonpressure tank cars range from 35 to 100 psi (251 to 689 kPa). Capacities range from 4000 to 45,000 gal (15 to 170 m^3). These tank cars are cylindrical with rounded heads.[6] *(See Figures 3.6 and 3.7.)*

(b) Pressure tank cars

According to Fitch and Wright in Section 9, Chapter 35, "Rail Transportation Systems," of the *Fire Protection Handbook,*

> Pressure tank cars typically transport hazardous materials, including flammable, nonflammable, or

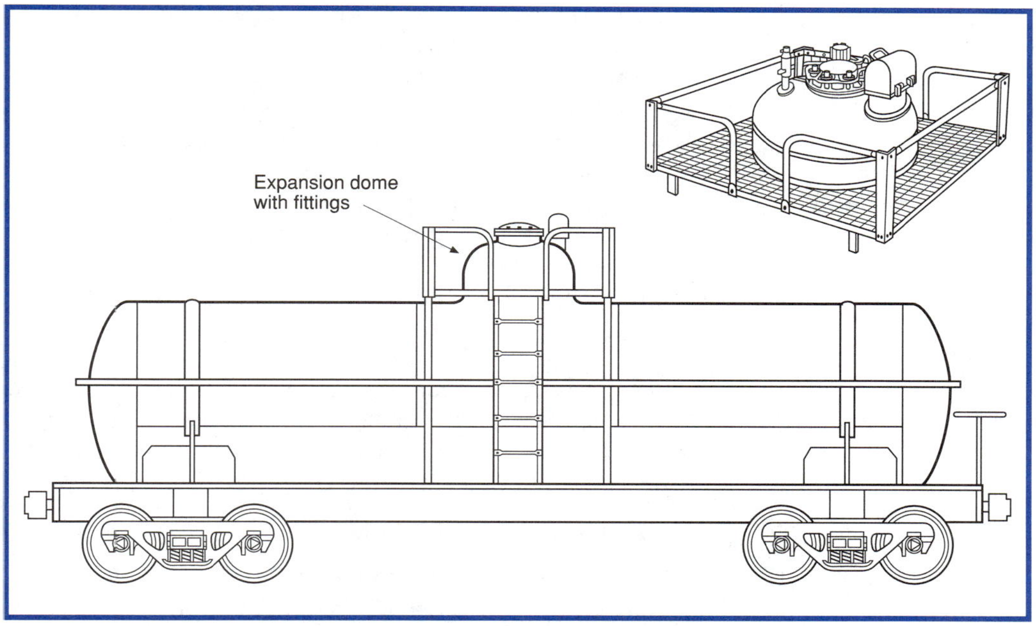

Figure 3.6 *Diagram of a typical nonpressure tank car, shown with an expansion dome. Older tank models, such as the one shown here, have the dome. (Source: Union Pacific Railroad)*

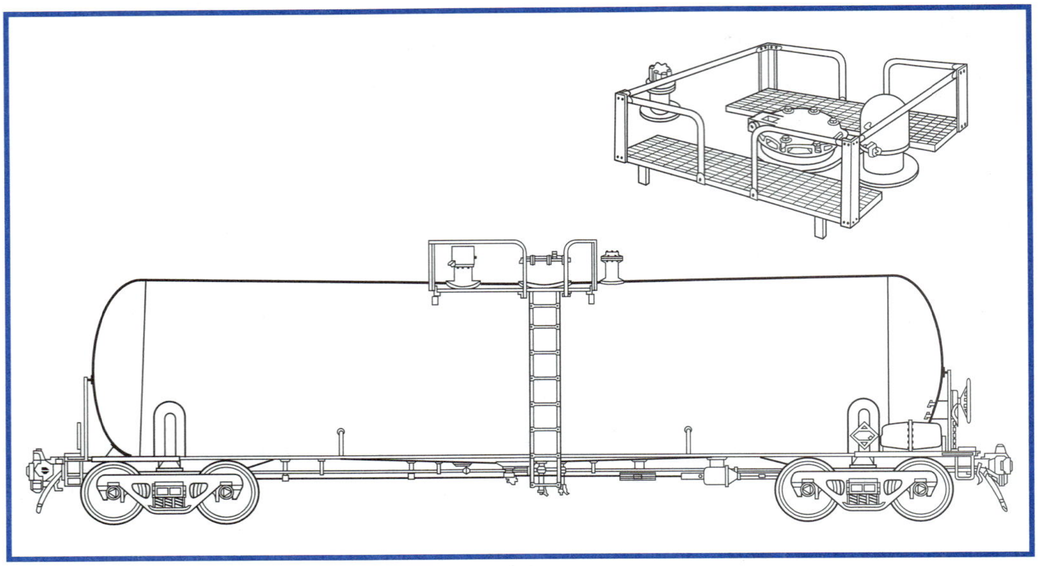

Figure 3.7 Diagram of a typical nonpressure tank car shown without an expansion dome, as is generally true of newer cars. (Source: Union Pacific Railroad)

poisonous gases at higher pressures. However, pressure tank cars can transport other commodities, depending upon the characteristics of the product or the process for loading and unloading the tank. Other products transported in pressure tank cars are ethylene oxide, pyrophoric liquids, sodium metal, motor fuel anti-knock compounds, bromine, anhydrous hydrofluoric acid, and acrolein.

Tank test pressures for these tank cars range from 100 to 600 psi (689 to 4137 kPa). Pressure tank cars range in capacity from 4000 to 45,000 gal (15 to 170 m^3).

Pressure tank cars are cylindrical, noncompartmented steel or aluminum tanks with rounded heads. They are top-loading, with fittings for loading and unloading, pressure, and gauging located inside protective housing mounted on a manway, of which there is typically one.

Pressure tank cars may be insulated and/or thermally protected. The top two-thirds of pressure tank cars without insulation and without jacketed thermal protection will be painted white.[7] *(See Figure 3.8.)*

(c) Cryogenic liquid tank cars

Cryogenic tank cars carry low-pressure [25 psi (172 kPa) or lower] liquids refrigerated to –155°F (–104°C) and below. These liquids typically include argon, ethylene, hydrogen, nitrogen, and oxygen. A cryogenic tank car is actually a tank-within-a-tank, the inner tank made of stainless steel or nickel. The space between the inner and outer tanks is filled with insulation and is under a vacuum.[8] *(See Figure 3.9.)*

3-2.1.1.2 Given examples of the following intermodal tank containers, identify each intermodal tank container by type:

Intermodal tank containers are being used more and more frequently in North America to transport a wide range of commodities, including an increasing number of hazardous materials. Among the factors that account for this increased use are their improved safety, their portability, and the lower transportation costs. Tank containers also offer the benefits of a multimodal transport system. Because they consist of a single metal tank mounted inside a sturdy metal supporting structure, they can be used interchangeably on several modes of transport, such as railroad cars, tank trucks, and ships.[9]

(a) Nonpressure intermodal tank containers

Nonpressure tank containers, sometimes referred to as intermodal portable tanks or IM portable tanks, are usually used to transport liquid or solid materials at pressures of up to 100 psi (690 kPa).[10] *(See Figure 3.10.)*

(b) Pressure intermodal tank containers

Fitch and Wright note in Section 9, Chapter 35, "Rail Transportation Systems," of the *Fire Protection Handbook* that pressure tank containers are designed to accommodate internal pressures of 100 psi to 500 psi

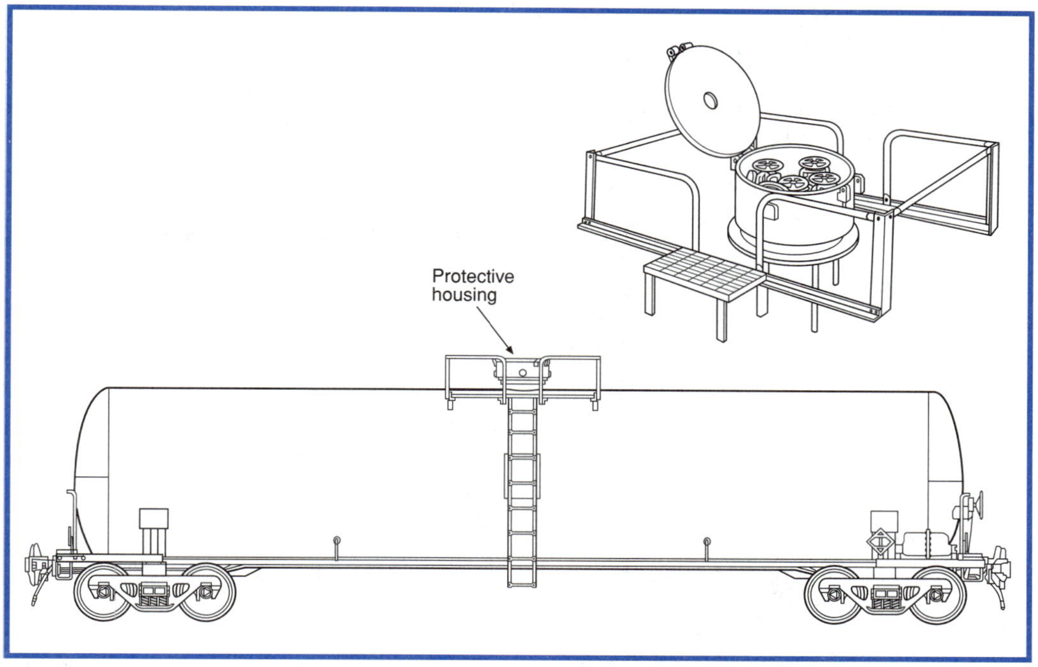

Figure 3.8 Diagram of a typical pressure tank car. (Source: Union Pacific Railroad)

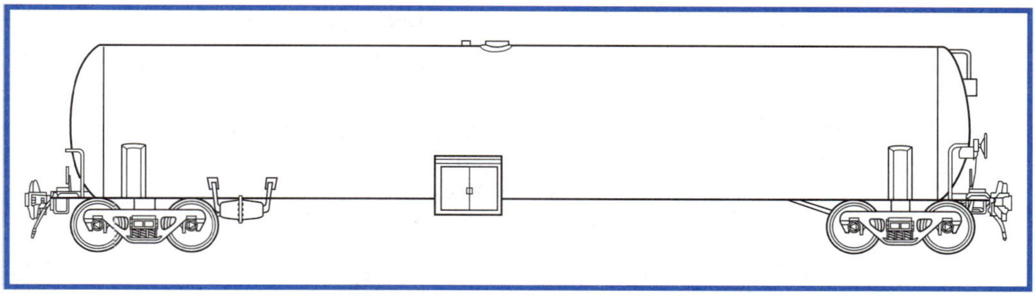

Figure 3.9 Diagram of a typical cryogenic liquid tank car. (Source: Union Pacific Railroad)

(690 kPa to 3450 kPa) and are generally used to transport gases liquefied under pressure, such as LP-Gas and anhydrous ammonia. They may also carry such liquids as motor fuel antiknock compound and aluminum alkyls.[11] *(See Figure 3.11.)*

3-2.1.1.3 Given examples of the following cargo tanks, identify each cargo tank by type:

(a) MC-306/DOT-406 cargo tanks
(b) MC-307/DOT-407 cargo tanks
(c) MC-312/DOT-412 cargo tanks
(d) MC-331 cargo tanks
(e) MC-338 cargo tanks
(f) Dry bulk cargo tanks

Cargo tanks are large containers used for hauling liquids in bulk. Sometimes referred to as tank motor vehicles or tank trucks, they are the most common vehicles used to transport combustible, flammable, and corrosive materials, as well as flammable and nonflammable compressed gases. *(See Figures 3.12–3.17.)*

3-2.1.1.4 Given examples of the following facility tanks, identify each fixed facility tank by type:

In Chapter 21, Section 3, "Storage of Flammable and Combustible Liquids," of the *Fire Protection Handbook,* Anthony M. Ordile, notes that "Tanks may be installed

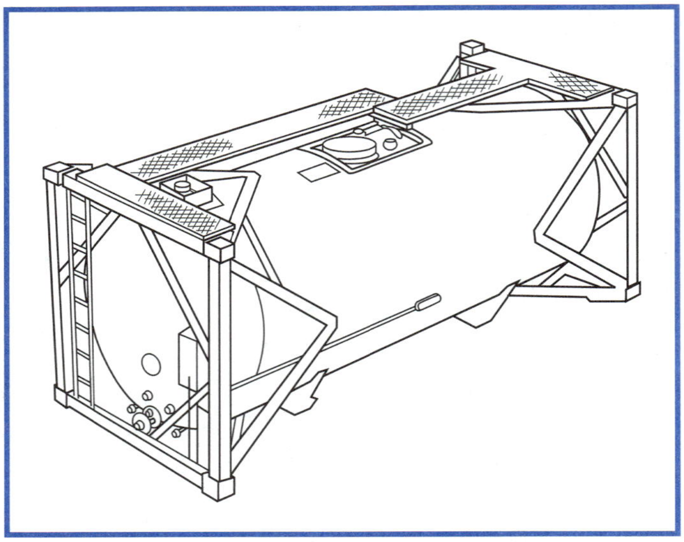

Figure 3.10 *Illustration of a nonpressure tank container. (Source: Union Pacific Railroad)*

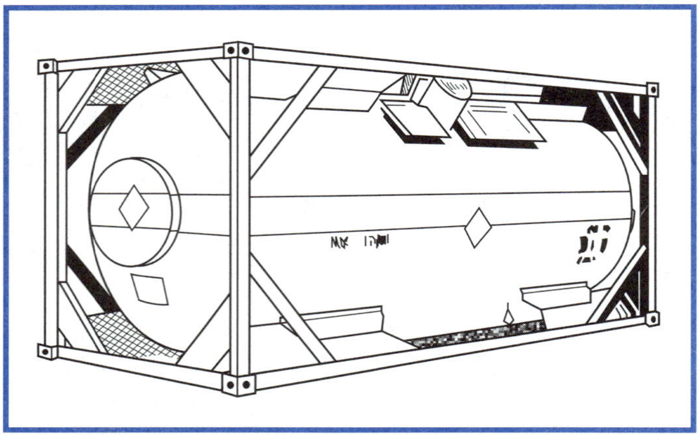

Figure 3.11 *Diagram of a typical pressure tank container. (Source: Union Pacific Railroad)*

aboveground, belowground, or, under certain conditions, inside buildings."[12] It is important that the responder be able to identify the difference between pressure and nonpressure tanks.

(a) Nonpressure facility tanks

Nonpressure tanks, also called atmospheric tanks, are designed for pressures of 0 to 0.5 psi (0 to 4 kPa). *(See Figure 3.18.)*

(b) Pressure facility tanks

Pressure tanks are divided into low-pressure storage tanks, for pressures of 0.5 psi to 15 psi (4 kPa to 103 kPa), and pressure vessels, for pressures above 15 psi (103 kPa). *(See Figure 3.19.)*

(c) Cryogenic liquid tanks

Cryogenic liquid tanks are heavily insulated with a vacuum in the space between the outer and inner shells. They are nonpressure tanks designed to carry refrigerated commodities such as carbon dioxide, nitrogen, argon, hydrogen, and oxygen.

3-2.1.1.5 Given examples of the following nonbulk packages, identify each package by type:

(a) Bags
(b) Carboys
(c) Cylinders
(d) Drums

3-2.1.2 Given examples of facility and transportation containers, identify the markings that differentiate one container from another.

Containers at fixed facilities may be marked with the NFPA 704 system, and transportation vehicles may be marked with DOT placards or identification numbers. Particular tanks or storage areas at fixed facilities may also be identified by labeling and pre-incident planning documents, as may the products they contain.

3-2.1.2.1 Given examples of the following marked transport vehicles and their corresponding shipping papers, identify the vehicle or tank identification marking:

There will be an identification marking on each transport vehicle that will be included on the shipping papers. This allows the responders to ensure that the shipping papers and vehicles match. The identification number also provides a way to contact the shipper for information about a specific vehicle.

(a) Rail transport vehicles, including tank cars
(b) Intermodal equipment including tank containers
(c) Highway transport vehicles, including cargo tanks

3-2.1.2.2 Given examples of facility containers, identify the markings indicating container size, product contained, and/or site identification numbers.

Containers at fixed facilities are often stenciled with a product name or some type of identification number that refers to a site plan or an emergency operations plan that identifies the product and the quantity stored.

3-2.1.3 Given examples of facility and transportation situations involving hazardous materials, identify the name(s) of the hazardous material(s) in each situation.

In order to develop the appropriate action options, the operational responder should be able to gather whatever information is necessary to identify the hazardous materials at an incident by name.

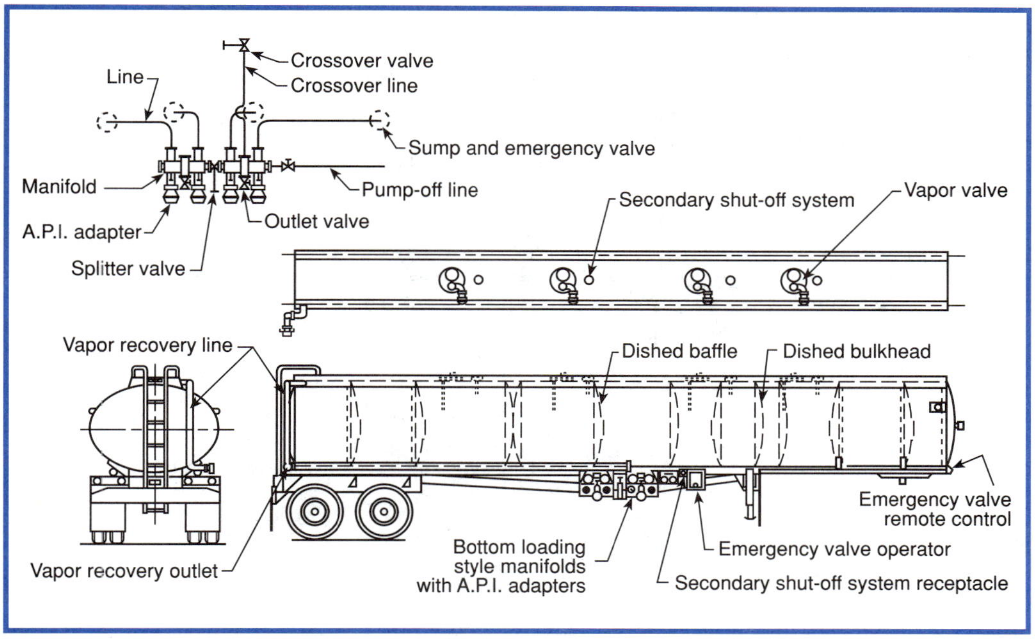

Figure 3.12 A typical MC-306 cargo tank. (Drawing courtesy of the Tractor Trailer Manufacturers Association)

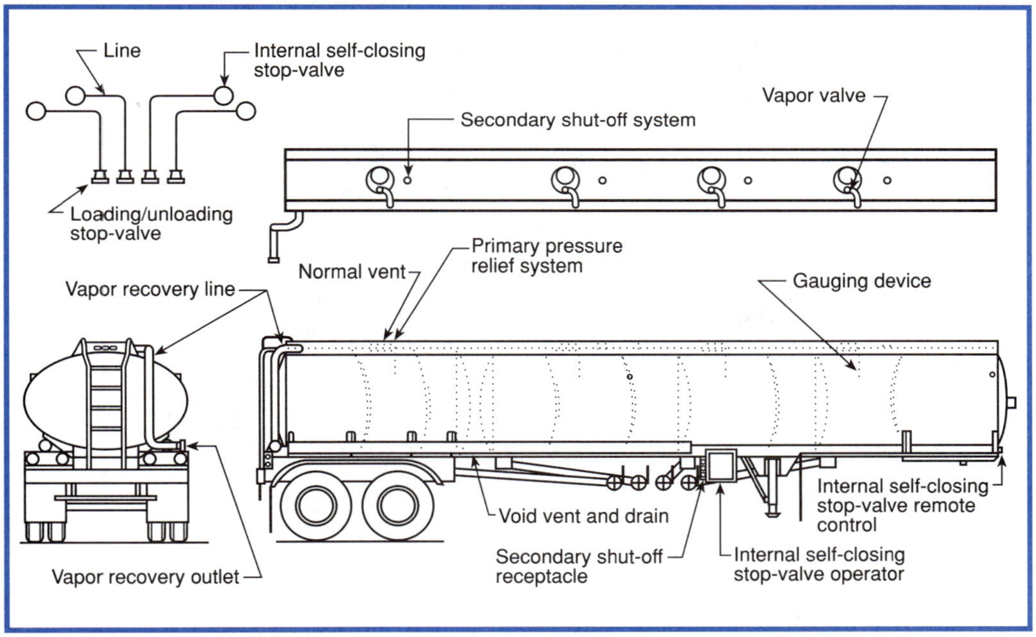

Figure 3.13 A typical DOT-406 cargo tank. (Drawing courtesy of the Tractor Trailer Manufacturers Association)

3-2.1.3.1 Identify the following information on a pipeline marker:

(a) Product
(b) Owner
(c) Emergency telephone number

Pipelines that carry hazardous materials must be identified, and the above information provided. *(See Figure 3.20.)*

3-2.1.3.2 Given a pesticide label, identify each of the following pieces of information; then match the piece of information to its significance in surveying the hazardous materials incident:

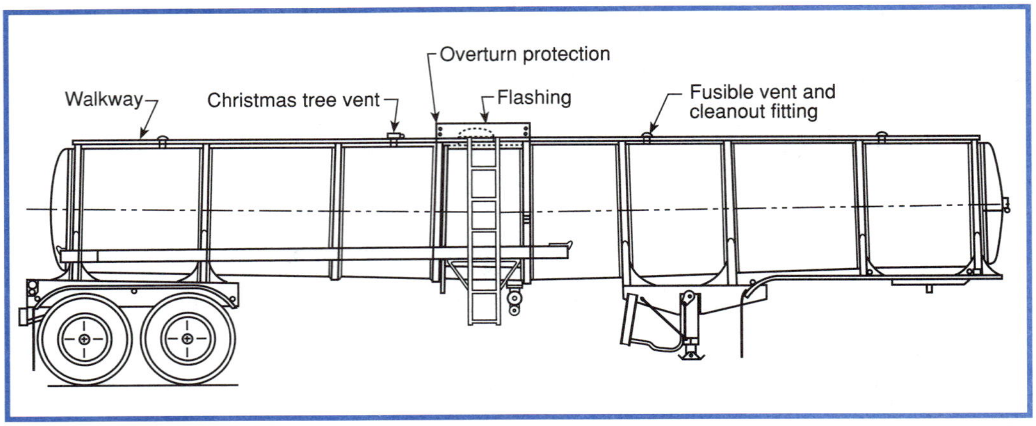

Figure 3.14 *A typical MC-307 cargo tank. (Drawing courtesy of the Tractor Trailer Manufacturers Association)*

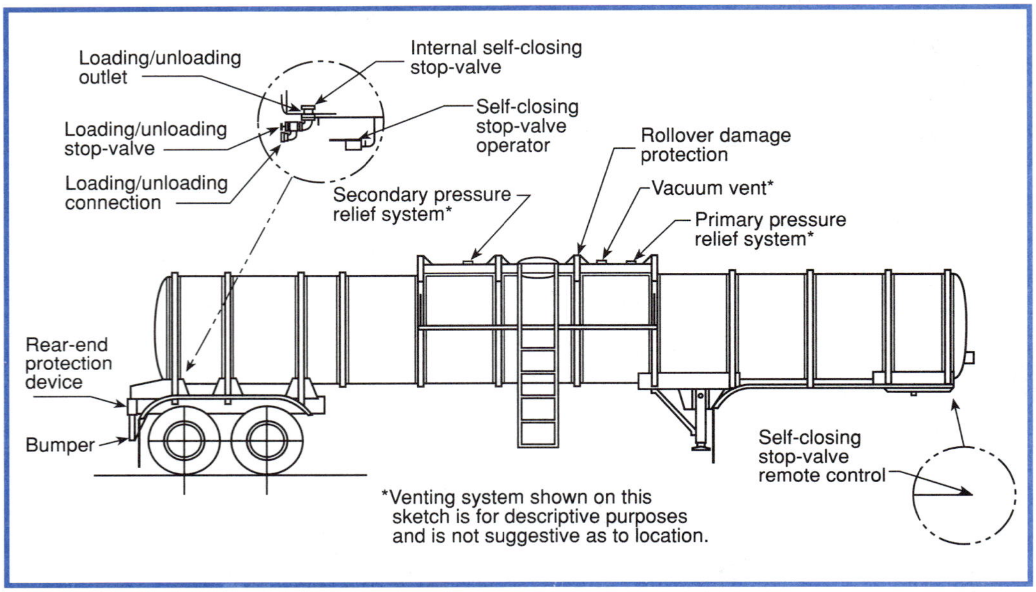

Figure 3.15 *A typical DOT-407 cargo tank. (Drawing courtesy of the Tractor Trailer Manufacturers Association)*

According to William J. Keffer and Matthew Woody, writing in Chapter 11, Section 4, "Pesticides," of the *Fire Protection Handbook,* pesticides are classified according to their primary or specific control purposes or to reflect the manner in which they are used. Among the pesticides classified by control purposes are insecticides, fungicides, herbicides, nematocides, and rodenticides. Among those classified by the manner in which they are used are fumigants.[13]

(a) Name of pesticide

The label contains the manufacturer's name for the pesticide.

(b) Signal word

Pesticide labels must have a "signal word" that indicates the relative hazard of the product. Table 3.2 lists the current warnings the EPA requires, based on the hazard of the active ingredient.

(c) Pest control product (PCP) number (in Canada)

In Canada, labels carry a pest control number that can be used to acquire additional information regarding a specific product. In the United States, labels carry an EPA registration number.

(d) Precautionary statement

Labels also carry a caution statement indicating the care that must be taken when using the product. Such statements in-

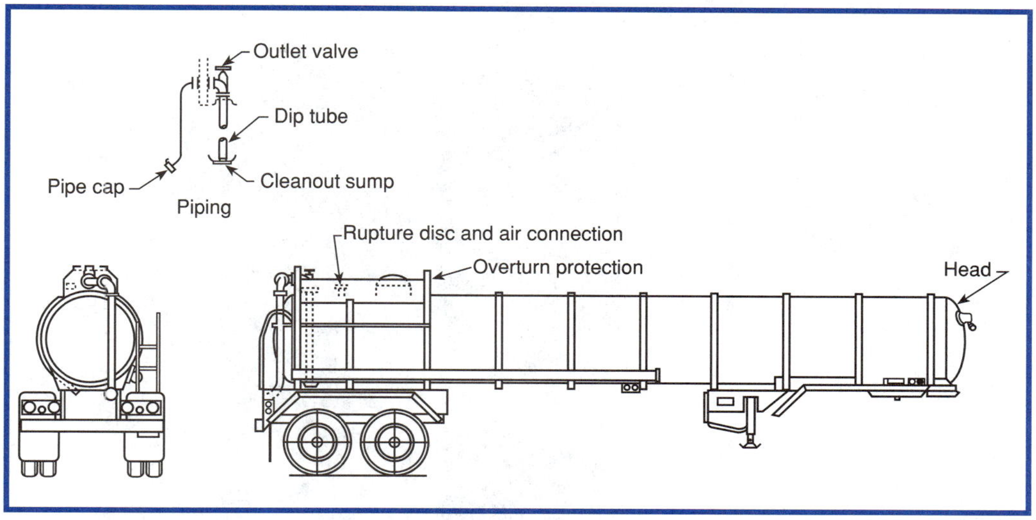

Figure 3.16 A typical MC-312 cargo tank. (Drawing courtesy of the Tractor Trailer Manufacturers Association)

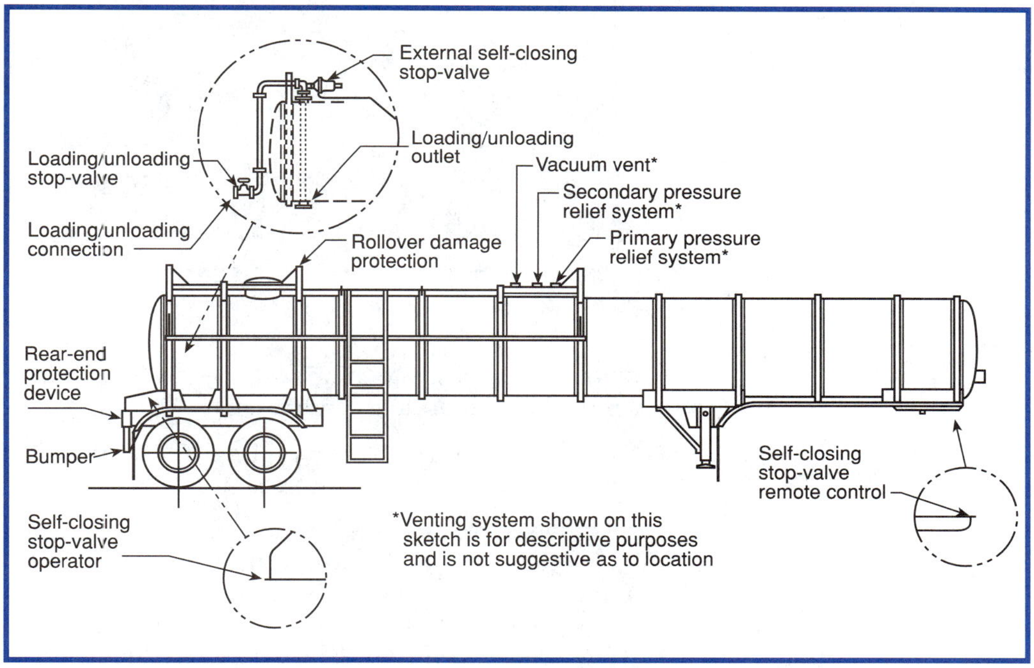

Figure 3.17 A typical DOT-412 cargo tank. (Drawing courtesy of the Tractor Trailer Manufacturers Association)

clude "Keep Out of Reach of Children," "Restricted Use Pesticide," or "Hazard to Humans and Domestic Animals."

(e) Hazard statement

Typically, a hazard statement indicates that the product poses an environmental hazard and advises against contaminating water supplies.

(f) Active ingredient

Each active ingredient in the pesticide is identified and the percentage indicated. Inert ingredients are also shown, but only by percentage.

3-2.1.4* Identify and list the surrounding conditions that should be noted by the first responders when surveying hazardous materials incidents.

A-3-2.1.4 The list of surrounding conditions should include: topography; land use; accessibility; weather conditions; bodies

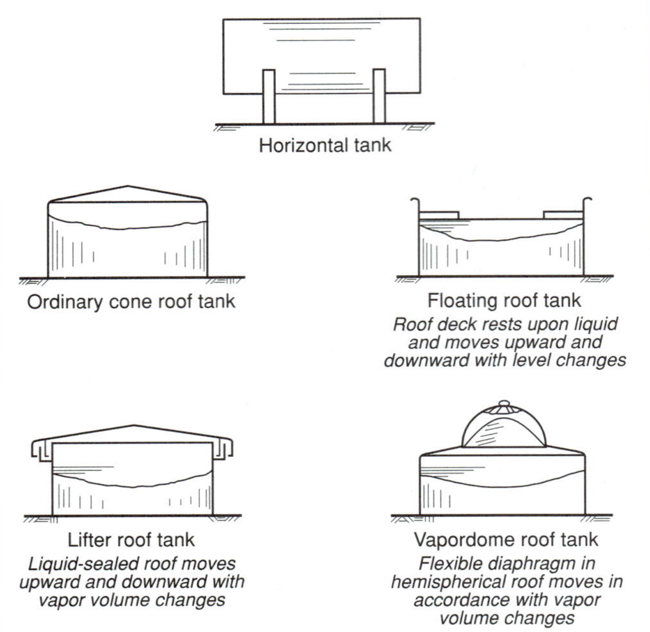

Figure 3.18 Common types of atmospheric storage tanks. (Source: Fire Protection Handbook, 18th edition)

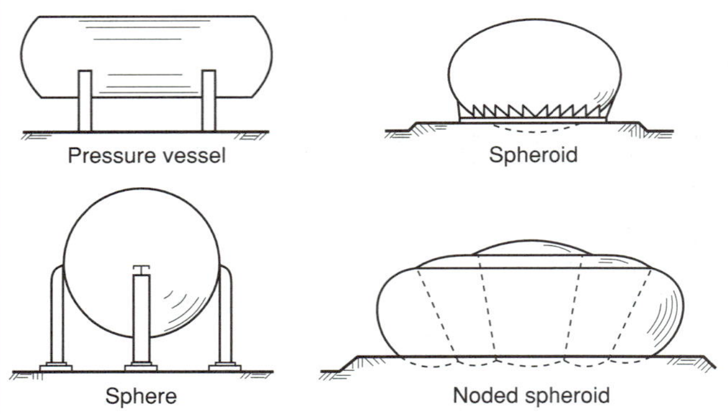

Figure 3.19 Common types of low-pressure tanks or pressure vessels. (Source: Fire Protection Handbook, 18th edition)

of water; public exposure potential; overhead and underground wires and pipelines; storm and sewer drains; possible ignition sources; adjacent land use such as rail lines, highways, and airports; and nature and extent of injuries. Building information such as floor drains, ventilation ducts, air returns, etc., also should be included when appropriate.

Surrounding conditions are important to the responder in that they influence the options available. It is important for the responder to think very broadly when considering the surrounding conditions.

Figure 3.20 Typical markings on a pipeline marker.

3-2.1.5 Give examples of ways to verify information obtained from the survey of a hazardous materials incident.

Responders should collect information about an incident continuously so that they can validate the information collected earlier. This information may be verified by, among other things, contacting CHEMTREC/CANUTEC/SETIQ to verify the hazard information found in emergency response guides, contacting the shipper to verify the products listed on shipping papers, and using additional references to confirm the emergency handling procedures.

See the Tentative Interim Amendment on p. 294 for new paragraphs 3-2.1.6 and A-3-2.1.6.

3-2.2 Collecting Hazard and Response Information.

Given known hazardous materials, the first responder at the operational level shall collect hazard and response informa-

Table 3.2 EPA Toxicity Categories

Category 1: Poison/Danger

All pesticide products meeting the following criteria:

Oral LD_{50} up to and including 50 mg/kg

Inhalation LD_{50} up to and including 0.2 mg/L

Dermal LD_{50} up to and including 200 mg/kg

Eye effects—corneal opacity not reversible within 7 days

Skin effects — corrosive

Must bear on the front panel the signal word "Danger." In addition, if the product was assigned to Category 1 on the basis of its oral, inhalation, or dermal toxicity (as distinct from skin and eye local effects), the word "Poison" must appear in red on a background of distinctly contrasting color and the skull and crossbones must appear in immediate proximity to the word "Poison."

Category 2: Warning

All pesticides meeting the following criteria:

Oral LD_{50} from 50 through 500 mg/kg

Inhalation LD_{50} from 0.2 through 2.0 mg/L

Dermal LD_{50} from 200 through 2000 mg/kg

Eye effects—corneal opacity reversible within 7 days (irritation persisting for 7 days)

Skin effects—severe irritation at 72 hours

Must bear on the front panel the signal word "Warning."

Categories 3 and 4: Caution

All pesticide products meeting the following criteria:

Oral LD_{50} greater than 500 mg/kg

Inhalation LD_{50} greater than 2.0 mg/L

Dermal LD_{50} greater than 2000 mg/kg

Eye effects—no corneal opacity

Skin effects—moderate irritation at 72 hours

Must bear on the front panel the signal word "Caution."

Source: *Fire Protection Handbook*, 18th edition.[14]

tion using material safety data sheets (MSDS), CHEMTREC/CANUTEC/SETIQ, and contacts with the shipper/manufacturer. The first responder at the operational level shall be able to:

In the *Fire Protection Handbook*, Charles Wright notes:

> Once a hazardous material is identified, information about the material's hazards, behavior characteristics, and suggested response options is collected. This information, which may be collected simultaneously with determining the extent of containment system damage, is used to predict the behavior of that material. The information to be collected is divided into six basic groups: (1) material identification information, (2) physical properties, (3) chemical properties, (4) physical hazards, (5) health hazards, and (6) response information. The task of obtaining, recording, and interpreting hazardous material information can be lengthy and rigorous. Various forms are being used to record hazard and response information.[15]

The information the responder at the operational level collects allows him or her to determine the defensive options that can be performed safely, given the personnel and equipment available. At the technician level, this same process continues, and the responder uses the information collected to determine whether it is feasible to conduct offensive operations.

3-2.2.1 Match the definitions associated with the DOT hazard classes and divisions of hazardous materials, including refrigerated liquefied gases and cryogenic liquids, with the class or division.

The responder should be able to match the hazard class or division of a hazardous material with the appropriate definition of that material. For example, the responder should be able to match the definition "consists of explosives that have a mass explosion hazard" with a Class 1, Division 1.1 material.

3-2.2.2 Identify two ways to obtain a material safety data sheet (MSDS) in an emergency.

MSDSs are available at fixed facilities and can often be found in transporting vehicles as well. A responder may obtain MSDSs from CHEMTREC or from the shipper, who may fax them to dispatch offices or to portable fax machines available to field personnel.

3-2.2.3 Using a material safety data sheet (MSDS) for a specified material, identify the following hazard and response information:

In the United States, MSDSs are required by the Occupational Safety and Health Administration (OSHA). Although OSHA provides a standard form, manufacturers may use similar forms of their own design that OSHA has approved.

Certain basic information specified by OSHA must appear on all forms. Responders should be familiar with this information and know how to locate it on an MSDS, which is a valuable source of product information. The responder should understand that, although the location of certain information on the MSDS may vary, the basic information outlined below can be found somewhere on the sheet. For example, information relating to storage found on one form in a section called "Precautions for Safe Handling and Use" may be found on another form in a section called "Special Protection Information."

(a) Physical and chemical characteristics

The information in this section provides the responder with information about such physical characteristics of the hazardous material as its vapor density, boiling point, specific gravity, water solubility, pH, and physical appearance. For example, a substance may be described as "white to pale yellow sticks, granules or powder, no odor."

(b) Physical hazards of the material

This section includes information about a material's fire and explosion hazards, including its flash point, autoignition temperature, and flammability limits, as well as information about the extinguishing agents that may be used on the material. This section may also provide information about hazards associated with fire control operations. For example, an entry may read, a water stream directed at molten material can scatter the material, increasing the flammability of any combustible material it contacts. This section may also recommend appropriate personal protective clothing and respiratory protection.

A separate reactivity section generally provides information about the material's stability and notes what the material will react with. For instance, an entry may read, "is a strong oxidizing agent that will increase the flammability of all combustible materials it contacts."

(c) Health hazards of the material
(d) Signs and symptoms of exposure
(e) Routes of entry
(f) Permissible exposure limits

The above information is generally contained in the health hazard section, which provides the responder with important data on the health hazards a material presents, including the threshold limit value (TLV), the routes of exposure, and the material's effects. Also provided is information about emergency first aid measures.

(g) Responsible party contact

Information about the material's manufacturer and possibly the names of its distributors is also provided, as are telephone numbers for emergency contacts.

(h) Precautions for safe handling (including hygiene practices, protective measures, procedures for cleanup of spills or leaks)

The MSDS also tells the responder what steps should be taken in the event of a spill or leak and how to dispose of such spilled or leaked material. For example, this section might instruct the responder to remove ignition sources or to cover the material with soda ash. And to dispose of the material, the responder might be advised to "mix slurry with wet sand and dispose of suitably in an approved landfill."

(i) Applicable control measures including personal protective equipment

This information will help the responder choose the appropriate respiratory protection, eye protection, protective gloves, and so on for working with the hazardous material. It may also indicate how the material should be stored and how to recognize improperly stored materials.

(j) Emergency and first aid procedures

Information about emergency and first aid procedures is often found with other health-related data. It will detail the actions that should be taken immediately if an individual is exposed to a hazardous material and recommend when to seek additional medical attention.

3-2.2.4 Identify the following:

(a) Type of assistance provided by CHEMTREC/CANUTEC/SETIQ
(b) Procedure for contacting CHEMTREC/CANUTEC/SETIQ
(c) Information to be furnished to CHEMTREC/CANUTEC/SETIQ

"CHEMTREC" stands for Chemical Transportation Emergency Center and is a public service of the Chemical Manufacturers Association, located in Washington, DC. CHEMTREC provides the on-scene commander with immediate advice by telephone and contacts the involved shipper for detailed assistance and response follow-up. It can also notify the National Response Center (NRC) of significant incidents and bridge a caller to the NRC to report a spill. CHEMTREC operates 24 hours a day and can be contacted throughout the United States and Canada.

CHEMTREC can usually provide hazard information warnings and guidance when given a material's four-digit identification number, the name of the product, and the nature of the problem. If the product is unknown or more detailed information and assistance is needed, the caller should attempt to provide as much of the following information as possible:

(a) The caller's name and a call-back number
(b) The guide number being used
(c) The name of the shipper or manufacturer

(d) The rail car or truck number
(e) The carrier's name
(f) The consignee
(g) Local conditions

At an incident, the caller should try to keep a phone line open to CHEMTREC so that they can provide guidance and assistance. CHEMTREC can also provide a teleconferencing bridge that allows them to connect technical experts to the caller's line as necessary.

CANUTEC is the Canadian Transport Emergency Center located in Ottawa, Canada, and operated by the Transport Dangerous Goods Directorate of Transport Canada. It provides technical assistance to emergency responders much the same as CHEMTREC. Personnel will provide technical information regarding the physical, chemical, toxicological, and other properties of the products involved in an incident; recommend remedial actions for fires, spills, or leaks; provide advice on protective clothing and emergency first aid; and contact the shipper, manufacturer, or others who are deemed necessary.

SETIQ is the Emergency Transportation System for the Chemical Industry in Mexico and provides the same services as CHEMTREC and CANUTEC.

3-2.2.5 Identify two methods of contacting the manufacturer or shipper to obtain hazard and response information.

The responder may contact the manufacturer or shipper through CHEMTREC/CANUTEC/SETIQ, as described above, or by using information provided on the shipping papers or on the MSDS.

See the Tentative Interim Amendment on p. 294 for new paragraphs 3-2.2.6 and 3-2.2.6.1.

3-2.3* Predicting the Behavior of a Material and Its Container.

Given an incident involving a single hazardous material, the first responder at the operational level shall predict the likely behavior of the material and its container. The first responder at the operational level shall be able to:

A-3-2.3 Predicting the likely behavior of a hazardous material and its container requires the ability to identify the types of stress involved and the ability to predict the type of breach, release, dispersion pattern, length of contact, and the health and physical hazards associated with the material and its container. Reference can be made to *A Textbook for Use in the Study of Hazardous Materials Emergencies,* the National Fire Academy's training program, *Hazardous Materials Incident Analysis*, *Hazardous Materials*; *Managing the Incident*, or "Managing the Hazardous Materials Incident," *Fire Protection Handbook.*

Ludwig Benner, Jr., in his *Textbook for Use in the Study of Hazardous Materials Emergencies,* 2nd edition, describes the process of predicting hazardous materials behavior as the ". . . visualization of an event's sequences in a 'mental movie' framework. . . . The responder needs to think in terms of events and then relate them to the prediction of the emergency events." The responder ". . . needs to focus on what the hazardous material is going to do . . . in order to influence the sequence of events."[16]

3-2.3.1 Given two examples of scenarios involving known hazardous materials, interpret the hazard and response information obtained from the current edition of the *North American Emergency Response Guidebook*, material safety data sheets (MSDS), CHEMTREC/CANUTEC/SETIQ, and shipper/manufacturer contacts.

Not only must the responder know where to find response information, but he or she must also be able to interpret that information in order to decide what actions are appropriate. The responder must also recognize that different emergency response guides may present conflicting information or emphasize one area more than another. It is necessary to gather, interpret, and choose the information that is most appropriate for a given situation.

3-2.3.1.1 Match the following chemical and physical properties with their significance and impact on the behavior of the container and/or its contents:

(a) Boiling point

Boiling point is the temperature of a substance when the vapor pressure exceeds atmospheric pressure and the liquid turns into a gas at the surface.

(b) Chemical reactivity

Chemical reactivity is the susceptibility of a material to release energy either by itself or in combination with other materials.

(c) Corrosivity (pH)

Corrosivity is a measure of a substance's tendency to deteriorate in the presence of another substance or in a particular environment. United States Federal Regulations define a corrosive material as a liquid or solid that causes visible destruction or irreversible alterations in human skin tissue at the site of contact or that causes steel to corrode at a severely accelerated rate. The degree of corrosiveness is measured by pH, which ranges from 1 to 14. A pH of 7 is neutral, while a pH below 7 is acidic and a pH above 7 represents a base.

(d) Flammable (explosive) range (LEL & UEL)

A material's flammable or explosive range is the difference between its upper and lower flammable limits. The lower flammable limit (LFL) is the minimum concentration of vapor to air below which a flame will not propagate in the presence of an ignition source. The upper flammable limit (UFL) is the maximum vapor-to-air concentration above which a flame will not propagate. If a vapor-to-air mixture is below the LFL, it is described as being "too lean" to burn; if it is above the UFL, it is "too rich" to burn. When the vapor-to-air ratio is somewhere between the LFL and the UFL, fires and explosions can occur, and the mixture is said to be in the flammable range. The flammable range for gasoline is 1.4 percent to 7.6 percent and the flammable range for carbon monoxide is 12.5 percent to 74 percent. It is important that the responder be aware of the range, as well as the upper and lower flammable limits.

If the responder suspects or knows that flammable vapors are present, he or she must determine the concentration of vapor in air. Combustible gas-detection instruments are used for this purpose.

(e) Flash point

The flash point of a liquid is the minimum temperature at which it gives off vapor in sufficient concentration to form an ignitable mixture with air. A liquid's flash point is the primary property or characteristic used to determine its relative degree of flammability. Since it is the vapors of flammable liquids that burn, vapor generation is a primary factor in determining the liquid's fire hazard.

(f) Ignition (autoignition) temperature

"Ignition temperature" and "autoignition temperature" are interchangeable terms. The ignition temperature of a substance, whether solid, liquid, or gaseous, is the minimum temperature required to cause self-sustained combustion in the absence of any source of ignition. The responder should look upon assigned ignition temperatures as approximations.

Ignition temperatures can be quite high, especially in relation to a liquid's flash point. For example, the flash point of gasoline is –45°F (–43°C), while its ignition temperature is well over 500°F (260°C).

(g) Physical state (solid, liquid, gas)

Hazardous materials are either solids, liquids, or gases, and the responder should understand the difference form makes on the hazards a material presents. For example, gases present significantly different hazards than solids.

(h) Specific gravity

Specific gravity is the ratio of the weight of a volume of liquid or solid to the weight of an equal volume of water, with the gravity of water being 1.0. A substance with a specific gravity of less than 1.0 will float on water, and one with a specific gravity greater than 1.0 will sink.

(i) Toxic products of combustion

All products of combustion should be considered toxic, but those produced by hazardous materials may be more toxic than those produced by nonhazardous materials. The danger that the products of combustion of hazardous materials are contaminated to a greater degree with higher levels of toxins than one would find in a regular structural fire increases the need for respiratory protection and for evacuation downwind of the fire. However, there are instances when burning hazardous materials, such as pesticides, may destroy the hazardous materials during the combustion process. Fire fighters must be aware that this is as true for outside fires as it is for structural fires.

(j) Vapor density

Vapor density measures the weight of a given vapor as compared with an equal volume of air, with air having a value of 1.0. A vapor density greater than 1.0 indicates it is heavier than air; a value less than 1.0 indicates it is lighter.

Vapor density can be important to the responder, since it will determine the behavior of free vapor at the scene of a liquid spill or gas release.

(k) Vapor pressure

Vapor pressure is the pressure at any given temperature at which the vapor and liquid phases of the substance are in equilibrium in a closed container. For example, the vapor pressure of diesel fuel increases with elevation due to reduced barometric pressure (lower atmospheric pressure). As a result, even fuels with high flash points can become flammable, depending on the altitude at which they are used.

(l) Water solubility

Water solubility, or the degree to which a substance is soluble in water, can be useful in determining effective extinguishing agents and methods. Response personnel should consider the property of solubility along with that of specific gravity.

3-2.3.1.2 Identify the differences among the following terms:

(a) Exposure and hazard

A person may be exposed to large quantities of a hazardous material in concentrations that do not present a hazard or to small amounts of a hazardous material that present a very high hazard.

(b) Exposure and contamination

A person exposed to a hazardous material may not necessarily be contaminated by it.

(c) Contamination and secondary contamination

Responders working in the hot zone may become contaminated during control operations. If they then carry that contamination outside the hot zone on their equipment, clothing, skin, or hair in sufficient quantities and are not adequately decontaminated, they may contaminate others. Substances that pose a high risk of secondary contamination include asbestos, mercaptans, pesticides, and PCBs. Materials that present little risk of secondary contamination include carbon monoxide, weak acids, and gasoline.

3-2.3.2* Identify three types of stress that could cause a container system to release its contents.

A-3-2.3.2 The three types of stress that could cause a container to release its contents are thermal stress, mechanical stress, and chemical stress.

Stress is defined by Ludwig Benner, Jr., in *A Textbook for Use in the Study of Hazardous Materials Emergencies,* 2nd edition, as "the applied force or system of forces that tend to strain or deform a body."[17] The "body" in question could refer to either a container or its contents. Responders are more likely to encounter this type of stress on the job than they are to encounter the two other types of stress to which containers are subject, irradiation and etiologic agents, or active microorganisms that move around.

3-2.3.3* Identify five ways in which containers can breach.

A-3-2.3.3 The five ways in which containers can breach are disintegration, runaway cracking, closures opening up, punctures, and splits or tears.

The performance objectives contained in 3-2.3.3 through 3-2.3.5 should be taught in a manner and language understandable to the audience. The intent is to convey the simple concepts that containers of hazardous materials under stress can open up and allow the contents to escape. This refers to both pressurized and nonpressurized containers. This content release will vary in type and speed. A pattern will be formed by the escaping product that will possibly expose people, the environment, or property, creating physical and/or health hazards. This overall concept is often referred to as a general behavior model and is used to estimate the behavior of the container and its contents under emergency conditions.

When a hazardous materials container loses its integrity, the incident will often escalate. The timing of such a release cannot always be predicted, and it will vary with the duration, intensity, and type of stress to which the container is subjected.

The responder must understand that a container may be stressed or its contents may be stressed and that there is a difference between the two phenomena. A container may degrade under stress. The material inside a container can either degrade the container or breach a container that has not been degraded.[18]

According to Charles Wright, factors that affect the intensity of the breach include ". . . type and duration of the stress being applied, behavior of the containment system under the stresses applied, behavior of the contents, location of the applied stresses, force of opening of the containment system, size of breach, and speed of breach event."[19]

3-2.3.4* Identify four ways in which containers can release their contents.

A-3-2.3.4 The four ways in which containment systems can release their contents are detonation, violent rupture, rapid relief, and spill or leak.

The types of release include detonation, disintegration of the container, and/or detonation of the contents; violent massive failure behavior, the runaway cracking of the container, and rapid-acceleration polymerization or oxidizing hazardous materials reactions that burst the container abruptly; rapid relief behavior, including pressure ruptures or safety valve operation; and spill or leak behavior, including gradual flow through openings, tears or splits, and punctures.[20]

3-2.3.5* Identify at least four dispersion patterns that can be created upon release of a hazardous material.

A-3-2.3.5 The seven dispersion patterns that can be created upon release of hazardous materials are hemisphere, cloud, plume, cone, stream, pool, and irregular.

Knowing how hazardous materials behave when they are released is important in determining the area potentially endangered. The dispersion pattern is influenced by the way the material is released, physical behavior of the material, and weather conditions.

3-2.3.6* Identify the three general time frames for predicting the length of time that exposures can be in contact with hazardous materials in an endangered area.

A-3-2.3.6 The three general time frames for predicting the length of time that an exposure can be in contact with hazardous materials in an endangered area are short-term (minutes and hours), medium-term (days, weeks, and months), and long-term (years and generations).

Factors that influence the length of time an exposure may last in an endangered area include the quantity of the material released, the method of dispersion, and the speed at which it is released. For example, did the container leak or did it detonate? The presence of secondary reactions will also influence the length of an exposure.

3-2.3.7* Identify the health and physical hazards that could cause harm.

A-3-2.3.7 The health and physical hazards that could cause harm in a hazardous materials incident are thermal, mechanical, poisonous, corrosive, asphyxiation, radiation, and etiologic.

Harm is the injury or damage caused by being exposed to the hazards of the released contents.

The hazards associated with the released contents are directly proportional to the concentrations of released materials and to the duration of contact.[21]

3-2.3.8* Identify the health hazards associated with the following terms:

(a) Asphyxiant
(b)* Chronic health hazard
(c) Convulsant
(d) Irritant/corrosive
(e) Sensitizer/allergen

A-3-2.3.8 Health Hazard Definitions.

(a) *Carcinogen:* A chemical that falls within any of the following categories:

1. It has been evaluated by the International Agency for Research on Cancer (IARC) and found to be a carcinogen or potential carcinogen
2. It is listed as a carcinogen or potential carcinogen in the *Annual Report on Carcinogens* published by the National Toxicology Program (NTP) (latest edition)
3. It is regulated by federal OSHA as a carcinogen (can be regulated additionally by states)

(b) *Corrosive:* A chemical that causes visible destruction of, or irreversible alterations in, living tissue by chemical action at the site of contact

(c) *Highly toxic:* A chemical that falls within any of the following categories:

1. A chemical that has a median lethal dose (LD_{50}) of 50 mg or less per kg of body weight when administered orally to albino rats weighing between 200 g and 300 g each
2. A chemical that has a median lethal dose (LD_{50}) of 200 mg or less per kg of body weight when administered by continuous contact for 24 hours (or less if death occurs within 24 hours) with the bare skin of albino rabbits weighing between 2 kg and 3 kg each
3. A chemical that has a median lethal concentration (LD_{50}) in air of 200 parts per million by volume or less of gas or vapor, or 2 mg per L or less of mist, fume, or dust, when administered by continuous inhalation for 1 hour (or less if death occurs within 1 hour) to albino rats weighing between 200 g and 300 g each

(d) *Irritant:* A chemical that is not corrosive but that causes a reversible inflammatory effect on living tissue by chemical action at the site of contact

(e) *Sensitizer:* A chemical that causes a substantial proportion of exposed people or animals to develop an allergic reaction in normal tissue after repeated exposure to the chemicals

(f) *Toxic:* A chemical that falls within any of the following categories:

1. A chemical that has a median lethal dose (LD_{50}) or more than 50 mg per kg but not more than 500 mg per kg of body weight when administered orally to albino rats weighing between 200 g and 300 g each
2. A chemical that has a median lethal dose (LD_{50}) of more than 200 mg per kg but not more than 1,000 mg per kg of body weight when administered by continuous contact for 24 hours (or less if death occurs within 24 hours) with the bare skin of albino rabbits weighing between 2 kg and 3 kg each
3. A chemical that has a median lethal concentration (LD_{50}) in air of more than 200 parts per million but not more than 3,000 parts per million by volume of gas or vapor, or more than 2 mg per L but not more than 200 mg per L of mist, fume, or dust, when administered by continuous inhalation for 1 hour (or less if death occurs within 1 hour) to albino rats weighing between 200 g and 300 g each

(g) *Target organ effects:* A target organ categorization of effects that can occur, including examples of signs and symptoms and chemicals that have been found to cause such effects. These examples are presented to illustrate the range and diversity of effects and hazards that can be encountered and is not intended to be all-inclusive.

1. *Hepatotoxins.* Chemicals that produce liver damage (signs and symptoms: jaundice, liver enlargement; chemicals: carbontetrachloride, nitrosamines)
2. *Nephrotoxins.* Chemicals that produce kidney damage (signs and symptoms: edema, protein urea; chemicals: halogenated hydrocarbons, uranium)
3. *Neurotoxins.* Chemicals that produce their primary toxic effects on the nervous system

   a. *Central Nervous System Hazards:* Chemicals that cause depression or stimulation of consciousness or otherwise injure the brain

b. *Peripheral Nervous System Hazards:* Chemicals that damage the nerves that transmit messages to and from the brain and the rest of the body (signs and symptoms: numbness, tingling, decreased sensation, change in reflexes, decreased motor strength; examples: arsenic, lead, toluene, styrene)

4. Agents that decrease hemoglobin in the blood of function; deprive the hematopolatic body tissues of oxygen system (signs and symptoms: cyanosis, loss of consciousness; chemicals: carbon monoxide, benzene)
5. Agents that irritate the lung or damage the pulmonary tissue (signs and symptoms: cough, tightness in chest, shortness of breath; chemicals: silica, asbestos, HCL)
6. *Reproductive toxins.* Chemicals that affect the reproductive capabilities, including chromosomal damage (mutations) and effects on fetuses (teratogenesis) (signs and symptoms: birth defects, sterility; chemicals: lead, DBCP)
7. *Cutaneous hazards.* Chemicals that affect the dermal layer of the body (signs and symptoms: defatting of the skin, rashes, irritation; chemicals: ketones, chlorinated compounds)
8. *Eye hazards.* Chemicals that affect the eye or visual capacity (signs and symptoms: conjunctivitis, corneal damage; chemicals: organic solvents, acids)

A-3-2.3.8(b) Chronic health hazards include carcinogen, mutagen, and teratogen.

Responders need to be able to recognize the effect(s) that hazardous materials can have on human beings. Knowing the class of health hazard for a particular chemical will help the responder evaluate the risk and readily identify possible reactions to the exposure. The product may have more than one type of reaction on an individual, and reaction to a particular product may vary with the individual. Depending on the type of health hazard the product possesses, the reaction may be immediate, delayed, or chronic.

See the Tentative Interim Amendment on pp. 294 and 295 for new paragraphs 3-2.3.9 and A-3-2.3.9.

3-2.4* Estimating the Potential Harm.

The first responder at the operational level shall estimate the potential harm within the endangered area at a hazardous materials incident. The first responder at the operational level shall be able to:

A-3-2.4 The process for estimating the potential outcomes within an endangered area at a hazardous materials incident includes determining the dimensions of the endangered area, estimating the number of exposures within the endangered area, measuring or predicting concentrations of materials within the endangered area, estimating the physical, health, and safety hazards within the endangered area, identifying the areas of potential harm within the endangered area, and estimating the potential outcomes within the endangered area.

The operational level responder must be able to estimate the area of potential harm. Responders at this level are not expected to engage in intricate calculations or even to use sophisticated computer modeling, but they should be able to make general estimates based on the hazard information collected so that they can begin evacuations and safely implement defensive operations. As an incident becomes more complex, technician level responders would probably become involved, and they would be able to make more definitive predictions about the endangered area.

3-2.4.1* Identify a resource for determining the size of an endangered area of a hazardous materials incident.

A-3-2.4.1 Resources for determining the size of an endangered area of a hazardous materials incident are the current edition of the *North American Emergency Response Guidebook* and plume dispersion modeling results from facility pre-incident plans.

The *North American Emergency Response Guidebook* recommends isolation and evacuation distances for some hazardous materials. CHEMTREC, CANUTEC, or SETIQ may provide additional information.

3-2.4.2 Given the dimensions of the endangered area and the surrounding conditions at a hazardous materials incident, estimate the number and type of exposures within that endangered area.

Exposures include people, the environment, and property. Once the responder has estimated the size and location of the endangered area, he or she can determine what is inside the perimeter. Factors influencing the decision include the time of day, the type of occupancies involved, and the type of area involved. Is it rush hour, for example? Is the occupancy a petrochemical plant? Is the area congested or is it rural?

3-2.4.3 Identify resources available for determining the concentrations of a released hazardous material within an endangered area.

Various types of monitoring equipment and dispersion modeling programs are available for determining the concentrations of a released hazardous material. In most cases, however, responders at the operational level would not have this type of equipment. Nonetheless, they should understand what can be used and know how to acquire it and the technical assistance needed to operate it. For example, they should be aware of any company in their area that handles hazardous materials and know whether the company has personnel and equipment available to monitor hazardous conditions.

Responders should also know whether they can ask a regional hazardous materials response team to assist them. State or county environmental agencies or health departments can often provide monitoring equipment and personnel. However, responders should plan ahead and make these arrangements before an incident occurs, not at 3:00 A.M. on a rainy night when an overturned cargo tanker begins leaking hazardous materials all over the highway.

3-2.4.4* Given the concentrations of the released material, identify the factors for determining the extent of physical, health, and safety hazards within the endangered area of a hazardous materials incident.

A-3-2.4.4 The factors for determining the extent of physical, health, and safety hazards within an endangered area at a hazardous materials incident are surrounding conditions, an indication of the behavior of the hazardous material and its container, and the degree of hazard.

Responders must determine the extent of physical harm that can be expected in an endangered area and compare the gains they may receive from intervening—or not intervening—before they can determine the actions they should or should not take. Factors that influence this decision are the quantity and concentration of the hazardous materials released, the number of exposures in the endangered area, and the manner in which the exposures will be subjected to the hazardous material. Is the material a liquid or gas, for example? How far away from the source are the exposures? How fast is the material being released?

3-3 Competencies — Planning the Response

3-3.1 Describing Response Objectives for Hazardous Materials Incidents.

Given at least two scenarios involving hazardous materials incidents (one facility and one transportation), the first responder at the operational level shall describe the first responder's response objectives for each problem. The first responder at the operational level shall be able to:

Up to this point, we have addressed the competencies that allow the responder to gather the information necessary to make appropriate decisions when determining response objectives. This section outlines the competencies necessary for using this information to develop defensive options that can be safely implemented to influence the outcomes of the incident. Remember, actions are limited by the resources available. Responders should not take any action until they have a clear idea of what they are trying to accomplish.

In the *Fire Protection Handbook,* Wright notes,

> The planning process begins as part of the pre-emergency response planning efforts prior to the incident and continues on the scene of the incident, again from a safe location. Federal, state, and local agencies, industry, and carrier personnel may be called upon to help.
>
> The process of response planning is based on the following tasks.
>
> 1. Determine the response objectives.
> 2. Determine the available response options that could favorably change the outcomes.
> 3. Identify the personal protective equipment for the response options.
> 4. Identify an appropriate decontamination process for each response option.
> 5. Select the response options within the response community's capabilities that will most favorably change the outcomes.
> 6. Develop a plan of action including safety considerations.[22]

3-3.1.1 Given an analysis of a hazardous materials problem and the exposures already lost, identify the steps for determining the number of exposures that could be saved by the first responder with the resources provided by the authority having jurisdiction and operating in a defensive fashion.

To determine the number of exposures that might be saved, the responder must first determine the total number of exposures and the number that have already been lost, then estimate the effectiveness of the chosen action options. The worksheet shown in Figure 3.21 can be used to help work out this analysis.

3-3.1.2 Given an analysis of a hazardous materials incident, describe the steps for determining defensive response objectives.

The key to these response objectives is that they need to be limited to actions that protect persons, the environment, or property without actually controlling the release. Defensive actions taken from a safe distance to either control the release or keep it from spreading are appropriate, however.

Worksheet for Estimating the Effect of Each Response Option

Exposures/Harm	Amount that could be saved	Amount that could be saved with option 1	Amount that could be saved with option 2	Amount that could be saved with option 3	Amount that could be saved with option 4	Amount that could be saved with option 5	Amount that could be saved with option 6
People Death	#	#	#	#	#	#	#
People Injuries	#	#	#	#	#	#	#
Property Damage	$	$	$	$	$	$	$
Environ. Damage	$	$	$	$	$	$	$

Figure 3.21 *Completing this worksheet can help to analyze the exposure risk. (Source: Fire Protection Handbook, 18th edition)*

3-3.2 Identifying Defensive Options.

Given simulated facility and transportation hazardous materials problems, the first responder at the operational level shall identify the defensive options for each response objective. The first responder at the operational level shall be able to:

After responders have determined what or who to protect, they must determine how to protect them. Operational level responders must remember that their actions are expected to be defensive in nature.

3-3.2.1 Identify the defensive options to accomplish a given response objective.

The available defensive options fall into two categories: containment and confinement. This is also part of offensive operations for the technician, too, but the responder at this level is expected to take actions without actually stopping the release.

Some broad general control methods that might be available at this level include absorption; dilution with water; dams, dikes, and diversions; and vapor dispersion.

3-3.2.2 Identify the purpose for, and the procedures, equipment, and safety precautions used with, each of the following control techniques:

(a) Absorption

Absorption can be described as the process by which one substance, such as a liquid, combines with another substance, such as a solid, by becoming physically part of that substance.

Two things should be kept in mind when using sorbents. First, the sorbent must be compatible with the material being absorbed. And second, the sorbent material must be handled as a hazardous waste and disposed of correctly once it has been contaminated.

A number of sorbents are available commercially in the form of booms, pads, pillows, and so on. Other materials, such as commercial granular products, sand, soil, sawdust, and vermiculite, may also be used as sorbents. The responder should know where to acquire large quantities of these materials and establish a method for obtaining them 24 hours a day in the event of an emergency.

(b) Dike, dam, diversion, retention

Although substantial hazardous liquids spills can pose insurmountable problems, many lesser spills can be controlled by diking, damming, diversion, or retention. These techniques are the most commonly used methods of controlling releases because they can be improvised with a little ingenuity. Earthen dikes or dams can be erected quickly under favorable conditions. Trenches can be used to collect spilled liquids. And commercial booms can be used to control spills on waterways.

(c) Dilution

Dilution refers to the application of water to water soluble hazardous materials to reduce the hazard. Responders must take care when using water to check for any water reactive behavior. They must also remember that dilution will increase the total volume of liquid that must be retained.

(d) Remote valve shutoff
(e) Vapor dispersion

Water spray can be used to disperse or move vapors away from certain materials. The gas concentration of some materials, such as liquefied petroleum gas, can be reduced below the lower flammable limit.

(f) Vapor suppression

Vapor suppression refers to the reduction or elimination of vapors emanating from a spilled or released material. While vapor suppression does not change the nature of the hazardous material, it is an important mitigation procedure because it can greatly reduce the immediate hazard associated with the presence of an uncontrolled vapor.

3-3.3 Determining Appropriateness of Personal Protective Equipment.

Given the name of the hazardous material involved and the anticipated type of exposure, the first responder at the operational level shall determine whether available personal protective equipment is appropriate for implementing a defensive option. The first responder at the operational level shall be able to:

Responders at this level are not expected to use specialized chemical-protective clothing. Rather, they are expected to use the type of protective clothing they normally wear in their working environment. For example, fire fighters would wear structural fire-fighting protective clothing, while the employee of an industrial facility might use liquid splash-protective clothing.

Responders must understand the differences among the various types of protective clothing and the levels of protection they afford. The level of protective clothing available to operational level responders is a significant factor when considering what type of defensive operations they can safely undertake and when they should request additional expertise and specialized equipment.

3-3.3.1* Identify the appropriate respiratory protection required for a given defensive option.

A-3-3.3.1 The minimum requirement for respiratory protection at hazardous materials incidents (emergency operations until concentrations have been determined) is positive pressure self-contained breathing apparatus. Therefore, the minimum for the first responder at the operational level is positive pressure self-contained breathing apparatus.

OSHA 1910.120, Subpart L, 4iiiD, requires that "Employees engaged in emergency response and exposed to hazardous substances shall wear positive pressure self-contained breathing apparatus while engaged in emergency response until such time that the individual in charge of the IMS [incident commander] determines through the use of air monitoring that a decreased level of respiratory protection will not result in hazardous exposure to employees."[23]

This does not mean that the responder at the operational level cannot use other types of respiratory protection. Once the material has been identified and an appropriate type of protection has been determined, the protection can be worn for the emergency. The incident commander should make this decision only after consulting with the hazardous materials branch safety officer.

3-3.3.1.1 Identify the three types of respiratory protection and the advantages and limitations presented by the use of each at hazardous materials incidents.

The three types of respiratory protection are the air purifying respirator (APR), the supplied-air respirator (SAR), and the self-contained breathing apparatus (SCBA). APRs are lightweight, and they provide the user with more movement and travel distance than the other two types of respiratory protection. However, APRs cannot be used in oxygen-deficient atmospheres and must be worn only in atmospheres in which the hazard has been identified and the concentrations are within allowable limits.

SARs are supplied with air by an external source, usually a compressor or compressed air cylinders located away from the actual work site. SARs can be used in oxygen-deficient atmospheres, they can operate longer than SCBA, and they are lighter to wear than SCBA. However, the SARs' hoses limit the distance the wearer can travel and can become tangled or twisted. In addition, the wearer must enter and leave the site at the same point.

Positive pressure SCBA provides the highest level of respiratory protection available. It can be used in oxygen-deficient atmospheres and does not restrict the distance the wearer may travel or path they may take. However, the positive pressure SCBA's limited air supply—2 hours at the most—will limit the length of time it can be used, thus controlling the distance the wearer may travel. This limitation will be even greater for individuals not in good physical condition. In addition, the weight of the SCBA may cause the wearer to exert additional physical effort, which may also shorten the period of effectiveness. *(See Table 3.3.)*

3-3.3.1.2 Identify the required physical capabilities and limitations of personnel working in positive pressure self-contained breathing apparatus.

There are certain limitations on the use of SCBA. Positive pressure SCBA places a strain on the wearer's cardiovascular system because of the additional weight. In general, the better the aerobic capacity, the longer a person can operate before running out of air. This dif-

Table 3.3 Respirator, Protection Equipment

Type	Advantages	Limitations
1. Positive pressure self-contained breathing apparatus	• Provides highest level of protection against airborne contaminants and oxygen deficiency	• Bulky, heavy • Finite air supply limits work duration • May impair movement in confined spaces
2. Positive pressure supplied-air respirators	• Longer work periods than with SCBA • Less bulky and heavy than SCBA • Protects against airborne contaminants	• Impairs mobility • MSHA/NIOSH limits hose to 300 ft (91 m) • As length of hose is increased, minimum approved airflow may not be delivered at the facepiece • Air line is vulnerable to damage, chemical contamination, and degradation. Decontamination of hoses may be difficult • Worker must retrace steps to leave work area • Requires supervision/ monitoring of the air supply line • Not approved for use in atmospheres immediately dangerous to life or health (IDLH) or in oxygen-deficient atmospheres unless equipped with an emergency egress unit-only SCBA that can provide immediate emergency respiratory protection in case of air line failure
3. Air purifying respirator [including powered air purifying respirators (PAPRs)]	• Enhance mobility • Lighter in weight than an SCBA	• Cannot be used in IDLH or oxygen-deficient atmosphere (less than 19.5 percent oxygen at sea level) • Limited duration of protection. May be hard to gauge safe operating time in field conditions • Only protects against specific chemicals and up to specific concentrations • Use requires monitoring of contaminants and oxygen levels • Can only be used: 1. Against gas and vapor contaminants with adequate warning properties, or 2. For specific gases or vapors provided that the service is known and a safety factor is applied or if the unit has an end-of-service-life indicator (ESLI)

ference can be substantial. In addition, some individuals are claustrophobic and simply cannot wear SCBA. OSHA regulations require that an individual be medically certified to wear respiratory protection safely.

NFPA 1500, *Standard on Fire Department Occupational Safety and Health Program*, requires that all responders using SCBA be medically certified annually by a physician.[24] The certifying physician should consult ANSI Z88.6, *Standard for Respiratory Protection-Respirator Use—Physical Qualifications for Personnel*, to determine which medical review is appropriate.[25] NFPA 1500 also requires that SCBA users be trained, tested, and certified regularly in the safe and proper use of the equipment. *(See Table 3.4.)*

3-3.3.2 Identify the appropriate personal protective clothing required for a given defensive option.

Given the name of the material involved in an incident and the type of exposure, the responder should be able to determine what type of personal protective equipment is required when implementing defensive options.

3-3.3.2.1 Identify skin contact hazards encountered at hazardous materials incidents.

There are a number of skin contact hazards, including burns, rashes, and absorption of toxic substances, so protecting exposed skin is critical.

3-3.3.2.2 Identify the purpose, advantages, and limitations of the following levels of protective clothing at hazardous materials incidents:

(a) Structural fire-fighting protective clothing
(b) High temperature-protective clothing

Table 3.4 Relative Advantages and Disadvantages of SCBA

Type	Description	Advantages	Disadvantages	Comments
Entry-and-Escape SCBA				
Open-Circuit SCBA	Supplies clean air to wearer from cylinder Wearer exhales air directly to atmosphere	• Operated in positive pressure mode, provides highest respiratory protection now available. Warning alarm signals when 20 to 25 percent of air supply remains	• Shorter operating time (30, 45, 60 minutes), heavier weight [up to 35 lb (15.9 kg)] than closed- circuit SCBA	• Operating time may vary depending on size of air tank, physical fitness, and work rate of individual
Closed-Circuit SCBA (Rebreather)	Recycles exhaled gases (CO_2, O_2, nitrogen) by removing CO_2 with alkaline scrubber and replenishing consumed oxygen with oxygen from liquid or gaseous source	• Longer operating time (up to 4 hours), lighter weight [21 to 30 lb (9.5 to 13.6 kg)] than open-circuit apparatus • Warning alarm signals when 20 to 25 percent of oxygen supply remains • Oxygen supply is depleted before CO_2 sorbent scrubber supply, protecting wearer from CO_2 breakthrough	• At very cold temperatures, scrubber efficiency may be reduced, CO_2 breakthrough may occur • Units retain heat exchanged in exhalation, generate heat in CO_2 scrubbing operations, adding to danger of heat stress • Auxiliary cooling devices may be required • When worn outside encapsulating suit, breathing bag may be permeated by chemicals, contaminating breathing apparatus and respirable air • Decontamination of breathing bag may be difficult	• Positive pressure units offer more protection than negative-pressure units, which are not recommended on hazardous waste sites. While these devices may be certified as closed-circuit SCBAs, NIOSH cannot certify closed-circuit SCBAs as positive pressure devices due to limitations in certification procedures defined in 30 *CFR,* Part 11
Escape-Only SCBA	Supplies clean air from an air cylinder or from oxygen-generating chemical Approved for escape only	• Lightweight [10 lb (4.5 kg) or less], low bulk, easy to carry • Available in pressure-demand, continuous flow modes	• Cannot be used for entry	• Provides only 5 to 15 minutes of respiratory protection, depending on model, wearer breathing rate

(c) Chemical-protective clothing

1. Liquid splash-protective clothing
2. Vapor-protective clothing

It is important to remember that no single type of protective clothing will protect the wearer against all possible hazards. This is true even of chemical-protective clothing.

3-3.4* Identifying Emergency Decontamination Procedures.

The first responder at the operational level shall identify emergency decontamination procedures. The first responder at the operational level shall be able to:

A-3-3.4 Refer to *Hazardous Materials Response Handbook*, National Fire Protection Association, Quincy, MA.

Decontamination, or contamination reduction, is critical to health and safety at a hazardous materials incident. It protects responders from hazardous substances that may contaminate and eventually permeate their personal protective equipment and the other equipment they use at the incident. Decontamination also minimizes the transmission of harmful substances from one control zone to another and helps protect the environment. Decontamination procedures must be specific for the type of hazard encountered.

3-3.4.1 Identify ways that personnel, personal protective equipment, apparatus, and tools and equipment become contaminated.

Contamination occurs when responders come in contact with hazardous substances at an incident. If the responders are adequately protected, only the garments they are wearing or the equipment they are using in the hot zone will be contaminated. All contaminants must be removed from the responders' personal protective clothing before the clothing itself is removed.

3-3.4.2 Describe how the potential for secondary contamination determines the need for emergency decontamination procedures.

Operational level personnel who inadvertently or in the performance of an emergency rescue enter the hot zone can carry contaminants out of the hot zone on their protective clothing or equipment. Emergency decontamination procedures must be implemented immediately to minimize the threat of secondary contamination.

3-3.4.3 Identify the purpose of emergency decontamination procedures at hazardous materials incidents.

Emergency, or gross, decontamination is designed to remove contaminants that pose an immediate threat to life, and, in most cases, will not remove all contaminants.

3-3.4.4 Identify the advantages and limitations of emergency decontamination procedures.

Emergency decontamination can be implemented without establishing a formal decontamination corridor. However, it only provides gross decontamination, so the victim may still be exposed to contaminants and may pose a threat of secondary contamination.

See the Tentative Interim Amendment on p. 295 for new paragraphs 3-3.4.5 and 3-3.4.6.

3-4 Competencies — Implementing the Planned Response

3-4.1 Establishing and Enforcing Scene Control Procedures.

Given scenarios for facility and/or transportation hazardous materials incidents, the first responder at the operational level shall identify how to establish and enforce scene control including control zones, emergency decontamination, and communications. The first responder at the operational level shall be able to:

3-4.1.1 Identify the procedures for establishing scene control through control zones.

The site control process must be put into place very quickly at each hazardous materials incident to maintain control of the scene. The size of the control zone is based on the degree of hazard present.

3-4.1.2 Identify the criteria for determining the locations of the control zones at hazardous materials incidents.

Initially, the responder will probably determine where to locate the control zones using recommendations from emergency response guides, such as the *North American Emergency Response Guidebook*'s initial isolation and evacuation distances, or the advice of such organizations as CHEMTREC or CANUTEC. In addition, the responder will rely on his or her own observations of the incident and on an assessment of related information.

As the incident progresses, the responder may adjust the zones based on sampling and monitoring results, on evaluations of the extent of contamination and the path it might take in case of a leak, and on the space needed to support control operations.

3-4.1.3 Identify the basic techniques for the following protective actions at hazardous materials incidents:

(a) Evacuation

Evacuation is defined by the *North American Emergency Response Guidebook* as the process of moving people at risk from the area threatened to safey.[26] There must be opportunity and enough time to warn the people in the affected area and enough time for them to get ready and leave that area. Evacuees should be sent upwind of the threatened area by a specific route to a place far enough away from the incident that they will not have to be moved again if the conditions change. They must be kept in one place so that they can be decontaminated and receive medical treatment if necessary.

(b) Sheltering in-place protection

Sheltering in-place protection means either to direct people to seek immediate shelter inside a building or to remain inside a building in the hot zone or the warm zone.[27] Certain protective actions must be taken inside that building, such as closing windows and doors, shutting down HVAC equipment (which draws in outside air), and staying away from windows.

3-4.1.4 Identify the considerations associated with locating emergency decontamination areas.

Such considerations include the ability to control runoff and to minimize exposure to others through secondary contamination.

3-4.1.5* Demonstrate the ability to perform emergency decontamination.

A-3-4.1.5 Refer to *Hazardous Materials Response Handbook*, National Fire Protection Association, Quincy, MA.

3-4.1.6* Identify the items to be considered in a safety briefing prior to allowing personnel to work on a hazardous materials incident.

See the Tentative Interim Amendment on p. 296 for revised paragraph 3-4.1.6.

The following items should be presented during a safety briefing:

(a) Preliminary evaluation
(b) Hazard identification
(c) Description of the site
(d) Task(s) to be performed
(e) Length of time for task(s)
(f) Required personal protective clothing
(g) Monitoring requirements
(h) Notification of identified risks

These are some of the most important factors to consider, but there may be others that are important to include depending on the type of incident.

A-3-4.1.6 Refer to NIOSH/OSHA/USCG/EPA *Occupational Safety and Health Guidance Manual for Hazardous Waste Site Activities.*

See the Tentative Interim Amendment on p. 296 for new paragraphs A-3-4.1.6(b).

3-4.2* Initiating the Incident Management System (IMS).

Given simulated facility and/or transportation hazardous materials incidents, the first responder at the operational level shall initiate the incident management system (IMS) specified in the local emergency response plan and the organization's standard operating procedures. The first responder at the operational level shall be able to:

A-3-4.2 See A-2-4.1.

One of the key elements of conducting a safe and effective control operation at a hazardous materials incident is the implementation of an effective incident management system. For an incident management system to be effective, it must be part of a pre-incident plan and be adopted as a standard operating procedure for emergency responders in a given area. NFPA 1561, *Standard on Incident Management System,*[28] provides guidance on what an effective incident management system should provide in order to operate as effectively as possible. The National Inter-Agency Incident Management System (NIIMS) lists the following components of its incident command system:

(a) Common terminology
(b) Modular organizations
(c) Integrated communications
(d) Unified command structure
(e) Consolidated action plans
(f) Manageable span of control

3-4.2.1 Identify the role of the first responder at the operational level during hazardous materials incidents as specified in the local emergency response plan and the organization's standard operating procedures.

The local emergency response plan should outline the role of emergency responders at the operational level. Primarily, that role includes responding to an emergency, assessing the nature of the incident, implementing initial defensive actions, notifying other involved parties, and asking for additional assistance when needed.

3-4.2.2 Identify the levels of hazardous materials incidents as defined in the local emergency response plan.

3-4.2.3 Identify the purpose, need, benefits, and elements of an incident management system (IMS) at hazardous materials incidents.

3-4.2.4 Identify the considerations for determining the location of the command post for a hazardous materials incident.

The initial command post may well be the first-arriving unit at the incident. As more equipment and personnel arrive, however, the incident commander may use a designated command post, which may be a specially designed vehicle. The IC may also use radios or telephones to disseminate information. At more complex incidents, an emergency operations center may actually be set up.

Each incident should have only one command post. That post should be clearly marked, and access to it should be controlled. The responder should consider locating the command post in an area where it would not have to be moved.

3-4.2.5 Identify the procedures for requesting additional resources at a hazardous materials incident.

It is extremely important that responders at every level know what type of resources are available and understand how to request them. It is not uncommon for a responder to reply, "Gee, I didn't know it was available," when asked why they did not ask for a particular type of assistance.

3-4.2.6* Identify the authority and responsibilities of the safety officer.

A-3-4.2.6 The hazardous materials safety officer should meet all the competencies for the responder at the level of operations being performed.

A hazardous materials branch safety officer is an individual who directs the safety of operations within the hot and warm zones. A hazardous materials branch safety officer should be designated specifically at all hazardous material incidents (CFR 1910.120). The hazardous materials safety officer has the following responsibilities:

(a) Obtains a briefing from the incident commander or incident safety officer and the hazardous materials branch safety officer
(b) Participates in the preparation of and monitors the implementation of the incident safety considerations (including medical monitoring of entry team personnel before and after entry)
(c) Advises the incident commander/sector officer of deviations from the incident safety considerations and of any dangerous situations
(d) Alters, suspends, or terminates any activity that is judged to be unsafe

The position of hazardous materials branch safety officer is critical, as can be seen by the position's responsibilities as outlined in A-3-4.2.6. The incident commander may be responsible for implementing tasks at an incident, but the branch safety officer has the authority to see that they are accomplished safely in the hot and warm zones. At most incidents, there is only one safety officer. At more complex incidents, however, there may be additional assistants.

3-4.3 Using Personal Protective Equipment.

The first responder at the operational level shall demonstrate the ability to don, work in, and doff the personal protective equipment provided by the authority having jurisdiction. The first responder at the operational level shall be able to:

Not only should responders know all about the protective clothing and equipment they are given, but they must also be able to use it.

3-4.3.1 Identify the importance of the buddy system in implementing the planned defensive options.

One purpose of the buddy system is to keep track of everyone working at an incident and to make sure they are all safe. No one involved in operations at an incident works alone: everyone either is part of a team or has a partner. *(See Figure 3.22.)*

3-4.3.2 Identify the importance of the backup personnel in implementing the planned defensive options.

During emergency operations, responders often work in conditions that may deteriorate rapidly and unexpectedly, even with the best of planning. Thus, it is vitally important that back-up personnel are available, that they are equipped with the same level of personal protective equipment as the personnel they are backing up, and that they can be deployed immediately in the event of an emergency.

__Figure 3.22__ Working in pairs increases responder safety. If one worker is injured, the other can assist or go for help. These A level technicians work regularly as partners on incidents, and these shared experiences have increased their understanding of each others' hand signals and the ability to anticipate when assistance in needed. (Photo courtesy of Henrik G. de Gyor)

3-4.3.3 Identify the safety precautions to be observed when approaching and working at hazardous materials incidents.

An incident should be approached from upwind and uphill whenever possible, and the approach should be calculated and deliberate. Binoculars can help responders identify the material involved, and monitoring equipment can help them assess the hazard and determine what protective equipment they should use from a safe distance.

Responders working at an incident should be aware of what is happening around them. Is there an increase in the rate of venting? Does the fire seem bigger than it did? Does the problem seem to be lessening? Is there a change in atmospheric conditions? Is it getting windier? Has the wind changed direction? These are a few examples of the questions responders should ask themselves while working at a hazardous materials incident.

3-4.3.4 Identify the symptoms of heat and cold stress.

The two most serious heat problems are heat exhaustion and heat stroke. Heat exhaustion is characterized by fatigue, headache, nausea, dizziness, and profuse sweating. It usually occurs when a person is dehydrated from not having adequate liquid intake. Heat stroke is characterized by hot, dry skin because of the inability to sweat. It may occur quickly, and the victim will exhibit confusion and impaired judgment.

Cold stress may occur if responders are exposed to prolonged cold temperatures. Hypothermia is one of the more severe manifestations of cold stress. Victims will exhibit shivering, apathy, listlessness, drowsiness, slow pulse, a low respiratory rate, and possible freezing of the extremities. If the victim is exposed to water, either by sweating or if clothing becomes wet, this will increase the possibility of cold stress.

3-4.3.5 Identify the physical capabilities required for, and the limitations of, personnel working in the personal protective equipment as provided by the authority having jurisdiction.

The physical and medical requirements for personnel wearing respiratory protection were discussed in the commentary to 3-3.3.1.2. In addition to those requirements, responders must have the physical stamina to wear the protective clothing and equipment provided and to work under strenuous conditions. That is why it is so important to conduct realistic training exercises that require responders to demonstrate their true abilities.

A job-oriented physical fitness test should be given to new responders and administered annually to existing responders. This is the only way to determine fitness for duty before placing personnel into physically strenuous situations.

3-4.3.6 Match the function of the operational components of the positive pressure self-contained breathing apparatus provided to the hazardous materials responder with the name of the component.

This allows responders to demonstrate their knowledge of the positive pressure self-contained breathing apparatus, which consists of a full facepiece, an exhalation valve, a breathing tube, a regulator, an air-supply hose, a cylinder, a cylinder valve, a bypass valve, a main line valve, and a harness assembly.

3-4.3.7 Identify the procedures for cleaning, disinfecting, and inspecting respiratory protective equipment.

Manufacturers and suppliers of the various types of respiratory equipment furnish guidelines and instructions for their use, maintenance, and cleaning. These instructions should be followed.

3-4.3.8 Identify the procedures for donning, working in, and doffing positive pressure self-contained breathing apparatus.

3-4.3.9 Demonstrate donning, working in, and doffing positive pressure self-contained breathing apparatus.

3-4.4 Performing Defensive Control Actions.

Given a plan of action for a hazardous materials incident within their capabilities, the first responder at the operational level shall demonstrate defensive control actions set out in the plan. The first responder at the operational level shall be able to:

3-4.4.1 Using the type of fire-fighting foam or vapor suppressing agent and foam equipment furnished by the authority having jurisdiction, demonstrate the proper application of the fire-fighting foam(s) or vapor suppressing agent(s) on a spill or fire involving hazardous materials.

3-4.4.2 Identify the characteristics and applicability of the following foams:

(a) Protein

Protein foam concentrates produce dense, viscous foams of high stability, high heat resistance, and good resistance to burnback, but they are less resistant to breakdown by fuel saturation than are AFFF and fluoroprotein foams. They are nontoxic and biodegradable.

(b) Fluoroprotein

Fluoroprotein foams are very effective in fire-fighting situations where the foams become coated with fuel because of their "fuel shedding" properties. They are used in subsurface injection systems such as in storage tank fires and other in-depth crude petroleum or hydrocarbon fuel fires. They possess superior vapor securing and burnback resistance characteristics. In addition, they demonstrate better compatibility with dry chemical agents than do regular protein-type foams. They are biodegradable and nontoxic.

(c) Special purpose

1. Polar solvent alcohol-resistant concentrates

These types of foam concentrates produce foam that is resistant to breakdown when used on water-soluble or water-miscible materials or on polar solvents, such as alcohols, lacquer or enamel thinners, and acetone. The most common exhibit AFFF characteristics on hydrocarbons and produce a floating gel-like mass for foam buildup on water-miscible fuels.

2. Hazardous materials concentrates

Vapor-mitigating foams have been developed that are relatively stable on many hazardous liquids. One type is an alcohol-resistant fire-fighting foam that has been additionally stabilized to lengthen its effectiveness as a foam and its stability on toxic, flammable, or corrosive liquids. Another type is medium-expansion foams that are specially formulated to be stable on either acidic or alkaline hazards. In general, these foams should be applied to spills of toxic liquids only by trained personnel.

(d) Aqueous film-forming foam (AFFF)

AFFFs are composed of synthetically produced materials that form air-foams similar to protein-based foams. In addition, they are capable of forming water-solution films on the surface of flammable liquids. AFFFs have low viscosity and have fast spreading and leveling characteristics. They also produce a continuous aqueous layer of solution under the foam. This film is self-healing following mechanical disruption and continues to spread because there is a reservoir of nearby foam. Film effectiveness may be reduced on hot surfaces and aromatic hydrocarbons. AFFFs are nontoxic and biodegradable.

(e) High expansion

High-expansion foams are agents for control of Class A and Class B fires and are particularly suited for total flooding of confined spaces. They are suitable for transporting wet foam masses to inaccessible places. Their use outdoors may be limited by the effects of weather.

3-4.4.3 Given the appropriate tools and equipment, demonstrate how to perform the following defensive control activities:

(a) Absorption
(b) Damming
(c) Diking
(d) Dilution
(e) Diversion
(f) Retention
(g) Vapor dispersion
(h) Vapor suppression

The best way to prepare personnel to conduct the above operations is to subject them to a training exercise that allows them to perform these operations while wearing the appropriate personal protective clothing and equipment.

3-4.4.4 Identify the location and describe the use of the mechanical, hydraulic, and air emergency remote shutoff devices as found on cargo tanks.

Emergency shutoff valves on MC-306 tanks are usually mechanical and are located at both the front and rear of the cargo tanks. (The shutoff valve for the DOT-406 is shown in Figure 3.13.)

On the MC-331 there are two remote methods of closure. Both closures are required to operate by mechanical and thermal means. One is located at the front of the cargo tank and the other is located at the rear of the vehicle. *(See Figure 3.23.)*

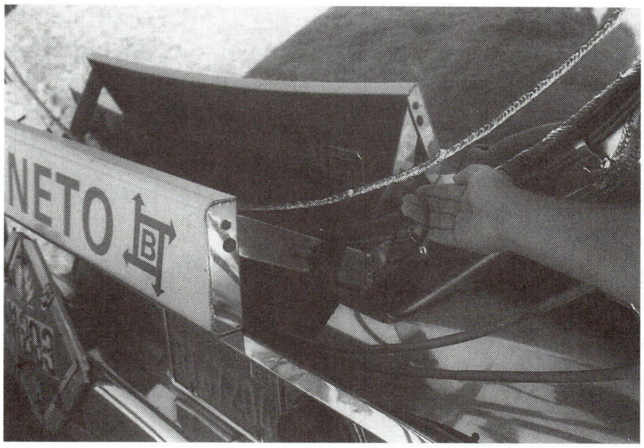

***Figure 3.23** A manual shutoff at the rear of an MC-306 cargo tank. The shutoff for a DOT-406 tanker is shown in Figure 3.13.*

3-4.4.5 Describe the objectives and dangers of search and rescue missions at hazardous materials incidents.

This broadly stated competency requires only a general response, since search and rescue operations are so varied in nature and in complexity. If circumstances mandate such an operation, responders are obliged to take actions necessary to locate and rescue or account for the victims within the limitations of the operational level.

In performing such an operation, responders will expand their size-up of the incident. The hazards associated with search and rescue operations are obvious: rescuers expose themselves to increased hazards and risks.

3-5 Competencies – Evaluating Progress

3-5.1 Evaluating the Status of Defensive Actions.

Given simulated facility and/or transportation hazardous materials incidents, the first responder at the operational level shall evaluate the status of the defensive actions taken in accomplishing the response objectives. The first responder at the operational level shall be able to:

All responders should understand why their efforts must be evaluated. If they are not making progress, the plan must be reevaluated to determine why progress is not being made.

3-5.1.1 Identify the considerations for evaluating whether defensive options are effective in accomplishing the objectives.

To decide whether the actions being taken at an incident are effective and the objectives are being achieved, the responder must determine whether the incident is stabilizing or increasing in intensity.

3-5.1.2 Describe the circumstances under which it would be prudent to withdraw from a hazardous materials incident.

There is no reason to remain in the immediate vicinity of an incident when nothing can be done to mitigate it and the situation may be about to deteriorate. If flames are impinging on an LP-Gas vessel, for example, and there is no way to provide the necessary volume of water to cool it, it would be prudent to withdraw to a safe distance.

3-5.2 Communicating the Status of the Planned Response.

The first responder at the operational level shall communicate the status of the planned response to the incident commander and other response personnel. The first responder at the operational level shall be able to:

3-5.2.1 Identify the methods for communicating the status of the planned response to the incident commander through the normal chain of command.

When two-way radios are used, the incident management system should establish standard procedures for selecting the appropriate channels to communicate with the incident commander.

3-5.2.2 Identify the methods for immediate notification of the incident commander and other response personnel about critical emergency conditions at the incident.

A procedure should be established to allow responders to notify the incident commander immediately when conditions become critical and personnel are threatened. This may take the form of a pre-established emergency radio message or tone that signifies danger, for example, or it might be repeated blasts on an air horn. The message should not be delayed while responders try to locate a specific person in the chain of command.

3-6 Competencies — Terminating the Incident

(No competencies currently required at this level.)

References Cited in Commentary

1. Arthur E. Cote, ed., *Fire Protection Handbook*, 18th edition, National Fire Protection Association, Quincy, MA, 1997, p. 10-107.
2. Ibid., p. 10-113.
3. Ibid., p. 10-113.
4. Ibid., p. 10-110, 10-113.
5. Ibid., p. 9-286.
6. Ibid., p. 9-286.
7. Ibid., p. 9-286.
8. Ibid., p. 9-287.
9. Ibid., p. 9-290.
10. Ibid., p. 9-292.
11. Ibid., p. 9-292.
12. Ibid., p. 3-235.
13. Ibid., p. 4-135.
14. Ibid., p. 4-136.
15. Ibid., p. 10-113.
16. Benner, Ludwig, Jr., A *Textbook for Use in the Study of Hazardous Materials Emergencies*, 2nd edition, Lufred Industries, Inc., Oakton, VA, 1978, pp. 5 and 6.
17. Ibid., p. 71.
18. Ibid., p. 19.
19. Cote, *Fire Protection Handbook*, p. 10-118.
20. Benner, *A Textbook for Use in the Study of Hazardous Materials Emergencies*, p. 25.
21. Cote, *Fire Protection Handbook*, p. 10-118.
22. Ibid., p. 10-120.
23. OSHA 1910.120, Subpart L, 4iiiD, U.S. Government Printing Office, Washington, DC.
24. NFPA 1500, *Standard on Fire Department Occupational Safety and Health Program*, 1997 edition.

25. ANSI Z88.6, *Standard for Respiratory Protection-Respirator Use—Physical Qualifications for Personnel,* 1984 edition.
26. *North American Emergency Response Guidebook,* U.S. Department of Transportation, Washington, DC, 1996, p. 340.
27. Ibid., p. 340.
28. NFPA 1561, *Standard on Fire Department Incident Management System,* 1995 edition.

CHAPTER 4

Competencies for the Hazardous Materials Technician

4-1 General

4-1.1 Introduction.

Hazardous materials technicians shall be trained to meet all competencies at the first responder awareness and operational levels and the competencies of this chapter. Hazardous materials technicians also shall receive any additional training to meet applicable United States Department of Transportation (DOT), United States Environmental Protection Agency (EPA), Occupational Safety and Health Administration (OSHA), and other appropriate state, local, or provincial occupational health and safety regulatory requirements.

The technician level competencies are achieved through more advanced training and build upon the skills required at the awareness and operational levels. Training programs at this level must ensure that trainees have first mastered the competencies in Chapter 2 and Chapter 3 of NFPA 472.

4-1.2 Definition.

Hazardous materials technicians are those persons who respond to releases or potential releases of hazardous materials for the purpose of controlling the release. Hazardous materials technicians are expected to use specialized chemical protective clothing and specialized control equipment.

The role of the responder at the technician level is significantly different from the roles of the responder at the awareness and operational levels. At those levels, individuals were likely to be those first on the scene, or those whose normal duties include initial response to emergencies that involve hazardous materials. Accordingly, their actions are limited because their primary duty is to reduce or eliminate access to the immediate area of the incident and to minimize the potential harm of a release of hazardous materials.

The technician, on the other hand, is asked to assume a more aggressive role in controlling an incident. The technician will need to approach the point of release to plug, patch, or otherwise stop a hazardous substance spill.

4-1.3* Goal.

The goal of this chapter shall be to provide the hazardous materials technician with the knowledge and skills to perform the following tasks safely. Therefore, in addition to being competent at both the first responder awareness and operational levels, the hazardous materials technician shall be able to:

For greater details on the skills and knowledge required for the hazardous materials technician (HMT), texts such as *Emergency Management of Hazardous Materials Incidents* by John E. Bowen can be extremely helpful.[1]

(a) Analyze a hazardous materials incident to determine the magnitude of the problem in terms of outcomes by completing the following tasks:

1. Survey the hazardous materials incident to identify special containers involved, to identify or classify unknown materials, and to verify the presence and concentrations of hazardous materials through the use of monitoring equipment
2. Collect and interpret hazard and response information from printed resources, technical resources, computer data bases, and monitoring equipment
3. Determine the extent of damage to containers
4. Predict the likely behavior of released materials and their containers when multiple materials are involved
5. Estimate the size of an endangered area using computer modeling, monitoring equipment, or specialists in this field

The HMT is expected to be able to operate monitoring equipment in order to identify the presence and concentrations of hazardous materials and to have an in-depth knowledge of containers. The HMT should be able to access and interpret a wide variety of resources for hazard and response information as well as to find ways to identify hazards based on minimal information at the scene.

The responder at the technician level is expected to be able to predict more definitively than the responder at the operational level how the materials will behave when released.

Finally, the HMT should know either what computer modeling systems are available or how to get help from someone who can conduct modeling simulations of the dispersion patterns for various hazardous materials.

(b) Plan a response within the capabilities of available personnel, personal protective equipment, and control equipment by completing the following tasks:

1. Identify the response objectives for hazardous materials incidents

It is important to note the difference between this competency and the corresponding competency at the operational level. At the operational level, the responder is asked to "describe" response objectives; at the technician level, the technician will be asked to "identify" response objectives. Identifying a response objective requires a higher level of competency than describing a response objective because the responder must first acquire the information necessary to evaluate the objective and then determine the appropriate course of action.

The response objectives available at this level are defensive, offensive, or nonintervention. The responder must identify clear objectives, that is, determine the harmful results one wants to prevent or reduce.

2. Identify the potential action options available by response objective

At this level, the responder is again asked to identify the options available to achieve the response objectives that have been identified. This is done by considering the choices, given the resources and time available and the risk at hand. Some of these options may include separating the hazard from potential exposures, establishing barriers or dikes, diluting the material, or transferring the product to an undamaged container.

3. Select the personal protective equipment required for a given action option

Responders at this level must know more about personal protective equipment because technicians are expected to be involved in offensive operations. This may mean that they have to work in specialized chemical-protective clothing, such as a totally encapsulating suit. *(See Figure 4.1.)*

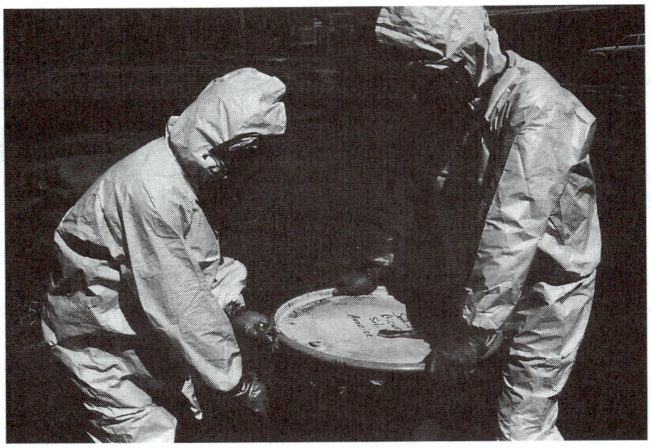

Figure 4.1 *Hazardous materials technicians control a leak from a drum.*

4. Select the appropriate decontamination procedures

It is imperative that technician level responders be able to select the appropriate decontamination procedures because they may come in contact with hazardous materials while conducting such offensive operations as plugging or patching.

5. Develop a plan of action, including safety considerations, consistent with the local emergency response plan and the organization's standard operating procedures, and within the capability of the available personnel, personal protective equipment, and control equipment

After the response objectives have been identified, the plan of action outlines these objectives and identifies the personnel and equipment necessary to accomplish them.

(c) Implement the planned response to favorably change the outcomes consistent with the organization's standard operating procedures and safety considerations by completing the following tasks:

1. Perform the duties of an assigned hazardous materials branch position within the local incident management system (IMS)

At this level, the responder should be able to perform assigned roles in the incident management system. Generally, the hazardous materials technician is expected to fill a role related to their expertise, such as decontamination, research, or medical treatment.

2. Don, work in, and doff appropriate personal protective clothing, including, but not limited to, both liquid splash- and vapor-protective clothing with appropriate respiratory protection
3. Perform the control functions identified in the plan of action

Responders at the technician level must be able to demonstrate their ability to select and use the appropriate equipment and to implement the defensive control functions chosen.

(d) Evaluate the progress of the planned response by evaluating the effectiveness of the control functions

(e) Terminate the incident by completing the following tasks:

1. Assist in the incident debriefing
2. Assist in the incident critique
3. Provide reports and documentation of the incident

A-4-1.3 The following site safety plan considerations are referenced from the *Standard Operating Safety Guides*, EPA, June 1992:

(a) Site description
(b) Entry objectives
(c) On-site organization
(d) On-site control
(e) Hazard evaluation
(f) Personal protective equipment
(g) On-site work plans
(h) Communication procedures
(i) Decontamination procedures
(j) Site safety and health plan.

4-2 Competencies — Analyzing the Incident

4-2.1 Surveying the Hazardous Materials Incident.

The hazardous materials technician shall identify special containers involved and, given the appropriate equipment, identify or classify unknown materials, verify the identity of the hazardous materials, and determine the concentration of hazardous materials. The hazardous materials technician shall be able to:

At this level, the HMT should be able to identify the characteristics of special containers that might indicate the presence of hazardous materials. The responder is also expected to be able to conduct an analysis that will identify and classify unknown materials. Special containers include high-pressure containers (identified by their rounded ends), cryogenic cargo tanks or cylinders, and casks for radioactive materials.

4-2.1.1 Given examples of various specialized containers, identify each container by name and identify the material, and its hazard class, that is typically found in the container.

4-2.1.1.1 Given examples of the following railroad cars, identify each car by type and identify at least one material, and its hazard class, that is typically found in each car:

(a) Cryogenic liquid tank cars

Cryogenic tank cars carry low-pressure liquids — usually at 25 psi (172 kPa) or lower that are refrigerated to –155°F (–104°C) or below. The cryogenic tank car is a tank-within-a-tank. The space between the inner and outer tanks is filled with insulation and normally maintained under a vacuum.

Cryogenic cars are distinguished by the absence of top fittings: the fittings are enclosed in cabinets either at ground level on both sides or at the end of the car. Among the materials that may be shipped in cryogenic tank cars are argon, ethylene, hydrogen, nitrogen, and oxygen (*see Figure 4.2*).

Figure 4.2 *Cryogenic transport vehicles have an inner shell of nickel or carbon steel to safeguard against the product inside from reacting with the shell due to low temperatures. On the tank trucks shown, the product pressure vent is under the large number on the back. (Photo courtesy Distrigas, Everett, MA)*

Another type of cryogenic tank car is the box tank. This type of tank is built inside a 40-ft (12-m) box car, and its fittings are located inside the doors on both sides.

(b) High-pressure tube cars

In the *Fire Protection Handbook*, Roger K. Fitch and Charles Wright note:

> The high pressure tube car is a 40-foot (12-m) box-type open-frame car. Inside the frame is a visible cluster of 30 stainless steel, uninsulated cylinders, arranged horizontally and permanently attached

to the car. Tank test pressures of these tube cars range up to 5000 psi (345,000 kPa). These tube cars transport helium, hydrogen, or oxygen in the gaseous form.

A steel case encloses each end of the tube car. Loading and unloading fittings and safety devices are located in a walk-in cabinet at one end of the car. Safety relief devices, either safety relief valves or safety vents, are found on each cylinder. For cars transporting flammable gases, safety relief devices are equipped with ignition devices to burn off any released material.[2]

All cylinders contain the same material. *(See Figure 4.2.)*

(c) Nonpressure tank cars
(d) Pneumatically unloaded hopper car

According to Fitch and Wright, in the *Fire Protection Handbook,* pneumatically unloaded covered hopper cars are covered hopper cars that are unloaded through pressure differential, or pneumatics, by the application of air pressure. The tank car specifications are used in building these containers. Even though the pressure is used only during loading and unloading, tank test pressures for the car range from 20 to 80 psi (138 to 551 kPa). Dry caustic soda is one of the commodities transported in this type of car."[3]

(e) Pressure tank cars

4-2.1.1.2 Given examples of the following intermodal tanks, identify each intermodal tank by type and identify at least one material, and its hazard class, that is typically found in each tank:

(a) Nonpressure intermodal tanks:

1. IM-101 (IMO Type 1 internationally) portable tank

These tanks are built to withstand maximum allowable working pressures (MAWP) of 25.4 psi to 100 psi (172 kPa to 6890 kPa). They may be used to transport both nonhazardous and hazardous materials, including toxic, corrosive, and flammable materials. Internationally, an IM-101 portable tank is called an IMO Type 1 tank container.

2. IM-102 (IMO Type 2 internationally) portable tank

Fitch and Wright note in the *Fire Protection Handbook*:

These tanks are designed to handle lower MAWP, that is from 14.5 psi to 25.4 psi (103 kPa to 172 kPa). They transport materials such as liquor, alcohols, some corrosives, pesticides, insecticides, resins, industrial solvents, and flammables with flash points between 32 and 140°F (0 and 60°C). More often, they transport various nonregulated materials, such as food commodities. Internationally, an IM-102 tank is called an IMO Type 2 tank container.[4]

(b) Pressure intermodal tanks (DOT 51) (IMO Type 5 internationally)
(c) Specialized intermodal tanks:

1. Cryogenic intermodal tanks (IMO Type 7 internationally)

Cryogenic tank containers carry refrigerated liquid gases, such as liquefied argon, oxygen, helium, ethylene, and nitrogen. They consist of a tank-within-a-tank with insulation between the inner and outer tanks. The space between the tanks is normally maintained under a vacuum.

2. Tube modules

While they are not actually portable tanks, tube modules are used to transport bulk gases. This rigid bulk packaging consists of several horizontal seamless steel cylinders, from 9 in. to 48 in. (229 mm to 1219 mm) in diameter, that are permanently mounted inside an open frame with a boxlike compartment at one end enclosing the loading and unloading fittings and safety devices. Service pressures range from 3000 psi to 5000 psi (20,685 kPa to 345,000 kPa). Among the materials shipped in tube modules are nonliquefied gases such as helium, nitrogen, and oxygen.

4-2.1.1.3 Given examples of the following cargo tanks, identify at least one material, and its hazard class, that is typically found in each tank:

(a) Dry bulk cargo tanks
(b) MC306/DOT-406 cargo tanks
(c) MC307/DOT-407 cargo tanks
(d) MC312/DOT-412 cargo tanks
(e) MC331 cargo tanks
(f) MC338 cargo tanks

Often the shape of the vehicle can offer clues to its cargo in an emergency. Figure 4.3 shows the various shapes of road trailers for quick reference.

4-2.1.1.4 Given examples of the following facility tanks, identify at least one material, and its hazard class, that is typically found in each tank:

(a) Nonpressure tank
(b) Pressure tank

4-2.1.1.5 Given examples of the following nonbulk containers, identify at least one material, and its hazard class, that is typically found in each container:

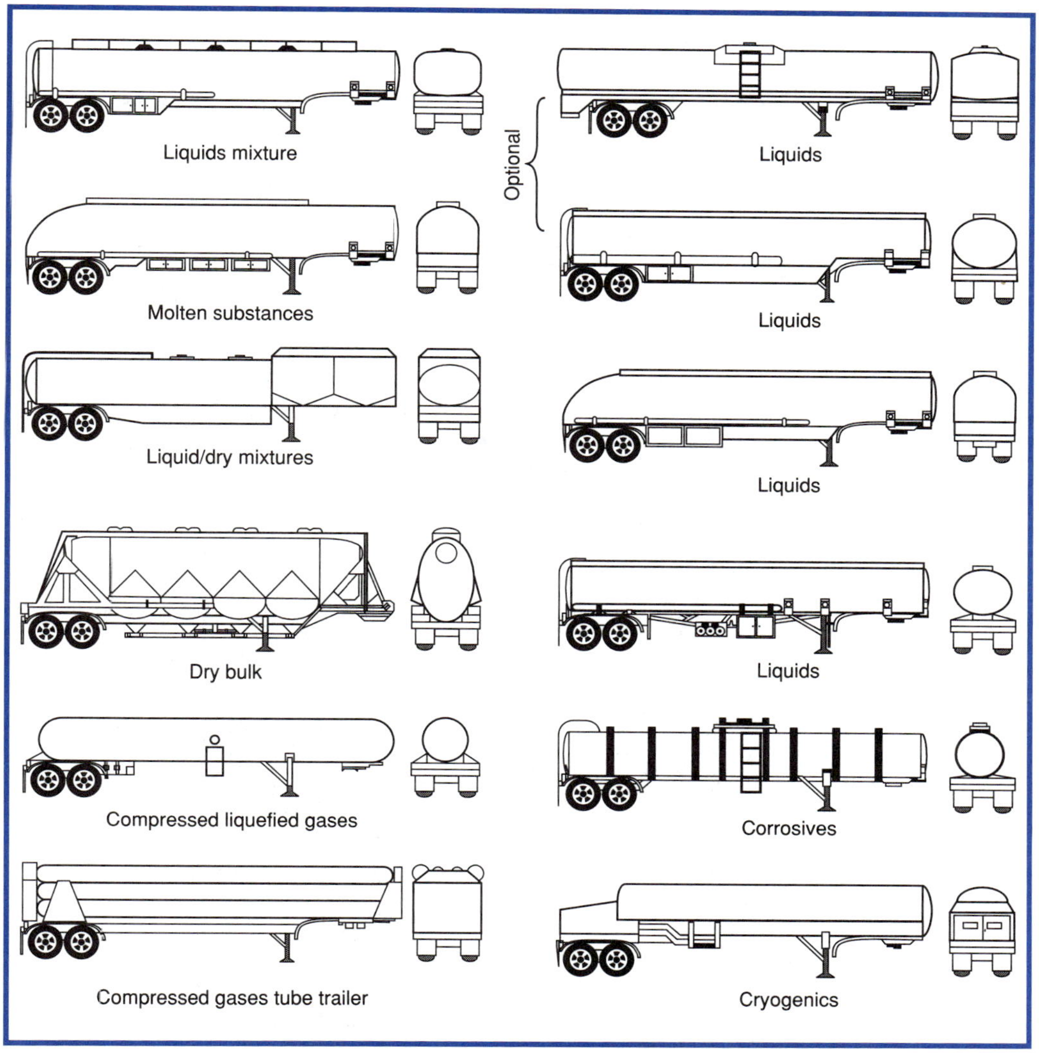

***Figure 4.3** Shape is often the only key to identifying the cargo of a trailer truck at an accident scene. The shapes of the most common vehicles are shown here. (Source: Fire Protection Handbook, 18th edition)*

(a) Bags
(b) Carboys
(c) Cylinders
(d) Drums

4-2.1.1.6 Given examples of the following radioactive materials packages, identify each package by type and identify at least one typical material found in each package:

(a) Type A
(b) Type B

See the Tentative Interim Amendment on p. 295 for new paragraph 4-2.1.1.7.

4-2.1.2 Given three examples of facility and transportation containers, identify the approximate capacity of each container.

Facility containers are often marked with their capacities. Transportation containers are required to be marked with their capacities.

4-2.1.2.1 Using the markings on the container, identify the capacity (by weight and/or volume) of the following examples of transportation vehicles:

(a) Cargo tanks

A data plate and a specification plate must be affixed to cargo tanks. These plates provide the volume and/or weight of the container.

(b) Tank cars

Tank cars must be marked by the U.S. Department of Transportation. Figure 4.4 shows an example of tank car markings.

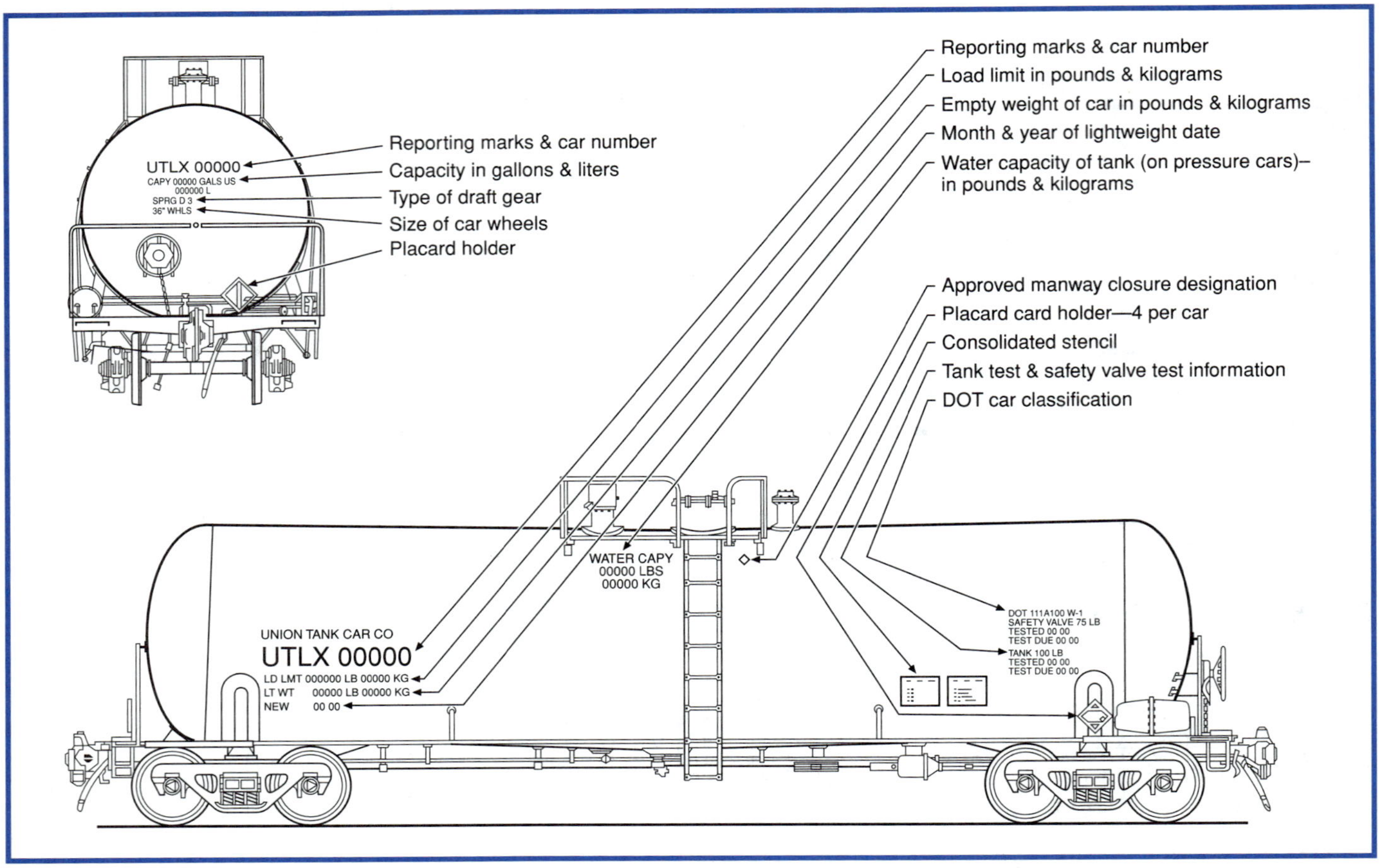

Figure 4.4 *Diagram of a tank car with markings identified. (Source: Union Tank Car Company)*

(c) Tank containers

The U.S. DOT also requires that tank containers have standardized markings. *(See Figure 4.5.)*

4-2.1.2.2 Using the markings on the container and other available resources, identify the capacity (by weight and/or volume) of each of the following facility containers:

(a) Nonpressure tank
(b) Pressure tank
(c) Cryogenic liquid tank

4-2.1.3* Given at least three unknown materials, one of which is a solid, one a liquid, and one a gas, identify or classify by hazard each unknown material.

The technician level responder is expected to be able to identify unknown materials in the event that a container's shipping papers, placards, MSDS, or other identifying items have been destroyed or are unavailable.

A-4-2.1.3 Suggested materials to identify can include the most commonly released materials that are identified on several lists annually (EPA, State of California).

4-2.1.3.1 Identify the steps in an analysis process for identifying unknown solid and liquid materials.

Unknown materials must be identified cautiously. Monitoring equipment can help identify the hazard class and, in some cases, even specific chemicals. Kits are also available to provide assistance in identification.

If the technician must take samples in order to conduct an analysis or approach the site to monitor it, he or she must use the proper level of protective clothing. In most cases, Level A should be used to ensure adequate protection. Responders must approach the site from upwind, wearing the appropriate level of protective clothing and working in at least pairs, with adequate backup personnel.

Kenneth York and Gerald Grey, in their text *Hazardous Materials/Waste Handling for the Emergency Responder,* recommend that

> . . . unless you are certain, beyond any doubt, as to what your hazard is, you should approach the incident employing the information listed below.

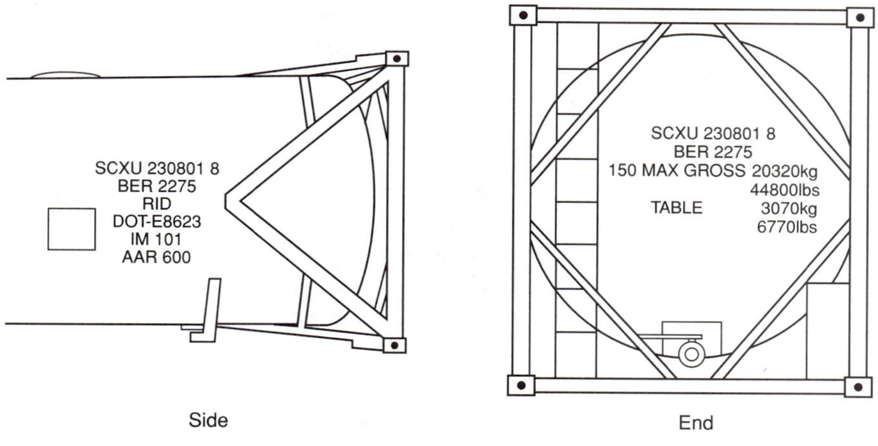

Figure 4.5 *Typical markings on a U.S. DOT tank container. (Source: Fire Protection Handbook, 18th edition)*

Assuming that you are not certain what all the hazards are, you should measure, in the order shown below, for:

- Radioactivity
- Combustibility
- Oxygen availability (deficiency)
- pH (if liquid)
- Hydrogen sulfide (if in areas of, or adjacent to, petroleum refining activities)
- Carbon monoxide (in a fire or post-fire incident)
- Organic vapor.[5]

4-2.1.3.2 Identify the steps in an analysis process for identifying an unknown atmosphere.

4-2.1.3.3 Identify the type(s) of monitoring equipment, test strips, and reagents used to determine the following hazards:

Hazardous materials response teams should develop protocols for monitoring the air during operations at hazardous materials incidents. A wide variety of monitoring equipment is available, and response teams must determine what is appropriate for the type of hazards they are likely to encounter. The response teams must also become proficient in calibrating, operating, and maintaining this equipment. Each instrument has its own operating characteristics and limitations, and responders must be familiar with them.

(a) Corrosivity (pH)

Corrosivity is measured by determining the pH of a material. This can be done using pH paper or pH meters. pH paper changes color, indicating the pH level. By comparing the color of the pH paper with the color chart provided, one can determine the pH of the material in question. Commercially available pH meters have a probe that is inserted into the material; the pH is indicated on the meter's display. These pH meters provide a more accurate reading than pH paper.

(b) Flammability

Combustible gas indicators (CGI) can be used to determine the presence of flammable vapors of hydrocarbon products. Certain instruments are specifically designed to monitor methane vapors only; they measure the flammable vapors as a percentage of the lower explosive limit. Flash point testers are also available for field use. These allow the responder to determine fairly accurately the flammability of an unknown material and the class of flammable or combustible liquid with which they are dealing.

(c) Oxidation potential
(d) Oxygen deficiency

Equipment used to monitor oxygen concentrations generally measures over a range of 0 to 25 percent oxygen in air. Some models contain an alarm that sounds if the oxygen level drops below 19.5 percent — the minimum adequate percentage of oxygen availability established by the U.S. Occupational Safety and Health Administration. For work in areas with oxygen measurements below this level, the responder must have an air-supplied respirator.

(e) Radioactivity

Radiation detectors are available to monitor alpha particles, beta particles, gamma rays, and neutron particles. Generally, such detectors measure two or more types of radiation. For example, the Geiger Counter, probably the most common type of radiation detector, can detect both gamma and beta radiation. However, it cannot effectively measure the amounts of beta radiation. Ion chambers can also measure radiation, but they are not effective on low-level radiation, either. *(See Figure 4.6.)*

Figure 4.6 *Small, hand-held radiation detectors are most useful for suspected leaks in nuclear medicine facilities.*

(f) Toxic levels

Several types of instruments can be used to measure toxic exposures. These include photoionization detectors, flame ionization detectors, infrared spectrophotometers, and detector tubes. Some of these instruments are designed to measure specific chemicals, such as hydrogen sulfide, and some may measure more than one. Detector tubes, which allow responders to evaluate potential hazards quickly, operate by drawing an air sample through a tube. This causes the material inside the tube to change color, indicating the concentration of the material in the air.

4-2.1.3.4* Identify the capabilities and limiting factors associated with the selection and use of the following monitoring equipment, test strips, and reagents:

A-4-2.1.3.4 These factors include, but are not limited to, operation, calibration, response time, detection range, relative response, sensitivity, selectivity, inherent safety, environmental conditions, and nature of hazard. Also refer to NIOSH/OSHA/USCG/EPA *Occupational Safety and Health Guidance Manual for Hazardous Waste Site Activities,* October 1985.

The key to successfully selecting and using sampling and monitoring instruments is intensive training. Personnel must thoroughly understand the operating characteristics and limitations of all the instruments available to them.

(a) Carbon monoxide meter

The carbon monoxide meter is limited in that it will measure only carbon monoxide. It may not indicate whether an area is oxygen-deficient, and it will not indicate the percent of the lower explosive limit. This information, if available, can warn responders that they have entered a flammable atmosphere. *(See Figure 4.7.)*

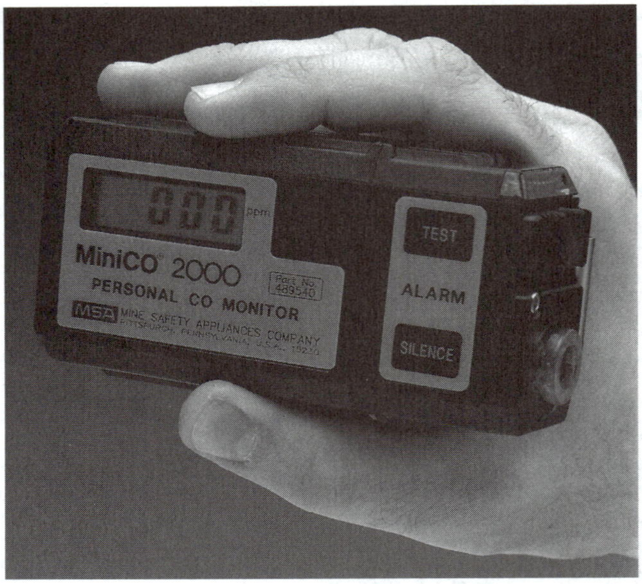

Figure 4.7 *This type of carbon monoxide meter, developed for use by an individual, contains an alarm that sounds when safe limits are exceeded. (Courtesy Mine Safety Appliance Co.)*

(b) Colorimetric tubes

Because colorimetric tubes are designed to read a specific material, responders need to know the material they are sampling. The tubes have a specific shelf life and are affected by both temperature and humidity, so tube supplies must be monitored to ensure that they are still usable. Colorimetric tubes may not be very accurate, giving responders only a general idea of the presence of the material for which they are testing. And it may be difficult to interpret the color change to determine the concentration of the material present. *(See Figure 4.8.)*

(c) Combustible gas indicator

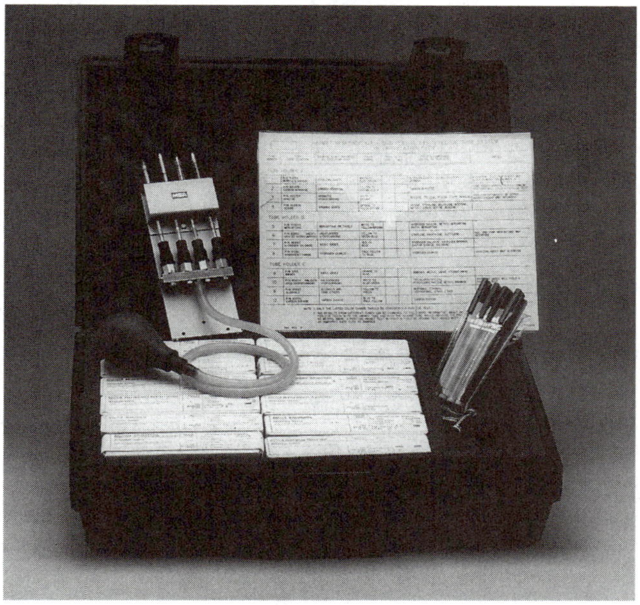

Figure 4.8 *The Haz Mat Detector Tube Kit allows sampling for multiple gases and vapors simultaneously. (Courtesy Mine Safety Appliance Co.)*

Figure 4.9 *A combustible gas indicator that uses an aspirator bulb to draw air samples from both immediate areas and remote locations. (Courtesy Mine Safety Appliance Co.)*

The combustible gas indicator (CGI) *(see Figure 4.9)* measures only whether the atmosphere contains a flammable material that is within a percentage of the lower explosive limit (LEL). It cannot identify other hazards, such as toxicity. In an atmosphere that contains more than 100 percent of the LEL, the needle on an analog CGI will go to the maximum, then return quickly to zero. If the operator is not watching closely, this shift may be missed.

Because the CGI only measures the LEL, the U.S. Environmental Protection Agency has established the following guidelines for working in areas that contain flammable vapors:

- <10 percent of LEL—continue working with caution
- 10 percent to 25 percent of LEL—continue working with continuous monitoring
- >25 percent of LEL—explosion hazard, withdraw from the area.

(d) Oxygen meter

Oxygen meters do not indicate what type of gas may be replacing the oxygen, nor do they indicate the toxicity of the gas. The sensing unit on an oxygen meter may be adversely affected by high concentrations of carbon monoxide or carbon dioxide. The sensing units also deteriorate over time and must be changed. Oxygen meters may be affected by changes in temperature, humidity, and atmospheric pressure, as well. *(See Figure 4.10.)*

(e) Passive dosimeter

Passive dosimeters, or passive samplers, are limited in several ways. For example, the responder must know what material is going to be sampled, and any other chemicals present that may interfere with the reading.

(f) Photoionization detectors
(g) pH indicators and/or pH meters

Both pH paper and strips may be difficult to read if the material sampled has been contaminated with oil, mud, or some other material. In addition, the personnel interpreting the paper or strips must have accurate color perception. pH meters can also be affected by oils or other contaminants.

To measure the corrosivity of a solid, the responder may place it in water and measure the pH of the water. Since measuring pH usually requires coming near or touching the material being sampled, responders must exercise extreme caution until they have determined the degree of hazard.

(h) Radiation detection instruments

Figure 4.10 *This monitoring device records oxygen levels and combustible gas levels simultaneously. (Courtesy Mine Safety Appliance Co.)*

It is important that the proper radiation detection equipment be available to determine the type of radiation hazard present. The more common instruments measure only gamma rays and will detect, but not measure, other types of radiation, such as beta radiation.

(i) Reagents
(j) Test strips

4-2.1.3.5* Given three hazardous materials, one of which is a solid, one a liquid, and one a gas, and the following monitoring equipment, test strips, and reagents, select the appropriate equipment and demonstrate the proper techniques to identify and quantify the materials:

(a) Carbon monoxide meter
(b) Colorimetric tubes
(c) Combustible gas indicator
(d) Oxygen meter
(e) pH indicators and/or pH meters
(f) Radiation detection instruments
(g) Reagents
(h) Test strips

The purpose of this competency is to have responders at this level demonstrate their ability to select the proper instrument and demonstrate its use.

A-4-2.1.3.5 For example, the techniques for the use of the monitoring equipment should include monitoring for lighter than air gases in a confined area, heavier than air gases and vapors in a confined area, and heavier than air gases and vapors in an unconfined area.

4-2.1.3.6 Demonstrate the field maintenance and testing procedures for the monitoring equipment, test strips, and reagents provided by the authority having jurisdiction.

Responders who operate monitoring equipment must know how to field-calibrate it in order to get accurate readings and must be able to perform minor field maintenance, such as replacing the sensing device in a combustible gas indicator.

4-2.1.4 Given a label for a radioactive material, identify vertical bars, contents, activity, and transport index, then describe the labeled item and its significance in surveying a radioactive materials incident.

The radioactive label provides responders with information about the level of radiation hazard a material presents. Radioactive White I, with a single vertical bar, is the lowest level hazard. Radioactive Yellow II, with two vertical bars, is the next highest level, and Radioactive Yellow III, with three vertical bars, is the highest level of hazard. These levels are based on the radiation activity of the material. The radiation level must be written on the label. On vehicles, as shown in Figure 4.11, these labels may not be easily accessible so recognition of the special shape of the transport vehicle is vital.

4-2.2 Collecting and Interpreting Hazard and Response Information.

Given access to printed resources, technical resources, computer data bases, and monitoring equipment, the hazardous materials technician shall collect and interpret hazard and response information not available from the current edition of the *North American Emergency Response Guidebook* or a material safety data sheet (MSDS). The hazardous materials technician shall be able to:

At the operational level, the responder must be able to collect hazard and response information from sources that, in general, are readily available, such as the *North American Emergency Response Guidebook*[6] or MSDSs. At this level, however, the technician responder must be able to collect and interpret information from a number of sources.

Technician level responders must understand the importance of using multiple resources for gathering hazard and response information. They should collect information from a variety of resources, compare that information, then make their decisions based on this

Figure 4.11 Radioactive materials that are used in medicine, in scientific research, and in power plants or military facilities are transported in a distinctively shaped cask trailer as shown here. In most cases, the shipper will have a private hazardous materials control team, either on staff or under contract, who will be able to assist responders at an accident or incident involving these materials.

comparison. Responders will generally give more weight to the more conservative information and base their actions on that information. It is important for them to remember that there will be different information, and some of it may conflict.

4-2.2.1* Identify and interpret the types of hazard and response information available from each of the following resources and explain the advantages and disadvantages of each resource:

A-4-2.2.1 For example, the significance of high concentrations of three airborne hazardous materials readings at scenarios relative to the hazards and harmful effects of the hazardous materials on the responders and the general public should be known.

(a) Hazardous materials data bases

A number of databases are available. CAMEO 3.0 (Computer-Aided Management of Emergency Operations) is probably the most widely used. It is available in both DOS and Macintosh applications. Other public-domain databases are also available to the responder, including OHM/TADS (Oil and Hazardous Materials Technical Assistance Database), RTECS (Registry of Toxic Effects of Chemical Substances), and CHRIS (Chemical Hazard Response Information System). Each database presents information a little differently and concentrates on different areas. Technician level responders should understand the differences among them and use those that are the most appropriate for handling a specific incident.

(b) Maps and diagrams
(c) Monitoring equipment

Monitoring equipment again provides a source of information regarding the hazards that are present. The responder should not rely on a single means of monitoring at any incident because the equipment could be affected by unknown materials and give a false reading. Technician level responders should have a sound understanding of the instruments they are using and recognize the value of not relying on a single source for determining the level of hazard present.

(d) Reference manuals

As with hazardous materials databases, there are a number of reference manuals available, such as *The Condensed Chemical Dictionary*,[7] the *Guide to Hazardous Chemical Reactions* (NFPA 491),[8] and *Dangerous Properties of Industrial Materials*[9] by Irving Sax, to name just a few. Each manual tends to emphasize information a little differently. For example, some will present quite a bit of information about medical hazards but very little about handling emergency incidents. The responder must understand this and recognize the value of gathering information from more than one source and comparing that information for a broader picture of the potential hazards.

(e) Technical information centers (i.e., CHEMTREC/CANUTEC/SETIQ)

Technical information centers such as CHEMTREC can provide the responder with valuable information during hazardous materials incidents, and it is important that responders know what assistance is available from these sources.

Using its database, CHEMTREC can provide initial response information on more than one million product-specific MSDSs. CHEMTREC can put the responder at the scene in contact with the shipper and can help the responder identify the materials involved in an incident using waybill numbers and other sources. In addition to contacting shippers, CHEMTREC can help the responder contact manufacturers and other technical specialists. If needed, CHEMTREC also can activate its emergency response mutual aid network, composed of more than 250 emergency response teams from chemical companies and private contractors that can respond to the scene of an incident and help those on site.

(f) Technical information specialists

Technical specialists can be a valuable asset to the responder, who may want to keep a directory of individuals who are able to provide technical assistance. However, the responder must remember that no individual is likely to have all the answers. For example, there are chemists who specialize in formulating perfumes and chemists who specialize in formulating explosives. Depending on the type of incident the responder is involved in, the assistance of one would be more appropriate than the assistance of the other.

Developing a network of people with technical knowledge is one of the most important things a responder can do. Because incidents differ, responders cannot rely on finding books or data bases that address all the possibilities.

See the Tentative Interim Amendment pp. 296–297 for revised paragraph 4-2.2.2.

4-2.2.2 Describe the following terms and explain their significance in the risk assessment process:

(a) Acid, caustic

Acids or caustics may cause the pressure within a container to rise, particularly if they become contaminated.

(b) Air reactivity

Materials that are potentially air-reactive can ignite if they are exposed to air, and the potential for container failure due to overpressurization exists.

(c) Boiling point

Boiling point is the temperature at which the transition from liquid to gaseous occurs. At this temperature, the vapor pressure of a liquid equals the surrounding atmospheric pressure so that the liquid rapidly becomes a vapor. Flammable materials with low boiling points generally present greater problems than those with high boiling points. For example, the boiling point of acetone is 133°F (56°C), and the boiling points for jet fuels range from 400°F to 550°F (204°C to 288°C).

(d) Catalyst

Catalysts are used to control the rate of a chemical reaction by either speeding it up or slowing it down. If used improperly, catalysts can speed up a reaction and cause failure of a container that cannot withstand either the pressure or the heat build-up.

(e) Chemical interactions

The chemical interaction of materials in a container may result in a build-up of heat that, in turn, causes an increase in pressure. The combined materials may be more corrosive than the material the container was originally designed to withstand, and the container may fail.

(f) Chemical reactivity

Chemical reactivity describes a substance's propensity to release energy or undergo change. Some materials are self-reactive or can polymerize. Others undergo violent reactions if they come in contact with other materials. Substances that are air-reactive will ignite or release energy when exposed to air.

Organic peroxides are examples of highly reactive materials. Other examples are corrosives, radioactive materials, oxidizing materials, pyrophoric substances, explosives, and water-reactive materials.

(g) Compound, mixture

Compounds have a tendency to break down into their component parts, sometimes in an explosive manner. If the compound nitroglycerine has been contaminated, for example, it can decompose explosively when heated or shocked.

(h) Concentration

When dealing with corrosives, the amount of acid or base is compared to the amount of water present. Concentrated acids are not the same as strong acids. It is possible to have a high concentration of a weak acid and a low concentration of a strong acid.

(i) Corrosivity (pH)

Corrosivity is measured by pH, which indicates the concentration of hydrogen ions in the material being tested. Title 40, *Code of Federal Regulations,* Part 261.22 defines a corrosive material as one with a pH of 2 or less, or of 12.5 or more.[10] Those with a pH of 2 or less are acidic, and those with a pH at or over 12.5 are bases.

(j) Critical temperatures and pressure

Critical temperature and pressure relate to the process of liquefying gases. The critical temperature is the minimum temperature at which a gas can be liquefied no matter how much pressure is applied. The critical pressure is the pressure that must be applied to bring a gas to its liquid state.

A gas cannot be liquefied above its critical temperature. The lower the critical temperature, the less pressure is required to bring a gas to its liquid state. If a liquefied gas container exceeds its critical temperature, the liquid will convert instantaneously to gas, which may cause the container to fail violently.

(k) Expansion ratio

The expansion ratio is the amount of gas produced by a given volume of liquid at a given temperature. For instance, liquid propane has an expansion ratio of liquid to gas of 270 to 1, while liquefied natural gas has an expansion ratio of 635 to 1. Obviously, the greater the expansion ratio, the more gas is produced, and the larger the endangered area becomes.

(l) Flammable (explosive) range (LEL & UEL)

There are several important things to remember about the flammable range of a material. One is the lower limit, and another is the width of the range. For example, gasoline has a lower flammable limit (LFL) of 1.4 percent and an upper flammable limit (UFL) of 7.6 percent. Carbon monoxide, on the other hand, has an LFL of 12.5 percent and a UFL of 74 percent.

(m) Fire point
(n) Flash point

It is important to take flash point into account when determining the level of hazard of flammable liquids. Aviation-grade gasoline (100-130 octane) has a flash point of −50°F (−45.5°C), and kerosene has a flash point of 100°F (37.8°C). A kerosene spill that occurs when the temperature is 25°F (−3.8°C) will present less danger than a spill that occurs when the temperature is 110°F (43°C). Gasoline would present a serious hazard even at 25°F (−3.8°C).

(o) Halogenated hydrocarbon

A hydrocarbon with halon atoms attached is a halogenated hydrocarbon. Halogenated hydrocarbons are used to produce such things as flammable liquids, combustible liquids, and liquids used as extinguishing agents. They are often more toxic than naturally occurring organic chemicals, and they all decompose into smaller, more harmful elements when exposed to high temperatures for long periods of time.

(p) Ignition (autoignition) temperature

The ignition temperature is the minimum temperature to which a material must be raised before it will ignite; it is also the temperature the ignition source must be. Carbon disulfide has an ignition temperature of 194°F (90°C), while ammonia has an ignition temperature of 1,204°F (651°C). Products with lower ignition temperatures are in greater danger of igniting than those with higher ignition temperatures.

(q) Inhibitor

Inhibitors are added to products to control their chemical reaction with other products. For example, an inhibitor is added to monomers, such as ethylene, when they are being shipped to keep them from polymerizing. If the inhibitor is not added or escapes during an incident, the material will begin to polymerize, which creates a very dangerous situation. The final result may be a violent rupture of the container.

(r) Instability

Materials that decompose spontaneously, polymerize, or otherwise self-react are generally considered unstable. They do not need to mix with other chemicals to react. Organic peroxides, for example, exhibit this characteristic. At low temperatures, they can be fairly stable, but they begin to decompose rapidly when exposed to higher temperatures, and once this reaction has begun, it cannot be stopped. The term *instability* is often used interchangeably with the term *reactivity*.

(s) Ionic & covalent compounds
(t) Maximum safe storage temperature (MSST)
(u) Melting point/freezing point

The melting point is the temperature at which a solid becomes a liquid. Materials with low melting points present problems because they easily become liquid and spread more readily. The reverse is also true, however. If the temperature of a liquid can be lowered, the responder may be able to convert it to a solid.

(v) Miscibility

The term *miscible* refers to the tendency or ability of two or more liquids to form a uniform blend, or to dissolve in each other. Liquids may be totally miscible, partially miscible, or not at all miscible.

(w) Organic and inorganic

Organic materials are derived from materials that are living or were once living, such as plants or decayed products, and they contain chains of two or more carbon atoms. An example of an organic material is methane (CH_4). Inorganic materials lack carbon chains, but they may contain a carbon atom. An example of an inorganic material that contains a carbon atom is carbon dioxide (CO_2).

Knowing whether a material is organic or inorganic can be helpful in choosing the proper instrumentation. Some organic materials are reactive with oxidizers. In addition, inorganic acids are generally stronger than organic acids at the same concentration. Organic acids are generally flammable, however; as a rule, they are also the toxic and explosive acids.

(x) Oxidation potential

Combining anything with oxygen is called *oxidation*. The rusting of steel is slow oxidation, while the burning of wood is rapid oxidation. The ability of a substance to oxidize is a measure of its propensity to yield oxygen. Oxygen is easily released, especially when heated, and it will accelerate the burning of combustible materials. The more readily a material gives up its oxygen molecule, the greater the hazard it presents. This is the case with oxidizing agents.

(y) pH

The pH of a substance is a numerical measure of its relative acidity or alkalinity. pH is an accurate determinant of a solution's hydrogen ion concentration.

The level of pH determines the type of container in which a material may be stored or transported. With a low pH of 2 or less, or a high pH of 12.5 or more, special containers are needed. Containers that do not meet the requirements will fail and release the product.

(z) Physical state (solid, liquid, gas)

The physical state a hazardous material takes plays a significant role in determining not only the measures that will be used to control a spill but often the hazards that it presents. A solid is much easier to contain than a liquid, and liquids that have to be diked or dammed while in a gaseous state generally cannot be contained.

(aa) Polymerization

Polymerization is a chemical reaction in which small molecules combine to form larger molecules. A hazardous polymerization takes place at a rate that releases large amounts of energy, which can cause a fire or explosion or burst a container. Materials that polymerize usually contain inhibitors that delay the reaction. *[See 4-2.2.2(q).]*

(bb) Radioactivity

The level and type of radioactivity determines the type of packaging a radioactive material needs. The greater the radioactivity, the greater the packaging requirements.

(cc) Saturated, unsaturated, and aromatic hydrocarbons

Saturated hydrocarbons *(alkanes)* are those in which the carbon atoms are linked by only single covalent bonds. In saturated hydrocarbons, all the carbon atoms are saturated with hydrogen. Examples include methane (CH_4) and ethane (C_2H_6). Unsaturated hydrocarbons *(alkenes* and *alkynes)* have at least one multiple bond between two carbon atoms somewhere in the molecule. Examples are ethylene (C_2H_4) and acetylene (C_2H_2).

Generally speaking, unsaturated hydrocarbons are more active chemically than saturated hydrocarbons. As a result, they are considered more hazardous.

Aromatic hydrocarbons contain the benzene "ring," which is formed by six carbon atoms and contains double bonds. Examples are benzene (C_6H_6) and toluene (C_7H_8).

(dd) Self-accelerating decomposition temperature (SADT)

(ee) Solution, slurry

A solution is a mixture in which all of the ingredients are completely dissolved. It is a homogeneous mixture of the molecules, atoms, or ions of two or more different substances.

A slurry is a pourable mixture of a solid and a liquid.

(ff) Specific gravity

Specific gravity is the weight of a solid or liquid compared to an equal volume of water. If a material has a specific gravity greater than 1.0 and it does not dissolve in water, it will sink. If its specific gravity is less than 1.0, it will float on water. This becomes important when conducting some types of damming or booming operations and when dealing with flammable liquids, which generally have specific gravities less than 1.0 and will be spread around when water is applied.

(gg) Strength

Strength is a term used to describe the concentration of a solution. In corrosives, it refers to the degree of ionization of the acid or base in water. Hydrochloric acid is a strong acid, for example, and acetic acid is a weak acid.

(hh) Sublimation

In sublimation, a substance passes directly from the solid state to the vapor state without passing through the liquid state. Solids such as naphthalene, used in mothballs, are an example. An increase in temperature increases the rate of sublimation. During an incident, a responder should assess the toxicity and flammability of the vapors of any spilled material that sublimes.

The opposite of sublimation is deposition.

(ii) Temperature of product

The temperature of a product will influence the measures taken to control an incident that involves that product. A product's temperature may also present hazards. An incident involving molten sulfur, for example, raises a different set of concerns than one involving a cryogenic material such as liquefied natural gas.

(jj) Toxic products of combustion

All products of combustion, from cigarette smoke to the smoke from a fire involving pesticides, have some toxic effects. Some materials generate more highly toxic products of combustion than others, and appropriate levels of protective clothing and equipment must be used to counter them.

(kk) Vapor density

Vapor density is the relative density of a vapor compared to air. The vapor density of air is 1.0. If a material has a vapor density higher than 1.0, it is heavier than air and will settle. Toluene, for example, has a vapor density of 3.14, and it will settle and pool in low-lying areas. If a vapor's density is less than 1.0, it is lighter than air and will rise and tend to dissipate.

(ll) Vapor pressure

Vapor pressure is the pressure exerted on the inside of a closed container by the vapor in the space above the liquid in the container. Products with high vapor pressures have a greater potential to breach their containers when heated, since the pressure increases as the temperature rises. Products with high vapor pressures are more volatile.

Vapor pressure is measured in mm of mercury. The vapor pressure of water is 21 mm mercury, and that of chlorine is 4,800 mm mercury.

(mm) Viscosity

Viscosity, a measure of the thickness of a liquid, determines how easily it flows. Liquids with high viscosity, such as heavy oils, must be heated to increase their fluidity. Liquids that are more viscous tend to flow more slowly, while those that are less viscous will spread more easily. During an incident, liquids that are less viscous are likely to flow away from a leaking container, expanding the endangered area.

(nn) Volatility

Volatility describes the ease with which a liquid or solid can pass into the vapor state. The higher a material's volatility, the greater its rate of evaporation. Vapor pressure is a measure of a liquid's propensity to evaporate. Thus, the higher a liquid's vapor pressure, the more volatile it is. During an incident, a volatile material will disperse in air and expand the endangered area.

(oo) Water reactivity

Water reactivity describes the sensitivity of a material to water without the addition of heat or confinement. The more sensitive materials release heat or flammable or toxic gases. Some materials even react explosively when they are exposed to water. Examples of water-reactive substances are sulfuric acid and sodium and aluminum chloride.

(pp) Water solubility

The ability of a substance to form a solution with water can be important when determining control methods. For example, gasoline is insoluble, while anhydrous ammonia is soluble.

4-2.2.3 Describe the heat transfer processes that occur as a result of a cryogenic liquid spill.

Because cryogenic liquids are kept at temperatures below –150°F (–100°C), cryogenic liquid spills will vaporize rapidly when exposed to the higher ambient temperatures of the atmosphere outside the tank. Expansion ratios for common cryogenics range from 560 to 1,445 to 1.

4-2.2.4* Given five hazardous material scenarios and the appropriate reference materials, identify the signs and symptoms of exposure to each material and the target organ effects of exposure to that material.

The responder at this level should be able to use various references to determine what effect various chemicals have on target organs. For example, *Emergency Care for Hazardous Materials Exposures*[11] is a good source for signs and symptoms and notes the chemicals that may have caused the effects.

A-4-2.2.4 The selection of scenarios to test the knowledge and ability to identify exposure symptoms should consider the following:

(a) Select materials common to the jurisdiction. This selection can be based on historical local records or any of the lists of materials that are commonly spilled throughout the country (i.e., chlorine, anhydrous ammonia, mineral acids, bases, aliphatic and aromatic solvents).

(b) Select concentrations and formulation of the materials common to the jurisdiction. It is especially important with pesticides to select realistic scenarios since the state of matter, behavior, and exposure routes can vary considerably from technical-grade materials to common-use formulations.

(c) Select weather conditions and release conditions appropriate to the jurisdiction since the behavior and the exposure hazards can vary considerably from summer conditions in the deep south to winter conditions in the north.

This is a new appendix item designed to help guide the exam creator in preparing a scenario to test this competency.

4-2.2.5 Given the scenario of a domestic gas line break and the readings from a combustible gas indicator, determine the area of evacuation.

4-2.2.6 Identify two methods for determining the pressure in bulk packaging or facility containers.

4-2.2.7 Identify one method for determining the amount of lading remaining in damaged bulk packaging or facility containers.

4-2.3* Describing the Condition of the Container Involved in the Incident.

Given simulated facility and transportation container damage, the hazardous materials technician shall describe the damage. The hazardous materials technician shall be able to:

A-4-2.3 The condition of the container should be described using one of the following terms:

(a) Undamaged, no product release
(b) Damaged, no product release
(c) Damaged, product release
(d) Undamaged, product release

These terms allow the responder to use standard terminology when assessing containers to determine how badly they have been damaged.

4-2.3.1* Given three examples of containers, DOT specification markings for nonbulk and bulk packaging, and the appropriate reference guide, identify the basic design and construction features of each container.

A-4-2.3.1 See Appendix D for the appropriate reference guides.

4-2.3.1.1 Identify the basic design and construction features, including closures, of the following bulk containers:

(a) Cargo tanks:

1. Dry bulk cargo tanks
2. MC-306/DOT-406 cargo tanks
3. MC-307/ DOT-407 cargo tanks
4. MC-312/DOT-412 cargo tanks
5. MC-331 cargo tanks
6. MC-338 cargo tanks

Cargo tank specifications are found in Title 49, *Code of Federal Regulations*, Part 178.[12] The U.S. Department of Transportation has established five classifications for cargo tanks: MC-306 (DOT-406), MC-307 (DOT-407), MC-312 (DOT-412), MC-331, and MC-338. The classifications in parentheses became effective October 1, 1993. There were some changes to the specifications, but both classifications of cargo tanks have the same general appearance.

For illustrations of these various car types, see Chapter 3 of NFPA 472 in this handbook.

(b) Fixed facility tanks:

1. Nonpressure tank
2. Pressure tank

According to Anthony M. Ordile, writing in the *Fire Protection Handbook*:

> The thickness of the metal used in tank construction is based not only on the strength required to hold the weight of the liquid, but also on an added allowance for corrosion. When intended for storing corrosive liquids, the specifications for the thickness of the tank shell are increased to provide additional metal and allow for the expected service life of the tank. In some cases, special tank linings are used to reduce corrosion. . . .
>
> All aboveground storage tanks should be built of steel or concrete, unless the character of the liquid necessitates the use of other materials. Both steel and concrete tanks resist heat from exposure fires.
>
> The required nominal thickness of shell plates must be the greater of the design shell thickness, including any corrosion allowance, or the hydrostatic test shell thickness, but in no case less than the values given in Table 4.1. . . .
>
> Concrete ranks require special engineering. Unlined concrete tanks should be used only for the storage of liquids with a specific gravity of 40 degrees API or heavier.[13]

For additional information see NFPA 30, *Flammable and Combustible Liquids Code*,[14] which provides specifications for fixed containers designed to store flammable and combustible liquids.

(c) Intermodal tanks:

1. Nonpressure intermodal tanks:

   a. IM-101 portable tank
   b. IM-102 portable tank

2. Pressure intermodal tanks (specification 51)
3. Specialized intermodal tanks:

   a. Cryogenic intermodal tanks
   b. Tube modules

In the *Fire Protection Handbook*, Charles Wright and Roger Fitch note that:

> Tank containers consist of a single, metal tank mounted inside a sturdy, metal supporting frame. This unique frame structure, built to international standards, makes tank containers multimodal (intermodal).
>
> The tank container tank is generally built as a cylinder enclosed at the ends by heads. Other

Table 4.1 Shell Plate Thicknesses

Nominal Tank Diameter in Ft (m)	Nominal Thickness in In. (mm)
Smaller than 50 ft (15.2 m)	3/16 in. (4.8 mm)
50 ft to, but not including, 120 ft (15.2 m–36.4 m)	1/4 in. (6.6 mm)
120 ft to 200 ft, inclusive (36.4 m–60.8 m)	5/16 in. (8 mm)
Over 200 ft (60.8 m)	3/8 in. (9.5 mm)

Source: *Fire Protection Handbook*, 18th edition.[15]

tank shapes . . . and configurations . . . exist but they are rare.

Ninety percent or more of the tanks are built of stainless steel, and the rest are constructed of mild steel. Aluminum and magnesium alloy tanks are available, but they cannot be used in water transport mode.

Minimum head and shell thickness are measured in terms of "equivalent thickness in mild steel" after forming. For regulated materials, the minimum thickness is 3/8 in. (9.5 mm). For stainless steel tanks, the minimum thickness for nonregulated materials is slightly less than 1/8 in. (3.2 mm). For regulated commodities, the minimum thickness is just under 3/16 in. (4.8 mm).

Most tanks are built according to the pressure-vessel standards of the American Society of Mechanical Engineers (ASME), and the welds are x-rayed.[16]

See the 18th edition of NFPA's *Fire Protection Handbook* for more information on tank containers.

(d) One-ton containers
(e) Pipelines

Pipelines are constructed according to standards established by the American Society of Mechanical Engineers (ASME).

(f) Railroad cars:

1. Cryogenic liquid tank cars
2. High-pressure tube cars
3. Nonpressure tank cars
4. Pneumatically unloaded hopper cars
5. Pressure tank cars

Roger Fitch and Charles Wright also note in the *Fire Protection Handbook*:

> Typically, tank cars are enclosed longitudinal cylinders (with or without compartments) with rounded ends called heads. Tank cars may or may not have underframes. If not, the tank must bear the stresses of train movement. Tank cars typically have railroad running gear and safety appliances. . . .
>
> Carbon steel is used in over 90 percent of tank car tanks, with aluminum making up most of the remainder. Stainless steel, referred to in the regulations as alloy steel, is used in a smaller number of cars. Nickel or nickel alloy is used for some tanks in acid or food services. Regulations specify the plate thickness of materials used to construct tank car tanks. *(See Table 4.2.)*[17]

For additional information about tank car construction, see the 18th edition of NFPA's *Fire Protection Handbook.*

(g) Intermediate bulk containers (also known as tote tanks)

4-2.3.1.2 Identify the basic design and construction features including closures of the following nonbulk containers:

(a) Carboys
(b) Drums
(c) Pressurized cylinders

4-2.3.1.3 Identify the basic design and construction features of the following radioactive materials containers:

(a) Type A package
(b) Type B package

Table 4.2 Minimum Tank and Jacket Plate Thickness

Minimum Plate Thickness After Forming	Common Use of Plate Thickness
Steel	
11 gauge (approximately 1/8 in.), also aluminum	Jacket of insulated tank cars, or jacket for thermally protected cars
7/16 in.	Tank for nonpressure tank cars, outer tank for nonpressure tank within a tank; or shell portion of outer tank for cryogenic liquid tank cars
1/2 in.	Head puncture resistance (head shield); or head portion of outer tank for cryogenic liquid tank cars
9/16 in.	Tank for steel pressure tank cars with tank test pressures of 200 psi and below
11/16 in.	Tank for steel pressure tank cars with tank test pressure of 300 psi and greater
3/4 in.	Tank for steel pressure tank cars in chlorine service
Aluminum	
1/2 in.	Tank for nonpressure aluminum tank cars
5/8 in.	Tank for aluminum pressure tank cars

Notes:

1. If high-tensile strength steels are used, plate thickness for pressure tank car tanks may be reduced but in no case should that thickness be less than 1/2 in.

2. Plate thickness for nonpressure steel tank cars with expansion domes is a function of where the plate is used in the tank and the diameter of the tank. Thickness ranges from 1/4 to 1/2 in. For tank cars built after 1969, minimum plate thickness is 7/16 in., except for tank cars with a diameter of 112 in. to 122 in. where the thickness is 1/2 in.

3. For SI units: 1 in. = 2.54 cm; 1 psi = 6.9 kPa.

See the Tentative Interim Amendment on p. 295 for new paragraph 4-2.3.1.4.

4-2.3.2 Describe how a liquid pipeline can carry different products.

Many different products can be transported through a single pipeline. This is done by means of a "pig" that isolates a product that may have just been transported from a different product that is to follow.

4-2.3.3 Given an example of a pipeline, identify the following:

(a) Ownership of the line
(b) Procedures for checking for gas migration
(c) Procedure for shutting down the line or controlling the leak
(d) Type of product in the line

The ownership of a line may be indicated with a pipeline marker. The responder can contact the company identified on the marker for information on the type of product in the line and for help in shutting down the line. Technician level responders should also consider acquiring pipeline maps for their area so they can preplan their response needs for pipeline incidents.

4-2.3.4* Identify the types of damage that a pressure container could incur.

A-4-2.3.4 Some of the types of damage that containers can incur include the following:

The types of damage listed below would be most common in tank cars and tank trucks.

(a) *Cracks.* A crack is a narrow split or break in the container metal that can penetrate through the metal of the container.

A cracked pressurized container should be considered to be critically damaged since it is generally difficult to determine the depth of a crack and thus difficult to establish the safest course of action to take. Cracks in the base metal, no matter how small, warrant off-loading the container. If the crack is associated with a dent, the tank car should not be moved until it has been off-loaded.

(b) *Scores.* A score is a reduction in the thickness of the container shell. It is an indentation in the container made by a relatively blunt object. A score is characterized by the relocation of the container or weld metal in such a way that the metal is pushed aside along the track of contact with the blunt object.

Scores that are not accompanied by a dent are not critical. Nor is a score critical if it crosses a welded seam and does not cut into the heat-affected area of the weld. If a score does cut into the heat-affected area of a welded seam, however, the situation is critical and the product should be off-loaded.

(c) *Gouges.* A gouge is a reduction in the thickness of the container. It is an indentation in the shell made by a sharp, chisel-like object. A gouge is characterized by the cutting and complete removal of the container or weld metal along the track of contact.

Gouges are similar to scores, and the same considerations apply.

(d) *Dents.* A dent is a deformation of the container metal. It is caused by impact with a relatively blunt object. With a sharp radius, there is the possibility of cracking.

Large dents are not serious unless gouges are also present. Longitudinal dents along the long axis of a tank are the most serious. Dents with a radius of less than 4 in. (10 cm) that occur in tank cars built before 1966 are critical, and tanks that are so damaged should be off-loaded without being moved. The situation is also critical if the tank car was built in 1966 or later and the radius of the dent is less than 2 in. (5 cm); in such cases, the tank car should be off-loaded without being moved.

4-2.3.5 Given examples of tank car damage, identify the type of damage in each example by name.

4-2.4 Predicting Likely Behavior of Materials and Their Containers When Multiple Materials Are Involved.

Given examples of both facility and transportation incidents involving multiple hazardous materials, the hazardous materials technician shall predict the likely behavior of the material in each case. The hazardous materials technician shall be able to:

This competency requires the hazardous materials technician to be able to predict the behavior of containers and contents when multiple hazardous materials are involved.

4-2.4.1 Identify at least three resources available that indicate the effects of mixing various hazardous materials.

NFPA 491, *Guide to Hazardous Chemical Reactions;*[18] Bretherick's *Handbook of Reactive Chemical Hazards;*[19] and Richard J. Lewis, Jr.'s *Hazardous Chemicals Desk Reference*[20] are examples of references that provide information about the mixture of various chemicals. This is by no means a complete listing of this type of reference.

4-2.4.2 Identify the impact of the following fire and safety features on the behavior of the products during an incident at a bulk storage facility and explain their significance in the risk assessment process:

(a) Fire protection systems

Fire protection systems allow responders to apply fire extinguishing agents sooner and to control an incident in its initial stages, thus reducing the threat to adjoining containers.

(b) Monitoring and detection systems

Monitoring and detection systems permit early notification of potential problems and allow responders to initiate control actions while an incident is still relatively small, thereby limiting the threat to other containers.

(c) Product spillage and control (impoundment and diking)

Dikes and other impoundment features are designed to contain spilled product and minimize the exposure to adjoining tanks. See NFPA 30, *Flammable and Combustible Liquids Code*,[21] for information about diking requirements.

(d) Tank spacing

Adequate tank spacing will minimize the hazard to uninvolved tanks. See NFPA 30, *Flammable and Combustible Liquids Code*,[22] for information about tank spacing requirements.

(e) Tank venting and flaring systems

Tank venting and flaring systems allow a tank to release pressure, thus minimizing the threat of a rupture and an increase in the size of the endangered area. See NFPA 30, *Flammable and Combustible Liquids Code*,[23] for information about venting requirements.

(f) Transfer operations

Transferring product from one tank to another minimizes the danger to surrounding containers.

4-2.5 Estimating the Likely Size of an Endangered Area.

Given various facility and transportation hazardous materials incidents, the hazardous materials technician shall estimate the likely size, shape, and concentrations associated with the release of materials involved in the incident by using computer modeling, monitoring equipment, or specialists in this field. The hazardous materials technician shall be able to:

4-2.5.1 Identify local resources for dispersion pattern prediction and modeling including computers, monitoring equipment, or specialists in the field.

The responder should be able to identify resources that will help predict dispersion patterns. These resources include the weather service; computer models; industrial facilities; colleges or universities; county, state, or federal agencies, such as health departments; environmental protection agencies; and the U.S. Coast Guard, among others. Responders must be able to predict dispersion patterns to determine which areas are likely to become endangered by a spill.

4-2.5.2 Given the concentrations of the released material, identify the steps for determining the extent of the hazards (e.g., physical, safety, and health) within the endangered area of a hazardous materials incident.

Once the responder has determined the concentrations of the materials that have been released, he or she must determine the acceptable exposure limits for those materials. This can be done using resources that list acceptable exposure values. This competency is necessary when dealing with, for example, sulfuric acid, the chemical with the highest quantity production in the United States. Sulfuric acid can come in many different strengths ranging from a mild acid to oleum or fuming sulfuric acid, which is a strong oxidizer.

4-2.5.2.1 Describe the following toxicological terms and exposure values and explain their significance in the risk assessment process:

The reader will notice that the various exposure values described in this section are based on values established by the American Council of Governmental and Industrial Hygienists (ACGIH), the U.S. Occupational Safety and Health Administration (OSHA), and the National Institute of Occupational Safety and Health (NIOSH). Responders should be familiar with all these terms because different references may use different values, and responders must understand the differences and similarities so that they can make the appropriate comparisons.

(a) Parts per million (ppm)
(b) Parts per billion (ppb)

The values used to establish exposure limits are quantified in parts per million or parts per billion. A good reference to remember is that 1 percent equals 10,000 ppm, 1 percent equals 1,000 ppb. So if you obtain a reading from a sampling instrument of 0.5 percent, that is equivalent to 5,000 ppm, or 500 ppb. If you then determine the TLV is 7,500 ppm, you can relate the reading from the instrument to determine the degree of hazard.

(c) Lethal dose (LD_{50})

The LD of a substance is a single dose that will cause the death of 50 percent of a group of test animals exposed to it by any route other than inhalation.

(d) Lethal concentrations (LC_{50})

The LC is the median lethal concentration of a hazardous material. It is defined as the concentration of a material in air that, on the basis of laboratory tests (inhalation route), is expected to kill 50 percent of a group of test animals when administered in a specific time period.

(e) Permissible exposure limit (PEL)

This is a term OSHA uses in its health standards covering exposures to hazardous chemicals. It is similar to the TLV/TWA established by the ACGIH. PEL, which generally relates to legally enforceable TLV limits, is the maximum concentration, averaged over 8 hours, to which 95 percent of healthy adults can be repeatedly exposed for 8 hours per day, 40 hours per week.

(f) Threshold limit value time-weighted average (TLV-TWA)

This is the maximum concentration, averaged over 8 hours, to which a healthy adult can be repeatedly exposed for 8 hours per day, 40 hours per week.

(g) Threshold limit value short-term exposure limit (TLV-STEL)

This is the maximum average concentration, averaged over a 15-minute period, to which healthy adults can be safely exposed for up to 15 minutes continuously. Exposure should not occur more than four times a day with at least 1 hour between exposures.

(h) Threshold limit value ceiling (TLV-C)

This is the maximum concentration to which a healthy adult can be exposed without risk of injury. It is comparable to the IDLH, and exposures to higher concentrations should not occur.

(i) Immediately dangerous to life and health value (IDLH)

This is the maximum level to which a healthy worker can be exposed for 30 minutes and escape without suffering irreversible health effects or impairment. If at all possible, exposure to this level should be avoided. If that is not possible, responders should wear Level A or Level B protection with positive pressure self-contained breathing apparatus or a positive pressure supplied-air respirator with an auxiliary escape system. This limit is established by OSHA and NIOSH.

4-2.5.2.2* Describe the following radiological terms and explain their significance in predicting the extent of health hazards and environmental impact in a hazardous materials incident:

(a) Types
(b) Measurement
(c) Protection

A-4-2.5.2.2

(a) Types:

1. Alpha

Alpha radiation involves the alpha particle, a positively charged particle emitted by some radioactive materials. It is less penetrating than beta and gamma radiation and is not considered dangerous unless ingested. If ingested, alpha radiation will attack internal organs.

2. Beta

Beta radiation involves the beta particle, which is much smaller but more penetrating than the alpha particle. Beta particles can damage skin tissue, and they can damage internal organs if they enter the body. Full protective clothing, including positive pressure self-contained breathing apparatus, will protect against most beta radiation.

3. Gamma

Gamma radiation is especially harmful since it has great penetrating power. Gamma rays are a form of ionizing radiation with high energy that travels at the speed of light. It can cause skin burns and can severely injure internal organs. Protective clothing is inadequate in preventing gamma radiation from harming the body.

(b) Units of measurement:

1. Activity
2. Quantity gamma
3. Absorbed dose

(c) Protection factors:

1. Half-life

Half-life is a measure of the rate of decay of a radioactive material. It indicates the time needed for one half of a given amount of radioactive material to change to another nuclear form or element.

2. Inverse square law
3. Time, distance, and shielding

Time, distance, and shielding are methods of protecting oneself from harmful exposures to radiation. The shorter the time of exposure, the lower the dosage. The farther the distance from the exposure, the lower the amount of radiation; this is calculated as inverse to the square of the distance. Shielding refers to blocking radiation by using varying thicknesses of different materials.

The radiation absorbed dose (rad) and the roentgen equivalent man (rem) were used for many years to measure the amount and effect of ionizing radiation absorbed by humans. While officially replaced by the gray and the sievert, both rad and rem are still used. The rad equals the energy absorption of 100 ergs per gram of irradiated material (an erg is a unit of work or energy). The rem is the absorbed dose of ionizing radiation that produces the same biological effect as 1 rad of X rays or gamma rays (which are equal). The rem of X rays and gamma rays is therefore equal to the rad; for each type of radiation the number of rads is multiplied by a specific factor to find the number of rems. The millirem, 0.001 rems, is also frequently used; the average radiation dose received by a person in the United States is about 180 millirems per year.

In the SI system (Systeme International d' Unite's, or International System of Units), the gray and the sievert are used to measure radiation absorbed; these units have largely superseded the older rad and rem. The gray (Gy), equal to 100 rads, is now the base unit. It is also expressed as the energy absorption of 1 joule per kilogram of irradiated material. The sievert (Sv) is the absorbed dose of radiation that produces the same biological effect as 1 gray of X rays or gamma rays. The sievert is equal to 100 rems, and has superseded the rem. The becquerel (Bq) measures the radioactive strength of a source, but does not consider effects on tissue. One becquerel is defined as one disintegration (or other nuclear transformation) per second.

Curie

A curie is the standard unit of radioactivity, being the quantity of a radioactive isotope that decays at a rate of 3.7×10^{10} disintegrations per second.

Roentgen

A roentgen is the international unit of the intensity of X rays or gamma rays. It is the quantity of radiation that would produce, in air, ions carrying a positive or negative charge equal to one electrostatic unit in 0.001293 grams of air.

4-2.5.2.3 Identify two methods for predicting the areas of potential harm within the endangered area of a hazardous materials incident.

4-2.5.3* Identify a method for estimating the outcomes within an endangered area of a hazardous materials incident.

An estimate is a series of predictions that attempts to provide an overall picture of potential outcomes. Responders must assess the information gathered during analysis and predict the outcome based on that assessment.

According to the National Fire Academy's (NFA) *Initial Response to Hazardous Materials Incidents, Course II: Concept and Implementation,* it is necessary to break an incident into three components: the product, the container, and the environment. Each of these can then be broken into three subgroups: damage, hazard, and vulnerability risk. In addition, incidents may have three elements that may occur separately or in conjunction with one another: a spill, a leak, or a fire. The estimate identifies the relationships between the three components of an incident and the three elements of an incident.

The NFA course states,

> An estimate is made by analyzing the physical, cognitive, and technical information that has been gathered. Then, by breaking the incident into the components dealing with product, container, environment and their respective subgroups, a conclusion can be drawn . . . [a] conclusion with some measure of quantifiable accuracy that suggests what the full impact(s) of the relationships will be.[24]

It is important to understand that this analysis continues throughout an incident. As new information is gathered, old estimates should be verified or new estimates made. Predictions, which should be based on worst-case scenarios, will allow the responder to develop an overall estimate of the incident's potential outcomes.

Incident commanders should keep in mind that the safety of both emergency personnel and the public is their primary objective. There may very well be times when the most prudent action is no action and the establishment of an appropriate evacuation area is the best possible course to take.

A-4-2.5.3 See A-3-2.4.

4-3 Competencies — Planning the Response

4-3.1 Identifying Response Objectives.

Given simulated facility and transportation problems, the hazardous materials technician shall describe the response objectives for each problem. The hazardous materials technician shall be able to describe the steps for determining response objectives (defensive, offensive, nonintervention) given an analysis of a hazardous materials incident.

In 3-3.1, the operational level responder is required to determine the appropriate response objectives for responders at that level. The options available at that level are either defensive or nonintervention. The response objectives for the hazardous materials technician (HMT) are expanded to include offensive operations.

In the *Fire Protection Handbook,* Charles Wright notes that:

> The first task in planning the response is to determine the response objectives (strategy) based on the estimated outcomes. The response objectives, based on the stage of incident, are the strategic goals for stopping the event now occurring or keeping future events from occurring. Two basic principles apply to these decisions.
>
> 1. One cannot influence events that have already happened or change the outcomes of those events; and
> 2. The earlier that the event sequence can be interrupted, the more acceptable the loss.
>
> The following steps should be taken when determining response objectives.
>
> 1. Estimate the exposures that could be saved. The level of response and the acceptable risk associated with a response is based on the exposures that can be saved. The number of exposures that could be saved is based on the estimated outcomes minus the exposures already lost.
>
> 2. Determine the response objectives. The response objectives, based on the stage of the incident, are the strategic goals for stopping the event now occurring or keeping future events from occurring. Decisions should focus on changing the actions of the stressors, the containment system, and the hazardous material. *(See Figure 4.12.)* [25]

4-3.2 Identifying the Potential Action Options.

Given simulated facility and transportation hazardous materials incidents, the hazardous materials technician shall identify the possible action options (defensive, offensive, and nonintervention) by response objective for each problem. The hazardous materials technician shall be able to identify the possible action options to accomplish a given response objective.

Because they can conduct offensive operations, HMTs can take actions that are not available to the responder at the operational level. Figure 4.13 shows options available to the HMT to accomplish response objectives.

The responder should note that many of the options available can be used either offensively or defensively. For example, the size of the endangered area may be changed defensively by placing barriers around the endangered area to contain a spill or offensively by entering the hot zone and plugging the leak. It should also be noted that the HMT may choose defensive operations as the most prudent method of dealing with an incident.

4-3.3 Selecting Personal Protective Equipment.

Given situations with known and unknown hazardous materials, the hazardous materials technician shall determine the appropriate personal protective equipment for the action options specified in the plan of action in each situation. The hazardous materials technician shall be able to:

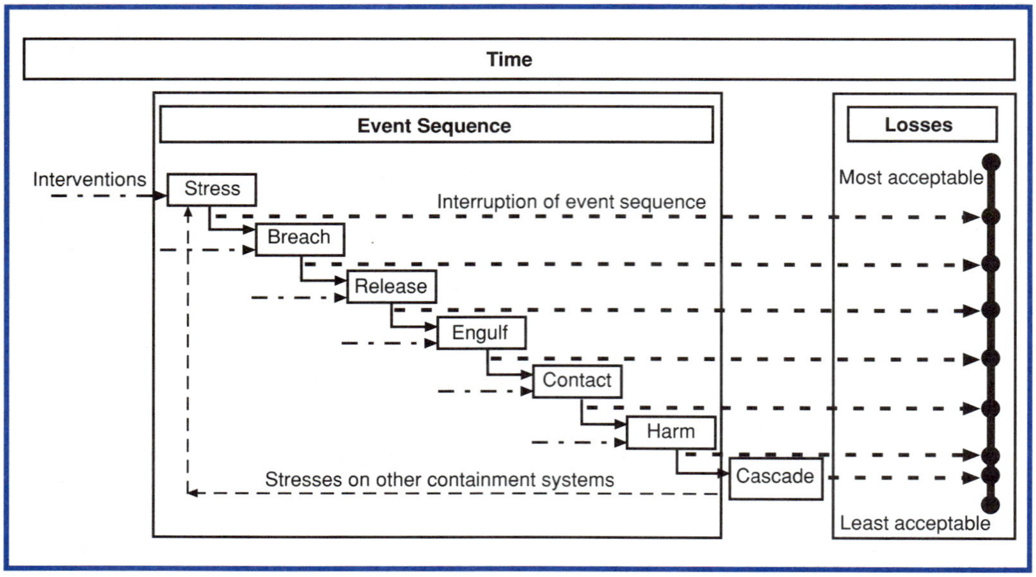

Figure 4.12 *This chart depicts the relationship of the events sequence and the losses. (Source: Fire Protection Handbook, 18th edition)*

Response Objective Analysis Form	Containment System ID
	Material

Event Sequence

Stress	Breach	Release	Engulf	Contact	Harm

Response Objectives

Change Applied Stresses	Change Breach Size	Change Quantity Release	Change Size of Danger Zone	Change Exposures Contacted	Change Severity of Harm

Sample Response Options

Move stressor Move stressed system Shield stressed system	Chill contents Limit stress levels Activate venting devices Mechanical repair	Change container position Minimize pressure differential Cap off breach Remove contents	Barriers Dikes and dams Adsorbents Absorbents Diluents Reactants Overpack	Provide sheltering Begin evacuation Personal protective equipment	Rinse off contaminant Increase distance from source Provide shielding Provide prompt medical attention

Figure 4.13 This response objective analysis worksheet is used for identifying response options in a hazardous materials incident by response objective. (Adapted from Ludwig Benner's A Textbook for Use in the Study of Hazardous Materials Emergencies, 2nd ed., Lufred Industries Inc., Oakton, VA, 1978.)

4-3.3.1 Identify the four levels of personal protective equipment (EPA/NIOSH or NFPA 471) and describe the equipment for each level and the condition under which each level is used.

4-3.3.2 Identify the factors to be considered in selecting the proper respiratory protection for a specified action option.

The type of respiratory protection required depends on many factors. A key factor is the level of protective clothing necessary to protect the HMT. Level A protection limits the user to positive pressure self-contained breathing apparatus or positive pressure supplied-air respirators. The responder should always use the highest level of protection until the levels of concentration have been determined.

4-3.3.2.1 Describe the advantages, limitations, and proper use of the following types of respiratory protection at hazardous materials incidents:

(a) Positive pressure self-contained breathing apparatus

SCBA is the primary type of breathing apparatus used by fire fighters. It does not restrict the wearer's mobility, and it provides the highest level of respiratory protection. The most commonly used units are rated at 30 to 60 minutes of protection. Units are available that provide longer periods of use. Actual time, however, will be substantially less for persons not at their best physical fitness level and under conditions of exhausting work. NFPA 1981, *Standard on Open-Circuit Self-Contained Breathing Apparatus for Fire Fighters,*[26] provides performance criteria for SCBA.

(b) Positive pressure air line respirators with required escape unit

Positive pressure air line respirators, which are lighter than SCBA, allow the user an unlimited supply of air. However, the air line supply unit restricts the user's travel distance to a maximum of 300 ft (92 m), and it must be kept clear of obstructions while the user is negotiating the incident scene. Under certain conditions, though, it is an ideal method of supplying air to the emergency worker.

It should be noted that, in some instances (when working in IDLH atmospheres, for example), the person wearing an air line respirator must have an emergency egress system available.

(c) Air purifying respirators

Air purifying respirators (APR), which use a filter or sorbent to remove airborne contaminants, are designed for use only in atmospheres that contain enough oxygen to sustain life. They should be used only when the hazard and concentration of the hazardous material is known, and the level must be within the limitations of the filter being used. The life of the filtering cartridges depends on the concentrations present, the type of filter material being used, and the breathing volume of the user.

APRs should not be used by initial responders to an emergency involving hazardous materials.

4-3.3.2.2 Identify the process for selecting the proper respiratory protection at hazardous materials incidents.

To determine the appropriate respiratory protection to wear during a specific incident, the responder must establish the name of the chemicals involved in the incident, the concentration of those chemicals, and the hazards they present. The responders must then determine the types of exposure that they would face based on the action chosen.

The minimum level of protection OSHA requires for emergency response is positive pressure self-contained breathing apparatus (SCBA). SCBA should be worn at least until the material has been identified and its concentrations determined.

4-3.3.2.3 Identify the operational components of air purifying respirators and air line respirators by name and describe their functions.

4-3.3.3 Identify the factors to be considered in selecting the proper chemical-protective clothing for a specified action option.

4-3.3.3.1 Describe the following terms and explain their impact and significance on the selection of chemical-protective clothing:

(a) Degradation

Degradation of chemical-protective clothing (CPC) can be either chemical or physical. The result of degradation is an increased likelihood that a hazardous material will permeate and penetrate the garments, thus endangering the health of the responder.

Chemical degradation can be minimized by avoiding unnecessary contact with chemicals and by undergoing effective decontamination procedures. It is important that the garments a responder wears are chosen based on their compatibility with the chemicals involved in an incident and that they have breakthrough times consistent with their expected use.

Protective clothing can also degrade physically, such as might occur when the garment rubs against a rough surface. CPC wearers should recognize the physical limitations of their garments and make every effort to avoid circumstances that may cause the material to be damaged physically.

NFPA 1991, *Standard on Vapor-Protective Suits for Hazardous Chemical Emergencies,*[27] NFPA 1992, *Standard on Liquid Splash-Protective Suits for Hazardous Chemical Emergencies,*[28] and NFPA 1993, *Standard on Support Function Protective Clothing for Hazardous Chemical Operations,*[29] contain criteria for abrasion or tear testing and for manufacturers' certification of CPC. When purchasing CPC, the responder should ascertain whether the garments can be certified to the appropriate NFPA CPC standard.

(b) Penetration

Penetration is the movement of a material through a suit's closures; these include zippers, buttonholes, seams, flaps, and other design features of CPC. Hazardous materials may also penetrate CPC through cracks or tears in the suit's fabric.

Protection against penetration is vital. A regular and routine program of inspection can help uncover conditions that could lead to penetration. CPC must also be properly stored and regularly maintained and tested in order to ensure that it can still provide the proper level of protection. NFPA 1991, 1992, and 1993 provide criteria for testing CPC for penetration resistance and for manufacturer's certification of CPC.

(c) Permeation

Different fabrics have different resistance levels to chemical permeation, and all will absorb chemicals over a period of time. NFPA 1991, 1992, and 1993 provide guidelines for manufacturer permeation testing and certification.

NFPA 1991, *Standard on Vapor-Protective Suits for Hazardous Chemical Emergencies,*[30] requires the manufacturer to provide documentation on a garment's permeation resistance for 3 hours against at least the following chemicals:

(a) Acetone*
(b) Acetonitrile
(c) Anhydrous ammonia
(d) Carbon disulfide
(e) Chlorine
(f) Dichloromethane
(g) Diethyl amine*
(h) Dimethyl formamide
(i) Ethyl acetate
(j) Hexane*
(k) Nitrobenzene
(l) Sodium hydroxide*
(m) Sulfuric acid*
(n) Tetrachloroethylene*
(o) Tetrahydrofuran* Toluene*

NFPA 1992, *Standard on Liquid Splash-Protective Suits for Hazardous Chemical Emergencies,*[31] and NFPA 1993, *Standard on Support Function Protective Clothing for Hazardous Chemical Operations,*[32] require that the manufacturer provide documentation on a garment's permeation resistance for 1 hour, to at least the chemicals noted with an asterisk in the list above.

Before buying CPC, the HMT should make sure that it meets, and has been certified as meeting, the appropriate standard. When choosing CPC for use at an incident, the HMT must be sure that the garment is compatible with the type of material to which it is going to be exposed. In any event, the wearer is advised to use extreme caution. Available data do not cover every situation the responder may encounter.

4-3.3.3.2 Identify at least three indications of material degradation of chemical-protective clothing.

Indications of material degradation are stiffness or excess pliability, tears, cuts or abrasions, and damage to zippers or other closures. This list is not all-inclusive, and users should check manufacturers' recommendations for the inspection of CPC.

4-3.3.3.3* Identify the three types of vapor-protective and splash-protective clothing and describe the advantages and disadvantages of each type.

A-4-3.3.3.3 Refer to the Chemical Manufacturers Association and Association of American Railroads Hazardous Materials Technical Bulletin *Recommended Terms for Personal Protective Equipment,* issued October 1985. Also refer to NFPA 1991, *Standard on Vapor-Protective Suits for Hazardous Chemical Emergencies;* NFPA 1992, *Standard on Liquid Splash-Protective Suits for Hazardous Chemical Emergencies;* and NFPA 1993, *Standard on Support Function Protective Clothing for Hazardous Chemical Operations.*

4-3.3.3.4 Identify the relative advantages and disadvantages of the following heat exchange units used for the cooling of personnel in chemical-protective clothing:

(a) Air cooled
(b) Ice cooled
(c) Water cooled

Wearing CPC can cause wearers to suffer increased heat stress. Thus, it is important for responders to be monitored closely while working in CPC.

Some CPC garments have temperature control features. Some have air-cooling systems that require an air line and large quantities of breathable air. Others incorporate water-cooling systems that require an ice supply or refrigeration units and a pump. This adds additional weight and bulk to the suit. Users should conduct a thorough evaluation of such units to make sure they are appropriate for the intended use.

There are also vests that can hold coolant packs. This requires a supply of the frozen coolant packs or an ice source at the scene. The vests add additional weight to the CPC.

4-3.3.3.5 Identify the process for selecting the proper protective clothing at hazardous materials incidents.

The HMT should determine the appropriate level of protection based on the criteria established by the EPA and OSHA in Table 4-3. The chemical-protective clothing chosen must be compatible with the chemicals to which it will be exposed. The HMT must determine whether the breakthrough times of the chosen garment will allow him or her enough time to enter the contaminated area safely, do the necessary work, leave the area, and undergo decontamination. In some cases, layering materials may provide increased protection. It is important to remember that no single garment will

Table 4.3 EPA/OSHA Protection Levels

Level of Protection	Equipment	Protection Provided	Should Be Used When:	Limiting Criteria
A	RECOMMENDED: Pressure-demand, full-facepiece SCBA or pressure- demand, supplied-air respirator with escape SCBA Fully encapsulating chemical-resistant suit Inner chemical- resistant gloves Chemical-resistant safety boots/shoes Two-way radio communications OPTIONAL: Cooling unit Coveralls Long cotton underwear Hard hat Disposable gloves and boot covers	The highest available level of respiratory, skin, and eye protection	The chemical substance has been identified and requires the highest level of protection for skin, eyes, and the respiratory system based on either: measured (or potential for) high concentration of atmospheric vapors, gases, or particulates or site operations and work functions involving a high potential for splash, immersion, or exposure to unexpected vapors, gases, or particulates of materials that are harmful to skin or capable of being absorbed through the intact skin Substances with a high degree of hazard to the skin are known or suspected to be present, and skin contact is possible Operations must be conducted in confined, poorly ventilated areas until the absence of conditions requiring Level A protection is determined	Fully encapsulating suit material must be compatible with the substances involved.
B	RECOMMENDED: Pressure-demand, full facepiece SCBA or pressure-demand supplied-air respirator with escape SCBA Chemical-resistant clothing (overalls and long-sleeved jacket; hooded, one- or two-piece chemical splash suit; disposable chemical-resistant one-piece suit)	The same level of respiratory protection but less skin protection than Level A. It is the minimum level recommended for initial site entries until the hazards have been further identified.	The type and atmospheric concentration of substances have been identified and require a high level of respiratory protection, but less skin protection. This involves atmospheres: with IDLH concentrations of specific substances that do not represent a severe skin hazard or containing less than 19.5 percent oxygen	Use only when the vapor or gases present are not suspected of containing high concentrations of chemicals that are harmful to skin or capable of being absorbed through the intact skin. Use only when it is highly unlikely that the work being done will generate either high concentrations of vapors, gases, or particulates or splashes of material that will affect exposed skin.

Table 4.3 (Continued)

Level of Protection	Equipment	Protection Provided	Should Be Used When:	Limiting Criteria
	Inner and outer chemical-resistant gloves Chemical-resistant safety boots/shoes Hard hat Two-way radio communications OPTIONAL: Coveralls Disposable boot covers Face shield Long cotton underwear		Presence of incompletely identified vapors or gases is indicated by direct-reading organic vapor detection instrument, but vapors and gases are not suspected of containing high levels of chemicals harmful to skin or capable of being absorbed through the intact skin. Use only when the vapor or gases present are not suspected of containing high concentrations of chemicals that are harmful to skin or capable of being absorbed through the intact skin.	
C	RECOMMENDED: Full facepiece, air purifying, canister-equipped respirator Chemical-resistant clothing (overalls and long-sleeved jacket; hooded, one- or two-piece chemical splash suit; disposable chemical-resistant one-piece suit) Inner and outer chemical-resistant gloves Chemical-resistant safety boots/shoes Hard hat Two-way radio communications OPTIONAL: Coveralls Disposable boot covers Face shield Escape mask Long cotton underwear	The same level of skin protection as Level B, but a lower level of respiratory protection	The atmospheric contaminants, liquid splashes, or other direct contact will not adversely affect any exposed skin. The types of air contaminants have been identified, concentrations measured, and a canister is available that can remove the contaminant. All criteria for the use of air purifying respirators are met.	Atmospheric concentration of chemicals must not exceed IDLH levels.
D	RECOMMENDED: Coveralls Safety boots/shoes Safety glasses or chemical splash goggles Hard hat OPTIONAL: Gloves Escape mask Face shield	No respiratory protection Minimal skin protection	The atmosphere contains no known hazard. Work functions preclude splashes, immersion, or the potential for unexpected inhalation of or contact with hazardous levels of any chemicals	This level should not be worn in the Exclusion Zone. The atmosphere must contain at least 19.5 percent oxygen.

protect a responder against all chemicals. The HMT should know the manufacturers' recommendations or how to find the information regarding the use of its CPC.

4-3.3.3.6 Given three examples of various hazardous materials, determine the appropriate protective clothing construction materials for a given action option using chemical compatibility charts.

4-3.3.3.7 Identify the physical and psychological stresses that can affect users of specialized protective clothing.

Specialized protective clothing, particularly fully encapsulating garments, increases the stress a responder may feel when working at a hazardous materials incident. Persons wearing CPC usually experience a loss of dexterity and mobility; the higher the level of protection, the greater this loss. Their visibility is also restricted, and their communications are affected. In addition, wearing CPC increases the likelihood of heat stress and heat exhaustion. Reductions in dexterity, mobility, visibility, and communication, in turn, create additional physical and mental stresses.

Familiarity with wearing and working in the garment will reduce any mental anxiety associated with garment wear. Thus, frequent drills are essential. It is important that the HMT be aware of these additional stresses and receive adequate rest and rehabilitation before, during, and after suit wear. Drinking fluids such as water before donning CPC will reduce some of the effects of excess heat.

4-3.4 Developing Appropriate Decontamination Procedures.

Given a simulated hazardous materials incident, the hazardous materials technician shall select an appropriate decontamination procedure and determine the equipment required to implement that procedure. The hazardous materials technician shall be able to:

4-3.4.1 Identify the advantages and limitations and describe an example where each of the following decontamination methods would be used:

There are basically two ways to decontaminate something: physically and chemically. Physical methods manually separate the chemical from the material being decontaminated by scrubbing or washing the material, or both. Physical decontamination is often easier than chemical decontamination, but it may not completely remove all the contaminants.

Chemical methods involve adding another chemical that changes the physical or chemical properties of one chemical into another or into a form that will facilitate its removal. Unfortunately, the chemical process involved could introduce other hazards. Care must be taken to collect all the contamination that has been removed by either method and to dispose of it properly.

(a) Absorption

Absorption is the process by which materials hold liquids. Many types of commercial absorbents are available. Sand or soil can also be used for this purpose, although they are more suited for decontaminating equipment or the area surrounding a spill than they are for decontaminating personnel. Absorbents are often readily available, but they must be disposed of properly since the absorbent substance will retain the properties of the material absorbed.

(b) Adsorption

Adsorption is a chemical method of decontamination involving the interaction of a hazardous liquid and a solid sorbent surface. Examples of adsorbents are activated charcoal, silica or aluminum gel, fuller's earth, and other clays. Adsorption produces heat and can cause spontaneous combustion. Adsorbents must also be disposed of properly.

(c) Chemical degradation

Chemical degradation is the natural breakdown of the contaminants as they age. An example of chemical degradation is the evaporation of a flammable liquid spill. The decontamination of an oil spill on a beach because of manual (pressure washer) or natural (wave action) actions is an example of physical degradation. Either of the two methods has limitations depending on such factors as the location of the spill and the toxicity of the material. In some cases, however, they are the most practical methods.

(d) Dilution

Dilution, which simply reduces the concentration of a contaminant, is best used on materials that are soluble or miscible in water, such as chlorine and ammonia. An advantage of dilution is that solutes, especially water, are generally available in large quantities. A disadvantage is that the run-off must be collected and disposed of in a container such as a kiddie pool. *(See Figure 4.14.)*

(e) Disposal

Disposal is the direct removal of a contaminant from a carrier. An example is the removal of a contaminated object from a piece of equipment. This type of decontamination may not entirely remove all contamination.

(f) Evaporation

In some cases, responders may allow a hazardous material simply to evaporate, particularly if the vapors do

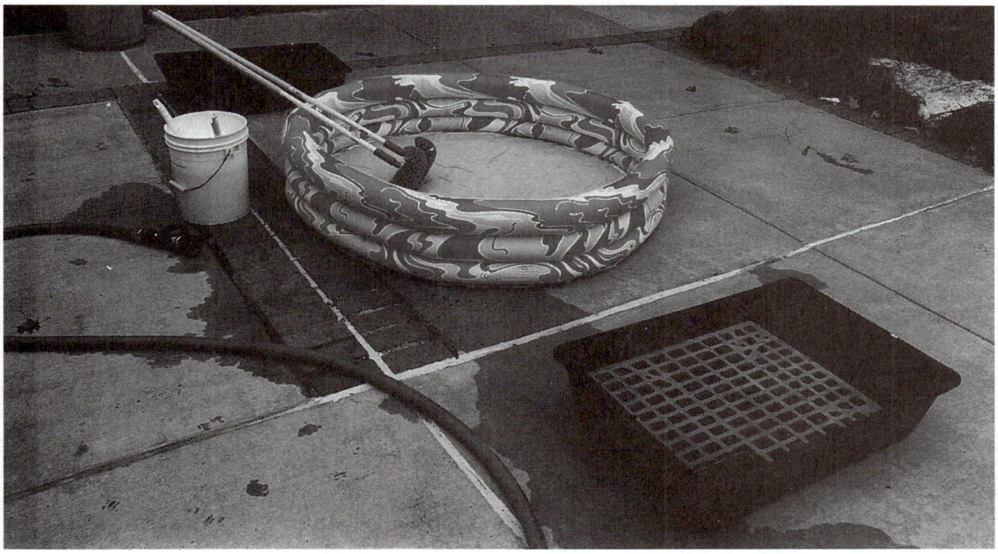

Figure 4.14 A kiddie pool is the most convenient way to prevent decontamination run-off. The pools are inexpensive and can be stored and transported easily.

not present a hazard. This may be the case with a small spill of gasoline, for example, as long as it does not present a vapor problem. Evaporation is an easy operation and requires minimal personnel. It is not as effective on porous surfaces as it is on nonporous surfaces, however, and it could take quite a while, depending on the quantity of the chemical involved.

(g) Neutralization

Neutralizers alter a contaminant chemically so that the resulting chemical is harmless. For example, the addition of soda ash to an acidic solution can increase the pH, making it a chemically harmless substance. Many neutralizing chemicals present hazards of their own, however, and should only be used by HMTs who are fully aware of the consequences. One advantage of neutralizers is that by rendering the remaining material harmless, they reduce the problem of disposal.

(h) Solidification

Commercial products are available that cause certain liquids to solidify. One advantage of solidification is that it allows responders to confine a small spill relatively quickly. As with other decontaminants, however, the resulting solid must be disposed of properly when the incident is over.

(i) Vacuuming

Vacuuming allows for the collection of materials, either liquid or solid, into containers. It is important that the equipment being used is appropriate for the material being vacuumed. If it is corrosive or flammable, for example, specialized equipment is needed.

(j) Washing

A very effective decontamination process for many materials involves washing the contaminated person, building, or equipment. Materials that are not soluble in water, such as oil-based contaminants, can be washed with detergent solutions. Washing equipment, protective clothing, and personnel is one of the easiest ways to decontaminate them. However, it is necessary to collect and properly dispose of any run-off.

4-3.4.2 Identify three sources of technical information for selecting appropriate decontamination procedures and identify how to contact those sources in an emergency.

Among the sources of technical information about decontamination are CHEMTREC, CANUTEC, SETIQ, MSDSs, product manufacturers, the National Response Center, and local or regional poison control centers.

4-3.5 Developing a Plan of Action.

Given simulated hazardous materials incidents in facility and transportation settings, the hazardous materials technician shall develop a plan of action, including safety considerations. The plan shall be consistent with the local emergency response plan and the organization's standard operating procedures and be within the capability of available personnel, personal protective equipment, and control equipment for that incident. The hazardous materials technician shall be able to:

According to Charles Wright, writing in the *Fire Protection Handbook:*

After selecting the response option for a hazardous material incident, a plan of action including safety and health considerations should be developed. This plan of action describes the response objectives and options and the personnel and equipment required to accomplish the objectives. The plan provides a permanent record of the decisions made at the incident. An organization's standard operating procedures provide the basis of this plan of action. Input from all segments of the response community is considered in developing the plan. Based on the specific incident conditions, the standard operating procedures are modified without having to write an entire plan for each incident.

A plan of action also outlines the safety and health procedures to protect responders and the public from the potential hazards at an incident. These procedures should address incident management, communications protocol (both internal and external), control zones for incident security, personal protective equipment use, decontamination procedures, and documentation. They also include designation of a safety sector and a safety officer, emergency medical care procedures, environmental monitoring, emergency procedures, and personnel monitoring.

Components for a typical plan of action would include the following:

1. Site description
2. Entry objectives
3. On-scene organization and coordination
4. On-scene control
5. Hazard evaluation
6. Personal protective equipment
7. On-scene work assignments
8. Communications procedures
9. Decontamination procedures
10. On-scene safety and health considerations including designation of the safety officer, emergency medical care procedures, environmental monitoring, emergency procedures, and personnel monitoring.[33]

4-3.5.1 Describe the purpose of, procedures for, equipment required, and safety precautions used with the following techniques for hazardous materials control:

(a) Adsorption
(b) Neutralization
(c) Overpacking
(d) Patching
(e) Plugging

Figure 4.15 shows the techniques used in plugging and patching.

4-3.5.2 Given MC-306/DOT-406, MC-307/DOT-407, MC-312/DOT-412, MC-331, and MC-338 cargo tanks, identify

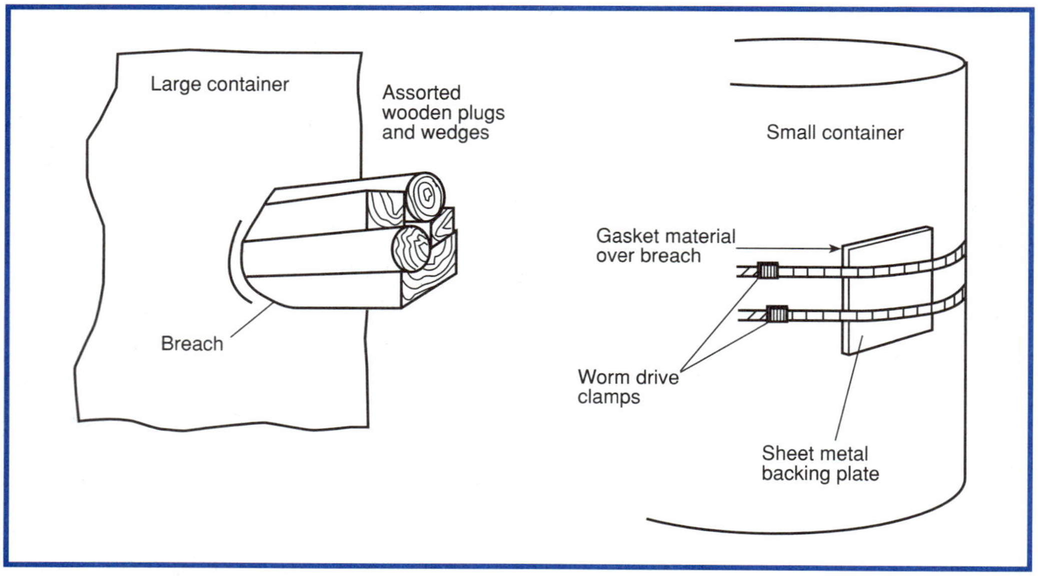

Figure 4.15 *Examples showing the use of plugging and patching materials.*

the common methods for product transfer from each type of cargo tank.

Transfer operations are complex and can be hazardous. The hazardous materials technician should be very cautious when considering this type of operation. Usually transfer operations are conducted by a technician with a tank car specialty, cargo tank specialty, or intermodal tank specialty *(see Chapters 9, 10 and 11)*; cleanup company; or by personnel from the shipper or manufacturer.

As Hildebrand and Noll point out in their text, *Handling Gasoline Tank Truck Emergencies: Guidelines and Procedures*,[34] the most common methods of product transfer for MC-306/DOT-406 cargo tanks are vacuum pumps, vehicles with power take-off (PTO) pumps, or air-driven portable pumps. This is true for most non-pressure cargo tanks.

Transfer operations involving pressure tanks present additional hazards and should be undertaken only by personnel with the necessary technician specialty training and skills.

4-3.5.3 Given a simulated hazardous materials incident, develop the safety considerations that must be included in the plan of action.

According to Title 29, *Code of Federal Regulations*, Part 1910.1200, Appendix C,[35] comprehensive control plans should address the following: analysis of hazards on the site and a risk analysis of those hazards, site map or sketch, site work (control) zones, use of buddy system, site communications, command post, standard operating procedures and safe work practices, medical assistance and triage area, and other relevant topics. This plan should be a part of the employer's emergency response plan or an extension of it to the specific site.

4-3.5.3.1 List and describe the safety considerations to be included.

4-3.5.3.2 Identify the points that should be made in a safety briefing prior to working at the scene.

4-3.5.4* Identify the atmospheric and physical safety hazards associated with hazardous materials incidents involving confined spaces.

The competency in new paragraph 4-3.5.4 became necessary after the promulgation of the OSHA regulations on confined space operations. The HMT should become very familiar with the OSHA regulations. Failure to comply has led to several substantial fines.

A-4-3.5.4 Safety hazards associated with confined spaces could include the following:

(a) Atmospheric hazards, such as the following:

1. Oxygen-deficient atmosphere
2. Oxygen-enriched atmosphere
3. Flammable/explosive atmosphere
4. Toxic atmosphere

(b) Physical hazards, such as the following:

1. Engulfment hazards
2. Falls/slips
3. Electrical hazards
4. Structural hazards
5. Mechanical hazards

4-3.5.5 Identify the pre-entry activities to be performed.

See the Tentative Interim Amendment on p. 295 for new paragraph 4-3.5.6.

4-4 Competencies — Implementing the Planned Response

4-4.1 Performing Incident Management Duties.

Given the local emergency response plan or organization's standard operating procedures and a simulated hazardous materials incident, the hazardous materials technician shall demonstrate the duties of an assigned hazardous materials branch position within the local incident management system (IMS). The hazardous materials technician shall be able to:

The emergency response plan is the link between the community's response plans and the operational personnel who are expected to implement those plans. Emergency response plans incorporate standard operating procedures (SOPs), which may identify the type of response appropriate to a particular type of incident, as well as site-specific procedures. The emergency response plan should also address alerting procedures, response and coordination procedures, personnel, the command structure, communications, and training.

4-4.1.1 Identify the role of the hazardous materials technician during an incident involving hazardous materials.

4-4.1.2 Identify the duties and responsibilities of the following hazardous materials branch functions within the incident management system:

(a) Backup
(b) Decontamination

The decontamination officer is responsible for the operations of the decontamination unit. They will report to the hazard sector/division officer and supervise decontamination operations.

(c) Entry

Entry may be supervised by an entry officer/leader, who supervises entry operations and makes recommendations concerning control activities in the hot zone.

(d) Hazardous Materials Branch Management

Hazardous materials branch manages the activities that apply directly to the primary mission, and the hazardous materials branch officer is responsible for allocating and assigning resources to control the incident. The incident commander, if qualified, may perform this function during small incidents.

(e) Hazardous Materials Branch Safety

The hazardous materials branch safety officer is designated by the incident commander. They must be knowledgeable in the operations being conducted at the emergency response site, with the specific responsibility of identifying and evaluating hazards and providing direction with respect to the safety of operations for the emergency.

(f) Information/research

Personnel assigned to information/research are responsible for developing, documenting, and coordinating the information gathered during an incident. This information will be used in the hazard and risk assessment and should include, but not be limited to, evacuation considerations and protective clothing and equipment selection.

(g) Reconnaissance

Those assigned to reconnaissance should gather information about the layout of the incident scene and any other factors that may have an influence on the incident. They may develop a checklist that includes information about such things as access and egress routes, the weather, utilities, drainage, topography, water supplies, exposures, and the number, type, and condition of containers.

(h) Resources

The resources officer keeps track of available personnel and equipment, which should be kept at a staging area until assigned. The resources officer must work very closely and coordinate with the operations officer. (This is also referred to as "logistics" in some incident management systems.)

4-4.1.3 Demonstrate setup of the decontamination corridor as specified in the planned response.

The decon corridor is a vital part of any drill or incident scene and should include the equipment shown in Figure 4.16.

Figure 4.16 *This decontamination corridor is being set up for training purposes. Once the operation has begun, the path in and out of the corridor will be marked with hazard tape or red cones.*

4-4.1.4 Demonstrate the decontamination process specified in the planned response.

4-4.2 Using Protective Clothing and Respiratory Protection.

The hazardous materials technician shall demonstrate the ability to don, work in, and doff both liquid splash and vapor-protective chemical-protective clothing and any other specialized personal protective equipment provided by the authority having jurisdiction, including the appropriate respiratory protection. The hazardous materials technician shall be able to:

4-4.2.1 Describe three safety procedures for personnel wearing vapor-protective clothing.

4-4.2.2* Describe three emergency procedures for personnel wearing vapor-protective clothing.

Because personnel wearing vapor-protective clothing may experience a loss of mobility, dexterity, vision, and communications capability, it is important for them to be closely monitored. *(See Figure 4.17.)* Back-up personnel wearing the same level of protective clothing must be available, and hand signals should be established to aid in communications. Personnel must also be monitored for the effects of heat, and a proper rehabilitation program should be in place to replenish fluids and allow for rest and recovery.

Figure 4.17 Chemical protective clothing adds special challenges to a hazardous materials response. The same encapsulating design that protects the responder also traps heat within the suit, creating heat stress—a potential health hazard on its own. Here, an A level technician is taking precautions against heat stress by wearing a self-cooling vest. The safety officer at right is ensuring that the frozen inserts are positioned correctly within the vest. (Photo courtesy of Henrik G. De Gyor)

A-4-4.2.2 Emergency procedures for personnel wearing vapor-protective clothing should include procedures for the following:

(a) Loss of air supply
(b) Loss of suit integrity
(c) Loss of verbal communications
(d) Buddy down in hot zone

4-4.2.3* Identify the procedures for donning, working in, and doffing the following types of respiratory protection:

(a) Air line respirator with required escape unit
(b) Air purifying respirator

A-4-4.2.3 Competency for wearing positive pressure self-contained breathing apparatus should have been met as part of Chapter 3.

4-4.2.4 Demonstrate donning, working in, and doffing chemical-protective clothing in addition to any other specialized protective equipment provided by the authority having jurisdiction.

HMTs should practice donning and doffing chemical-protective clothing to become proficient. One of the more effective ways to evaluate an HMT's ability to don and doff the protective clothing provided is to conduct training exercises that require putting on the personal protective equipment and to conduct simulated control activities, followed by simulated decontamination.

Because some types of chemical-protective clothing are very costly, it may be advisable to use garments that are no longer adequate for emergency response solely for training purposes. Haz mat training suits that are less expensive are also available; these allow for cost-effective training in the use of totally encapsulating suits.

4-4.2.5 Demonstrate the ability to record the use, repair, and testing of chemical-protective clothing according to manufacturer's specifications and recommendations.

It is very important to keep accurate records on the use, repair, and testing of chemical-protective clothing. Proper records will help identify possible problems or potential failures.

4-4.2.6 Describe the maintenance, testing, inspection, and storage procedures for personal protective equipment provided by the authority having jurisdiction according to the manufacturer's specifications and recommendations.

Chemical-protective clothing must be maintained properly according to the manufacturer's specifications. It is also important that garments be completely decontaminated before they are stored and that they be stored properly after use. Compatible components should be stored together so that the wrong item will not be used by mistake. An individual's chemical-protective clothing should be inspected visually before it is worn to ensure that it is still in usable condition.

4-4.3 Performing Control Functions Identified in Plan of Action.

Given various simulated hazardous materials incidents involving nonbulk and bulk packaging and facility containers, the hazardous materials technician shall select the tools, equipment, and materials for the control of hazardous materials incidents and identify the precautions for controlling releases from those packaging/containers. The hazardous materials technician shall be able to:

4-4.3.1* Given a pressure vessel, select the appropriate material or equipment and demonstrate a method(s) to contain leaks from the following locations:

The purpose of this competency is to allow the HMT to demonstrate the ability to choose the appropriate equipment and methods to control releases in various situations. The equipment necessary to conduct the following operations may vary depending on the type of material that is leaking and the physical properties of the damaged area, valve, or plug. For example, nonsparking tools should be used when working with flammable liquids or gases. And in some cases, special tools may be needed for certain valves. Such situations should be identified during pre-incident planning.

(a) Fusible metal of plug
(b) Fusible plug threads
(c) Side wall of cylinder

A patch placed over a leak in the side wall of a container and secured may control the leak.

(d) Valve blowout

If a valve has blown out, it may be possible to use a wooden plug to stop the flow temporarily until the line can be shut down or the container drained for replacement.

(e) Valve gland

Leaks from valve glands may be controlled by tightening the packing nut. It may also be possible to cap the outlet.

(f) Valve inlet threads

If there is a leak around the inlet threads of a valve, it may be possible to tighten the valve assembly.

(g) Valve seat

The valve should be tightened first to ensure that it is closed all the way. It may also be necessary to open and reclose the valve to clear debris that is preventing the valve from seating properly. In addition, it may be possible to cap the outlet.

(h) Valve stem assembly blowout

If the valve assembly has blown out, it may be possible to drive a wooden plug into the hole to gain temporary control depending on the pressure of the product in the container.

4-4.3.2* Given the fittings on a pressure container, demonstrate the ability to perform the following:

(a) Close valves that are open
(b) Replace missing plugs
(c) Tighten loose plugs

This competency is intended to allow the HMT to demonstrate the ability to choose the appropriate equipment and methods to control the above situations. For the competency to be most effective, the HMT should demonstrate these skills while wearing chemical-protective clothing and equipment.

A-4-4.3.1, A-4-4.3.2 Contact the Chlorine Institute for assistance in obtaining training on the use of the various chlorine kits.

4-4.3.3 Given a 55-gal (208-L) drum, demonstrate the ability to contain the following types of leaks using appropriate tools and materials:

(a) Bung leak

Bung leaks can often be stopped by tightening the bung with a bung wrench.

(b) Chime leak
(c) Forklift puncture

Because a puncture made by a forklift may be large and irregularly shaped, it may be plugged with a number of wooden plugs of different sizes or shapes. While an appropriate plugging or patching device is being assembled, it may be possible to stop the drum from leaking by turning it on its side, with the opening at the top.

(d) Nail puncture

Punctures can often be stopped with a wooden plug. A sheet metal screw and a gasket may also be used.

4-4.3.4 Given a 55-gal (208-L) drum and an overpack drum, demonstrate the ability to place the 55-gal drum into the overpack drum using the following methods:

When conducting overpacking operations manually, responders must take care to lift and move the drum properly so as to avoid back strain and injuries to hands or feet.

(a) Rolling slide-in

This method involves laying the drum on its side. Rollers are put underneath the drum, and the drum is rolled into the overpack drum. Items that may be used as rollers include lengths of pipe and other rounded materials.

(b) Slide-in

This involves laying a leaking drum on its side and sliding it into an overpack drum.

(c) Slip-over

This method involves placing the overpack drum over the top of the leaking drum and manually rotating it upright. A device called a drum "up-ender" is available commercially to assist with this type of operation.

4-4.3.5 Identify the maintenance and inspection procedures for the tools and equipment provided for the control of hazardous materials releases according to the manufacturer's specifications and recommendations.

4-4.3.6 Identify three considerations for assessing a leak or spill inside a confined space without entering the area.

Confined space operations are extremely dangerous, and the HMT must exercise the utmost caution during such operations. One of the most critical considerations is whether the confined space is oxygen-deficient. Another is whether it contains a flammable or toxic atmosphere.

4-4.3.7* Identify three safety considerations for product transfer operations.

A-4-4.3.7 The safety considerations for product transfer operations should include the following:

(a) Bonding
(b) Grounding
(c) Elimination of ignition sources and shock hazards

Whenever flammables are transferred, responders must ensure that appropriate safety precautions have been taken. Obviously, all ignition sources must be eliminated. In addition, proper grounding and bonding connections must be made. Bonding is the process of connecting two or more objects by means of a conductor. Grounding, a specific form of bonding, is the process of connecting one or more conductive objects to the ground.

4-4.3.8 Given an MC-306/DOT-406 cargo tank and a dome cover clamp, demonstrate the ability to install the clamp on the dome properly.

Because this type of cargo tank is used so frequently, the HMT should become familiar with it and know how to secure the dome cover clamp. Arrangements can sometimes be made with a local distributor to use a cargo tank for training purposes. *(See Figure 4.18.)*

4-4.3.9 Identify the methods and precautions used when controlling a fire involving an MC-306/DOT-406 aluminum shell cargo tank.

When exposed to fire, an MC-306/DOT-406 tank will melt, preventing the build-up of excessive pressure. Melting will occur only above the liquid level of the product.

According to Hildebrand and Noll in *Handling Gasoline Tank Truck Emergencies: Guidelines and Procedures*,

> A fully involved MC306/DOT406 cargo tank truck fire will require a substantial amount of foam for final control and extinguishment. Attempting to apply 95 gpm (360 L/min) of foam from a single 5-gal (18.9-L) foam concentrate container onto a 9000-gal (34,065-L) gasoline spill fire will ruin your day.
>
> There may be situations where a controlled burn of the fire may be [appropriate]. . . gasoline burns at the rate of approximately one foot per hour. Although this may extend the duration of the incident, it will usually minimize both groundwater and surface water contamination.[36]

Figure 4.18 *Being able to clamp the dome cover on a cargo tanker is a necessary skill for the hazardous materials technician.*

4-4.3.10 Describe at least one method for containing each of the following types of leaks in MC-306/DOT-406, MC-307/DOT-407, and MC-312/DOT- 412 cargo tanks:

(a) Dome cover leak
(b) Irregular-shaped hole
(c) Puncture
(d) Split or tear

There are a variety of methods to control leaks in cargo tanks. These may include the use of wooden plugs, patches, specially designed dome clamps, and others. The technician-level responder should be aware of the type of product at hand and with the compatible patching material types. It is also important that the responder have an opportunity to train with the above vehicles in order to have an understanding of the characteristics of each type of cargo tank and the special challenges each presents.

4-4.3.11* Describe three product removal and transfer considerations for overturned MC-306/DOT-406, MC-307/DOT-407, MC-312/DOT-412, MC-331, and MC-338 cargo tanks.

Each of the above cargo tanks will present different problems if the tank overturns and the product inside must be transferred. In many cases this decision should be left up to the appropriate technician specialist. A cargo tank hauling gasoline will require different procedures and equipment than a cargo tank of liquefied petroleum gas. Again, it is important for the responder to be familiar with the various types of cargo tanks common in the response area and to work with shippers to gain an understanding of the considerations for conducting product transfer operations. In many cases, if not most, product transfer operations will require the equipment and expertise of the shipper or a company involved in hazardous materials cleanup. The HMT needs to know where such assistance can be obtained and must have an understanding of the procedures and safety considerations involved.

A-4.4.3.11 Product removal and transfer considerations should include the following:

(a) Inherent risks associated with such operations
(b) Procedures and safety precautions
(c) Equipment required

4-5 Competencies—Evaluating Progress

All responders should understand why their efforts must be evaluated. If they are not making progress, the plan must be reevaluated to determine why progress is not being made. To decide whether the actions being taken at an incident are effective and the objectives are being achieved, the responder must determine whether the incident is stabilizing or increasing in intensity. There is no reason to remain in the immediate vicinity of an incident when nothing can be done to mitigate it and the situation may be about to deteriorate. If flames are impinging on an LP-Gas vessel, for example, and there is no way to provide the necessary volume of water to cool it, it would be prudent to withdraw to a safe distance.

4-5.1 Evaluating the Effectiveness of the Control Functions.

Given various simulated facility and transportation hazardous materials incidents involving nonbulk and bulk packaging and the plan of action, the hazardous materials technician shall evaluate the effectiveness of any control functions identified in the plan of action.

4-6 Competencies — Terminating the Incident

4-6.1 Assisting in the Debriefing.

Given various simulated facility and transportation hazardous materials incidents involving nonbulk and bulk packaging, the hazardous materials technician shall participate in the debriefing of the incident. The hazardous materials technician shall be able to:

4-6.1.1 Describe three components of an effective debriefing.

4-6.1.2 Describe the key topics of an effective debriefing.

4-6.1.3 Describe when a debriefing should take place.

4-6.1.4 Describe who should be involved in a debriefing.

Since hazardous materials incidents are fairly rare in most communities, with the exception of large industrial cities, a debriefing is very helpful to document all the actions taken to control the incident. The debriefing should be done as soon as practical so that the responders still have a fresh recall of all the incident details.

4-6.2 Assisting in the Incident Critique.

Given various simulated facility and transportation hazardous materials incidents involving nonbulk and bulk packaging, the hazardous materials technician shall provide operational observations of the activities that were performed in the hot and warm zones during the incident. The hazardous materials technician shall be able to:

4-6.2.1 Describe three components of an effective critique.

4-6.2.2 Describe who should be involved in a critique.

4-6.2.3 Describe why an effective critique is necessary after a hazardous materials incident.

4-6.2.4 Describe which written documents should be prepared as a result of the critique.

Again, because of the infrequency of hazardous materials incidents, it is essential that a critique be completed and circulated among all the personnel of the organizations involved in the incident. The critique report should try to focus on positive actions but should not ignore or discount areas where improvement is obviously needed. It is better to acquire knowledge from a good critique report than from a tragic experience at the next incident scene.

Some of this same information can be attained by reading critiques from other hazardous materials teams' operations. It is beneficial to all hazardous materials teams to publish critiques in any of the national emergency services magazines.

4-6.3 Providing Reports and Documentation.

Given a simulated hazardous materials incident, the hazardous materials technician shall complete the reporting and documentation requirements consistent with the organization's emergency response plan and standard operating procedures. The hazardous materials technician shall be able to:

4-6.3.1 Identify the reports and supporting documentation required by the local emergency response plan and the organization's standard operating procedures.

4-6.3.2 Demonstrate the proper completion of the reports required by the local emergency response plan and the organization's standard operating procedures.

4-6.3.3 Describe the importance of personnel exposure records.

4-6.3.4 Describe the importance of debriefing records.

4-6.3.5 Describe the importance of critique records.

4-6.3.6 Identify the steps in keeping an activity log and exposure records.

4-6.3.7 Identify the steps to be taken in compiling incident reports that meet federal, state, local, and organizational requirements.

4-6.3.8 Identify the requirements for compiling hot zone entry and exit logs.

4-6.3.9 Identify the requirements for compiling personal protective equipment logs.

4-6.3.10 Identify the requirements for filing documents and maintaining records.

References Cited in Commentary

1. John, E. Bowen, *Emergency Management of Hazardous Materials Incidents,* National Fire Protection Association, Quincy, MA, 1995.
2. Arthur E. Cote, ed., *Fire Protection Handbook,* 18th edition, National Fire Protection Association, Quincy, MA, 1997, pp. 9-287–9-288.
3. Ibid., p. 9-288.
4. Ibid., p. 9-292.
5. Kenneth J. York and Gerald L. Grey, *Hazardous Materials/Waste Handling for the Emergency Responder,* Fire Engineering, New York, 1989, p. 281.
6. *North American Emergency Response Guidebook.*
7. *Hawley's Condensed Chemical Dictionary,* Van Nostrand Reinhold Co., New York, 1996, Computer file.
8. NFPA 491, *Guide to Hazardous Chemical Reactions,* 1997 edition.
9. *Irving Sax, Dangerous Properties of Industrial Materials,* Van Nostrand Reinhold Co., New York, 1996, Computer file.
10. Title 40, *Code of Federal Regulations,* Part 261, U.S. Government Printing Office, Washington, DC.
11. Alvin C. Bronstein, *Emergency Care for Hazardous Materials Exposures,* 2nd edition, Mosby Yearbook, St. Louis, MO, 1994.
12. Title 49, *Code of Federal Regulations,* Part 178, U.S. Government Printing Office, Washington, DC.
13. Cote, *Fire Protection Handbook,* p. 3-236.
14. NFPA 30, *Flammable and Combustible Liquids Code,* 1996 edition.
15. Cote, *Fire Protection Handbook,* p. 3-236.
16. Cote, *Fire Protection Handbook,* p. 9-290.
17. Ibid., p. 9-283.
18. NFPA 491.
19. L. Bretherick, *Handbook of Reactive Chemical Hazards* Butterworths, Boston, 1995.
20. Richard J. Lewis, Sr., *Hazardous Chemicals Desk Reference,* Van Nostrand Reinhold, New York, 1996.
21. NFPA 30.
22. Ibid.
23. Ibid.
24. National Fire Academy, *Initial Response to Hazardous Materials Incidents, Course II: Concept and Implementation,* Emmitsburg, MD.
25. Cote, *Fire Protection Handbook,* pp. 10-122–10-123.
26. NFPA 1981, *Standard on Open-Circuit Self-Contained Breathing Apparatus for Fire Fighters,* 1997 edition.
27. NFPA 1991, *Standard on Vapor-Protective Suits for Hazardous Chemical Emergencies,* 1994 edition.
28. NFPA 1992, *Standard on Liquid Splash-Protective Suits for Hazardous Chemical Emergencies,* 1994 edition.
29. NFPA 1993, *Standard on Support Function Protective Clothing for Hazardous Chemical Operations,* 1994 edition.
30. NFPA 1991.
31. NFPA 1992.
32. NFPA 1993.
33. Cote, *Fire Protection Handbook,* p. 10-127.
34. Michael S. Hildebrand and Gregory C. Noll, *Handling Gasoline Tank Truck Emergencies: Guidelines and Procedures,* Fire Protection Publications, Stillwater, OK, 1991.
35. Title 29, *Code of Federal Regulations,* Part 1910.1200, Appendix C, U.S. Government Printing Office, Washington, DC.
36. Hildebrand and Noll, *Handling Gasoline Tank Truck Emergencies: Guidelines and Procedures.*

CHAPTER 5

Competencies for the Incident Commander

5-1 General

5-1.1 Introduction.

The incident commander shall be trained to meet all the competencies for the first responder awareness and operational levels and the competencies of this chapter. Incident commanders also shall receive any additional training to meet applicable United States Department of Transportation (DOT), United States Environmental Protection Agency (EPA), Occupational Safety and Health Administration (OSHA), and other appropriate state, local, or provincial occupational health and safety regulatory requirements.

The incident commander (IC) assumes control of an incident when it requires skills beyond the capabilities of the awareness level responder. Because the IC is the supervisor of the entire incident, several competencies that are identical to the technician level must be met as part of the IC training. These include technician level competencies that deal with planning and management of the incident. In addition, ICs must have additional skills for managing the operation. Technician level competencies for mitigating the situation (e.g., plugging and diking) that are more "hands-on" are not included in the competencies for an IC.

No matter what the level of the incident or the personnel operating at the incident, however, the IC must be trained and competent in the appropriate incident management system emergency operations plan, the risks of operating at the scene, state and federal resources, and the importance of decontamination.

The committee recognized that, in complex incidents involving the response of hazardous materials technicians or private sector specialist employees, the IC would use their expertise in formulating response objectives, action options, and the plan of action. The IC will rely on the hazardous materials branch officer *(see Chapter 7 of NFPA 472 for information on this new classification)* to directly supervise the team and provide appropriate technical information.

5-1.2 Definition.

The incident commander is that person who is responsible for all decisions relating to the management of the incident. The incident commander is in charge of the incident site.

It is extremely important from an incident management standpoint that a designated person be in charge and that he or she be clearly identified in the local emergency response plan. The IC works from the strategic level and develops the overall response objectives. The IC, however, should not become involved in carrying out tactical operations personally. Broadly speaking, the IC is responsible for the safety of response personnel and the public, for controlling the incident, and for minimizing harm to the environment and property. *(See Figure 5.1.)*

Even though the IC is responsible for directing and coordinating the response, some management functions may have to be delegated to others. The IC will establish a hazardous materials branch(s) to manage activities in the warm and hot control zones. This branch is managed by a hazardous materials branch officer, who reports to the IC or to operations.

A number of different agencies may be responsible for controlling and cleaning up the more complex hazardous materials incidents. These agencies may be local, county, state, or federal agencies; some incidents involve more than one agency from each jurisdiction. It is vital that these agencies be identified during pre-incident planning. The plans must establish protocols that spell out which agency is to be the lead agency during an incident. Some incident management systems establish what is called a "unified command" for multiagency or multijurisdictional incidents. When a unified command

Figure 5.1 An incident command system enables the incident commander to manage and direct operations. Here the incident commander, center, is describing the response plan to the responders who will enter the hot zone while the branch safety officer and the branch decon officers stand by awaiting their instructions. (Photo courtesy of Henrik G. de Gyor)

has been established, representatives from each agency may be identified as the lead person for that agency. Collectively, these lead persons will manage the incident. Generally, one individual of this group is designated as the spokesperson for the unified command.

5-1.3* Goal.

The goal of this chapter shall be to provide the incident commander with the knowledge and skills to perform the following tasks safely. Therefore, in addition to being competent at the awareness and operational levels, the incident commander shall be able to:

A-5-1.3 The following site safety plan considerations are referenced from the *Standard Operating Safety Guides*, EPA, June 1992:

(a) Site description
(b) Entry objectives
(c) On-site organization
(d) On-site control
(e) Hazard evaluation
(f) Personal protective equipment
(g) On-site work plans
(h) Communication procedures
(i) Decontamination procedures
(j) Site safety and health plan

(a) Analyze a hazardous materials incident to determine the magnitude of the problem in terms of outcomes by completing the following tasks:

1. Collect and interpret hazard and response information from printed resources, technical resources, computer data bases, and monitoring equipment
2. Estimate the potential outcomes within the endangered area at a hazardous materials incident

(b) Plan response operations within the capabilities and competencies of available personnel, personal protective equipment, and control equipment by completing the following tasks:

1. Identify the response objectives for hazardous materials incidents
2. Identify the potential action options (defensive, offensive, and nonintervention) available by response objective

3. Approve the level of personal protective equipment required for a given action option
4. Develop a plan of action, including safety considerations, consistent with the local emergency response plan and the organization's standard operating procedures and within the capability of available personnel, personal protective equipment, and control equipment

(c) Implement a response to favorably change the outcome consistent with the local emergency response plan and the organization's standard operating procedures by completing the following tasks:

1. Implement an incident management system (IMS), including the specified procedures for notification and utilization of nonlocal resources, e.g., private, state, and federal government personnel
2. Direct resources (private, governmental, and others) with expected task assignments and on-scene activities and provide management overview, technical review, and logistical support to private and governmental sector personnel
3. Provide a focal point for information transfer to media and local elected officials through the IMS structure

(d) Evaluate the progress of the planned response to ensure the response objectives are being met safely, effectively, and efficiently and adjust the plan of action accordingly by evaluating the effectiveness of the control functions

(e) Terminate the incident by completing the following tasks:

1. Transfer command (control) when appropriate
2. Conduct an incident debriefing
3. Conduct a multi-agency critique
4. Report and document the hazardous materials incident and submit the report to the proper entity

5-2 Competencies — Analyzing the Incident

5-2.1 Collecting and Interpreting Hazard and Response Information.

Given access to printed and technical resources, computer data bases, and monitoring equipment, the incident commander shall collect and interpret hazard and response information not available from the current edition of the *North American Emergency Response Guidebook* or a material safety data sheet (MSDS). The incident commander shall be able to identify and interpret the types of hazard and response information available from each of the following resources and explain the advantages and disadvantages of each resource:

(a) Reference manuals
(b) Hazardous materials data bases
(c) Technical information centers
(d) Technical information specialists
(e) Monitoring equipment

The IC is expected to understand the types of resources that are available and the types of information each can provide. For example, the IC is not expected to have an in-depth knowledge of computer data bases but should know the type of information that can be accessed in each of the major data bases included in the hazardous materials response plan. Similarly, the IC is not expected to be able to personally operate the various types of monitoring equipment used in the analysis of a hazardous materials incident, but he or she should be able to understand the functions and limitations of the various monitoring methods.

5-2.2 Estimating Potential Outcomes.

Given simulated facility or transportation incidents involving hazardous materials, the surrounding conditions, and the predicted behavior of the container and its contents, the incident commander shall estimate the potential outcomes within the endangered area. The incident commander shall be able to:

5-2.2.1 Identify the steps for estimating the number of exposures within the endangered area.

See 4-2.5.3 of NFPA 472 in this handbook.

5-2.2.2 Describe the following toxicological terms and exposure values and explain their significance in the risk assessment process:

(a) Parts per million (ppm)
(b) Parts per billion (ppb)
(c) Lethal dose (LD_{50})
(d) Lethal concentrations (LC_{50})
(e) Permissible exposure limit (PEL)
(f) Threshold limit value time-weighted average (TLV-TWA)
(g) Threshold limit value short-term exposure limit (TLV-STEL)
(h) Threshold limit value ceiling (TLV-C)
(i) Immediately dangerous to life and health value (IDLH)

The IC must have a level of knowledge beyond that required at the operational level in order to understand clearly the potential hazards of the products that may be involved in a hazardous materials incident. See 4-2.5.2.1 of NFPA 472 in this handbook for an explanation of each term.

5-2.2.3* Describe the following radiological materials terms and explain their significance in predicting the extent of health hazards and environmental impact in a hazardous materials incident:

(a) Types
(b) Measurement
(c) Protection

A-5-2.2.3

(a) Types:

1. Alpha
2. Beta
3. Gamma

(b) Units of measurement:

1. Activity
2. Quantity gamma
3. Absorbed dose

(c) Protection factors:

1. Half-life
2. Inverse square law
3. Time, distance, and shielding

See 4-2.5.2.2 of NFPA 472 in this handbook for commentary on this competency.

5-2.2.4 Identify two methods for predicting the areas of potential harm within the endangered area of a hazardous materials incident.

Predicting the areas of potential harm in the endangered area involves determining the potential concentrations of the hazardous material that has been released. This includes the toxicity of the concentrations and the length of time that persons in the endangered area would be exposed.

5-2.2.5 Identify the methods available to the organization for obtaining local weather conditions and predictions for short-term future weather changes.

5-2.2.6 Explain the basic toxicological principles relative to assessment and treatment of personnel exposed to hazardous materials, including the following:

To determine the risk to both patient and rescuer, the IC must understand some basic toxicological principles.

(a) Acute and delayed toxicity (chronic)

Acute toxicity refers to the sudden, severe onset of symptoms due to an exposure. The effects of delayed toxicity may not develop for hours or longer after an exposure. In some instances, such as biological exposures, symptoms may not appear until three or more days after the exposure.

(b) Routes of exposure to toxic materials

The routes of exposure, sometimes referred to as routes of entry, include the following:

(a) Inhalation—the process by which irritants or toxins enter the body through the lungs as a result of the respiratory process

(b) Ingestion—the process of consuming contaminated food or water

(c) Absorption—the process by which hazardous materials are absorbed into the body through the skin or other external tissues

(d) Injection—the process by which a toxic substance is introduced directly into the blood by a needle, cannula, or some other mechanical means. Contaminants entering the bloodstream through an open wound can be considered to be injected.

(c) Local and systemic effects

Local effects are those in which a toxic substance comes in direct contact with the skin or other tissue. Systemic effects are the effects a toxic product has on either the entire body or on a specific system or organ.

(d) Dose response

The chemical, biological, or radiological dose relationship refers to the response produced in the human body. It is a cause/effect relationship. The magnitude of the body's response will depend on the concentration of the exposure at the site, the material itself, and the dose administered.

(e) Synergistic effects

Toxicity, exposure, and dose must all be analyzed to understand the risk that more than one product will have on both the patient and the rescuer.

See the Tentative Interim Amendment on pp. 295–296 for new paragraph 5-2.2.7 and A-5-2.2.7.

5-3 Competencies — Planning the Response

5-3.1 Identifying Response Objectives.

Given simulated facility and transportation hazardous materials incidents, the incident commander shall identify the possible action options (defensive, offensive, and nonintervention) by response objectives for each problem. The incident commander shall be able to describe the steps for determining response objectives (defensive, offensive, and nonintervention) given an analysis of a hazardous materials incident.

Response objectives can include modifying the stress being applied to the container, changing the size of the breach, changing the quantity being released, changing the size of the endangered area, reducing exposures by moving people away from the hot zone, and reducing the level of harm. These objectives can be met either defensively, offensively, or through nonintervention. Obviously, the potential loss and exposures will be reduced if actions can be safely taken that will terminate the incident in a shorter period of time.

5-3.2 Identifying the Potential Action Options.

Given simulated facility and transportation hazardous materials incidents, the incident commander shall identify the possible action options (defensive, offensive, and nonintervention) by response objective for each problem. The incident commander shall be able to:

5-3.2.1 Identify the possible action options to accomplish a given response objective.

Many of the response options available can be used either offensively or defensively. For example, the size of the endangered area may be changed defensively by placing barriers around the endangered area to contain a spill. The offensive approach would be to enter the hot zone and plug the leak.

The IC may choose defensive operations as the most prudent method of dealing with an incident. For example, diking or blanketing a liquid spill of diesel fuel can often be accomplished easily. However, transferring that same product from a damaged tank truck to another tank truck would require specialized training and equipment that the technician level may or many not have. This task may be best completed by one of the new responder levels such as Technician with a Tank Car Specialty. Other operations, such as vent and burn techniques, should be attempted only by Technicians with a Tank Car Specialty (see Chapter 8 in NFPA 472).

The competency described in this section is identical to the technician level competency described in 4-3.2 of NFPA 472.

5-3.2.2 Identify the purpose of each of the following techniques for hazardous materials control:

(a) Adsorption
(b) Neutralization
(c) Overpacking
(d) Patching
(e) Plugging

Some of the methods listed for controlling an incident require a high degree of specialized training and the use of sophisticated technical equipment. The IC must be familiar with the purposes of these techniques, but does not necessarily have to be able to personally perform the more technical methods.

5-3.3 Approving the Level of Personal Protective Equipment.

Given situations with known and unknown hazardous materials, the incident commander shall approve the appropriate personal protective equipment for the action options specified in the plan of action in each situation. The incident commander shall be able to:

It is important to note here the difference between this competency for the IC and the similar competency for the hazardous materials technician (HMT). At this level, the IC is expected to "approve" the personal protective equipment chosen. The HMT and the hazardous materials branch officer are expected to be more knowledgeable, as a result of more advanced training, in "selecting" the appropriate personal protective clothing, which the IC must then approve.

5-3.3.1 Identify the four levels of chemical protection (EPA/NIOSH) and describe the equipment required for each level with the conditions under which each level is used.

The four levels of chemical protection and the equipment required are listed below.

Level A. The highest available level of respiratory, skin, and eye protection.

Equipment — Fully encapsulating suit constructed of material that is compatible with the substances involved and self-contained breathing apparatus.

Level B. The same level of respiratory protection but less skin protection than Level A. It is the minimum level recommended for initial site entries where the hazards have not yet been identified.

Equipment — Chemical-resistant clothing and self-contained breathing apparatus.

Level C. The same level of skin protection as Level B, but a lower level of respiratory protection.

Equipment — Chemical-resistant clothing and air purifying respirator.

Level D. No respiratory protection and minimal skin protection.

Equipment — Normal work clothes.

5-3.3.2 Describe the following terms and explain their impact and significance on the selection of chemical-protective clothing:

(a) Degradation

Degradation of chemical-protective clothing (CPC) can be either chemical or physical. The result of degradation is an increased likelihood that a hazardous material will permeate and penetrate the garments and endanger the health of the responder.

Chemical degradation can be minimized by avoiding unnecessary contact with chemicals and by undergoing effective decontamination procedures. It is important that the garments a responder wears be chosen based on their compatibility with the chemicals involved in an incident and that they have breakthrough times consistent with their expected use.

Protective clothing can also degrade physically, such as the damage that might be sustained when the garment rubs against a rough surface.

(b) Penetration

Penetration is the movement of a hazardous material through a suit's closures. These include zippers, buttonholes, seams, flaps, and other design features of CPC. Hazardous materials may also penetrate CPC through cracks or tears in the suit's fabric.

Protection against such material penetration is vital. A regular and routine program of protective garment inspection can help uncover conditions that could lead to penetration. CPC must also be properly stored to avoid creating "weak spots" along seams or folds in the garment and other avenues for penetration.

(c) Permeation

Different fabrics have different resistance levels to chemical permeation, and all will absorb chemicals over a period of time. NFPA 1991, *Standard on Vapor-Protective Suits for Hazardous Chemical Emergencies;*[1] NFPA 1992, *Standard on Liquid Splash-Protective Suits for Hazardous Chemical Emergencies;*[2] and NFPA 1993, *Standard on Support Function Protective Clothing for Hazardous Chemical Operations,*[3] provide guidelines for manufacturer permeation testing and certification.

5-3.3.3 Describe three safety considerations for personnel wearing vapor-protective, liquid splash-protective, and high temperature-protective clothing.

Working efficiently in protective clothing takes practice. Because personnel wearing vapor-protective clothing may experience a loss of dexterity, vision, and communications capability, it is important for these individuals to be closely monitored. Back-up personnel wearing the same level of protective clothing must be available to assist the first team workers in an emergency, and hand signals should be established to aid in communications. All responding personnel must also be monitored for the effects of heat at the scene. A proper on-scene rehabilitation program should be in place to replenish fluids and allow for rest and recovery for all individuals responding to an incident, but especially for those wearing protective garments for hot zone and warm zone work.

5-3.3.4 Identify the physical and psychological stresses that can affect users of personal protective equipment.

Personnel protective clothing, particularly fully encapsulating garments, increases the stress a responder may feel when working at a hazardous materials incident. Persons wearing CPC usually experience a loss of mobility and restricted visibility and communications. The higher the level of protection afforded by the garments, the greater these hindrances may be. Wearing CPC also increases the likelihood of heat stress and heat exhaustion in both fit and unfit individuals. While fit individuals may be able to work under conditions of extreme heat and physical exertion for longer periods of time without adverse medical problems, there is still a limit to any person's endurance. Medical monitoring for all personnel in protective clothing at the scene is strongly recommended. *(See Chapter 8 of NFPA 471.)*

See the Tentative Interim Amendment on p. 296 for new paragraph 5-3.3.5.

5-3.4 Developing a Plan of Action.

Given simulated facility and transportation hazardous materials incidents, the incident commander shall develop a plan of action consistent with the local emergency response plan and the organization's standard operating procedures that is within the capability of the available personnel, personal protective equipment, and control equipment. The incident commander shall be able to:

A plan of action will describe the response objectives and any options to achieving the objectives. The basis for the plan will be the organization's standard operating procedures and the local emergency response plan. Safety and health considerations, necessary personnel, and control equipment should be listed in the plan for each objective. The plan of action provides a permanent record of the incident and can be the outline for the incident critique.

5-3.4.1 Identify the steps for developing a plan of action.

The following components must be considered when developing a plan of action:

(a) Site restrictions
(b) Entry objectives
(c) On-scene organization and control
(d) Personal protective equipment selection
(e) Hazard evaluation
(f) Communications procedures
(g) Emergency procedures and personnel accountability

(h) Emergency medical care arrangements
(i) Rehabilitation plan
(j) Decontamination procedures
(k) On-scene work assignments (branches)
(l) Debriefing and critiquing of the incident once it is concluded

5-3.4.2 Identify the factors to be evaluated in selecting public protective actions including evacuation and sheltering in-place.

This evaluation is designed to reduce or prevent contamination of the public directly exposed to the hazardous material(s). If the members of the public at the scene are safe in their present location, and the structure where they are located can be protected from contamination (by closing windows and doors, turning off ventilation systems that may draw air in from outside, etc.), it is better to leave these individuals in place until the incident can be controlled. Even after hazardous materials responders have notified the public at the scene that they are to stay in their present location, reassurances of their safety and updates on the progress of the incident from hazardous materials responders are necessary to reduce any anxiety.

5-3.4.3 Given the local emergency response plan and/or the organization's standard operating procedures, identify which agency will perform the following:

(a) Receive the initial notification
(b) Provide secondary notification and activation of response agencies
(c) Make ongoing assessments of the situation
(d) Command on-scene personnel (incident management system)
(e) Coordinate support and mutual aid
(f) Provide law enforcement and on-scene security (crowd control)
(g) Provide traffic control and rerouting
(h) Provide resources for public safety protective action (evacuation or shelter in-place)
(i) Provide fire suppression services when appropriate
(j) Provide on-scene medical assistance (ambulance) and medical treatment (hospital)
(k) Provide public notification (warning)
(l) Provide public information (news media statements)
(m) Provide on-scene communications support
(n) Provide emergency on-scene decontamination when appropriate
(o) Provide operational-level hazard control services
(p) Provide technician-level hazard mitigation services
(q) Provide environmental remedial action ("cleanup") services
(r) Provide environmental monitoring

The Emergency Planning and Community Right-to-Know Act requires local emergency planning committees (LEPCs) to develop local plans for emergency response to hazardous materials incidents. The incident commander must understand the local emergency response plan, which should address the actions listed above and those agencies responsible.

Emergency response agencies should also develop their own standard operating procedures based on their roles in the local emergency plan. These procedures should address the actions listed and should indicate who is responsible for these actions, both inside and outside the agency, and how each task will be accomplished. For an example of standard operating procedures for EMS responders, please see Supplement 11.

See the Tentative Interim Amendment on pp. 297–298 for revised paragraph 5-3.4.3.

5-3.4.4 Identify the process for determining the effectiveness of an action option on the potential outcomes.

Before a response option is selected, the effect of that response option or combination of response options on the sequence of events and ultimately the outcomes should be reviewed by prioritizing the response options based on their effect on the outcomes.[4] *(See Table 5.1.)* A Plan "B" should also be formulated in case the first plan fails to achieve the desired outcomes. Constant evaluation is necessary during the course of an

Table 5.1 Worksheet for Estimating the Effect of Each Response Option

Exposures/Harm	Amount That Could Be Saved	Amount Saved with Option 1	Amount Saved with Option 2	Amount Saved with Option 3	Amount Saved with Option 4	Amount Saved with Option 5	Amount Saved with Option 6
People Deaths	#	#	#	#	#	#	#
People Injuries	#	#	#	#	#	#	#
Property Damage	$	$	$	$	$	$	$
Environmental Damage	$	$	$	$	$	$	$

Source: *Fire Protection Handbook*, 18th edition.[5]

incident to prevent unsafe or ineffective operations and to assess subsequent options.

5-3.4.5 Identify the safe operating practices/procedures that are required to be followed at a hazardous materials incident.

This following practices should be employed to ensure safe operations at a hazardous materials incident scene:

(a) The incident commander and hazardous materials responders have met all the competencies of their appropriate levels in NFPA 472.

(b) Activities that present a significant risk to the safety of members are limited to situations where there is a potential to save endangered lives.

(c) No risk to the safety of members is acceptable when there is no possibility to save lives or property.

(d) All personnel working in the warm zone or hot zone are under the supervision of a hazardous materials branch officer.

(e) Personnel accountability procedures are utilized.

(f) A rest and rehabilitation area is completed and ready for first responders to finish their assignment.

(g) A hazardous materials branch safety officer has been designated and is operating.

(h) Communications are established on one simple radio channel that is not used by anyone close enough to interfere. Hand signals are available as a backup if the radios fail.

(i) Appropriate protective clothing and protective equipment are used whenever the responder is exposed or potentially exposed to hazardous materials.

(j) A rapid intervention crew consisting of at least two responders is available for rescue of a member or team if necessary. Responders are operating in the hot zone in teams of two or more.

(k) All responders are monitored before they can proceed to work in personnel protective equipment in accordance with the guidelines in Chapter 8 of NFPA 471.

(l) Hazardous materials responders are aware of clues indicating the incident may be a chemical, biological, nuclear, or explosives incident. Efforts are made to notice secondary devices or attempts to disguise the true nature of the incident if terrorism is suspected.

5-3.4.5.1 Identify the importance of pre-incident planning relating to safety during responses to specific sites.

5-3.4.5.2 Identify the procedures for presenting a safety briefing prior to allowing personnel to work on a hazardous materials incident.

5-3.4.5.3* Identify at least three safety precautions associated with search and rescue missions at hazardous materials incidents.

A-5-3.4.5.3 Safety precautions should include the following:

(a) Buddy systems
(b) Backup team
(c) Personal protective equipment

5-3.4.5.4 Identify the advantages and limitations and describe an example where each of the following decontamination methods would be used:

(a) Absorption
(b) Adsorption
(c) Chemical degradation
(d) Dilution
(e) Disposal
(f) Evaporation
(g) Neutralization
(h) Solidification
(i) Vacuuming
(j) Washing

5-3.4.5.5* Identify the atmospheric and physical safety hazards associated with hazardous materials incidents involving confined spaces.

A-5-3.4.5.5 See A-4-3.5.4.

This is a new section that was added in response to the OSHA regulations on confined space operations. The incident commander should become very familiar with the OSHA regulations. Failure to comply has led to several substantial fines.

5-4 Competencies — Implementing the Planned Response

5-4.1 Implementing the Incident Management System.

Given a copy of the local emergency response plan, the incident commander shall identify the requirements of the plan, including the required procedures for notification and utilization of nonlocal resources (private, state, and federal government personnel). The incident commander shall be able to:

5-4.1.1 Identify the role of the incident commander during an incident involving hazardous materials.

One of the responsibilities of the incident commander is to obtain cleanup and restoration services. In some cases, this simply involves contacting the local communications center and asking that those services be dispatched to the scene. In others, the IC may have to contact a different agency to activate those services.

5-4.1.2 Identify the duties and responsibilities of the following hazardous materials branch functions within the incident management system:

This is a good example of a competency required of the incident commander that is *not* required of the technician. According to this requirement, the IC must be familiar with and able to control and organize all phases of the complete emergency operation, not just mitigation procedures. This is the "big picture" approach necessary to ensure smooth and efficient interaction between different responder skill levels and duties at the scene. Mitigation is only one vital part of that big picture.

(a) Backup
(b) Decontamination
(c) Entry
(d) Hazardous Materials Branch Management
(e) Hazardous Materials Branch Safety
(f) Information/research
(g) Reconnaissance
(h) Resources

5-4.1.3 Identify the steps for implementing the local and related emergency response plans as required under SARA Title III (EPCRA) Section 303 of the federal regulations or other state and local emergency response planning legislation.

Normally, emergency response plans are set in motion when someone notifies an emergency operations center that an incident has occurred. The emergency response plan then identifies the type of resources that are to be dispatched and determines whether there are any additional entities that should be notified. The IC should understand this process and be aware of which officials and/or agencies must be notified for each type or level of incident reported.

5-4.1.4 Given the local emergency response planning documents, identify the elements of each of the documents.

Title III of SARA (Superfund Amendments and Reauthorization Act) requires that an emergency plan contain certain elements. These issues must be addressed in the planning process.

The emergency plan must address the following items if they are not covered elsewhere:

(a) Pre-emergency planning and coordination with outside parties
(b) Personnel roles, lines of authority, training, and communications
(c) Emergency recognition and prevention
(d) Safe distances and places of refuge
(e) Site security and control
(f) Evacuation routes and procedures
(g) Decontamination
(h) Emergency medical treatment and first aid
(i) Emergency alerting and response procedures
(j) Critique response and follow-up
(k) Personal protective equipment (PPE) and emergency equipment

If the standard operating procedures for the hazardous materials response team adequately cover these elements, as is sometimes the case, they need not be included in the emergency plan.

5-4.1.5 Identify the elements of the incident management system necessary to coordinate response activities at hazardous materials incidents.

There are several different models for hazardous materials incident command systems, some of which are presented in other sections of this handbook including Supplements 5, 8, and 9. NFPA 1561, *Standard on Fire Department Incident Management System,*[6] also contains additional information. Each system generally has the same components, however, even though they may use some different titles. For example, hazardous materials branch officers, hazard sector officers, and hazardous materials group supervisors generally perform the same functions. Basically, they are responsible for implementing the incident action plan that deals with operations intended to control the hazardous materials portion of an incident.

Within the incident management system, there are generally five primary functional areas: the incident command, operations, planning, logistics, and finance. Usually, there will also be a public information officer and a safety officer. For hazardous materials incidents, additional functions are identified, including the hazardous materials branch and safety officers, the decontamination officer, information research and resources officer, and the entry/reconnaissance officer.

It is extremely important that the IC be familiar with the incident management system established in the local emergency response plan and be able to implement it promptly and appropriately.

5-4.1.6 Identify the primary local, state, regional, and federal government agencies and identify the scope of their regulatory authority (including the regulations) pertaining to the production, transportation, storage, and use of hazardous materials and the disposal of hazardous wastes.

The incident commander must know which agencies may become involved in a hazardous materials incident and be able to identify their regulatory authority. The local emergency response plan should identify these agencies and delineate their roles, authority, and functions for each incident type and response level.

5-4.1.7 Identify the government agencies and private sector resources offering assistance during a hazardous materials incident and identify their role and the type of assistance or resources available.

Some government agencies provide response or technical assistance to local authorities in specific cases. For example, the U.S. Coast Guard staffs three strategically located national strike teams that are trained and equipped to respond to major oil spills and chemical releases in U.S. waters. *(See Figure 5.2.)* The U.S. Environmental Protection Agency also has a response component called the environmental response team (ERT). The ERT is a group of scientists and engineers who are trained in sampling and analysis, hazard assessment, cleanup techniques, and other technical support.

Figure 5.2 *The U.S. Coast Guard can provide assistance at incidents. This military branch maintains a specialized team of regional responders trained to deal with hazardous materials incidents in the areas of their routine patrols.*

In addition, many state and local governments and private industries can provide technical assistance. The hazardous materials response teams from other municipalities or private industry can also be good resources for large incidents or for identifying specific hazardous material(s) that are not able to be identified at the scene through other methods.

The private sector also has many resources available to emergency responders, from providing technical advice and assisting with on-scene monitoring to providing specialized equipment. *(See Figure 5.3.)* In most areas, there are private sector companies that provide cleanup and disposal services. Some of these companies may even stage equipment in an area and fly personnel to the scene when a hazardous materials incident occurs. CHEMTREC/CANUTEC/SETIQ can put responders in touch with private sector resources if they are unfamiliar with any in their area.

The IC must know how to get specialized assistance when it is needed and must be familiar with the type of assistance available from each resource. These resources, both public and private, should be identified in the local emergency response plan. In situations involving services that must be contracted for in advance, arrangements should be addressed during the pre-incident planning phase so as not to complicate matters during an actual emergency.

5-4.2* Directing Resources (Private and Governmental).

Given a simulated hazardous materials incident and the necessary resources to implement the planned response, the incident commander shall demonstrate the ability to direct the resources in a safe and efficient manner consistent with the capabilities of those resources.

A-5-4.2 Criteria/factors should include the following:

(a) Task assignment (based upon strategical and tactical options)
(b) Operational safety
(c) Operational effectiveness
(d) Planning support
(e) Logistical support
(f) Administrative support

5-4.3 Providing a Focal Point for Information Transfer to Media and Elected Officials.

Given a simulated hazardous materials incident, the incident commander shall identify appropriate information to provide to the media and local, state, and federal officials. The incident commander shall be able to:

5-4.3.1 Identify the local policy for providing information to the media.

The emergency response plan and/or an agency's standard operating procedures should establish a procedure for providing information to the media, which the media can then make available to the public. If the public is not to panic, it must receive accurate information. The media can also help responders alert the public to possible evacuations or any other protective actions that may be necessary. In addition, the media can announce the locations of any evacuation centers and phone numbers to check on the welfare of friends or family.

Figure 5.3 Private industry provides specialized response personnel to assist in controlling hazardous materials incidents like the truck rollover shown here. The private contractors are usually paid by the shipper of the materials. In other cases, the private firm is under contract to the state or local municipality which recovers the cost of the cleanup from the shipper or the shipper's insurance carrier. This simple looking accident in New Jersey spilled 3000 of the 6000 gallons carried by this tanker. Much of the fuel contaminated a nearby river as run-off from the accident scene. The sand, shown in the foreground, is being used to dike the spill. (AP/Worldwide photo by Mike Sypniewski)

5-4.3.2 Identify the responsibilities of the public information officer at a hazardous materials incident.

The public information officer (PIO) should function as a part of the IC's staff. One person should be chosen to serve as spokesperson at an incident. This person should have training and experience in public information and media relations.

The PIO should establish a press area in a safe location and regularly provide the media with accurate information about the incident. There may be areas to which the press is not allowed access because of the hazards present. If the media is allowed to move about, however, the PIO should provide escorts for them or identify safe areas into which they may go unescorted.

5-5 Competencies — Evaluating Progress

5-5.1 Evaluating Progress of the Plan of Action.

Given simulated facility and transportation hazardous materials incidents, the incident commander shall evaluate the progress of the plan of action to determine whether the efforts are accomplishing the response objectives. The incident commander shall be able to:

5-5.1.1 Identify the procedures for evaluating whether the action options are effective in accomplishing the objectives.

To determine whether the actions being taken at an incident are effective and the objectives are being met, responders must determine whether the incident is stabilizing or increasing in intensity. Feedback will allow responders to modify either their strategic goals or the action options being implemented. This feedback should include information on the effectiveness of personnel, on personal protective clothing and equipment, on control zones, on decontamination procedures, and on the action options being implemented.

5-5.1.2 Identify the steps for comparing actual behavior of the material and the container to that predicted in the analysis process.

When comparing actual behavior to predicted behavior, the incident commander should determine whether events at an incident are happening as predicted, are occurring out of sequence, or are different than expected. The IC should also determine if events that were predicted to occur as part of the mitigation, response, or overall plan are occurring as anticipated. This evaluation process should continue until the incident has been terminated so that there are no "surprises" during the cleanup or overhaul phase.

5-5.1.3 Determine the effectiveness of the following:

(a) Personnel being used
(b) Personal protective equipment
(c) Established control zones
(d) Decontamination process

This competency is intended to allow the IC to show that he or she can analyze an incident to determine the effectiveness of the chosen action options in achieving the strategic goals. The competencies in 5-5.1.1 and 5-5.1.2 provide the basis for this analysis.

5-6 Competencies — Terminating the Incident

The steps involved in terminating the emergency phase of an incident are transferring command, debriefing, critiquing the incident, and after-action activities.

The incident debriefing involves gathering information from response personnel. This information should then be used to develop a chronological report of emergency activities.

The critique is a review of the incident intended to identify and document lessons learned. It should allow the participants to review response activities and determine what worked well and what didn't. The critique should be a positive process that allows responders to modify response procedures if problems are identified.

After-action activities include analyzing the information gathered during the debriefing and the critique, documenting that analysis, and following up as necessary to ensure that any recommendations made to improve emergency operations are implemented.

5-6.1 Transferring Command/Control.

Given the details of a simulated incident, the local emergency response plan, and the organization's standard operating procedures, the incident commander shall be able to:

5-6.1.1* Identify the appropriate steps to be taken to transfer command/control of the incident.

A-5-6.1.1 The appropriate steps to transfer command/control of the incident include the following:

(a) Fully brief the incoming command/control person on the details of the incident
(b) Communicate the transfer of command/control to all other interests involved in the incident

5-6.1.2 Demonstrate the transfer of command/control.

Transferring authority at an incident generally means transferring command, or the role of IC, from one person to another. This process should be identified in the incident management system's standard operating procedures. Authority may be transferred from one officer to another officer of higher rank or, in the case of some agencies, from one person to another person with a higher authority and more responsibility.

Authority may also be transferred when the emergency phase has ended and a non-emergency phase begins, as when cleanup and remediation activities must continue at the site. In such cases, it is likely that some agency, be it local, state, or federal, will be chosen to manage this phase. Whatever the case, procedures should be developed to identify who may be responsible for overseeing these operations.

5-6.2 Conducting a Debriefing.

Given the details of a simulated hazardous materials incident, the incident commander shall conduct a debriefing of the incident. The incident commander shall be able to:

The incident debriefing is not a critique; it is the gathering of information intended to provide an overall summary of the activities of each branch, sector, or division during an incident. The objectives of a debriefing are to identify who responded, what they did, when they did it, and how effective their operations were. The debriefing should also document any injuries suffered, note the type of treatment given, and indicate whether any medical follow-up is needed. Equipment that has been damaged should be reported and any unsafe conditions noted.

It is important that responders are told what materials they were exposed to, warned of any symptoms those materials might produce, and advised on the decontamination procedures that they should undergo. These procedures may include showering and washing or disposing of clothing.

5-6.2.1 Describe three components of an effective debriefing.

5-6.2.2 Describe the key topics in an effective debriefing.

5-6.2.3 Describe when a debriefing should take place.

5-6.2.4 Describe who should be involved in a debriefing.

5-6.2.5 Identify the procedures for conducting incident debriefings at a hazardous materials incident.

5-6.3 Conducting a Multi-Agency Critique.

Given details of a simulated multi-agency hazardous materials incident, the incident commander shall conduct a critique of the incident. The incident commander shall be able to:

The procedure for conducting a multi-agency critique is similar to that outlined in Section 5-6, although the process is a little more complicated. Ideally, the ICs of the various responding authorities should conduct an initial meeting to identify the specific personnel who should be involved in the critique in order to ensure that all responding agencies or groups are properly represented.

5-6.3.1 Describe three components of an effective critique.

5-6.3.2 Describe who should be involved in a critique.

5-6.3.3 Describe why an effective critique is necessary after a hazardous materials incident.

5-6.3.4 Describe what written documents should be prepared as a result of the critique.

5-6.3.5 Implement the procedure for conducting a critique of the incident.

5-6.4 Reporting and Documenting the Hazardous Materials Incident.

Given a simulated hazardous materials incident, the incident commander shall demonstrate the ability to report and document the incident consistent with the local, state, and federal requirements. The incident commander shall be able to:

5-6.4.1 Identify the reporting requirements of the federal, state, and local agencies.

The IC must be aware of the reporting requirements necessary to deal with a hazardous materials incident. In many cases, the responsibility for reporting the incident to specific governmental agencies is outlined in an agency's, jurisdiction's, or organization's standard operating procedures. However, the IC must ensure that the proper agencies have been notified and that the proper reports have been completed.

5-6.4.2 Identify the importance of documentation for a hazardous materials incident, including training records, exposure records, incident reports, and critique reports.

Questions about an incident may not arise until someone files a claim some time after the incident is over. If information documenting the incident is not available, it could have serious ramifications for all personnel involved. Thus, both documenting information about personnel training and exposure and keeping incident and critique reports on file is critical to ensuring that answers to questions that might arise about the handling of an incident can be efficiently, accurately, and appropriately answered. Typically, the IC may be asked to explain the operations undertaken and the use of personnel during the incident, as well as why certain decisions were made or not made.

5-6.4.3 Identify the steps in keeping an activity log and exposure records for hazardous materials incidents.

The incident commander should assign someone to maintain a record of incident events. This will be helpful in completing the incident analysis and conducting the critique.

Personnel exposure records should also be maintained as required by federal and, in many cases, state law. The IC should assign someone to gather the necessary information about the type of exposure to which personnel were subjected, the exposure level and the length of the exposure, the type of personal protective clothing and equipment personnel were using, and the type of decontamination personnel underwent. Any on-scene medical assistance that personnel received should also be documented.

5-6.4.4 Identify the requirements for compiling hazardous materials incident reports found in the local emergency response plan as well as the organization's standard operating procedures.

5-6.4.5 Identify the requirements for filing documents and maintaining records found in the local emergency response plan and the organization's standard operating procedures.

See the Tentative Interim Amendment on p. 296 for new paragraph 5-6.4.6.

References Cited in Commentary

1. NFPA 1991, *Standard on Vapor-Protective Suits for Hazardous Chemical Emergencies,* National Fire Protection Association, Quincy, MA, 1994.
2. NFPA 1992, *Standard on Liquid Splash-Protective Suits for Hazardous Chemical Emergencies,* National Fire Protection Association, Quincy, MA, 1994.
3. NFPA 1993, *Standard on Support Function Protective Clothing for Hazardous Chemical Operations,* National Fire Protection Association, Quincy, MA, 1994.
4. Arthur E. Cote, ed., *Fire Protection Handbook,* 18th edition, National Fire Protection Association, Quincy, MA, 1997, p. 10-123.
5. Ibid., p. 10-125.
6. NFPA 1561, *Standard on Fire Department Incident Management System,* National Fire Protection Association, Quincy, MA, 1995.

CHAPTER 6

Competencies for Private Sector Specialist Employees

6-1 General

6-1.1 Introduction.

Private sector specialist employees are those persons who, in the course of their regular job duties, work with or are trained in the hazards of specific chemicals or containers within their organization's area of specialization. In response to emergencies involving hazardous materials in their organization's area of specialization, they could be called upon to provide technical advice or assistance to the incident commander relative to specific chemicals or containers for chemicals. Private sector specialist employees shall receive training or demonstrate competency in their area of specialization annually. Private sector specialist employees also shall receive any additional training to meet applicable United States Department of Transportation (DOT), Occupational Safety and Health Administration (OSHA), United States Environmental Protection Agency (EPA), and other appropriate state, local, or provincial occupational health and safety regulatory requirements.

Private sector specialist employees respond to hazardous materials incidents under different circumstances. They respond to incidents within their facility, in and outside their assigned work area, and outside their facility. Persons responding away from the facility or within the facility outside their assigned work area respond as a member of a hazardous materials response team or as a private sector specialist employee as outlined in this chapter. When responding to incidents away from their assigned work area, private sector specialist employees shall be permitted to perform only at the response level at which they have been trained.

Persons responding to a hazardous materials incident within their work area are not required to be trained to the levels specified by this chapter. Persons within their work area who have informed the incident management structure of an emergency as defined in the facility's emergency response plan; who have adequate personal protective equipment and adequate training in the procedures they are to perform; and who have employed the buddy system can take limited action in the danger area (e.g., turning a valve) before the emergency response team arrives. The limited action taken must be addressed in the emergency response plan. Once the emergency response team arrives, these persons shall be restricted to the actions that their training level allows and must operate under the incident command structure.

In this 1997 edition, the title "off-site specialist employee" has been changed to "private sector specialist employee." The committee made this change to more accurately describe the potential duties of these employees. Private sector specialist employees are not just assigned to respond to off-site hazardous materials incidents. They respond to incidents within their facility, in and outside their assigned work area, and outside their facility. In many cases, private sector specialist employees are part of the emergency response team for the company. *(See Figure 6.1.)*

This 1997 edition also outlines the actions and conditions under which other employees may be allowed to perform without meeting any of the competency levels described in this chapter. For example, consider a chemical technician who is responsible for a piece of machinery that combines several chemicals (raw product) into a new product for the company to market. If there is a spill or release of one of the chemicals that is a hazardous material, the chemical technician is allowed to take some simple actions to mitigate the incident, such as turning off a valve. However, the employee must first inform the incident management structure of an emergency before taking any actions; have adequate personnel protective equipment; have training in both the PPE and the procedures needed for mitigation; and break off all actions when the emergency response team arrives.

Figure 6.1 Private sector specialist employees must wear the appropriate protective clothing and breathing apparatus, just as those in the public sector do when responding to a similar level of emergency. Here, this Level B responder is sealing a breach in a piping system. As an employee of the facility, this worker is most familiar with the contents of the pipe and its hazards.

Private sector specialist employees may also be sent to the scene of hazardous materials incidents off site to provide incident commanders with technical advice or assistance. Among the companies these individuals may represent are chemical manufacturers, transportation companies, users of products, and container manufacturers.

All competencies for private sector specialist employees at every level apply to the individuals' areas of specialization and include only those chemicals and containers to which the individual is expected to respond. The private sector specialist employee must perform all activities in a manner consistent with the organization's emergency response (E/R) plan and standard operating procedures (SOPs), and with the available resources.

6-1.2 Scope.

This chapter will address competencies for the following private sector specialist employees:

(a) Private sector specialist employee C
(b) Private sector specialist employee B
(c) Private sector specialist employee A

6-2 Private Sector Specialist Employee C

6-2.1 General.

6-2.1.1 Introduction. The private sector specialist employee C shall meet the competencies at the first responder awareness level (Chapter 2) relative to their organization's area of specialization and the additional competencies in Section 6-2 of this chapter.

6-2.1.2 Definition. The private sector specialist employee C is that person who responds to emergencies involving chemicals and/or containers within his or her organization's area of specialization. Consistent with the organization's emergency response plan and standard operating procedures, the private sector specialist employees C can be called upon to gather and record information, provide technical advice, and/or arrange for technical assistance. A private sector specialist employee C does not enter the hot or warm zone at an emergency.

6-2.1.3 Goal. The private sector specialist employee C shall be competent at the first responder awareness level relative to their organization's area of specialization. The private sector specialist employee C shall have the knowledge and skills to perform the following duties and tasks safely:

(a) Assist the incident commander in analyzing the magnitude of an emergency involving chemicals or containers for chemicals by completing the following tasks:

1. Provide information on the hazards and harmful effects of specific chemicals
2. Provide information on the characteristics of specific containers for chemicals

(b) Assist the incident commander in planning a response to an emergency involving chemicals or containers for chemicals by completing the following tasks:

1. Provide information on the potential response options for chemicals or containers for chemicals

6-2.2 Competencies — Analyzing the Incident.

6-2.2.1 Providing Information on the Hazards and Harmful Effects of Specific Chemicals. Given a specific chemical(s) used in his or her organization's area of specialization and the appropriate material safety data sheet (MSDS) or other appropriate resource, the private sector specialist employee C shall advise the incident commander of the chemical's hazards and harmful effects. The private sector specialist employee C shall be able to:

Private sector specialist employees at Level C are expected to provide information about the chemical involved in an incident. The items listed in 6-2.2.1.1 represent the minimum requirements needed to determine proficiency in this area. Additional resources include *DOT North American Emergency Response Guidebook* (NAERG)[1] and the Association of American Railroads' *Emergency Handling of Hazardous Materials and Surface Transportation*,[2] among others.

6-2.2.1.1 Identify the following hazard information from the material safety data sheet (MSDS) or other appropriate resource:

(a) Physical and chemical characteristics
(b) Physical hazards of the chemical (including fire and explosion hazards)
(c) Health hazards of the chemical
(d) Signs and symptoms of exposure
(e) Routes of entry
(f) Permissible exposure limits
(g) Reactivity hazards
(h) Environmental concerns

6-2.2.1.2 Identify how to contact CHEMTREC/CANUTEC/SETIQ.

This requirement can be met by determining whether the responder can find the correct telephone number listed in the NAERG. The company to which the product belongs may include the telephone number in MSDSs, on labels, on containers, and in shipping papers. The number must be included in the E/R plan or standard operating procedures of the specialist employee's organization.

6-2.2.1.3 Identify the resources available from CHEMTREC/CANUTEC/SETIQ.

CHEMTREC/CANUTEC/SETIQ can provide information on products, fax MSDSs, and contact manufacturers, mutual-aid responders, and contractors for hire.

CHEMTREC stands for Chemical Transportation Emergency Center and is a public service of the Chemical Manufacturers Association, located in Washington, DC. CHEMTREC provides the on-scene commander with immediate advice by telephone and contacts the involved shipper for detailed assistance and response follow-up. It can also notify the National Response Center (NRC) of significant incidents or bridge a caller to the NRC to report a spill. CHEMTREC operates 24 hours a day and can be contacted throughout the United States and Canada.

CHEMTREC can usually provide hazard information warnings and guidance when given a material's four-digit identification number, the name of the product, and the nature of the problem. If the product is unknown or more detailed information and assistance is needed, the caller should attempt to provide as much of the following information as possible:

(a) Caller's name and call-back number
(b) Guide number being used
(c) Name of the shipper or manufacturer
(d) Rail car or truck number
(e) Carrier's name
(f) Consignee
(g) Local conditions

At an incident, a phone line should be kept open to CHEMTREC so that they can provide guidance and assistance. CHEMTREC can also provide a teleconferencing bridge that will connect technical experts to a caller's line as necessary.

CANUTEC is the Canadian Transport Emergency Center located in Ottawa, Canada, and operated by the Transport Dangerous Goods Directorate of Transport Canada. It provides technical assistance to emergency responders much the same as CHEMTREC. Personnel will provide technical information regarding the physical, chemical, toxicological, and other properties of the products involved in an incident; recommend remedial actions for fires, spills, or leaks; provide advice on protective clothing and emergency first aid; and contact the shipper, manufacturer, or others who are deemed necessary.

SETIQ is the Emergency Transportation System for the Chemical Industry in Mexico and provides the same services as CHEMTREC and CANUTEC.

6-2.2.1.4 Given their organization's emergency response plan and standard operating procedures, identify additional resources of hazard information, including a method of contact.

Private sector specialist employees at Level C must be able to contact knowledgeable personnel, as prescribed in the organization's E/R plan or standard operating procedures. They should also know where to find the organization's plan to locate the appropriate information.

6-2.2.2 Providing Information on Characteristics of Specific Containers. Given examples of facility and transportation containers for chemicals in their organization's area of specialization, the private sector specialist employee C shall advise the incident commander of the characteristics of the containers. The private sector specialist employee C shall be able to:

6-2.2.2.1 Identify each container by name.

Private sector specialist employees at Level C must be able to identify the containers, such as tank cars, cargo tanks, drums, and cylinders, routinely used in the manufacture, storage, and transport of hazardous materials. *(See Figure 6.2.)* Specialist employees may already know about these containers, or they may learn about them from such resources as other company specialists, the CMA's *Packaging for Transporting Hazardous and Non-hazardous Materials,*[3] and their own companies' packaging guides.

6-2.2.2.2 Identify the markings that differentiate one container from another.

Private sector specialist employees at Level C should be able to identify various container markings used in their work area including tank car marks and numbers,

Figures 6.2 Private sector specialist employees must be familiar with the containers used in the routine storage and transport of hazardous materials, as well as the facility's emergency plans, piping cutoffs, and access points that public sector responders will need to find in case of an emergency.

cargo tank numbers, portable tank numbers, and fixed facility tank markings. Figures 6.3(a) and 6.3(b) show the various warning placards and labels required by the U.S. Department of Transportation.

6-2.2.2.3 Given their organization's emergency response plan and standard operating procedures, identify the resources available that can provide information about the characteristics of the container.

Among the resources that can provide the responder with information about the characteristics of the container are, for example, knowledgeable persons in the responder's organization, container manufacturers, the Association of American Railroads (AAR), CHEMTREC, and various carriers.

6-2.3 Competencies — Planning the Response.

6-2.3.1 Providing Information on Potential Response Options for Specific Chemicals. Given a specific chemical used in their organization's area of specialization and an appropriate material safety data sheet (MSDS) or other appropriate resource, the private sector specialist employee C shall advise the incident commander of the response information for that chemical by being able to:

By virtue of their job duties, their knowledge of specific chemicals, or their access to appropriate resources within their organizations, private sector specialist employees at Level C must be able to provide the incident commander with response information. This information may include the physical and chemical properties of the hazardous material involved in an incident, health and environmental data, and containment and reactivity data.

6-2.3.1.1 Obtain the following response information:

(a) Precautions for safe handling, including hygiene practices, protective measures, and procedures for cleanup of spills/leaks
(b) Applicable control measures, including personal protective equipment
(c) Emergency and first aid procedures

6-2.3.1.2 Identify additional resources for obtaining response information.

Additional resources the private sector specialist employee might use include the NAERG, the AAR's EAG, knowledgeable persons in his or her organization, CHEMTREC/CANUTEC/SETIQ, and the National Fire Protection Association (NFPA).

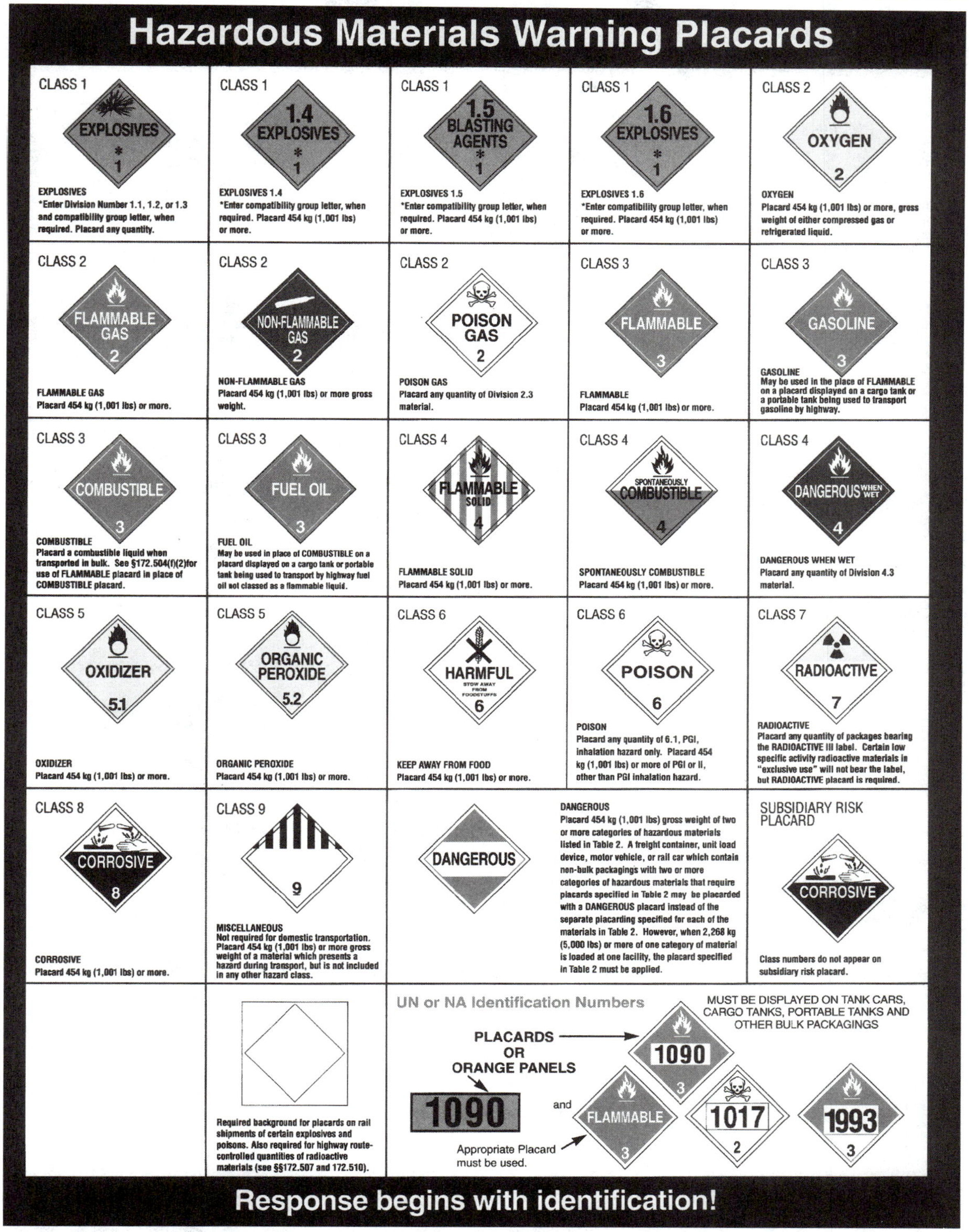

Figure 6.3(a) *The U.S. Department of Transportation's Chart 10 shows the warning placards required for the transport of hazardous materials. All private sector specialists should be familiar with the various markings, labeling, and placarding required for materials used in their organization's area of specialization. (U.S. Department of Transportation)*

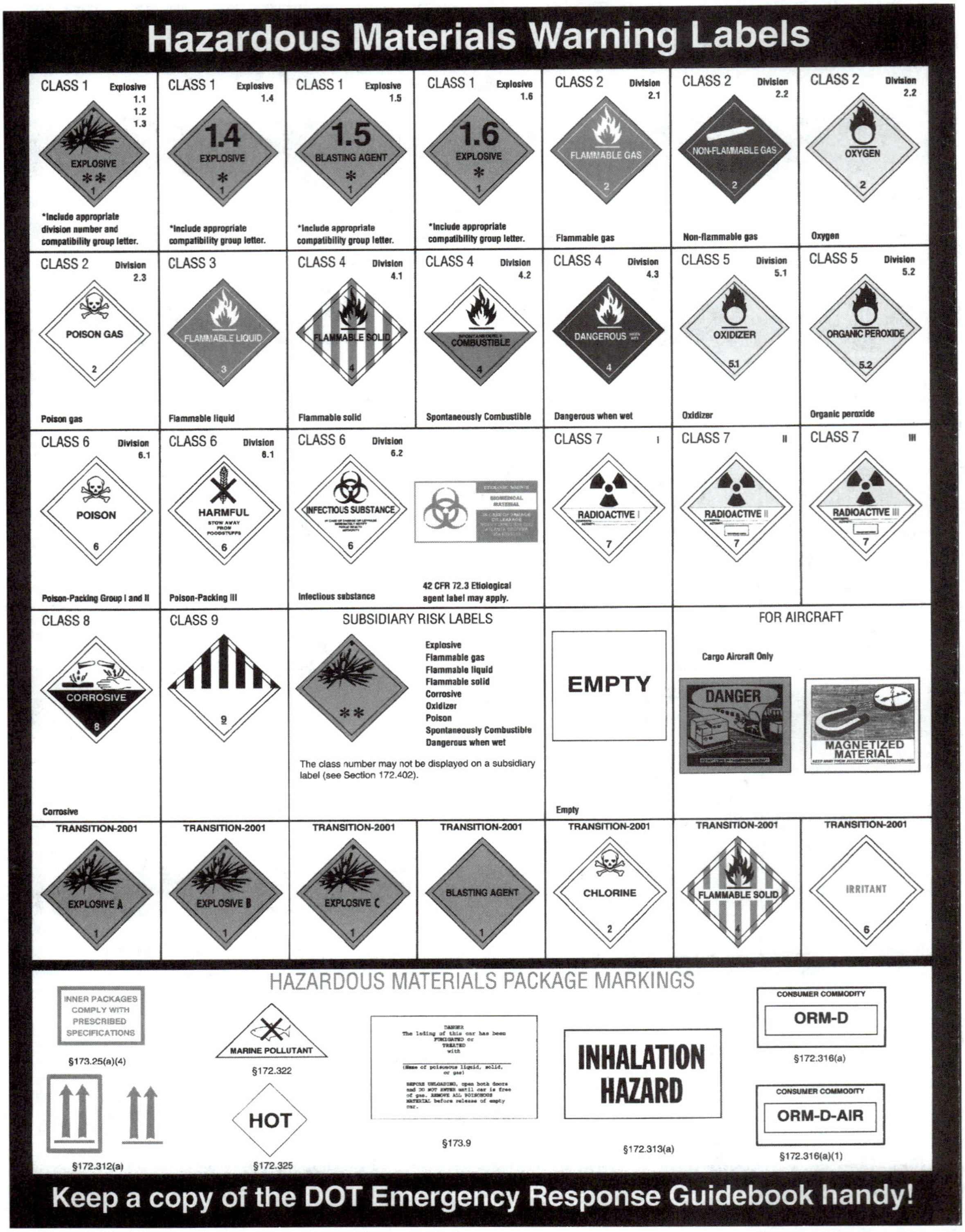

Figure 6.3(b) *The U.S. Department of Transportation's Chart 10 shows the warning labels required for the transport of hazardous materials.*

6-3 Private Sector Specialist Employee B

6-3.1 General.

6-3.1.1 Introduction. The private sector specialist employee B shall be trained to meet the competencies at the private sector specialist employee C level and the additional competencies in Section 6-3 of this chapter.

6-3.1.2* Definition. The level B private sector specialist employee is that person who, in the course of their regular job duties, works with or is trained in the hazards of specific chemicals or containers within their individual area of specialization. Because of their education, training, or work experience, the private sector specialist employee B can be called upon to respond to incidents involving these chemicals or containers. The private sector specialist employee B can be used to gather and record information, provide technical advice, and provide technical assistance (including work within the hot zone) at the incident consistent with their organization's emergency response plan and standard operating procedures and the local emergency response plan.

Private sector specialist employees at Level B are expected by their organization to respond *only* within their field of expertise. They may have expertise in a number of fields, including the following:

(a) Product specialties
(b) Industrial hygiene/toxicological specialties
(c) Environmental waste/remediation specialties
(d) Monitoring specialties
(e) Container specialties
(f) Material handling, such as loaders and unloaders
(g) Maintenance specialties

Private sector specialist employees at the B level need only meet those competencies required in their area of specialization.

A-6-3.1.2 An example of a private sector specialist employee B is a person who regularly loads and unloads tank trucks of the specific chemical involved in the incident as part of their regular job. At a hazardous materials incident, this person would be assigned the task of transferring the contents of the damaged tank truck into another container. The private sector specialist employee B would not be involved with chemicals for which the responder has not been trained. This person would leave the hot or warm zone when this work is completed.

6-3.1.3* Goal. The goal of these competencies is to ensure that the private sector specialist employee B has the knowledge and skills to safely perform the duties and responsibilities assigned in their organization's emergency response plan and standard operating procedures. Therefore, within their individual area of specialization, the private sector specialist employee B shall be able to:

(a) Assist the incident commander in analyzing the magnitude of an incident involving chemicals or containers for chemicals by completing the following tasks:

1. Provide and interpret information on the hazards and harmful effects
2. Provide and interpret information on the characteristics of specific containers
3. Provide information on concentrations of chemicals from exposure monitoring, dispersion modeling, or any other predictive method

(b) Assist the incident commander in planning a response to an incident involving chemicals or containers for chemicals by completing the following tasks:

1. Provide information on the potential response options and their consequences for specific chemicals or containers for chemicals
2. Provide information on the personal protective equipment requirements for a specific chemical
3. Provide information on the decontamination methods for a specific chemical
4. Provide information on the federal/provincial regulations that relate to the handling and disposal of a specific chemical
5. Develop a plan of action (within the capabilities of the available resources), including safety considerations, for handling chemicals or containers for chemicals consistent with their organization's emergency response plan and standard operating procedures

(c) Implement the planned response, as developed with the incident commander, for chemicals or containers for chemicals, consistent with their organization's emergency response plan and standard operating procedures and within the capabilities of the available resources, by completing the following tasks:

1. Perform response options specified in the plan of action, as agreed upon with the incident commander and consistent with their organization's emergency response plan and standard operating procedures (within the capabilities of the available resources)
2. Don, work in, and doff personal protective equipment needed to implement the response options

(d) Assist the incident commander to evaluate the results of implementing the planned response by completing the following tasks:

1. Provide feedback on the effectiveness of the response options taken
2. Provide reporting and subsequent documentation of the incident involving chemicals as required

A-6-3.1.3 The following site safety plan considerations are referenced from the *Standard Operating Safety Guides*, EPA, June 1992:

(a) Site description
(b) Entry objectives
(c) On-site organization
(d) On-site control
(e) Hazard evaluation
(f) Personal protective equipment
(g) On-site work plans
(h) Communication procedures
(i) Decontamination procedures
(j) Site safety and health plan

6-3.2 Competencies — Analyzing the Incident.

6-3.2.1 Providing and Interpreting Information on Hazards of Specific Chemicals. Given a specific chemical within their individual area of specialization and an appropriate material safety data sheet (MSDS) or other appropriate resource, the private sector specialist employee B shall advise the incident commander of the chemical's hazards and harmful effects and the potential consequences based on the incident. The private sector specialist employee B shall be able to:

6-3.2.1.1 Given a specific chemical, identify and interpret the following hazard information:

(a) Physical and chemical characteristics
(b) Physical hazards of the chemical (including fire and explosion hazards)
(c) Health hazards of the chemical
(d) Signs and symptoms of exposure
(e) Routes of entry
(f) Permissible exposure limits
(g) Reactivity hazards
(h) Environmental concerns

All private sector specialist employees at Level B must be able to locate the above hazard information in their organization's MSDSs and understand it. The product specialist described in 6-3.1.2 must be able to interpret the above information and give advice to the incident commander. If Level B responders cannot interpret this information, they must be able to contact the individuals in their organization who can interpret it. For an example of a typical MSDS, see the code and commentary in Chapter 2 of NFPA 472.

6-3.2.1.2 Given examples of specific chemicals and the appropriate resources (as identified in their organization's emergency response plan and standard operating procedures), predict the potential behavior of the chemicals based on the damage found, including the consequences of that behavior.

Private sector specialist employees at Level B should be able to predict what will happen when a liquid, solid, or gas is released from its container. What will occur, for example, if the chemical is exposed to air? Will it react, vaporize, or ignite?

6-3.2.1.3 Identify the general types of hazard information available from the other resources identified in their organization's emergency response plan and standard operating procedures.

Among the types of hazard information available to the private sector specialist employee from sources identified in the organization's E/R plan and standard operating procedures are containment techniques, medical treatment protocols, container design, reactivity data, and decontamination and mitigation procedures.

6-3.2.2 Providing Information on Characteristics of Specific Containers. Given a container for specific chemicals, the private sector specialist employee B shall advise the incident commander of the characteristics and potential behavior of that container. The private sector specialist employee B shall be able to:

All private sector specialist employees at Level B should be able to identify the person or persons in their organizations they can contact for information on such things as damage assessment, fitting arrangement, and the probability of container failure.

6-3.2.2.1 Given examples of containers for specific chemicals, identify the purpose and operation of the closures found on those containers.

Private sector specialist employees must be able to identify the following containers if they are used in their organization:

(a) Nonbulk containers

1. Drums
    a. type of bungs and seal caps
    b. closed and open
    c. head drums
    d. closure rings
    e. safety relief devices
2. Cylinders
    a. valves
    b. valve caps
    c. relief devices
    d. purge devices

(b) Bulk containers

1. Tote bins
    a. valves
    b. bungs, safety, and relief devices
    c. spouts

d. secondary closures
e. purge devices
f. couplings

2. Cargo tanks

a. venting devices
b. valves
c. relief purge devices
d. connections
e. manways
f. emergency shutoff valves
g. excess flow valves
h. gauging devices
i. sampling devices
j. secondary closures
k. safety relief devices

3. Tank cars

a. valves
b. safety and relief devices
c. connections
d. sampling valves
e. vapor and liquid valves
f. heater coils
g. caps
h. bottom outlet
i. dome cover
j. dome gasket, etc.

4. Hopper cars and hopper trucks

a. gates
b. manways

5. ISO containers

a. venting devices
b. valves
c. relief purge devices
d. connections
e. manways
f. emergency shutoff valves
g. excess flow valves
h. gauging devices
i. sampling devices
j. secondary closures
k. safety and relief devices

This list should also include any other types of containers, such as sample containers and supersacks, that the responder's organization uses. The private sector specialist employee B should know how to contact the organization's container specialist, who can provide this type of information.

6-3.2.2.2 Given a chemical container, list the types of damage that could occur.

Such damage might include punctures, scores, gouges, blown rupture disks, damaged gaskets, corrosion, damaged "O" rings, liner failure, weld seam failure, cracked bungs, and frictional damage on drums, among other things.

The private sector specialist employee B should know how to contact the organization's container specialist, who can provide this type of information.

6-3.2.2.3 Given examples of containers for specific chemicals and the appropriate resources (as identified in their organization's emergency response plan and standard operating procedures), predict the potential behavior of the containers and the consequences, based on the damage found.

Based on the types of damage listed in 6-3.2.2.2, all Level B private sector specialist employees should be able to assess potential container failures. They should know, for example, that a scored pressurized container may BLEVE, that a sheared valve on a cylinder may cause the container to rocket, that a bulging drum may rupture, and that damaged or stripped threads may cause a product release. Figure 6.4 shows an example of the warning signs that lead to detection of a leak.

Figure 6.4 *This plugged drum has the warning signs of leakage that a private sector specialist employee should be able to spot. The first sign is corrosion, visible on the far left; the second is the denting and scratches, visible along the seam side by the second plug; and the third is the evidence of seepage below the larger hole that has been plugged.*

6-3.2.2.4 Given their organization's emergency response plan and standard operating procedures, identify resources (including a method of contact) knowledgeable in the design, construction, and damage assessment of containers for chemicals.

These resources may include, but are not limited to, chemical and mechanical engineers, packaging specialists, and container manufacturers. The carrier, especially the cargo tank carrier, may be another resource.

6-3.2.3 Providing Information on Concentrations of Chemicals. Given a chemical and the applicable monitoring equipment provided by their organization for that chemical or the available predictive capabilities (e.g., dispersion modeling, exposure modeling), the private sector specialist employee B shall advise the incident commander of the concentrations of the released chemical and the implications of that information to the incident. The private sector specialist employee B shall be able to:

6-3.2.3.1 Identify the appropriate monitoring equipment.

Private sector specialist employees at Level B, who are trained to select and use monitoring equipment as part of their regular duties, should be able to identify the equipment appropriate for monitoring a chemical used in their areas of specialization. The equipment should be operated in accordance with the manufacturer's instructions.

6-3.2.3.2 Use the appropriate monitoring equipment provided by their organization to determine the actual concentrations of a specific chemical.

6-3.2.3.3 Given information on the concentrations of a chemical, interpret the significance of that concentration information to the incident relative to the hazards and harmful effects of the chemical.

The private sector specialist employee B should be able to interpret the results of monitoring in terms of known hazards. When unable to do so, the specialist employee should be able to contact the appropriate person in the organization who can.

6-3.2.3.4 Demonstrate field calibration and testing procedures, as necessary, for the monitoring equipment provided by their organization.

6-3.2.3.5 Given their organization's emergency response plan and standard operating procedures, identify the resources (including a method of contact) capable of providing monitoring equipment, dispersion modeling, or monitoring services.

Level B private sector specialist employees should be familiar with their organizations' E/R plan, standard operating procedures, and other resources so that they can identify the industrial hygienist, the site safety officer, the equipment supplier, and any other source who can provide this information.

6-3.3 Competencies – Planning the Response.

6-3.3.1 Providing Information on Potential Response Options and Consequences for Specific Chemicals. Given specific chemicals or containers within their individual area of specialization and the appropriate resources, the private sector specialist employee B shall advise the incident commander of the potential response options and their consequences. The private sector specialist employee B shall be able to:

6-3.3.1.1 Given a specific chemical and an appropriate material safety data sheet (MSDS), identify and interpret the following response information:

(a) Precautions for safe handling, including hygiene practices, protective measures, and procedures for cleanup of spills or leaks

Using their organizations' MSDSs, private sector specialist employees at Level B should be able to determine what personal protective equipment is needed to deal with spills and decontamination procedures, taking into consideration the class and state of the material, the external hazards, and the possible secondary hazards.

When dealing with flammables, for example, the Level B specialist employee should eliminate ignition sources, use spark-proof tools, and consider using foam to suppress vapors. When dealing with corrosives, the Level B specialist employee should ensure that the equipment and tools specific to the materials involved in the incident are compatible with the material and type of neutralizing materials being used. For example, certain chemicals may react with some metal shovels, pumps, and hoses.

When dealing with poison, the Level B specialist employee should consider evacuation or "protection in place"; should not allow eating, smoking, or gum chewing in hazardous areas; and should ensure that any personal protective equipment and tools that have been used are properly decontaminated.

(b) Applicable control measures, including personal protective equipment

Level B private sector specialist employees should be able to locate and identify the above information from an MSDS. Interpreting specific control and remediation procedures may require the expertise of a product specialist, an industrial hygienist, or some other appropriate person in the organization.

(c) Emergency and first aid procedures

The first aid section of an MSDS is generally comprehensive and self-explanatory. The private sector specialist employee B should pay particular attention to the use and availability of antidotes.

6-3.3.1.2 Given their organization's emergency response plan and standard operating procedures, identify additional resources for interpreting response information for a chemical.

Private sector specialist employees at Level B should be able to demonstrate how to access additional sources of assistance from other resources, such as CHEMTREC/CANUTEC/SETIQ.

6-3.3.1.3 Describe the advantages and limitations of the potential response options for a specific chemical.

The private sector specialist employee at Level B should be able to associate the appropriate response option to the chemicals for which they are expected to respond.

For example, Table 6.1 lists three possible options.

6-3.3.1.4 Given their organization's emergency response plan and standard operating procedures, identify resources (including a method of contact) capable of:

(a) Repairing containers for chemicals
(b) Removing the contents of containers for chemicals
(c) Cleanup and disposal of chemicals or containers for chemicals

The private sector specialist employee B should be able to locate individuals or other organizations, identified by such organizational resources as the E/R plan and standard operating procedures, who can accomplish the following tasks, tasks they normally perform in their day-to-day activities:

Normal Job Function	Task(s)
Material handler	Repair containers
Container specialist	
Material handler	Removing container contents
Loader/unloader	
Container specialist	
Environmental specialist	Cleaning up site Disposing of chemicals

Table 6.1 Examples of Response Options

Event	Response	Advantages	Disadvantages
Pesticide fire	Allow to burn	Minimal run-off Minimal containment	Products of combustion Demand on fire departments
Acid spill	Neutralize run-off	Reduces hazard Lessens corrosivity	Exposure from process Vapor release
Poisonous liquid releasing vapor	Apply foam blanket	Suppresses vapor	Contributes to contamination, increases cleanup

6-3.3.2 Providing Information on Personal Protective Equipment Requirements. Given specific chemicals or containers for chemicals within their individual area of specialization and the appropriate resources, the private sector specialist employee B shall advise the incident commander of the appropriate personal protective equipment necessary for various response options. The private sector specialist employee B shall be able to:

6-3.3.2.1 Given a specific chemical and an appropriate material safety data sheet (MSDS), identify personal protective equipment, including the materials of construction, that will be compatible with that chemical.

6-3.3.2.2 Given their organization's emergency response plan and standard operating procedures, identify other appropriate resources (including a method of contact) capable of identifying the personal protective equipment that is compatible with a specific chemical.

Some of the resources a Level B private sector specialist employee can use to identify personal protective equipment compatible with a specific chemical are compatibility charts, data bases, and PPE manufacturers' literature.

6-3.3.2.3 Given an incident involving a specific chemical and the response options for that problem, determine whether the personal protective equipment provided by the organization is appropriate for the options presented.

All private sector specialist employees at Level B who are trained to select and/or use PPE should be able to identify, interpret, and apply compatibility data from compatibility charts and to consider the limitations associated with the use of Level A and Level B equipment, especially if there is potential for fire.

6-3.3.3 Providing Information on Decontamination Methods. Given a specific chemical within their individual area of specialization and the available resources, the private sector specialist employee B shall identify appropriate decontamination methods for various response options. The private sector specialist employee B shall be able to:

6-3.3.3.1 Given a specific chemical and a material safety data sheet (MSDS) or other resource, obtain the potential methods for removing or neutralizing that chemical.

The private sector specialist employee B should be able to point out the sections on an MSDS that include decontamination and neutralization information or be able to contact an individual in the organization who can provide this information.

6-3.3.3.2 Given a specific chemical and a material safety data sheet (MSDS) or other resource, identify the circumstances under which disposal of contaminated equipment would be necessary.

Materials that cannot be decontaminated, such as porous materials like leather or wood; limited-use equipment, such as one-time-use protective clothing; or equipment for which decontamination procedures are unknown may have to be disposed of through bagging. The Level B private sector specialist employee should be able to clearly identify the appropriate disposal methods and when their use may be necessary.

6-3.3.3.3 Given their organization's emergency response plan and standard operating procedures, identify resources (including a method of contact) capable of identifying potential decontamination methods.

One such resource is Chapter 7, "Decontamination," of NFPA 471 in this handbook.

6-3.3.4 Providing Information on Handling and Disposal Regulations. Given a specific chemical within their area of specialization and the available resources, the private sector specialist employee B shall advise the incident commander of the federal or provincial regulations that relate to the handling, transportation, and disposal of that chemical. The private sector specialist employee B shall be able to:

6-3.3.4.1 Given a specific chemical and a material safety data sheet (MSDS) or other resource, identify federal or provincial regulations that apply to the handling, transportation, and disposal of that chemical.

Among the regulations that apply to the handling, transportation, and disposal of chemicals are Title 49 of CFR-DOT, Title 40 of CFR-EPA, and, in Canada, TDG and/or MOE. The agencies that handle these regulations should be contacted by someone identified in the organization's E/R plan or standard operating procedures as the person responsible for making notifications according to regulations.

6-3.3.4.2 Given a specific chemical and a material safety data sheet (MSDS) or other resource, identify the agencies (including a method of contact) responsible for compliance with the federal or provincial regulations that apply to the handling, transportation, and disposal of a specific chemical.

The agencies responsible for compliance with regulations applying to the handling, transportation, and disposal of a specific chemical include the Occupational Safety and Health Administration (OSHA), which covers emergency response activities; the U.S. Department of Transportation (DOT), which deals with transportation; and the Environmental Protection Agency (EPA), which handles hazardous materials disposal in the United States. Transport Canada, Environment Canada, and Labor Canada cover the same issues for the provinces.

These agencies should be contacted by someone identified in the organization's E/R plan or standard operating procedures as the person responsible for making the necessary notifications according to regulations.

6-3.3.4.3 Given their organization's emergency response plan and standard operating procedures, identify resources for information pertaining to federal or provincial regulations relative to the handling and disposal of a specific chemical.

The private sector specialist employee B should be able to contact a knowledgeable person, such as an environmental engineer, chemist, or specialist, within their organization who will know where in the organization's E/R plan or standard operating procedures the needed information can be located.

6-3.3.5 Developing a Plan of Action. Given a simulated incident involving chemicals or containers used in their individual area of specialization, the private sector specialist employee B shall (in conjunction with the incident commander) develop a plan of action, consistent with their organization's emergency response plan and standard operating procedures, for handling chemicals or containers in that incident. The plan of action developed shall be within the capabilities of the available resources and shall include safety considerations. The private sector specialist employee B shall be able to:

6-3.3.5.1 Given the organization's emergency response plan and standard operating procedures, identify the process for development of a plan of action, including safety considerations.

Each potential hazardous materials incident is required to have an overall plan of action. However, private sector specialist employees at Level B are expected to develop an action plan for only those tasks and procedures associated with their areas of expertise and regular job duties. They are also expected to define the processes needed to execute that plan.

For example, loader/unloaders who transload material as part of their normal duties may be called upon to develop an action plan for performing the same procedure at the scene of a hazardous materials incident and to define the steps and safety considerations required to execute that plan.

6-3.4 Competencies — Implementing the Planned Response.

6-3.4.1 Performing Response Options Specified in the Plan of Action. Given an assignment by the incident commander in their individual area of specialization, the private sector specialist employee B shall perform the assigned actions consistent with their organization's emergency response plan and standard operating procedures. The private sector specialist employee B shall be able to:

6-3.4.1.1 Perform assigned tasks consistent with their organization's emergency response plan and standard operating procedures and the available personnel, tools, and equipment (including personal protective equipment), including the following:

(a) Confinement activities
(b) Containment activities
(c) Product removal activities

6-3.4.1.2* Identify factors that can affect an individual's ability to perform the assigned tasks.

A-6-3.4.1.2 Such factors include heat, cold, working in confined space, working in personal protective equipment, working in a flammable or toxic atmosphere, and pre-existing health conditions.

6-3.4.2 Using Personal Protective Equipment. Given an assignment within their individual area of specialization that is consistent with their organization's emergency response plan and standard operating procedures, the private sector specialist employee B shall be able to:

6-3.4.2.1 Don, work in, and doff the appropriate respiratory protection and protective clothing for the assigned tasks.

6-3.4.2.2 Identify the safety considerations for personnel wearing personal protective equipment, including:

(a) Buddy system

All responders at a hazardous materials incident must work in a minimum of two-person teams. Each person must be within sight or sound of the other person at all times during the incident.

(b) Backup personnel

Safety procedures require that backup responders dress in the same level of protection as those on the entry team. Backup personnel may have to enter the same hazardous area as the primary entry team workers to perform a rescue and should be prepared to do so at any time.

(c) Symptoms of heat and cold stress

Safety procedures require that personnel be monitored for symptoms such as abnormal pulse, temperature, respiration, changes in skin color, and decreased mental alertness during or shortly after exposure to a hazardous material. Chapter 8, "Medical Monitoring," of NFPA 471 in this handbook contains the appropriate benchmarks for detecting heat or cold stress for persons working at a hazardous materials incident as well as other medical symptoms indicating potential acute and chronic health problems related to a hazardous materials exposure.

(d) Limitations of personnel working in personal protective equipment

Safety procedures establish time limits for wearing personal protective clothing during an incident. Other limiting factors include the responder's level of physical fitness, endurance ability, and the psychological condition of the individual responder.

(e) Indications of material degradation of chemical-protective clothing

Safety procedures require that responders evaluate signs of material degradation including discoloration, the loss of integrity and flexibility, the formation of blisters, and melting or stretching of material.

(f) Physical and psychological stresses on the wearer

Safety procedures required to maintain the overall well-being of the responder include monitoring responders for signs of stress related to work in the hazardous materials incident environment. Such stress may cause a rise in body temperature, loss of body fluids, elevated pulse and respiration rates, vertigo, nausea, changes in skin color, disorientation, anxiety, and incoherence. See Chapter 8 of NFPA 471 in this handbook for more information on this topic.

(g) Emergency procedures and hand signals

Safety procedures require that responders maintain visual contact and that they demonstrate appropriate hand signals for loss of air and emergency escape assistance.

6-3.4.2.3 Identify the procedures for cleaning, sanitizing, and inspecting personal protective equipment provided by the organization.

These procedures should be performed in accordance with the manufacturers' recommendations and the organization's standard operating procedures concerning the use and maintenance of personal protective equipment.

6-3.5 Competencies — Evaluating Progress.

6-3.5.1 Providing an Evaluation of the Effectiveness of Selected Response Options. Given an incident involving specific chemicals or containers for chemicals within their individual area of specialization, the private sector specialist employee B shall advise the incident commander of the effectiveness of the selected response options. The private sector specialist employee B shall be able to:

6-3.5.1.1 Identify the criteria for evaluating whether or not the selected response options are effective in accomplishing the objectives.

These criteria must be based on the desired outcome. The responder must determine how the hazards to personnel, the environment, and property affect the outcome sought. Effective options result in diminished hazards, stabilization, or complete mitigation.

6-3.5.1.2 Identify the circumstances when it would be prudent to withdraw from a chemical incident.

The responder should withdraw from a chemical incident when the following conditions exist:

(a) Intervention will not or cannot produce a favorable outcome;
(b) The immediate hazard level is unacceptable;
(c) The incident is worsening as a result of the option selected.

6-3.5.2 Reporting and Documenting the Incident. Given a simulated incident involving chemicals or containers for chemicals used in their individual area of specialization, the private sector specialist employee B shall complete the reporting and subsequent documentation requirements consistent with their organization's emergency response plan and standard operating procedures. The private sector specialist employee B shall be able to:

6-3.5.2.1 Identify the importance of documentation (including training records, exposure records, incident reports, and critique reports) for an incident involving chemicals.

Organizations require documentation in order to help establish preventive and corrective actions. Documentation of hazardous materials incidents is also mandated by governmental regulation. Documentation is also required for emergency response training, medical monitoring, and PPE certification. Regulatory organizations require documentation for similar reasons. Finally, documentation is frequently used for trend analysis in hazardous materials incident prevention assessments.

6-3.5.2.2 Identify the steps used in keeping an activity log and exposure records.

Most emergency response plans require that an employee's name and identifying code (usually a social security number) be recorded with each of the functions performed at a hazardous materials incident. In addition, the time and duration of each activity must be accurately documented. Exposure records are compiled in a similar manner, listing the materials to which the employee may be exposed, the duration of exposure, the manner in which the contaminant was identified, and the name of the person who made that determination.

6-3.5.2.3 Identify the requirements for compiling incident reports.

These requirements are a means of providing a factual, objective format for defining the who, what, where, when, and how of an incident.

6-3.5.2.4 Identify the requirements for compiling hot zone entry and exit logs.

This information is required so that those in charge of an incident can monitor an employee's health and keep track of the work performed and the time spent in the hot zone. See 6-3.5.2.2 for more information.

6-3.5.2.5 Identify the requirements for compiling personal protective equipment logs.

Personal protective equipment logs should include information about use time, inspections, testing, and the results of inspection and decontamination procedures for each garment or suit used. This documentation should also include a list of the contaminants to which the equipment has been exposed during its lifetime of use, as well as the duration of each exposure.

6-3.5.2.6 Identify the requirements for filing documents and maintaining records.

Most organizations keep records to protect themselves and their employees and to provide a written account of the incident. Appropriate sources within the organization, such as regulatory specialists, should be consulted for both internal and external reporting requirements.

6-4 Private Sector Specialist Employee A

6-4.1 General.

6-4.1.1 Introduction. The private sector specialist employee A shall be trained to meet the competencies at the private sector specialist employee C level (Section 6-2 in this chapter) and hazardous materials technician level (Chapter 4) relative to the chemicals and containers used in their organization's area of specialization.

Private sector specialist employees at Level A can provide the incident commander with considerable assistance since Level A training deals with a range of products and containers specific to their employing organization and is usually equivalent to that of the hazardous materials technician for these specific products and containers.

However, Level A private sector specialist employees need only demonstrate those technician-level competencies that apply to the materials and containers for which they are expected to respond at their company's property.

6-4.1.2 Definition. The private sector specialist employee A is that person who is specifically trained to handle incidents involving chemicals or containers for chemicals used in their organization's area of specialization. Consistent with their organization's emergency response plan and standard operating procedures, the private sector specialist employee A shall be able to analyze an incident involving chemicals within their organization's area of specialization, plan a response to that incident, implement the planned response within the capabilities of the resources available, and evaluate the progress of the planned response.

6-4.1.3 Goal. The goal of this level of competence is to ensure that the private sector specialist employee A has the knowledge and skills to safely perform the duties and responsibilities assigned in their organization's emergency response plan and standard operating procedures. Therefore, in addition to being competent at the private sector specialist employee C and the hazardous materials technician levels, the private sector specialist employee A shall be able to, in conjunction with the incident commander:

(a) Analyze an incident involving chemicals and containers for chemicals used in their organization's area of specialization to determine the magnitude of the incident by completing the following tasks:

1. Survey an incident involving chemicals and containers for chemicals, including the following:

   a. Identify the containers involved

The private sector specialist employee at Level A should be able to identify the characteristics of any onsite containers that might indicate the presence of hazardous materials. These special containers include high-pressure containers (identified by their rounded ends), cryogenic cargo tanks or cylinders, and casks used for radioactive materials.

   b. Identify or classify unknown materials

The private sector specialist employee at Level A is expected to be able to identify unknown materials likely to be at hand in the employer's manufacturing or storage facilities in the event that a container's shipping papers, placards, MSDS, or other identifying items have been destroyed or are unavailable.

   c. Verify the identity of the chemicals

2. Collect and interpret hazard and response information from printed resources, technical resources, computer data bases, and monitoring equipment for chemicals

Private sector specialist employees at Level A must understand the importance of using multiple resources for gathering hazard and response information. These responders should collect information from a variety of resources, be able to appropriately compare that information, and then make decisions based on this comparison and evaluation. Most responders generally give more weight to the more conservative information and base their actions on that information.

3. Determine the extent of damage to containers of chemicals

The terms listed below allow the responder to use standard terminology when assessing containers to determine how badly they have been damaged. The condition of the container should be described using one of the following terms:

(a) Undamaged, no product release
(b) Damaged, no product release
(c) Damaged, product release
(d) Undamaged, product release

4. Predict the likely behavior of the chemicals and containers for chemicals

After the chemical is identified, information about the chemical's hazards and behavior should be collected from appropriate reference sources. This information, which may be obtained simultaneously with determining the extent of container/packaging damage, is used to predict the behavior of the chemical and its container.

5. Estimate the potential outcomes of an incident involving chemicals and containers for chemicals

An estimate is a series of predictions that attempts to provide an overall picture of potential outcomes. Responders must assess the information gathered during analysis and predict the outcome based on that assessment.

(b) Plan a response (within the capabilities of available resources) to an incident involving chemicals and containers for chemicals used in their organization's area of specialization by completing the following tasks:

1. Identify the response objectives for an incident involving chemicals and containers for chemicals

The private sector specialist employee at Level A should note that many of the options available can be used either offensively or defensively. For example, the size of the potential endangered area may be changed defensively by diking to contain a spill or offensively by entering the hot zone and plugging the leak. It should also be noted that defensive operations may be the most prudent method of dealing with many hazardous materials.

2. Identify the potential action options for each response objective for an incident involving chemicals and containers for chemicals

Figure 4.13, in the commentary of NFPA 472, Chapter 4 of this handbook, shows options available to the private sector specialist employee at Level A for accomplishing response objectives.

3. Select the personal protective equipment required for a given response option for an incident involving chemicals and containers for chemicals

The responder should always use the highest level of protection until the chemicals likely to be involved in an incident can be positively identified and the level of concentration can be determined. Determining the most appropriate type of respiratory protection required at each incident depends on many factors. A key factor is the level of protective clothing necessary to protect the private sector specialist employee A.

Level A protection limits the user to positive pressure self-contained breathing apparatus or positive pressure supplied-air respirators.

4. Select the appropriate decontamination procedures, as necessary, for an incident involving chemicals and containers for chemicals

There are basically two ways to decontaminate something: physically and chemically. Physical methods manually separate the chemical from the material being decontaminated by scrubbing or washing the material, or both. Physical decontamination is often easier than chemical decontamination, but it may not completely remove all the contaminants.

Chemical methods involve changing one chemical into another or into a form that will facilitate its removal. Unfortunately, the chemical process involved could introduce other hazards. Care must be taken to collect all the contamination that has been removed by either method and to dispose of it properly.

5. Develop a plan of action (within the capabilities of the available resources), including safety considerations, for handling an incident involving chemicals and containers for chemicals consistent with their organization's emergency response plan and standard operating procedures

According to Charles Wright, writing in the *Fire Protection Handbook*, 18th edition:

> After selecting the response option for a hazardous materials incident, a plan of action including safety and health considerations should be developed. This plan of action describes the response objectives and options and the personnel and equipment required to accomplish the objectives. The plan provides a permanent record of the decisions made at the incident. An organization's standard operating procedures provide the basis of this plan of action. . . .
>
> Components for a typical plan of action include the following:
>
> 1. Site description
> 2. Entry objectives
> 3. On-scene organization and coordination
> 4. On-scene control
> 5. Hazard evaluation
> 6. Personal protective equipment
> 7. On-scene work assignments
> 8. Communications procedures
> 9. Decontamination procedures
> 10. On-scene safety and health considerations including designation of the safety officer, emergency medical care procedures, environmental monitoring, emergency procedures, and personnel monitoring.[4]

Obviously, the complexity of an incident will determine the detail identified in the plan of action. Each of the above items must be considered, however, in order to ensure that nothing is being overlooked.

(c) Implement the planned response (as developed with the incident commander) to an incident involving chemicals and containers for chemicals used in their organization's area of specialization consistent with their organization's emergency response plan and standard operating procedures by completing the following tasks:

1. Don, work in, and doff appropriate personal protective equipment provided by their organization for use with chemicals

Private sector specialist employees at Level A should practice donning and doffing chemical-protective clothing to become proficient. One of the more effective ways to evaluate the ability to don and doff the protective clothing provided is to conduct training exercises that require putting on the personal protective equipment and to conduct simulated control activities, followed by simulated decontamination.

Because some types of chemical-protective clothing are very costly, it may be advisable to use garments that are no longer adequate for emergency response. Hazardous materials training suits that are less expensive are also available; these allow for cost-effective training in the use of totally encapsulating suits.

2. Perform control functions, as agreed upon with the incident commander, for chemicals and containers for chemicals

The purpose of this competency is to allow the private sector specialist employee A to demonstrate the ability to choose the appropriate equipment and methods to control a simulated incident. The equipment necessary to conduct the operations may vary depending on the type of material that is leaking and the physical properties of the damaged area, valve, or breach. For example, non-sparking tools should be used when working with flammable liquids or gases. And in some cases, special tools may be needed for certain valves. Such situations should be identified during pre-incident planning.

(d) Evaluate the results of implementing the planned response to an incident involving chemicals and containers for chemicals used in their organization's area of specialization

References Cited in Commentary

1. *North American Emergency Response Guidebook,* U.S. Department of Transportation, Washington, DC, 1996.
2. *Emergency Handling of Hazardous Materials in Surface Transportation,* Association of American Railroads, Washington, DC, 1992.
3. CMA's *Packaging for Transporting Hazardous and Non-hazardous Materials,* Chemical Manufacturers Association, Washington, DC, 1989.
4. Arthur E. Cote, ed., *Fire Protection Handbook,* 18th edition, National Fire Protection Association, Quincy, MA, 1997, p. 10-127.

CHAPTER 7

Competencies for the Hazardous Materials Branch Officer

7-1 General

7-1.1 Introduction.

The hazardous materials branch officer shall be trained to meet all competencies for the first responder at the awareness, operational, and technician levels and the competencies of this chapter. The hazardous materials branch officer also shall receive any additional training to meet applicable United States Department of Transportation (DOT), United States Environmental Protection Agency (EPA), Occupational Safety and Health Administration (OSHA), and other appropriate state, local, or provincial occupational health and safety regulatory requirements.

The hazardous materials branch officer is a new level that has added to the 1997 edition of NFPA 472. *(See Figure 7.1.)* The committee created this new designation to meet the need for a team leader. In the fire department's chain-of-command, for example, each team or company has an assigned team leader to supervise the fire fighters. In addition, each team or group is supervised by an incident commander who may oversee one or more companies or teams.

The hazardous materials branch officer has the same technical competencies as a technician and completes the chain-of-command needed at an incident, which, in turn, can increase the safety and efficiency at the hazardous materials incident site.

In complex incidents involving numerous chemicals or more than one central location, the incident commander (IC) would use the hazardous materials branch officer's expertise in formulating response objectives, action options, and the plan of action. In addition, the IC would rely on the hazardous materials branch officer to provide direct supervision of the team to accomplish the objectives. More than one team can now work at an incident and each have its own leader.

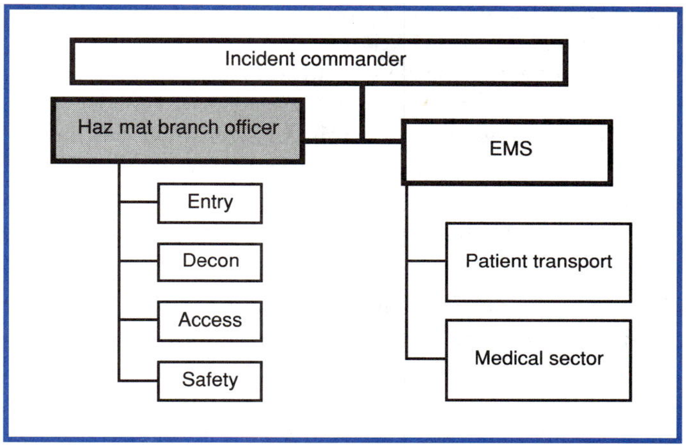

Figure 7.1 This incident command chart shows the role of the hazardous materials branch officer. This new command-level post, which requires technician-level competencies, functions as a tactical adviser to the incident commander and as a team leader to direct the technicians while entering and working within the hot and warm zones.

7-1.2 Definition.

The hazardous materials branch officer is that person who is responsible for directing and coordinating all operations assigned to the hazardous materials branch by the incident commander.

Again, different incident management systems may use words such as *sector, group,* or *division,* instead of "branch." If the duties assigned are identical, the competencies required are the same no matter which words are used to describe this level.

7-1.3 Goal.

The goal of this chapter shall be to provide the hazardous materials branch officer with the knowledge and skills to perform the following tasks safely. Therefore, in addition to being competent at the awareness, operational, and technician levels, the hazardous materials branch officer shall be able to:

(a) Analyze a hazardous materials incident to determine the magnitude of the problem by estimating the potential outcomes within the endangered area

(b) Plan a response within the capabilities and competencies of available personnel, personal protective equipment, and control equipment by completing the following tasks:

1. Identify the response objectives for hazardous materials incidents
2. Identify the potential action options (defensive, offensive, and nonintervention) available by response objective
3. Determine the level of personal protective equipment required for a given action option
4. Provide recommendations to the incident commander for the development of a plan of action for the hazardous materials branch consistent with the local emergency response plan and the organization's standard operating procedures and within the capability of available personnel, personal protective equipment, and control equipment

The hazardous materials branch officer can perform many of the same planning functions as an incident commander, as outlined above in (a) and (b). However, the branch officer can only recommend that various actions be taken. It is the IC who must consider each incident in its entirety and make the final decision.

(c) Implement a response to favorably change the outcomes consistent with the local emergency response plan and the organization's standard operating procedures by completing the following tasks:

1. Implement the incident management system as it directly relates to the specified procedures for hazardous materials branch operations
2. Direct hazardous materials branch resources (private, governmental, and others) with expected task assignments and on-scene activities and provide management overviews, technical review, and logistical support to hazardous materials branch resources

(d) Evaluate the progress of the planned response to ensure that the response objectives are being met safely, effectively, and efficiently and adjust the plan of action accordingly by evaluating the progress of the plan of action

(e) Terminate the incident by completing the following:

1. Conduct a debriefing for hazardous materials branch personnel
2. Conduct a critique for hazardous materials branch personnel
3. Report and document the hazardous materials branch operations

7-2 Competencies — Analyzing the Incident

7-2.1 Estimating Potential Outcomes.

Given simulated facility or transportation incidents involving hazardous materials, the surrounding conditions, and the predicted behavior of the container and its contents, the hazardous materials branch officer shall estimate the potential outcomes within the endangered area.

Outcomes are the result of implementing the response objectives. These objectives can include the following:

(a) Modifying the stress being applied to the container
(b) Changing the size of the breach
(c) Changing the quantity being released
(d) Changing the size of the endangered area
(e) Reducing exposures
(f) Reducing the level of harm

Another prudent objective that should always be considered is "what if we do nothing and keep everyone away."

The outcomes can be the result of defensive, offensive, or nonintervention actions. Several potential outcomes can be considered by the incident commander. Each will have its own risks, potential for success, and technical expertise required for successful completion. Each option must be thought through to its end or outcome. Only if the outcome can improve the situation, should it be considered.

7-3 Competencies — Planning the Response

7-3.1 Selecting the Level of Personal Protective Equipment.

Given situations with known and unknown hazardous materials, the hazardous materials branch officer shall select the appropriate personal protective equipment for the action options specified in the plan of action in each situation.

The branch officer can "select" the level of PPE, but the IC must "approve" the selection. The type of respiratory protection required depends on many factors. A key factor is the level of protective clothing necessary for protection into the hot zone. The responder should always use the highest level of protection until the specific hazardous material and the levels of concentration have been determined. For "unknown" situations, Level A PPE should be used.

7-3.2 Developing a Plan of Action.

Given simulated facility and transportation hazardous materials incidents, the hazardous materials branch officer shall develop a plan of action consistent with the local emergency response plan and the organization's standard operating procedures that is within the capability of the available personnel, personal protective equipment, and control equipment. The hazardous materials branch officer shall be able to:

A plan of action will describe the response objectives and any options to achieving the objectives. Again, with each objective should be an estimate of the likely outcome. The basis for the plan will be the estimate of the potential outcomes, the organization's standard operating procedures, and the local emergency response plan. In the plan, safety and health considerations, necessary personnel, and control equipment should be listed for each objective. This plan provides a permanent record of the incident and can be the outline for the incident critique.

7-3.2.1 Identify the order of the steps for developing a plan of action.

The following components need to be considered when developing a plan of action:

(a) Site restrictions
(b) Entry objectives
(c) On-scene organization and control
(d) Personal protective equipment selection
(e) Hazard evaluation
(f) Communications procedures
(g) Emergency procedures and personnel accountability
(h) Emergency medical care arrangements
(i) Rehabilitation plan
(j) Decontamination procedures
(k) On-scene work assignments (branches)
(l) Debriefing and critiquing

7-3.2.2 Identify the factors to be evaluated in selecting public protective actions, including evacuation and shelter in-place.

The goal of this evaluation should be to reduce or prevent contamination of those members of the public who are directly exposed to the hazardous material(s). If these individuals are safe in their present location and the structure in which they are housed can be protected from contamination by such methods as closing windows and doors and turning off ventilation systems that may draw air in from outside, it may be better to leave these civilians in place until the incident can be controlled. Even after hazardous materials responders have notified the public that they must remain in their present location, responders should provide these individuals with constant updates on the progress of the incident and reassurances of their safety.

7-3.2.3 Given the local emergency response plan or the organization's standard operating procedure, identify procedures to accomplish the following tasks:

(a) Make ongoing assessments of the situation
(b) Command on-scene personnel (incident management system) assigned to the hazardous materials branch
(c) Coordinate hazardous materials support and mutual aid
(d) Provide resources for public protection action (evacuation or shelter in-place)
(e) Coordinate with fire suppression services as it relates to hazardous materials incidents
(f) Coordinate hazardous materials branch control, containment, or confinement operations
(g) Coordinate with the medical branch to ensure proper medical assistance (ambulance) and medical treatment (hospital)
(h) Coordinate on-scene decontamination when appropriate
(i) Coordinate activities with those of the environmental remedial action ("cleanup") services

7-3.2.4 Identify the process for determining the effectiveness of an action option on the potential outcomes.

Direct observations from the technicians and the branch officer should be compared against the expected outcomes as listed in the plan of action. If time is a factor, specific time frames should be determined before any actions are started. At the agreed upon times, reports should be forward to the IC.

7-3.2.5 Identify the procedures for presenting a safety briefing prior to allowing personnel to work on a hazardous materials incident.

Some of the areas that should be evaluated in the safety briefing include the following:

(a) Incident commander, branch officers, and all hazardous materials responders have met all the competencies for their appropriate levels in accordance with NFPA 472.

(b) Activities that present a significant risk to the safety of members are limited to situations that offer the potential to save endangered lives.

(c) No risk to the safety of members is acceptable when there is no possibility to save lives or property.

(d) All personnel working in the warm zone or hot zone are under the supervision of a branch officer.

(e) Personnel accountability procedures are being utilized.

(f) A rest and rehabilitation area ready for first responders to finish their assignments is described and its location identified.

(g) A hazardous materials branch safety officer has been designated and is operational.

(h) Communications have been established on one simplex radio channel that is not used by anyone close enough to interfere. Hand signals are available as a backup if the radios fail.

(i) Appropriate protective clothing and protective equipment are used whenever the responder is exposed, or potentially exposed, to the hazardous materials.

(j) A rapid intervention crew consisting of at least two responders is available for rescue of a member or team if the need arises. Responders operating in the hot zone are operating in teams of two or more.

(k) Medical monitoring of all responders before they can proceed to work in personnel protective equipment, in accordance with the guidelines in Chapter 8, "Medical Monitoring" of NFPA 471 in this handbook, is established and briefly reviewed.

(l) Responders are warned to be aware of any clues indicating that the incident may be a chemical, biological, nuclear, or explosives incident. If terrorism is suspected, responders are alert to the possibility of secondary devices or attempts to disguise the true nature of the incident.

7-4 Competencies — Implementing the Planned Response

7-4.1 Implementing the Incident Management System.

Given a copy of the local emergency response plan, the hazardous materials branch officer shall identify the requirements of the plan, including the required procedures for notification and utilization of nonlocal resources (private, state, and federal government personnel). The hazardous materials branch officer shall be able to:

There are several different models for incident management systems. Each system generally has the same components, even though different titles for the various responders are sometimes used. For example, hazardous materials branch officers, hazard sector officers, and hazardous materials group supervisors generally perform the same functions. Basically, these workers are responsible for implementing the incident action plan that deals with any operations intended to control the hazardous materials portion of an incident. Overall direction and approval of the action plan is the duty of the incident commander.

Within the incident management system, there are generally five primary functional areas:

(a) Incident command
(b) Operations
(c) Planning
(d) Logistics
(e) Finance (in some cases)

Usually, there will also be a public information officer and an incident safety officer. For hazardous materials incidents, additional functions are identified, including the hazardous materials branch and safety officers, the decontamination officer, the rehabilitation officer, the information research and resources officer, and the entry/reconnaissance officer.

7-4.1.1 Identify the process and procedures for obtaining cleanup and restoration services in the local emergency response plan or organization's standard operating procedures.

7-4.1.2 Identify the steps for implementing the local and related emergency response plans as required under SARA Title III Section 303 of the federal regulations or other local emergency response planning legislation.

7-4.1.3 Given the local emergency planning documents, identify the elements of each of the documents.

7-4.1.4 Identify the elements of the incident management system necessary to coordinate response activities at hazardous materials incidents.

7-4.1.5 Identify the primary local, state, regional, and federal government agencies and identify the scope of their regulatory authority (including the regulations) pertaining to the production, transportation, storage, and use of hazardous materials and the disposal of hazardous wastes.

The branch officer must know which agencies may become involved and their regulatory authority in a hazardous materials incident. The local emergency response plan should identify these agencies and delineate their roles, authority, and functions.

7-4.1.6 Identify the governmental agencies and private sector resources offering assistance to the hazardous materials branch during a hazardous materials incident and identify their role and type of assistance or resources available.

Some government agencies provide response or technical assistance to the local hazardous materials response teams. For example, the U.S. Coast Guard staffs three strategically located National Strike Teams that are trained and equipped to respond to major oil spills and chemical releases. The U.S. Environmental Protection Agency also has a response component called the Environmental Response Team (ERT). The ERT is a group of scientists and engineers who are trained in sampling and analysis, hazard assessment, cleanup techniques, and other avenues of technical support. In addition, many state, local governments, and private industries can provide technical assistance. For example, hazardous materials response teams from other municipalities or private industry can be a great resource for large incidents and may have specialized monitoring equipment and knowledge to help identify complex or obscure hazardous material(s).

The private sector also has many resources available to emergency responders, from providing technical advice and assisting with on-scene monitoring to providing specialized equipment. In most areas, there are private-sector companies that provide cleanup and disposal services. Some of these companies may even stage equipment in an area and fly personnel to the scene when a hazardous materials incident occurs. CHEMTREC/CANUTEC/SETIQ offers referrals to private-sector resources.

The branch officer must know how to get specialized assistance when it is needed and must be familiar with various types of public and private sector assistance available. These resources and their contacts should be identified in the local emergency response plan.

7-4.2* Directing Resources (Private and Governmental).

Given a simulated hazardous materials incident and the necessary resources to implement the planned response, the hazardous materials branch officer shall demonstrate the ability to direct the hazardous materials branch resources in a safe and efficient manner consistent with the capabilities of those resources.

A-7-4.2 These abilities should include the following:

(a) Task assignment (based upon strategical and tactical options)
(b) Operational safety
(c) Operational effectiveness
(d) Planning support
(e) Information/research
(f) Logistical support
(g) Administrative support

7-4.3 Providing a Focal Point for Information Transfer to Media and Elected Officials.

Given a simulated hazardous materials incident, the hazardous materials branch officer shall demonstrate the ability to act as a resource to provide information to the incident commander or the public information officer for distribution to the media and local, state, and federal officials. The hazardous materials branch officer shall be able to:

7-4.3.1 Identify the local policy for providing information to the media.

7-4.3.2 Identify the responsibilities of the public information officer at a hazardous materials incident.

7-5 Competencies — Evaluating Progress

7-5.1 Evaluating Progress of the Plan of Action.

Given simulated facility and transportation hazardous materials incidents, the hazardous materials branch officer shall evaluate the progress of the plan of action to determine whether the efforts are accomplishing the response objectives. The hazardous materials branch officer shall be able to:

7-5.1.1 Identify the procedures for evaluating whether the action options are effective in accomplishing the objectives.

To determine whether the actions being taken at an incident are effective and the objectives are being met, responders must frequently reevaluate whether the incident is stabilizing or increasing in intensity. By comparing the predicted outcomes in the action plan to what is unfolding in the actual incident, the branch officer will have another indication of progress. Feedback from the entry teams and safety officer and other observations will allow the hazardous materials branch officer to recommend modifying the action options to the incident commander. This feedback should include information on the effectiveness of personnel, on personal protective clothing and equipment, on control zones, on decontamination procedures, and on the action options being implemented.

7-5.1.2 Identify the steps for comparing actual behavior of the material and the container to that predicted in the analysis process.

When comparing actual behavior to predicted behavior, the branch officer should determine whether events at an incident are happening as predicted, are occurring out of sequence, or are different than expected. The branch officer should also determine whether events that were predicted to occur have actually occurred at the incident. This evaluation and reevaluation process should continue until the incident has been terminated to minimize "surprises" during the cleanup or overhaul phase of the incident response.

7-5.1.3 Determine the effectiveness of the following:

(a) Hazardous materials response personnel being used
(b) Personal protective equipment
(c) Established control zones
(d) Control, containment, or confinement operations
(e) Decontamination process

7-6 Competencies — Terminating the Incident

7-6.1 Terminating the Emergency Phase of the Hazardous Materials Incident.

Given a simulated hazardous materials incident, the hazardous materials branch officer shall demonstrate the ability to terminate the emergency phase of the incident consistent with the local emergency response plan and the organization's standard operating procedures. The hazardous materials branch officer shall be able to:

7-6.1.1 Identify the steps required in terminating the emergency phase of a hazardous materials incident.

The steps involved in terminating the emergency phase of an incident include the following:

(a) Transferring command
(b) Debriefing
(c) Critiquing the incident
(d) After-action activities, such as restocking any disposables or damaged equipment

7-6.1.2 Identify the procedures for conducting incident debriefings at a hazardous materials incident.

7-6.1.3 Identify the steps in transferring authority as prescribed in the local emergency response plan or the organization's standard operating procedures.

7-6.2 Conducting a Debriefing.

Given the details of a simulated hazardous materials incident, the hazardous materials branch officer shall demonstrate the ability to conduct a debriefing of the incident for all units assigned to the hazardous materials branch. The hazardous materials branch officer shall be able to:

The incident debriefing involves gathering information from response personnel as soon as possible after terminating the incident. This information should then be used to develop a chronological report of emergency activities.

7-6.2.1 Describe three components of an effective debriefing.

7-6.2.2 Describe the key topics in an effective debriefing.

7-6.2.3 Describe when a debriefing should take place.

7-6.2.4 Describe who should be involved in a debriefing.

7-6.2.5 Identify the procedures for conducting incident debriefings at a hazardous materials incident.

7-6.3 Conducting a Critique.

Given the details of a simulated hazardous materials incident, the hazardous materials branch officer shall demonstrate the ability to conduct a critique of the incident for all units assigned to the hazardous materials branch. The hazardous materials branch officer shall be able to:

The critique is a review of the incident intended to identify and document the lessons learned from the actual incident response. This process should allow the participants to review response activities and determine what worked well and what didn't. The critique should be conducted in a positive manner that allows responders to modify response procedures if problems are identified without assessing blame.

After analyzing the information gathered during the debriefing and the critique and documenting that analysis, the termination process should also include a plan to follow up as necessary to ensure that any recommendations made to improve emergency operations are implemented.

7-6.3.1 Describe three components of an effective critique.

7-6.3.2 Describe who should be involved in a critique.

7-6.3.3 Describe why an effective critique is necessary after a hazardous materials incident.

7-6.3.4 Describe what written documents should be prepared as a result of the critique.

7-6.3.5 Identify the procedure for conducting a critique of the incident.

7-6.3.6 Identify the requirements for conducting a post-incident analysis as defined in the local emergency response plan, the organization's standard operating procedures, or federal, state, and local regulations.

7-6.4 Reporting and Documenting the Hazardous Materials Incident.

Given a simulated hazardous materials incident, the hazardous materials branch officer shall demonstrate the ability to report and document the incident consistent with the local, state, and federal requirements. The hazardous materials branch officer shall be able to:

The branch officer must be aware of the reporting requirements associated with a hazardous materials incident. In many cases, the responsibility for reporting to specific agencies is outlined in the responding agency or organization's standard operating procedures. However, the branch officer must ensure that the proper agencies have been notified and that the proper reports have been made.

7-6.4.1 Identify the reporting requirements of federal, state, and local agencies.

7-6.4.2 Identify the importance of documentation for a hazardous materials incident, including training records, exposure records, incident reports, and critique reports.

Throughout the incident, the branch officer should assign someone to maintain a record of incident events as they occur. This will be helpful in completing the post-incident analysis and conducting the critique because the "live" report will convey information as it unfolded. Reconstructing an incident after-the-fact often results in a flawed timeline and misinterpretation of events.

Personnel exposure records must also be maintained at the scene in accordance with federal and state laws. The necessary information about the type of exposure to which personnel were subjected, the exposure level, the length of the exposure, the type of personal protective clothing and equipment personnel were using, and the type of decontamination personnel underwent should be included as part of each responder's record. Any on-scene medical assistance that personnel received should also be documented.

7-6.4.3 Identify the steps in keeping an activity log and exposure records for hazardous materials incidents.

7-6.4.4 Identify the requirements found in the local emergency response plan and the organization's standard operating procedures for compiling hazardous materials incident reports.

7-6.4.5 Identify the requirements for filing documents and maintaining records as defined in the local emergency response plan and the organization's standard operating procedures.

CHAPTER 8

Competencies for the Hazardous Materials Branch Safety Officer

8-1 General

8-1.1* Introduction.

The hazardous materials branch safety officer shall be trained to meet all the competencies for the first responder at the awareness, operational, and technician levels and the competencies of this chapter. The hazardous materials branch safety officer also shall receive any additional training to meet applicable United States Department of Transportation (DOT), United States Environmental Protection Agency (EPA), Occupational Safety and Health Administration (OSHA), and other appropriate state, local, or provincial occupational health and safety regulatory requirements.

The hazardous materials branch safety officer is a new level that has been added to the 1997 edition of NFPA 472. The committee created the safety officer competency level to designate a responder who can operate in both the warm zone and the hot zone with all of the competencies contained in the awareness, operations, and technician levels with additional safety training not required by these other competency Levels. *(See Figure 8.1.)*

In most cases, the incident safety officer, as described in 3-2.2 of NFPA 1561, *Standard on Fire Department Incident Management System*,[1] will not be able to serve as the hazardous materials branch safety officer. An ISO usually is certified at the operations level rather than at the technician level. Many hazardous materials response teams therefore also assign a technician to the position of "branch safety officer" on the hazardous materials response team regardless of the technician's training or experience.

The competencies establishing the new level of hazardous materials branch safety officer have been formulated to provide for the increased safety concerns of the hazardous materials response team and its personnel through performance-based competencies and training standards.

A-8-1.1 These competencies are intended to address even situations when no "hazardous materials branch" is established, such as when only defensive (operational level) activities are being conducted.

If only defensive activities (i.e., at the operational level) are being conducted, the hazardous materials branch safety officer shall be trained to at least the operational level and in addition shall meet the competencies of this chapter.

If the functions and responsibilities of the hazardous materials branch safety officer are performed by the overall incident safety official or on-scene incident commander, that individual shall meet the competencies of this chapter.

8-1.2* Definition.

The hazardous materials branch safety officer is that person who works within an incident management system (IMS) to ensure that recognized safe practices are followed within the hazardous materials branch. The hazardous materials branch safety officer will be called upon to provide technical advice or assistance regarding safety issues to the hazardous materials branch officer and incident safety officer at a hazardous materials incident.

A-8-1.2 Under this section, the hazardous materials branch safety officer is given specific responsibilities. It should be understood that even though these duties are to be carried out by the hazardous materials branch safety officer, the incident commander still has overall responsibility for the implementation of these tasks.

8-1.3 Goal.

The goal of this chapter shall be to provide the hazardous materials branch safety officer with the knowledge and skills to evaluate a hazardous materials incident for safety and ensure that recognized safe operational practices are followed. Therefore, in addition to being knowledgeable at the level of operations being performed, the hazardous materials branch safety officer shall be able to:

Figure 8.1 The hazardous materials branch safety officer, with competencies at the technician level in addition to advanced safety training, advises the incident commander on the risks and potential health hazards involved in an incident. In addition, the safety officer maintains records related to the health and safety of responders and coordinates their medical supervision before, during, and after an incident response. (Photo courtesy of Henrik G. de Gyor)

(a) Analyze a hazardous materials incident to determine the magnitude of the problem in terms of safety by observing a scene and reviewing and evaluating hazard and response information as it pertains to the safety of all persons within the hazardous materials branch

(b) Assist in planning a safe response within the capabilities of available response personnel, personal protective equipment, and control equipment by completing the following tasks:

1. Identify the safety precautions for potential action options
2. Provide recommendations regarding safety considerations
3. Assist in the development of a plan of action
4. Review the plan of action and provide recommendations regarding safety
5. Review the selection of personal protective equipment required for a given action option
6. Review the decontamination operations
7. Ensure that the proper emergency medical services are provided

(c) Ensure the implementation of a safe planned response consistent with the local emergency response plan, the organization's standard operating procedures, and safety considerations by completing the following tasks:

1. Perform the duties of the hazardous materials branch safety officer within the local incident management system (IMS)
2. Identify safety considerations for personnel performing the control functions identified in the plan of action
3. Conduct safety briefings for personnel performing the control functions identified in the plan of action
4. Assist in the implementation and enforcement of safety considerations
5. Maintain communications within the incident command structure during the incident
6. Monitor status reports of activities in the hot and warm zones
7. Ensure the implementation of exposure monitoring (personnel and environment)

(d) Evaluate the progress of the planned response to ensure that the response objectives are being met safely by completing the following tasks:

1. Identify deviations from safety considerations and any dangerous situations
2. Alter, suspend, or terminate any activity that can be judged to be unsafe

(e) Assist in terminating the incident by completing the following tasks:

1. Perform the reporting, documentation and follow-up required of the hazardous materials branch safety officer
2. Assist in the debriefing of hazardous materials branch personnel
3. Assist in the incident critique

8-2 Competencies — Analyzing the Incident

8-2.1 Determining the Magnitude of the Problem in Terms of Safety.

Given various simulated facility and transportation hazardous materials incidents involving nonbulk and bulk packaging, the hazardous materials branch safety officer shall observe a scene and review and evaluate hazard and response information as it pertains to the safety of all persons within the hazardous materials branch. The hazardous materials branch safety officer shall be able to:

Hazardous materials branch safety officers should be able to identify the characteristics of special containers that might indicate the presence of hazardous materials, based on their technician level training. Many of the competencies in this section are either similar or identical to the technician level. The committee felt, however, that a second cycle of training and certification in the knowledge and skills of the technician level with a new emphasis on safety was necessary. The hazardous materials branch safety officer is responsible for monitoring the safe operation of the hazardous materials response team and should have the most demanding education and training available.

The hazardous materials branch safety officer is also expected to be able to conduct analyses that will identify and classify unknown materials. This information may be available from other hazardous materials responders already on site. Once the hazardous materials branch safety officer has determined that the material at the incident is a known or unknown hazardous material, the magnitude of mitigating actions and the level of PPE can then be defined and the safety precautions identified.

Predicting the magnitude of potential harm in the endangered area involves determining the potential concentrations of the hazardous material that has been, or potentially could be, released. This includes estimating the toxicity of the concentrations and the length of time responders could be exposed to the material in question without being personally endangered by that exposure.

8-2.1.1* Describe the following radioactive materials terms and explain their significance in predicting the extent of health hazards and environmental impact in a hazardous materials incident:

(a) Types
(b) Measurement
(c) Protection

A-8-2.1.1 See A-4-2.5.2.2.

8-2.1.2 Describe the following toxicological terms and exposure values and explain their significance in the risk assessment process:

The hazardous materials branch safety officer should be familiar with these terms since different references, such as the American Council of Governmental and Industrial Hygienists (ACGIH), the U.S. Occupational Safety and Health Administration (OSHA), and the National Institute of Occupational Safety and Health (NIOSH), may use different values in their reference materials and chemical exposure guides. Responders must understand the similarities and differences between the various information resources so that they can make appropriate comparisons between the sometimes differing information.

(a) Parts per million (ppm)
(b) Parts per billion (ppb)

The values used to establish the preceding exposure limits are quantified in parts per million or parts per billion. A good rule of thumb is that 1 percent equals 10,000 ppm, 1 percent equals 1000 ppb. So, a reading from a sampling instrument of 0.5 percent is equivalent to 5000 ppm, or 500 ppb. If the threshold limit valve (TLV) is then determined to be 7500 ppm, the reading from the instrument can be used to determine the degree of hazard.

(c) Lethal dose (LD_{50})

The LD of a substance is a single dose that will cause the death of 50 percent of a group of test animals exposed to it by any route other than inhalation.

(d) Lethal concentrations (LC_{50})

The LC is the median lethal concentration of a hazardous material. It is defined as the concentration of a material in air that, on the basis of laboratory tests (inhalation route), is expected to kill 50 percent of a group of test animals when administered in a specific time period.

(e) Permissible exposure limit (PEL)

This is a term OSHA uses in its health standards covering exposures to hazardous chemicals. It is similar to the TLV/TWA established by the ACGIH. PEL, which generally relates to legally enforceable TLV limits, is the maximum concentration, averaged over 8 hours, to which 95 percent of healthy adults can be repeatedly exposed for 8 hours per day, 40 hours per week.

(f) Threshold limit value time-weighted average (TLV-TWA)

This is the maximum concentration, averaged over 8 hours, to which a healthy adult can be repeatedly exposed for 8 hours per day, 40 hours per week.

(g) Threshold limit value short-term exposure limit (TLV-STEL)

This is the maximum average concentration, averaged over a 15-minute period, to which healthy adults can be safely exposed for up to 15 minutes continuously.

Exposure should not occur more than four times a day with at least one hour between exposures.

(h) Threshold limit value ceiling (TLV-C)

This is the maximum concentration to which a healthy adult can be exposed without risk of injury. It is comparable to the immediately dangerous to life and health value (IDLH), and exposures to higher concentrations should not occur.

(i) Immediately dangerous to life and health value (IDLH)

This is the maximum level to which a healthy worker can be exposed for 30 minutes and escape without suffering irreversible health effects or impairment. If at all possible, exposure to this level should be avoided. If that is not possible, responders should wear Level A or Level B protection with positive pressure self-contained breathing apparatus or a positive pressure supplied-air respirator with an auxiliary escape system. This limit is established by OSHA and NIOSH.

8-2.1.3 Explain the basic toxicological principles relative to assessment and treatment of personnel exposed to hazardous materials, including the following:

To determine the risk to the hazardous materials responder, the hazardous materials branch safety officer must understand these basic toxicological principles.

(a) Acute and delayed toxicity

Acute toxicity refers to the sudden, severe onset of symptoms due to an exposure. The effects of delayed toxicity may not develop for hours or longer after an exposure; in some instances, such as biological exposures, symptoms may not appear until three or more days after the exposure.

(b) Dose-response

The chemical, biological, or radiological dose relationship refers to the response produced in the human body. It is a cause/effect relationship. The magnitude of the body's response will depend on the concentration at the site, the concentration of the material itself, and the dose administered.

(c) Local and systemic effects

Local effects are those in which a toxic substance comes in direct contact with the skin or other tissue. Systemic effects are the effects a toxic product has on either the entire body or on a specific system or organ.

(d) Routes of exposure to toxic materials

The routes of exposure, sometimes referred to as routes of entry, include the following:

(a) Inhalation — the process by which irritants or toxins enter the body through the lungs as a result of the respiratory process

(b) Ingestion — the process of consuming contaminated food or water

(c) Absorption — the process by which hazardous materials are absorbed into the body through the skin or other external tissues

(d) Injection — the process by which a toxic substance is introduced directly into the blood by a needle cannula or some other mechanical means. Contaminants entering the bloodstream through an open wound can be considered to be injected.

(e) Synergistic effects

Toxicity, exposure, and dose must all be analyzed to understand the risk that more than one product will have on both the patient and the responder.

8-2.1.4* Identify five conditions where the hazards from flammability would require chemical-protective clothing with thermal protection.

Information about a materials fire and explosion hazards, including flash point, autoignition temperature, and flammability limits, as well as information about the extinguishing agents that may be used must be gathered. Reference sources can provide information about hazards associated with fire control operations. For example, an entry in a reference source may read ". . . a water stream directed at molten material can scatter the material, increasing the flammability of any combustible material it contacts." The reference source may also recommend appropriate personal protective clothing and respiratory protection.

Many reference sources will have a separate reactivity section with information about a material's stability and what the material will react with. For instance, an entry may read ". . . it is a strong oxidizing agent that will increase the flammability of all combustible materials it contacts."

A-8-2.1.4 Conditions where protective clothing with thermal protection might be required if entry was made into an area where flammability was a concern can include the following:

(a) Unknown materials involved
(b) Oxygen-enriched atmosphere
(c) Detectable percent of LEL on monitoring instruments
(d) Materials with a wide flammable range present
(e) Reactive materials present

8-2.1.5* Identify five conditions where personnel would not be allowed to enter the hot zone.

A-8-2.1.5 Conditions under which personnel would not be allowed in the hot zone include the following:

(a) Decontamination procedures not established or in place
(b) Advanced first aid and transportation not available
(c) Flammable atmosphere present
(d) Oxygen-enriched atmosphere of 23.5 percent or greater present
(e) Runaway reaction occurring
(f) Appropriate personal protective clothing not available
(g) No effective action can be taken
(h) Risk outweighs benefit
(i) Personnel not properly trained
(j) Insufficient personnel to perform tasks

8-2.1.6 Given the names of five hazardous materials and at least three reference sources, identify the physical and chemical properties and their potential impact on the safety of personnel at an incident involving each of the materials.

Information about the physical and chemical characteristics of a hazardous material will include its vapor density, boiling point, specific gravity, water solubility, pH, and physical appearance. For example, a substance can be described as "white to pale yellow sticks, granules, or powder, no odor."

8-2.1.7 Given the names of five hazardous materials and at least three reference sources, identify the health concerns and their potential impact on the safety and health of personnel at an incident involving each of the materials.

8-2.1.8* Given the names of five hazardous materials and a description of their containers, identify five hazards or physical conditions that would impact the safety of personnel at an incident involving each of the materials.

A-8-2.1.8 Examples of scenarios that would help prepare emergency responders for situations they might encounter in the field include the following:

(a) Ammonia leaking from a fitting or valve of a railroad tank car
(b) Chlorine leaking from the valve stem of a 150-lb (68-kg) cylinder
(c) Lacquer thinner leaking from a hole in a 55-gal (208-L) drum
(d) Gasoline leaking from a hole in the side of an aluminum tank truck
(e) Carbaryl, a powdered insecticide, found stored in a broken cardboard drum

8-2.1.9 Given at least three unknown materials, one of which is a solid, one a liquid, and one a gas, identify or classify by hazard each unknown material.

The hazardous materials branch safety officer is expected to be able to identify unknown materials in the event that a container's shipping papers, placards, MSDS, or other identifying items have been destroyed or are unavailable. Unknown materials must be identified cautiously. In some cases, monitoring equipment can help identify the hazard class and, sometimes, even specific chemicals. See Chapter 4 of NFPA 472 for more information on this competency.

If responders must take samples in order to conduct an analysis or must approach the site to monitor it, they must use the proper level of protective clothing. In most cases, Level A should be used to ensure adequate protection. For maximum safety, responders must approach the site from upwind, wearing the appropriate level of protective clothing, and work in a minimum of two-person teams, with adequate backup personnel. These actions should be closely monitored by the hazardous materials branch safety officer.

8-2.1.9.1 Identify steps in an analysis process for identifying unknown solid and liquid materials.

8-2.1.9.2 Identify steps in an analysis process for identifying an unknown atmosphere.

8-2.1.9.3 Identify the type(s) of monitoring equipment, test strips, and reagents used to determine the following hazards:

A wide variety of monitoring equipment is available, and response teams must determine what is appropriate for the type of hazards they are likely to encounter. The hazardous materials branch safety officer must be able to evaluate the selection process to ensure that no mistakes are made. This knowledge must also include any safety considerations or procedures in the use of monitoring or test equipment. The hazardous materials branch safety officer must also be proficient in calibrating, operating, and maintaining this equipment. Each instrument has its own operating characteristics and limitations, and the hazardous materials branch safety officer must be familiar with them.

(a) Corrosivity (pH)

Corrosivity is measured by determining the pH of a material. This can be done using pH paper or pH meters. pH paper changes color, indicating the pH level. By comparing the color of the pH paper with the color chart provided, one can determine the pH of the material in question. pH meters have a probe that is inserted into the material; the pH is indicated on the meter's display. pH meters provide a more accurate reading than pH paper.

(b) Flammability

Combustible gas indicators (CGI) can be used to determine the presence of flammable vapors of hydrocarbon products. Certain instruments are specifically designed to monitor methane vapors only; they measure the flammable vapors as a percentage of the lower explosive limit. Flash point testers are also available for field use. These allow the responder to determine fairly accurately the flammability of an unknown material and the class of flammable or combustible liquid with which they are dealing.

(c) Oxidation potential
(d) Oxygen deficiency

Equipment used to monitor oxygen concentrations generally measures over a range of 0 to 25 percent oxygen in air. Some models contain an alarm that sounds if the oxygen level drops below 19.5, which is the minimum adequate percentage of oxygen availability established by the U.S. Occupational Safety and Health Administration. Below this level, the hazardous materials branch safety officer must ensure that all responders have an air-supplied respirator or self-contained breathing apparatus.

(e) Radioactivity

Radiation detectors are available to monitor alpha particles, beta particles, gamma rays, and neutron particles. Generally, such detectors measure two or more types of radiation. For example, the Geiger counter, probably the most common type of radiation detector, can detect both gamma and beta radiation. However, it cannot effectively measure the amounts of beta radiation. The ion chamber, another radiation measurement tool, is also not effective for measuring low-level radiation.

(f) Toxic levels

Several types of instruments can be used to measure toxic exposures. These include photoionization detectors, flame ionization detectors, infrared spectrophotometers, and detector tubes. Some of these instruments are designed to measure specific chemicals, such as hydrogen sulfide. Others may measure more than one type of toxin. Detector tubes, which allow responders to evaluate potential hazards quickly, operate by drawing an air sample through a tube. In response to the sample, material inside the tube changes color, with the intensity of the color change corresponding to the concentration of the material in the air sample.

8-2.1.9.4* Identify the capabilities and limiting factors associated with the selection and use of the following monitoring equipment, test strips, and reagents:

(a) Carbon monoxide meter
(b) Colorimetric tubes
(c) Combustible gas indicator
(d) Oxygen meter
(e) Passive dosimeter
(f) Photoionization detectors
(g) pH indicators and/or pH meters
(h) Radiation detection instruments
(i) Reagents
(j) Test strips

A-8-2.1.9.4 Such limiting factors include, but are not limited to, operation, calibration, response time, detection range, relative response, sensitivity, selectivity, inherent safety, environmental conditions, and nature of hazard. Also refer to *Standard Operating Safety Guides*, EPA, June 1992.

The key to successfully selecting and using sampling and monitoring instruments is intensive training. Personnel must thoroughly understand the operating characteristics and limitations of all the instruments available to them. This competency is especially important for the hazardous materials branch safety officer because inappropriate or incorrectly used instruments can lead a hazardous materials team to draw inaccurate conclusions about such things as the identity of a material and its concentration.

8-2.1.9.5 Given three hazardous materials, one of which is a solid, one a liquid, and one a gas, and the following monitoring equipment, select and demonstrate the appropriate equipment to identify and quantify the materials:

(a) Carbon monoxide meter
(b) Colorimetric tubes
(c) Combustible gas indicator
(d) Oxygen meter
(e) pH papers and/or pH meters
(f) Radiation detection instruments
(g) Reagents
(h) Test strips

The purpose of this competency is to have the hazardous materials branch safety officers demonstrate their ability to select the proper instrument and demonstrate its use.

8-2.1.9.6 Demonstrate the field maintenance and testing procedures for the monitoring equipment, test strips and reagents provided by the authority having jurisdiction.

Responders who operate monitoring equipment must know how to field-calibrate it in order to get accurate readings and must be able to perform minor field maintenance, such as replacing the sensing device in a combustible gas indicator. The hazardous materials branch safety officer must be able to monitor this calibration process to ensure it is done in an accurate, safe manner.

8-3 Competencies — Planning the Response

Again, these competencies are similar to those of the technician level, but an extra emphasis has been placed on safety for the hazardous materials branch safety officer level. The hazardous materials branch safety officer should note that many of the response options available can be used either offensively or defensively. For example, the size of the endangered area may be changed defensively by placing barriers around the endangered area to contain a spill or offensively by entering the hot zone and plugging the leak. It should also be noted that the hazardous materials branch safety officer can recommend defensive operations as the most prudent method of dealing with an incident.

8-3.1* Identifying the Safety Precautions for Potential Action Options.

Given various simulated facility and transportation hazardous materials incidents involving nonbulk and bulk packaging, the hazardous materials branch safety officer shall assist in planning a safe response within the capabilities of available response personnel, personal protective equipment, and control equipment. The hazardous materials branch safety officer shall be able to:

A-8-3.1 Potential action options are either defensive or offensive in nature. See NFPA 471, *Recommended Practice for Responding to Hazardous Materials Incidents.*

8-3.1.1* Identify five specific safety precautions to observe while mitigating each of the hazards or conditions identified in 8-2.1.8.

A-8-3.1.1 Safety precautions to observe while mitigating hazards or conditions can include the following:

(a) Elimination of ignition sources
(b) Using monitoring instruments
(c) Stabilizing the container
(d) Establishing emergency evacuation procedures
(e) Ensuring availability of hose lines and foam, when appropriate
(f) Evacuating exposures
(g) Isolating the area
(h) Protecting in place
(i) Wearing proper protective equipment

8-3.1.2* Identify five safety precautions associated with search and rescue missions at hazardous materials incidents.

A-8-3.1.2 Safety precautions to be observed during search and rescue missions at hazardous materials incidents can include the following:

(a) Ensuring availability of appropriate personal protective clothing for all personnel
(b) Using monitoring instruments
(c) Maintaining an escape path
(d) Knowledge of approved hand signals by all personnel
(e) Ensuring availability of communications equipment for each team
(f) Preplanning the search sequence prior to entry

8-3.2 Providing Recommendations Regarding Safety Considerations.

Given various simulated facility and transportation hazardous materials incidents involving nonbulk and bulk packaging, the hazardous materials branch safety officer shall provide the incident safety officer, hazardous materials branch officer, and incident commander with observation-based recommendations regarding considerations for the safety of on-site personnel. The hazardous materials branch safety officer shall be able to identify five recommendations to the incident commander regarding safety considerations on the hazards or conditions for each of the hazardous materials and containers identified in 8-2.1.8.

This is one of the most important functions of the hazardous materials branch safety officer at the scene of an incident. The ability to quickly and accurately identify potential safety problems using observations of the achievements of the responders, knowledge of containers and hazardous materials, and information about the plan of action can only be obtained through experience, intensive training, and education.

8-3.3 Assisting in the Development of a Plan of Action.

Given various simulated facility and transportation hazardous materials incidents involving nonbulk and bulk packaging, the hazardous materials branch safety officer shall assist the incident safety officer and hazardous materials branch officer in the development of a safe plan of action. The hazardous materials branch safety officer shall be able to:

8-3.3.1* Identify the importance and list five benefits of pre-emergency planning relating to specific sites.

A-8-3.3.1 Benefits of pre-emergency planning include the following:

(a) Identifies and mitigates hazards during the planning process
(b) Familiarizes personnel with facility
(c) Identifies 24-hour responsible parties
(d) Identifies built-in containment systems
(e) Identifies the location of utility and other shutoff/shutdown valves and switches
(f) Identifies location of facility map
(g) Identifies location and quantities of hazardous materials
(h) Identifies vulnerable populations
(i) Identifies facility response capabilities

8-3.3.2* Identify and name five hazards and precautions to be observed when approaching a hazardous materials incident.

A-8-3.3.2 Hazards to observe when approaching a hazardous materials incident include the following:

(a) Inhalation hazard
(b) Dermal hazard
(c) Flammable hazard
(d) Reactive hazard
(e) Electrical hazard
(f) Mechanical hazard

8-3.3.3* List the elements of safety considerations.

A-8-3.3.3 The following are the elements of a site safety plan referenced from the *Standard Operating Safety Guides*, EPA, June 1992:

(a) Site description
(b) Entry objectives
(c) On-site organization
(d) On-site control
(e) Hazard evaluation
(f) Personal protective equipment
(g) On-site work plans
(h) Communication procedures
(i) Decontamination procedures
(j) Site safety and health plan

8-3.3.4 Given an organizations pre-incident plan and a simulated hazardous materials incident involving one of the hazardous materials and containers described in 8-2.1.8, develop safety considerations for the incident.

8-3.4 Providing Recommendations Regarding Safety and Reviewing the Plan of Action.

Given a proposed plan of action for an incident involving one of the hazardous materials and containers described in 8-2.1.8, the hazardous materials branch safety officer shall identify to the incident safety officer, hazardous materials branch officer, and incident commander the safety precautions for the plan of action. The hazardous materials branch safety officer shall be able to:

8-3.4.1 Ensure that the safety considerations in the proposed plan of action are consistent with the local emergency response plan and the organization's standard operating procedures.

8-3.4.2 Make recommendations to the incident commander on the safety considerations in the proposed plan of action.

8-3.5 Reviewing Selection of Personal Protective Equipment.

Given various simulated facility and transportation hazardous materials incidents involving nonbulk and bulk packaging, the hazardous materials branch safety officer shall demonstrate the ability to review the selection of personal protective equipment required for a given action option. The hazardous materials branch safety officer shall be able to:

8-3.5.1 Identify the four levels of chemical protection (EPA/NIOSH) and describe the equipment required for each level and the conditions under which each level is used.

8-3.5.2 Identify five safety considerations for personnel wearing vapor-protective, liquid splash-protective, and high temperature-protective clothing.

8-3.5.3 Given the names of five different hazardous materials and a chemical compatibility chart for chemical-protective clothing, identify the chemical-protective clothing that would provide the appropriate protection to the wearer for each of the five substances.

8-3.5.4* Given the names of five different hazardous materials, identify appropriate chemical-protective clothing levels for typical action options.

A-8-3.5.4 Typical action options can include surveying the scene, sampling, monitoring, plugging, and patching.

8-3.5.5 Demonstrate proper methods for donning, doffing, and using all personal protective equipment provided by the authority having jurisdiction for use in hazardous materials response activities.

8-3.6 Reviewing the Proposed Decontamination Plan.

Given a site-specific decontamination plan by the hazardous materials branch officer or incident commander for a simulated hazardous materials incident, the hazardous materials branch safety officer shall review the plan to identify safety considerations prior to plan implementation. The hazardous materials branch safety officer shall be able to:

8-3.6.1 Identify the advantages and limitations and describe an example where each of the following decontamination methods would be used:

(a) Absorption
(b) Adsorption
(c) Chemical degradation
(d) Dilution
(e) Disposal
(f) Evaporation
(g) Neutralization
(h) Solidification
(i) Vacuuming
(j) Washing

8-3.6.2 Identify how personnel, personal protective equipment, apparatus, tools, and equipment become contaminated, as well as the importance and limitations of decontamination procedures.

8-3.6.3 Explain the need for decontamination procedures at hazardous materials incidents.

8-3.6.4 Identify three sources of technical information for selecting appropriate decontamination procedures and identify how to contact those sources in an emergency.

8-3.6.5 Identify the considerations associated with the placement, location, and setup of the decontamination corridor.

8-3.6.6 Identify the decontamination procedures as defined by the authority having jurisdiction for personnel and personal protective equipment at hazardous materials incidents.

8-3.6.7 Given three reference sources and a simulated hazardous materials incident involving two or more different chemicals, develop a site-specific personnel decontamination plan that is consistent with the local emergency response plan and the organization's standard operating guidelines.

8-3.7 Ensuring Provision of Proper Emergency Medical Services.

Given a simulated hazardous materials incident, the hazardous materials branch safety officer shall review the emergency medical services plan to ensure that response personnel are provided medical care. The hazardous materials branch safety officer shall be able to:

8-3.7.1* Identify the elements required in an emergency medical services plan.

A-8-3.7.1 The elements of an emergency medical services plan according to NFPA 473, *Standard for Competencies for EMS Personnel Responding to Hazardous Materials Incidents,* include the following:

(a) EMS control activities
(b) EMS component of an incident management system
(c) Medical monitoring of personnel utilizing chemical-protective and high temperature-protective clothing
(d) Triage of hazardous materials victims
(e) Medical treatment for chemically contaminated individuals
(f) Product and exposure information gathering and documentation

8-3.7.2 Identify the importance of an on-site medical monitoring program.

8-3.7.3 Identify three resources for the transportation and care of the injured persons exposed to hazardous materials.

8-4 Competencies — Implementing the Planned Response

8-4.1 Performing the Duties of the Hazardous Materials Branch Safety Officer.

Given various simulated facility and transportation hazardous materials incidents involving nonbulk and bulk packaging, the hazardous materials branch safety officer shall perform the duties of their position in a manner consistent with the local emergency response plan, the organization's standard operating procedures, and safety considerations. The hazardous materials branch safety officer shall be able to:

8-4.1.1 Identify the duties of the hazardous materials branch safety officer as defined in the organization's standard operating procedures.

8-4.1.2 Demonstrate proper performance of the duties of the hazardous materials branch safety officer as defined in the organization's standard operating procedures.

8-4.2 Monitoring Safety of Response Personnel.

Given a simulated hazardous materials incident and safety considerations, the hazardous materials branch safety officer shall ensure that personnel perform their tasks in a safe manner by identifying the safety considerations for the control functions identified in the plan of action. The hazardous materials branch safety officer shall be able to:

8-4.2.1 Identify the safe operating practices that are required to be followed at a hazardous materials incident as stated in the local emergency response plan and the organization's standard operating procedures.

8-4.2.2 Identify how the following factors influence heat and cold stress for hazardous materials response personnel:

(a) Activity levels
(b) Duration of entry
(c) Environmental factors
(d) Hydration
(e) Level of PPE
(f) Physical fitness

8-4.2.3 Identify the methods that will minimize the potential harm from heat and cold stress.

8-4.2.4 Identify the safety considerations that will minimize the psychological and physical stresses on personnel wearing vapor-protective, liquid splash-protective, and high temperature-protective clothing.

8-4.2.5 Describe five conditions where it would be prudent to withdraw from a hazardous materials incident.

Hazardous materials response teams should develop protocols for monitoring the air during operations at hazardous materials incidents and for reporting these findings periodically to the hazardous materials branch safety officer as well as to other command-line staff, in accordance with their response plan. Any new or increasing stresses on the containment system should be carefully evaluated on a continuing basis to determine if withdrawal may be necessary. Withdrawal conditions can be identical to conditions that preclude initial commitment of personnel on arrival.

8-4.3 Conducting Safety Briefings.

Given a simulated hazardous materials incident and safety considerations, the hazardous materials branch safety officer shall conduct safety briefings for personnel performing the control functions identified in the plan of action. The hazardous materials branch safety officer shall be able to demonstrate the proper procedure for conducting a safety briefing to personnel for an incident involving one of the hazardous materials and its container identified in 8-2.1.8, as specified by the organization's standard operating procedures.

The following issues should be included in the safety briefing:

(a) Ensure that the incident commander, branch officers, and all hazardous materials responders have met all the competencies of their appropriate levels in accordance with NFPA 472

(b) Explain that activities that present a significant risk to the safety of members are limited to situations with the potential to save endangered lives

(c) Explain that no risk to the safety of members is acceptable when there is no possibility of saving lives or property

(d) Ensure that all personnel working in the warm zone or hot zone are under the supervision of a branch officer

(e) Explain personnel accountability procedures that are utilized

(f) Ensure that a rest and rehabilitation area is completed and ready for the first responders to finish their assignment

(g) Explain that communications have been established on one simplex radio channel that is not used by anyone close enough to interfere. Also, explain that hand signals are available as a backup if the radios fail

(h) Ensure that appropriate protective clothing and protective equipment will be used whenever the responder is exposed, or potentially exposed, to the hazardous materials

(i) Ensure that a rapid intervention crew consisting of at least two responders is available for rescue of a member or a team if the need arises. Emphasize that responders operating in the hot zone shall operate in teams of two or more

(j) Explain the medical monitoring of all responders before they can proceed to work in personal protective equipment, in accordance with Chapter 8, "Medical Monitoring," of NFPA 471 in this handbook

(k) Ensure that all responders are aware of clues that can indicate that an incident may be a chemical, biological, nuclear, or explosives incident. If terrorism is suspected, responders are informed to be alert to the possibility of secondary devices or attempts to disguise the true nature of the incident.

8-4.4 Implementing and Enforcing Safety Considerations.

Given a simulated hazardous materials incident and safety considerations, the hazardous materials branch safety officer shall assist the incident commander, the incident safety officer, and the hazardous materials branch officer in implementing and enforcing the safety considerations. The hazardous materials branch safety officer shall be able to:

The following is an excerpt from NFPA 1521, *Standard for Fire Department Safety Officer,* that outlines a good approach to enforcing safety procedures:

> 2-3 Authority of the Health and Safety Officer (HSO).
>
> 2-3.1 The health and safety officer shall have the responsibility to identify and cause correction of safety and health hazards.
>
> 2-3.2 The health and safety officer shall have the authority to cause immediate correction of situations that create an imminent hazard to members.
>
> 2-3.3 Where nonimminent hazards are identified, a health and safety officer shall develop actions to correct the situation within the administrative process of the fire department. The fire department health and safety officer shall have the authority to bring notice of such hazards to whomever has the ability to cause correction.[2]

A hazardous materials response team's standard operating procedures should contain these requirements for both the hazardous materials branch safety officer and the incident safety officer.

8-4.4.1 Identify whether the boundaries of the established control zones are clearly marked, consistent with the safety considerations, and are being maintained.

8-4.4.2 Identify whether the on-site medical monitoring that are required by the authority having jurisdiction is being performed.

8-4.4.3 Given an entry team, a backup team, and a decontamination team wearing personal protective clothing and equipment, identify that each team is properly protected and prepared to safely perform its assigned tasks.

8-4.4.3.1 Identify whether the selection of clothing and equipment is consistent with safety considerations.

8-4.4.3.2 Identify whether each team has examined the clothing for barrier integrity and the equipment to ensure proper working order.

8-4.4.3.3 Identify whether protective clothing and equipment have been donned in accordance with the organization's standard operating procedures and the manufacturer's recommendations.

8-4.4.4 Identify whether each person entering the hot zone has a specific task assignment, understands the assignment, is properly trained to perform the assigned task(s), and is working with a designated partner at all times during the assignment.

8-4.4.5 Identify whether a backup team with the appropriate level of personal protective equipment is prepared at all times for immediate entry into the hot zone during entry team operations.

8-4.4.6 Identify whether the decontamination process specified in the safety considerations is in place before any entry into the hot zone.

8-4.4.7 Identify that each person exiting the hot zone and each tool or piece of equipment is decontaminated in accordance with the safety considerations and the degree of hazardous materials exposure.

8-4.4.8 Demonstrate the proper procedure for recording the names of the individuals exiting the hot zone, as specified in the local emergency response plan and the organization's standard operating procedures.

8-4.4.9* Identify three safety considerations that can minimize secondary contamination.

A-8-4.4.9 Safety considerations that can minimize secondary contamination include the following:

(a) Control zones are established and enforced
(b) All people and equipment exiting the hot zone are decontaminated
(c) Personnel performing decontamination are properly trained
(d) Personnel performing decontamination are properly protected

See NFPA 473, *Standard for Competencies for EMS Personnel Responding to Hazardous Materials Incidents.*

8-4.5 Maintaining Communications.

Given a simulated hazardous materials incident and the safety considerations, the hazardous materials branch safety officer shall maintain routine and emergency communications within the incident command structure at all times during the incident. The hazardous materials branch safety officer shall be able to:

8-4.5.1* Identify three types of communications systems used at hazardous materials incident sites.

A-8-4.5.1 Communications systems include in-suit radio communications, hand-held portable radios, air horns, and hand signals.

8-4.5.2 Identify whether each person assigned to work in the hot zone understands the emergency alerting and response procedures specified in the safety considerations prior to entry into the hot zone.

8-4.6 Monitoring Status Reports.

Given a simulated hazardous materials incident and the safety considerations, the hazardous materials branch safety officer shall monitor routine and emergency communications within the incident command structure at all times during the incident. The hazardous materials branch safety officer shall be able to identify whether entry team members regularly communicate the status of their work assignment to the hazardous materials branch officer.

8-4.7 Implementing Exposure Monitoring.

Given a simulated hazardous materials incident and the safety considerations, the hazardous materials branch safety officer shall assist the incident commander, the incident safety officer, and the hazardous materials branch officer in implementing exposure monitoring.

8-4.8

The hazardous materials branch safety officer shall identify that exposure monitoring (personnel and environment) as specified in the organization's standard operating procedures and safety considerations is performed.

8-5 Competencies — Evaluating Progress

8-5.1 Identifying Deviations from Safety Considerations and Any Dangerous Situations.

Given simulated facility and transportation hazardous materials incidents involving nonbulk and bulk packaging, and given simulated deviations from the safety considerations for activities in both the hot and warm zones and simulated dangerous conditions, the hazardous materials branch safety officer shall evaluate the progress of the planned response to ensure that the response objectives are being met safely. The hazardous materials branch safety officer shall be able to:

8-5.1.1 Identify those actions that deviate from the safety considerations or otherwise violate generally accepted safe operating practices, organizational policies, or applicable occupational safety and health laws, regulations, codes, standards, or guidelines.

8-5.1.2 Identify dangerous conditions that develop or are identified during work in the hot or warm zones that threaten the safety or health of persons in those zones.

8-5.1.3 Identify the signs and symptoms of psychological and physical stresses on personnel wearing vapor-protective, liquid splash-protective, and high temperature-protective clothing.

8-5.2 Taking Corrective Actions.

Given various simulated facility and transportation hazardous materials incidents involving nonbulk and bulk packaging, and given simulated deviations from the safety considerations for activities in both the hot and warm zones and simulated dangerous conditions, the hazardous materials branch safety officer shall take such corrective actions as are necessary to ensure the safety and health of persons in the hot and warm zones. The hazardous materials branch safety officer shall be able to:

8-5.2.1 Send emergency communications to, and receive emergency communications from, the incident safety officer, entry team personnel, the hazardous materials branch officer, and others as appropriate regarding safe working practices and conditions.

8-5.2.1.1* Given a hazardous situation or condition that has developed or been identified following initial hot zone entry, demonstrate the application of the emergency alerting procedures specified in the safety considerations to communicate the hazard and emergency response information to the affected personnel.

A-8-5.2.1.1 Examples of such situations or conditions can include, but are not limited to, the following:

(a) Fire or explosion
(b) Container failure
(c) Sudden change in weather conditions
(d) Failure of entry team personal protective clothing and/or equipment
(e) Updated information on identification of hazardous materials(s) involved warranting reassessment of level of protective clothing and equipment being used

8-5.2.1.2 Given a demonstrated emergency alert via hand signal by a member of the entry team operating within the hot zone, identify the meaning of that signal as specified in the safety considerations.

8-5.2.2 Identify the procedures to alter, suspend, or terminate any activity that can be judged to be unsafe, as specified in the local emergency response plan and the organization's standard operating procedures.

8-5.2.3 Demonstrate the procedure for notifying the appropriate individual of the unsafe action and for directing alternative safe actions, in accordance with the safety considerations and the organization's standard operating procedures.

8-5.2.4 Demonstrate the procedure for suspending or terminating an action that could result in an imminent hazard condition, in accordance with the safety considerations and the organization's standard operating procedures.

8-6 Competencies — Terminating the Incident

8-6.1 Providing Reports and Documentation.

Given various simulated facility and transportation hazardous materials incidents involving nonbulk and bulk packaging, the hazardous materials branch safety officer shall complete and submit the reports, documentation, and follow-up required of the hazardous materials branch safety officer. The hazardous materials branch safety officer shall be able to:

8-6.1.1 Identify the safety reports and supporting documentation required by the local emergency response plan and the organization's standard operating procedures.

8-6.1.2 Demonstrate the proper completion of the safety reports required by the local emergency response plan and the organization's standard operating procedures.

8-6.1.3 Describe the importance of personnel exposure records.

8-6.2 Debriefing of Hazardous Materials Branch Personnel.

Given various simulated facility and transportation hazardous materials incidents involving nonbulk and bulk packaging, the hazardous materials branch safety officer shall debrief hazardous materials branch personnel regarding site-specific occupational safety and health issues. The hazardous materials branch safety officer shall be able to:

8-6.2.1* Identify five health and safety topics to be addressed in an incident debriefing.

A-8-6.2.1 Topics can include, but are not limited to, the following:

(a) The identity of the hazardous materials to which personnel have been or may have been exposed
(b) The signs and symptoms of exposure to the hazardous material(s) involved in the incident
(c) The signs and symptoms of critical incident stress
(d) The duration of a recommended observation period for such signs and symptoms
(e) Procedures to follow in the event of delayed presentation of such signs or symptoms
(f) The name of the individual responsible for post-incident medical contact
(g) Safety and health hazards remaining at the site

8-6.2.2 Demonstrate the proper procedure for debriefing hazardous materials branch personnel regarding site-specific occupational safety and health areas of concern, as specified in the safety considerations, local emergency response plan, and the organization's standard operating procedures.

8-6.3 Assisting in the Incident Critique.

Given various simulated facility and transportation hazardous materials incidents involving nonbulk and bulk packaging, the hazardous materials branch safety officer shall provide safety and health-related critical observations of the activities that were performed in the hot and warm zones during the incident.

8-6.4

Given the safety considerations and hazardous materials branch safety officer's report for a simulated incident, the hazardous materials branch safety officer shall demonstrate the proper procedure for verbally presenting the following in accordance with the local emergency response plan and the organization's standard operating procedures:

(a) Safety and health-related critical observations of the activities that were performed in the hot and warm zones during the incident

(b) Recorded violations of the safety considerations or generally accepted safe operating practices, organizational policies, or applicable occupational safety and health laws, regulations, codes, standards, or guidelines

(c) Injuries or deaths that occurred as a result of reasonably unforeseen dangerous conditions that developed during the incident

(d) Injuries or deaths that occurred as a result of violations of the safety considerations or generally accepted safe operating practices, organizational policies, or applicable occupational safety and health laws, regulations, codes, standards, or guidelines

(e) The proper course of action(s) that would likely have prevented the injuries or deaths that occurred as a result of the safety violations identified in (d)

(f) Deficiencies or weaknesses in the safety considerations, local emergency response plan, and organizational standard operating procedures that were noted during or following the incident

References Cited in Commentary

1. NFPA 1561, *Standard on Fire Department Incident Management System,* National Fire Protection Association, Quincy, MA, 1997.
2. NFPA 1521, *Standard for Fire Department Safety Officer,* National Fire Protection Association, Quincy, MA, 1997.

CHAPTER 9

Competencies for the Technician with a Tank Car Specialty

9-1 General

9-1.1 Introduction.

Technicians with a tank car specialty shall meet all competencies of the first responder awareness, operational, and hazardous materials technician levels and the competencies of this chapter. The technician with a tank car specialty also shall receive any additional training to meet applicable United States Department of Transportation (DOT), United States Environmental Protection Agency (EPA), Occupational Safety and Health Administration (OSHA), and other appropriate state, local, or provincial occupational health and safety regulatory requirements.

In the 1987 edition of NFPA 472, one of the competencies required for the hazardous materials specialist (subsequently incorporated into the hazardous materials technician in 1992) was merely to "describe" specific techniques. In the commentary on that competency, Martin F. Henry wrote the following: "The task is generally performed by people with particular expertise and responsibility for the operation, under the supervision and control of responders." The specific techniques listed in that competency were transferring liquids and gases, flaring liquids and gases, hot tapping, and venting and burning.

Now in this new Chapter 9 of NFPA 472, it is now required that competency in performing these tasks be demonstrated. For example, 9-4.1.7 reads: "Given the appropriate equipment and resources, demonstrate the following:

(a) Transferring of liquids and vapors
(b) Flaring of liquids and vapors
(c) Venting"

The new specialty levels introduced in Chapters 9, 10, and 11 of this 1997 edition of NFPA 472 cover extremely hazardous and highly skilled operations that have not had any standardized training or certification previously. The technician with a tank car specialty, the technician with a cargo tank specialty, and the technician with an intermodal tank specialty are levels that are above OSHA's technician and specialist levels and are not defined by the present OSHA regulation (Title 29, *Code of Federal Regulations*, Part 1910.120). Table 9.1 offers a comparison of the various levels described by NFPA and OSHA.

9-1.2 Definition.

Technicians with a tank car specialty are those persons who provide support to the hazardous materials technician, provide oversight for product removal and movement of damaged tank cars, and act as a liaison between technicians and other outside resources. These technicians are expected to use specialized chemical-protective clothing and specialized control equipment.

9-1.3 Goals.

The goal of this chapter shall be to provide the technician with a tank car specialty with the knowledge and skills to perform the following tasks safely. In addition to being competent at the hazardous materials technician level, the technician with a tank car specialty shall be able to:

(a) Analyze a hazardous materials incident involving tank cars to determine the magnitude of the problem in terms of outcomes by completing the following tasks:

  1. Determine the type and extent of damage to tank cars
  2. Predict the likely behavior of tank cars and their contents in an emergency

(b) Plan a response for an emergency involving tank cars within the capabilities and competencies of available

Table 9.1 NFPA and OSHA Comparison

NFPA 472, 1997 edition	OSHA 1910.120
Chapter 2, First Responder Awareness	1910.120 (q)(6)(i), First Responder Awareness
Chapter 3, First Responder Operations	1910.120 (q)(6)(ii), First Responder Operations
Chapter 4, Hazardous Materials Technician	1910.120 (q)(6)(iii), Hazardous Materials Technician
Chapter 5, Incident Commander	1910.120 (q)(6)(v), On Scene Incident Commander
Chapter 6, Private Sector Specialist Employee B and C	1910.120 (q)(5), Specialist Employee
Chapter 6, Private Sector Specialist Employee A	1910.120 (q)(6)(iv), Specialist
Chapter 7, Hazardous Materials Branch Officer	No OSHA equivalent
Chapter 8, Hazardous Materials Branch Safety Officer	No OSHA equivalent
Chapter 9, Technician with a Tank Car Specialty	No OSHA equivalent
Chapter 10, Technician with a Cargo Tank Specialty	No OSHA equivalent
Chapter 11, Technician with an Intermodal Tank Specialty	No OSHA equivalent

personnel, personal protective equipment, and control equipment by completing the following tasks:

1. Determine the response options (offensive, defensive, and nonintervention) for a hazardous materials emergency involving tank cars
2. Ensure that the options are within the capabilities and competencies of available personnel, personal protective equipment, and control equipment

(c) Implement the planned response to a hazardous materials incident involving tank cars

9-1.4 Mandating of Competencies.

This standard does not mandate that hazardous materials response teams performing offensive operations on tank cars have technicians with a tank car specialty. Technicians operating within the bounds of their training as listed in Chapter 4 of this standard are able to intervene in railroad incidents. However, if a hazardous materials response team desires to train some or all its technicians to have in-depth knowledge of tank cars, this chapter sets out the required competencies.

The committee wanted to be perfectly clear that existing and new responders at the hazardous materials technician level can still perform the operations on tank cars that they have always been qualified to do. This new specialty level covers those highly technical skills and knowledge needed only rarely in a major accident. For example, the skills required by the competency in 9-4.1.7 are skills that the technician normally does not possess. A hazardous materials response team may have a few members trained to this level or a request can be made to the railroad, shipper, or manufacturer to bring someone with this specialty to the incident scene. Because of the relative newness of this level, it is unrealistic to expect to see responders with either the training or certification necessary to achieve this specialty level in the near future.

The committee wants to be clear that this specialty level is not mandated for any hazardous materials response team or its members. Arrangements to request assistance are perfectly appropriate and are encouraged in these situations.

9-2 Competencies — Analyzing the Incident

9-2.1 Determining the Type and Extent of Damage to Tank Cars.

Given examples of damaged tank cars, technicians with a tank car specialty shall describe the type and extent of damage to each tank car and its fittings. Technicians with a tank car specialty shall be able to:

In this document, tank cars are grouped into the following five types:

(a) Nonpressure tank cars, known as general service or low-pressure tank cars, transport hazardous and non-hazardous materials at vapor pressures below 25 psig (40 psia) at 105°F–115°F (90°C–95°C). Tank test pressures for nonpressure tank cars are 60 psi and 100 psi (414 kPa–690 kPa). Capacities range from 4,000 gal (15,140 L) to 45,000 gal (170,325 L).

(b) Pressure tank cars typically transport hazardous materials, including Class 2 (flammable, nonflammable, and poison gases) materials, at pressures greater than 40 psia (276 kPa) at 20°C (68°F). They may also transport flammable liquids. Tank test pressures for these tank cars are 100 psi, 200 psi, 300 psi, 340 psi, 400 psi, 500 psi, and 600 psi (4137 kPa). They range in capacity from 4,000 gal (15,140 L) to 45,000 gal (170,325 L).

(c) Cryogenic liquid tank cars carry low-pressure, usually 25 psig (172 kPa) or lower, refrigerated liquids (−130°F and below). Materials typically found in these tanks include argon, ethylene, hydrogen, nitrogen, and oxygen.

(d) High-pressure tube cars are 40-ft (12.2 m), box-type, open frame cars. Inside the frame is a visible cluster of 30 seamless, noninsulated, 40-ft (12.2 m) steel cylinders arranged horizontally and permanently attached to the car. Tank test pressures of these cylinders vary from 3000 psi to 5000 psi (20,685 kPa–34,475 kPa). These high-pressure tube cars transport helium, hydrogen, or oxygen in the gaseous form.

(e) Pneumatically unloaded covered hopper cars are built to tank car specifications. Covered hopper cars are unloaded by pressure differential *(pneumatic)* through the application of air pressure. Although the pressure is used only during unloading, tank test pressures for the car range from 20 psi to 80 psi (138 kPa–552 kPa). Dry caustic soda is one material frequently transported in this type of car.

9-2.1.1 Given the specification mark for a tank car and the appropriate reference materials, describe the car's basic construction and features.

Tank cars are built to precisely defined standards established by the DOT and the AAR. A tank car's specification mark indicates the standards that were followed when the tank car was constructed. *(See Figure 9.1.)* This specification mark is stenciled on both sides of the tank. As you face the side of the car, the specification mark will be to the right (at the opposite end from the reporting marks, or initials, and number). The specification mark is also stamped into the head of the tank where it is not readily visible.

Specification information may also be obtained from the railroad, shipper, car owner, or the Association of American Railroads (from the car's certificate of construction) using the car's initials and number.

9-2.1.2 Point out the "B" end of the car.

The "B" end of the car is the end where the hand brake is mounted. The placement of all nomenclature is based on facing the "B" end of the car. Additional information about tank cars and their markings, along with a diagram of marking locations, is found in Chapter 4 of this handbook.

9-2.1.3 Given examples of various tank cars, point out and explain the design and purpose of each of the following tank car components, when present.

It is important for technicians with a tank car specialty to be able to identify and explain the various components of a tank car so they can communicate the condition at a hazardous materials incident scene involving a tank car.

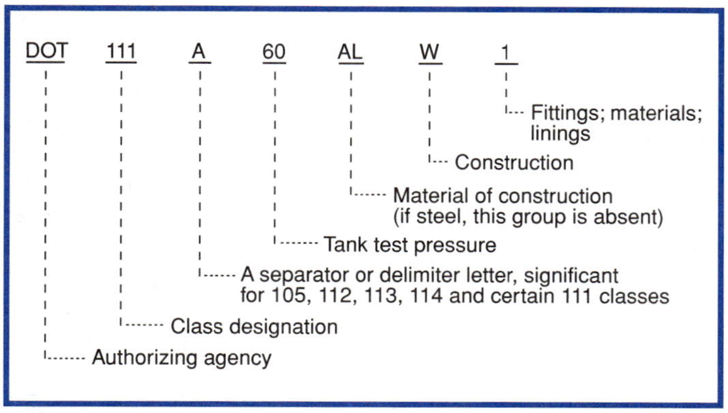

Figure 9.1 *Explanation of specification marking.*

(a) Tank, including shell, and head

Each tank car tank is made up of a shell enclosed at the ends by heads. The shell is constructed of two to seven metal plates formed into rings. Heads are made from plates pressed into an ellipsoidal shape. The components (rings and heads) are fusion-welded together, although on older nonpressure tank cars the tank car components were riveted together.

As they are built, representative samples of the tanks are X-rayed to identify possible flaws in metal or welds. Steel tank car tanks are heated to 1100°F (600°C) for one hour to relieve metal stresses caused by welding. Finally, they are hydrostatically tested.

Tank car tanks may have as many as six compartments, with each compartment constructed as a separate tank. Compartments within the same tank car may have different capacities and may transport different commodities. Tank car tanks with multiple compartments are identified by the multiple sets of fittings on top of the car, one set for each compartment.

(b) Head shield

Head shields (head puncture resistance) are used to protect the heads of tank cars that transport flammable gases, ethylene oxide, and anhydrous ammonia from punctures. These "half head" or trapezoidal-shaped plates of steel are applied to the lower half of each head. For jacketed-tank cars, either "full" or "bottom half" head shields may be incorporated in the head jacket.

(c) Jacket

A jacket is the thin outer covering used to hold both insulation and jacketed thermal protection in place, as well as to protect the insulation or thermal protection from the weather. Wooden blocks or metal brackets hold the jacket away from the tank.

(d) Lining/cladding

The interiors of some tank cars are lined or clad with materials to protect the tank from the corrosive or reactive effects of the contents or to maintain the purity of the contents.

A lining is a covering applied in strips or sections and fastened to the inside of the tank after the tank is constructed. Rubber is the most commonly used lining in tank cars used to transport hazardous materials. Glass, lead, nickel, polyurethane, and polyvinyl chloride are also used as linings.

Claddings are coverings applied to the base metal before the plate is formed. Nickel and stainless steel are used as cladding materials.

(e) Heater coils—interior vs. exterior

Some tank cars are equipped with a series of continuous parallel pipes or coils mounted internally (inside the tank) or externally (outside the tank). Steam, water, or hot oil from an external source is run through these coils to heat thick or solidified materials (i.e., asphalts, fused solids, heavy fuel oils, phenol, sulfur, metallic sodium, or petroleum waxes) to make them flow more easily when unloading. Cooling coils may be used to cool materials like metallic sodium.

(f) Underframe—continuous vs. stub sill

The continuous underframe is a one-piece assembly, attached to the tank by the center anchor and tank bands at the body bolster, that bridges the trucks of a tank car. This continuous underframe absorbs the draft and buff forces associated with train movement.

The stub sill type of frame is a short, longitudinal structural member welded to both ends of the tank to accommodate the coupler and draft gear. It also attaches the tank to its truck. With this type of underframe, the tank transmits the draft and buff forces associated with train movement.

(g) Shelf couplers

A top and bottom shelf coupler is a type of coupler with a vertical restraint mechanism on the top and bottom. It reduces the potential for coupler disengagement and possible head puncture.

(h) Body bolster

The body bolster is a structural cross member, mounted at right angles to the underframe, used to cradle the tank. Tank cars have two body bolsters, one at each end of the tank.

(i) Trucks (pin and bowl)

The truck consists of wheels, axles, side frames, springs, truck bolster, and center bowl and pin. It supports one end of the car and allows it to be moved on the rail.

9-2.1.4 Given examples of tank cars (some jacketed; some not jacketed), point out the jacketed tank cars.

Jacketed cars can be recognized by one or more of the following visual indicators:

(a) Flashing (shroud or cover) over the body bolster or tank bands
(b) Flat appearance of ends or flat sections on sides of tank car
(c) Rough appearance of visible welds, including lap welds, with welds generally thinner than the tank welds

9-2.1.5 Describe the difference between "insulation" and "thermal protection" on tank cars.

Insulation is used to safeguard the contents of the tank car from outside temperatures. It may be used on both pressure and nonpressure tank cars and is always used on cryogenic liquid tank cars. Fiberglass and polyurethane foams are the most common types of insulating materials. Cork is used to insulate tanks used for hydrocyanic acid. "Perlite" is used in cryogenic liquid cars. The insulation is concealed by a jacket.

Thermal protection is used on certain tank cars to protect them from flame impingement from either a pool or torch fire. It is designed to keep tank metal temperatures below 800°F (427°C) for 100 minutes (pool fire exposure) or 30 minutes (torch fire exposure). This thermal protection is used primarily on tank cars transporting Class 2.1 (liquefied flammable gases) like propane.

9-2.1.6 Describe the difference between "jacketed" and "sprayed-on" thermal protection on tank cars.

The following two types of thermal protection are currently being used:

(a) Jacketed thermal protection—mineral wool or various man-made ceramic fiber blankets held in place by a metal jacket
(b) Sprayed-on thermal protection—a rough textured coating sprayed on to the tank or the jacket, protecting the tank by expanding when exposed to fire.

Jacketed thermal protection is the most common type of thermal protection in use today.

9-2.1.7 Describe the difference between "interior" and "exterior" heater coils on tank cars.

Interior heater coils are inside the tank. If they should become damaged, product can be released from the inlet or outlet pipes on the tank can. Exterior heater coils are not in contact with the product at all.

9-2.1.8 Given examples of various fittings arrangements for pressure, nonpressure, cryogenic, and CO_2 tank cars (including examples of each of the following fittings), point out and explain the design, construction, and operation of each of the following fittings, when present:

(a) Fittings for loading and unloading tank cars, including the following:

1. Bottom outlet valves (top operated with stuffing box, bottom operated — internal or external ball, wafer-sphere)

A bottom outlet valve is used to load or unload the tank from the bottom. It can be any of the following types:

(a) Plug-type valve that is operated from the top of the tank, called a "top-operated bottom outlet valve"
(b) Ball-type valve mounted inside or outside the tank, operated from ground level with some type of operating handle
(c) Wafersphere (butterfly valve) mounted outside the tank, operated from ground level with some type of operating handle

2. Liquid valve/vapor valve (ball vs. plug type)

Liquid valves are typically angle valves, either plug type or ball type, and are mounted on the manway cover plate. Liquid valves are closed by a plug, attached by a chain, that is inserted into the valve orifice. Liquid valves are found in 1-in., 2-in., and 3-in. (25-mm, 51-mm, and 76-mm) sizes. Liquid valves are interchangeable with vapor valves and 2-in. and 3-in. (51-mm and 76-mm) liquid valves may be used on the same car. A gasket is used to complete the seal between the liquid valve and the manway cover plate.

An eduction line is a pipe that extends to within 1 in. to 2 in. (25 mm to 51 mm) of the bottom of the tank or into a sump. In many cases, an excess flow valve is attached between the liquid valve and the eduction line, just below the manway cover plate.

Vapor valves are typically angle valves, either plug type or ball type, and are mounted on the manway cover plate. Vapor valves are closed by a plug, attached by a chain, that is inserted into the valve orifice. Vapor valves are found in 1-in., 2-in., and 3-in. (25-mm, 51-mm, and 76-mm) sizes. Vapor valves are interchangeable with liquid valves. A gasket is used to complete the seal between the vapor valve and the manway cover plate.

3. Excess flow valve

Excess flow valves are attached inside the tank between the manway cover plate and the eduction line. They almost completely cut off the flow of product when the valve is sheered off in an accident. They operate either by product flow or, when the car is overturned, by gravity. Under normal conditions, gravity keeps the excess flow valves open, but higher flow rates associated with valves being sheered off or hoses breaking closes them. When the tank car is turned over, gravity closes the valves.

4. Air valve

On nonpressure tank cars, the valve that controls the flow of vapor is called an air valve. Unloading is accomplished from pressure/gravity generated from the contents or by pressurizing the tank with air, nitrogen, or other gas. On nonpressure tank cars, the air valve is usually smaller than the liquid valve.

On occasion, the vapor valve may be removed and replaced with a blind flange bolted to the cover plate. The blind flange reduces the possibility of tampering and subsequent release of the contents.

5. Bottom outlet nozzle

The bottom outlet nozzle is the pipe or flange from the bottom of the tank to the bottom outlet.

6. Quick fill hole cover

The fill hole on nonpressure acid cars is used for loading and unloading the tank.

7. Flange for manway, valves, etc.

The flange for manways, valves, and so on is the rim used for strengthening the connection of fittings to the tank.

8. CO_2 tank car fittings

Fittings for CO_2 tank cars typically include two angle valves for loading and unloading, two pressure regulator valves, two sample valves (long pole/short pole used for gauging the amount of product), one safety valve, and one vent.

9. Cryogenic liquid tank car fittings

(b) Fittings for pressure relief, including the following:

1. Safety relief devices (safety valve, safety vent, combination safety valve)

Pressure relief devices are designed to reduce the build-up of excess internal pressure caused by commodity vaporization and expansion. They may be mounted on the manway cover plate or tank shell. Pressure relief devices include the following:

(a) Safety relief valves are pressure relief devices with the valve held closed by one or more springs.

When pressure in the safety relief valve exceeds the safety relief valve setting, the valve opens. The valve recloses when the tank pressure is reduced below the safety relief valve setting. The safety relief valve on a pressure tank car is usually set at 75 percent of the tank test pressure, but may be set as high as 82.5 percent of the tank test pressure.

(b) Safety vents are pressure relief devices that use a frangible disc, also called a rupture disc, to seal the vent opening. This disc is designed to rupture at a predetermined pressure to relieve internal pressure. Once ruptured, the safety vent does not reclose. Rupture discs are made of metal (lead is no longer authorized by the AAR), plastic, rubber, or a combination of metal, plastic, and rubber. Safety vents are used primarily on nonpressure tank cars, but may not be used with flammable liquids and poisons.

(c) Combination safety relief valves incorporate rupture discs and breaking pins in series with spring-operated valves. This type of safety relief valve is typically mounted on the manway cover plate and is usually found on tank cars transporting chlorine or sulfur dioxide. The spring is external to the tank and is protected from the lading by the rupture disc and breaking pin.

2. Pressure regulators on CO_2 cars and liquefied atmospheric gases in cryogenic liquid tank cars

These are devices to release vapors from the tank when the contents become heated.

3. Staged safety relief system for a CO_2 car

The staged safety relief system accounts for the release of vapors in order to keep the liquid in the tank in autorefrigeration during transportation. Relief valves have different settings to operate at different pressures.

4. Vacuum relief valve (negative pressure or vacuum)

A vacuum relief valve is designed to prevent excessive internal negative pressure build-up [a vacuum greater than –0.75 psig (–5.2 kPa)]. The vacuum relief valve, used during unloading with a bottom outlet that is operable from ground level, opens to admit air when a vacuum occurs, then recloses after normal conditions have been restored.

(c) Fittings for gauging, including the following:

Gauging devices are mounted on the manway cover plate and are used to measure the amount of commodity in a tank. These devices measure either innage, the amount of liquid in the tank, including liquefied or cryogenic gases, or outage the amount of vapor space left in the tank.

The following two types of gauging devices are used on pressure tank cars:

(a) Open-type gauging devices—slip tube gauging device with either quick release cover or screw cover
(b) Closed-type gauging devices—rod type magnetic or tape type magnetic

1. Open gauging devices, e.g., slip tube

Open-type gauging devices release liquid once the liquid level in the tank reaches the bottom of a fixed- or adjustable-length tube.

2. Closed gauging devices, e.g., magnetic

Closed-type gauging devices use a float coupled with a magnet on a measuring rod or a dial indicator to show the liquid level of the commodity.

3. Other gauging devices (T-bar, long/short pole)

The "T," or notch, of the gauge bar is mounted inside the manway of the tank. Liquid to the top of the notch or the bottom of the "T" indicates appropriate outage, normally 2 percent.

The long pole/short pole type gauging device resembles the sample line on pressure tank cars. It consists of a valve and fixed-length tube that extends into the tank to a specified level for measuring outage.

(d) Miscellaneous fittings, including the following:

1. Thermometer well

A thermometer well, mounted on the manway cover plate, consists of a closed tube that extends into the tank. It is filled with a small amount of permanent antifreeze. Some brands of this antifreeze may be flammable. By inserting a thermometer into the tube, the temperature of the commodity inside the tank can be measured.

2. Sample line

A sample line may be mounted on the manway cover plate and is used to obtain a sample of the commodity without otherwise opening the tank. For flammable gases, the sample line has an excess flow valve on the end inside the tank.

3. Manway, manway cover plate, hinged and bolted manway cover, protective housing

All tank cars have a manway. A manway is an opening on top of the tank car large enough to allow access to the tank's interior for cleaning, inspecting the interior, and making repairs.

The manway on pressure tank cars is closed with a permanent 20-bolt manway cover plate that is used for attaching fittings. A gasket is used between the manway and its cover plate to form a seal.

A protective housing is mounted on the manway. This housing protects the valves and fittings within from mechanical damage in a derailment. The protective housing has a hinged cover that must be opened to reach the valves and fittings.

4. Washout

A washout is a closed-off opening in the bottom of the tank car tank that is used to facilitate cleaning or purging the tank. Once the closure is removed, there is no control of the commodity flow.

5. Sump

A sump is a closed depression in the bottom of the tank. It allows the eduction line to extend slightly below the bottom of the tank to more completely unload the tank.

9-2.1.9 Given examples of various fitting arrangements on tank cars (including CO_{242} and cryogenic liquid tank cars) with the following fittings included, point out the location(s) where each fitting is likely to leak and a reason for the leak:

(a) Bottom outlet valve/top-operated bottom outlet valve (with stuffing box)
(b) Liquid valve/vapor valve (ball vs. plug type)
(c) Air valve
(d) Bottom outlet nozzle
(e) Quick fill hole cover
(f) Flange for manway, valves, etc.
(g) Safety relief valve
(h) Safety vent (with rupture/frangible) disk
(i) Combination safety valve
(j) Pressure regulators on CO_2 cars and liquefied atmospheric gases in cryogenic liquid tank cars
(k) Vacuum relief valve (negative pressure or vacuum)
(l) Open gauging devices, e.g., slip tube
(m) Closed gauging devices, e.g., magnetic
(n) Thermometer well
(o) Sample line
(p) Manway, manway cover plate, hinged and bolted manway cover, protective housing
(q) Washout

This competency is a good example of the difference between the technician level and the tank car specialty level. The competency in 4-2.3.4.1 for the technician level states, "Identify the types of damage that a pressure container could incur." This knowledge can be learned from a lecture, reviewing graphics, or studying reference sources. The competency for the technician with a tank car specialty, however, requires hands-on training with a "damaged tank car." The technician with a tank car specialty should have an intimate, detailed knowledge of tank cars. Table 9.2, from the Tank Car Safety Course of the Union Pacific Railroad, offers guidance in assessing and repairing damaged car fittings. There are still some competencies that can use "actual or simulated" equipment or tanks and they are specifically noted, such as in 9-2.1.11.

9-2.1.10 Given examples of each of the following types of tank car damage, identify the type of damage:

(a) Crack

A crack is a narrow split or break in the container metal that can penetrate through the metal of the container. Cracks are typically associated with dents and rail burns. Some characteristics of cracks including the following:

(a) Cracks typically occur in tension areas, not compression areas.

(b) Cracks cause failure because they can grow under stress.

(c) Cracks can grow at speeds approaching the speed of sound.

(d) Crack growth is very rapid in brittle steels and relatively slow in ductile steels.

(b) Score, gouge, wheel burn, rail burn

A score is a reduction in the thickness of the container shell. It is an indentation in the container made by a relatively blunt object. A score is characterized by the relocation of the container or weld metal in such a way that the metal is pushed aside along the track of contact with the blunt object.

A gouge is a reduction in the thickness of the container. It is an indentation in the shell made by a sharp, chisel-like object. A gouge is characterized by the cutting and complete removal of the container or weld metal along the track of contact.

Wheel burns, sometimes called spot burns, are similar to a score in that the prolonged contact of the wheel with the tank reduces the thickness of the tank pushing the metal aside at the point of contact.

Long dents with cold work at the bottom of the dent are called "rail burns." *[See 9-2.1.10(e).]*

(c) Puncture

A puncture is a hole in the tank.

(d) Flame impingement

Flame impingement is fire striking the surface of the tank, either in the liquid space or in the vapor space.

(e) Dent

Table 9.2 Guidelines for Assessing and Repairing Damaged Tank Car Fittings

Location of Leaks	Probable Cause	Basic Repair Methods
	Potential Locations of Leaks from Loading and Unloading Fittings	
Liquid or vapor valve (ball or plug type)		
• Liquid or vapor leak from threaded orifice in valve	Valve not completely closed Plug missing or loose Plug or seat worn	Close valve Replace and/or tighten plug To be handled by a tank car specialist
• Liquid or vapor leak from seat between valve and the manway cover plate	Loose flange nuts Bad gasket	Tighten flange nuts To be handled by a tank car specialist
• Liquid or vapor leak around valve stem	Packing retainer loose Missing split ring packing	Tighten packing retainer To be handled by a tank car specialist
Fill hole cover		
• Liquid or vapor leak around fill hole cover or missing	Loose cover nuts Fill hole gasket damaged	Tighten loose cover nuts To be handled by a tank car specialist
Manway cover		
• Liquid or vapor leak between manway nozzle and manway cover	Loose cover nuts Manway gasket damaged or missing	Tighten loose cover nuts To be handled by a tank car specialist
Top operating mechanism (stuffing box) for bottom outlet valve		
• Liquid or vapor leak from cover of stuffing box	Loose packing gland nut Defective packing material	Tighten packing gland nuts To be handled by a tank car specialist
Bottom outlet		
• Liquid leak from bottom outlet cap	Bottom outlet valve open Bottom outlet cap/plug loose Bottom outlet cap gasket missing or defective	Close bottom outlet valve Tighten bottom outlet cap/plug To be handled by a tank car specialist
Liquid line flange		
• Liquid leak from flange	Loose flange nuts Missing or defective gasket	Tighten flange nuts To be handled by a tank car specialist
	Potential Locations of Leaks from Pressure/Vacuum Relief Fittings	
Safety relief valve (external, internal, or combination)		
• Liquid or vapor leak from joint between base of valve and manway cover*	Loose flange nuts	Tighten flange nuts
• Liquid or vapor leak from valve seat*	"O" ring or washer installed incorrectly or damaged from normal wear ***Caution:*** Spring or stem may be broken and not repairable in the field Potentially overloaded tank	To be handled by a tank car specialist; **do not remove or "gag" the safety relief valve**
• Liquid or vapor leak from valve seat*	Valve stem bent or broken Overloaded tank	To be handled by a tank car specialist To be handled by a tank car specialist
Safety vent		
• Liquid or vapor leak from opening in center of safety vent	Ruptured frangible disc (rupture disc) Liquid indicates overloaded or splash without overload	Replace frangible disc with new disc identical to the ruptured disc
Vacuum relief valve		
• Liquid or vapor leak from under cap	"O" ring off seat or valve stem bent Solidified product	To be handled by a tank car specialist To be handled by a tank car specialist

Table 9.2 (continued)

Location of Leaks	Probable Cause	Basic Repair Methods
Potential Locations of Leaks from Fittings for Gauging		
Open-type gauging device, slip tube with quick release or screw cover		
• Liquid or vapor leak from gauging device control valve orifice plug	Gauging device control valve not closed; plug in valve is loose or missing	Close gauging device control valve Tighten plug in control valve
• Liquid or vapor leak from joint between gauging device and manway cover plate	Loose flange nuts	Tighten loose flange nuts
• Liquid or vapor leak from around cover at base of fitting	Loose flange nuts	Tighten loose flange nuts
• Liquid or vapor leak around gauge rod packing gland	Packing gland nut loose Packing material defective or missing	Tighten gauging device cover To be handled by a tank car specialist
Closed-type gauging device, magnetic		
• Liquid or vapor leak from base of gauging device cover	Broken pipe	Tighten gauging device cover **Do not remove cover**
• Liquid or vapor leak from seal between gauging device and manway cover plate	Loose flange nuts	Tighten flange nuts
Closed-type gauging device, tape-type		
• Liquid or vapor leak from seal between gauging device and manway cover plate	Loose flange nuts	Tighten flange nuts
Potential Locations of Leaks from Miscellaneous Fittings		
Sample line		
• Liquid or vapor leak from sample line orifice or around plug	Sample line valve not closed Plug missing or loose	Close sample line valve Replace and/or tighten plug
• Liquid or vapor leak from joint between base of sample line and manway cover	Damaged sample line pipe	To be handled by a tank car specialist
Thermometer well		
• Liquid or vapor leak from thermometer well cap	Loose cap with damaged thermometer well pipe Missing or defective "O" ring in cap or on nipple with damaged thermometer well pipe	Tighten cap; **do not remove cap** To be handled by a tank car specialist; **do not remove cap**
• Liquid leaking from between thermometer well nipple and manway cover	Damaged thermometer well pipe	To be handled by a tank car specialist: **do not tighten thermometer well nipple!!**
• Thermometer well nipple broken off with no leak	Mechanical damage to thermometer well nipple	To be handled by a tank car specialist
Heater coil—internal		
• Liquid leak from inlet or outlet pipes at bottom of tank	Condensation—residue from material used for heating contents Damage to internal heater coils	Tighten caps. If leak continues, contact a tank car specialist To be handled by a tank car specialist
Washout		
• Liquid leaking from around seal between tank and washout plate	Flange nuts loose Gasket defective	Tighten flange nuts clockwise To be handled by a tank car specialist
• Liquid leaking from plug in washout plate	Tell-tale plug loose	Tighten plug

Source: Union Pacific Railroad, *Participant's Manual: Tank Car Safety Course,* April 1997.

NOTE: Liquid leaks indicate overload or splash from valve functioning, due to impact of car.

A dent is a deformation of the container metal. It is caused by impact with a relatively blunt object. When there is a sharp radius of curvature associated with the dent, the possibility of cracking exists.

Long dents with cold work at the bottom of the dent are called "rail burns."

(f) Corrosion

Corrosion is pitting of the tank metal, thus reducing the thickness and, possibly, the strength of the tank metal.

9-2.1.11* Given examples (actual or simulated) of scores, gouges, wheel burns, and rail burns, perform each of the following tasks:

(a) Use a depth gauge to measure the depth of each score, gouge, wheel burn, and rail burn

The tank car dent gauge is a "go/no-go" device used to compare the radius of curvature of a dent in a tank car tank to accepted standards in order to determine the severity of damage. It is called a "go/no-go" because, depending on the reading, a tank car can be pulled out of service (if the measurement is below accepted standards).

(b) Point out where each score, gouge, wheel burn, and rail burn crosses a weld, if that condition exists

(c) Measure the depth of the weld metal removed for any point where the score, gouge, wheel burn, and rail burn crosses a weld

(d) Given examples (actual or simulated) of where a score, gouge, wheel burn, and rail burn crosses a weld, determine if the "heat-affected zone" has been damaged

A-9-2.1.11 The heat-affected zone is an area in the metal next to the actual weld. This zone is less ductile than either the weld or the metal due to the effect of the welding process. The heat-affected zone is vulnerable to cracks.

9-2.1.12 Given examples (actual or simulated) of dents and rail burns, perform each of the following tasks:

The technician with a tank car specialty will perform these tasks in a manner appropriate to the rail equipment used. These tasks should be performed using personal protective equipment appropriate for the material involved and the working conditions.

(a) Use a dent gauge to measure the radius of curvature for each dent or rail burn

The technician with a tank car specialty will use a dent gauge to determine whether the radius of curvature in a tank is critical or not critical.

(b) Identify those examples that include cracks at the point of minimum curvature

The technician with the tank car specialty will identify cracks at the point of minimum curvature and explain the significance of this condition.

9-2.1.13 Given examples of damaged tank car fittings, describe the extent of damage to those fittings.

The technician with a tank car specialty will describe the extent of damage to tank car fittings — for example, damaged and not leaking; damaged and leaking; repairable or not, and so forth.

9-2.1.14 Given examples of tank car tank damage, describe the extent of damage to the tank car tank.

The technician with a tank car specialty will describe the extent of damage to a tank car tank — for example, damaged and not leaking; damaged and leaking; repairable or not, and so on. The technician will also determine the depth of score, gouge, wheel burn or rail burn, radius of curvature of dents and rail burns, amount and location of corrosion, presence of cracks, and so on, as appropriate for the example.

9-2.1.15 Given a tank car and the appropriate equipment and reference material, determine the pressure in the tank car, using either of the following methods:

(a) A pressure gauge
(b) The temperature of the contents

The technician with a tank car specialty will determine the pressure in the tank car using a pressure gauge attached to the tank car through one of the fittings. Alternatively, the temperature of the material can be obtained and checked against temperature pressure charts to determine the pressure of the contents. This alternative method is unlikely to be used in an emergency.

9-2.1.16* Given a tank car, use the car's gauging device to determine the amount of lading in it.

The technician with a tank car specialty will use various types of gauging devices to determine the innage (amount of liquid) or outage (amount of vapor space) in a tank car.

A-9-2.1.16 Other methods for determining the amount of liquid include shipping papers, the presence of frost line, the use of touch to feel for the colder liquid level, and the use of heat sensors.

9-2.2 Predicting the Likely Behavior of the Tank Car and Its Contents.

Technicians with a tank car specialty shall predict the likely behavior of the tank car and its contents. The technician with a tank car specialty shall be able to:

Again, these competencies build on the competencies of the hazardous materials technician. The hazardous materials technician with a tank car specialty will have expertise in predicting the likely behavior of the tank car and its contents. In some cases, a private sector specialist employee A may also have these same skills and knowledge, but only for the specific tank car and chemical used by his or her company. For example, an employee of a petrochemical enterprise may be the resident expert on tank cars that carry gasoline. If the appropriate training or certification has been completed, this person can operate at the same level as the technician with a tank car specialty, but only for tank cars that carry gasoline used by the petrochemical company.

9-2.2.1 Given the following types of tank cars, describe the likely breach/release mechanisms associated with each type.

(a) Nonpressure tank cars
(b) Pressure tank cars
(c) Cryogenic liquid tank cars
(d) High-pressure tube cars
(e) Pneumatically unloaded covered hopper cars

The technician with a tank car specialty should be able to discuss the different types of breach and release mechanisms for various stress conditions on these tank cars.

9-2.2.2 Describe the difference in the following types of construction materials used in tank cars and their significance in assessing tank damage:

(a) Carbon steel
(b) Alloy steel
(c) Aluminum

Carbon steel is used in over 90 percent of the tank car tanks in use today, with aluminum making up most of the remainder. Stainless steel, referred to as alloy steel, is used in a smaller number of cars. Nickel or nickel alloy is used for some tanks that are used to transport acid or food. The minimum plate thickness of materials used to construct tank cars is specified by regulation.

9-2.2.3 Discuss the significance of selection of lading for compatibility with tank car construction material.

The technician with a tank car specialty will be able to explain the consequences of having an incompatible material in a tank car tank.

9-2.2.4 Describe the significance of "lining" and "cladding" on tank cars in assessing tank damage.

The interiors of some tank cars are lined or clad with materials to protect the tank from the corrosive or reactive effects of the contents or to maintain the purity of the contents. During an emergency, responders must consider the potential effects of lining or cladding damage.

9-2.2.5 Describe the significance of the jacket on tank cars in assessing tank damage.

An undamaged jacket may serve as a heat shield from radiated heat. Also, the jacket is not designed to hold the product, so mechanical damage to the jacket may not be indicative of the extent of damage to the tank itself.

9-2.2.6 Describe the significance of "insulation" and "thermal protection" on tank cars in assessing tank damage.

Insulation is used to safeguard the contents of the tank car from outside temperatures.

Thermal protection is used on certain tank cars to protect them from flame impingement from either a pool or torch fire. It is designed to keep tank metal temperatures below 800°F for 100 minutes (pool fire exposure) or 30 minutes (torch fire exposure).

9-2.2.7 Describe the significance of "jacketed" and "sprayed-on" thermal protection on tank cars in assessing tank damage.

Both provide the same function.

9-2.2.8 Describe the significance of "interior" and "exterior" heater coils on tank cars in assessing tank damage.

Exterior heater coils pose less of a problem when damaged because they are outside of the tank and have no contact with the contents. However, interior heater coils inside the tank can allow the contents to get outside the tank because the coil is connected to a heater coil inlet on the outside of the tank. Without a cap, there is no control of the flow.

9-2.2.9 Describe the significance of each of the following types of tank car damage on different types of tank cars in assessing tank damage:

(a) Crack

Since it is difficult to determine when a crack is critical, accurate and timely decisions must be made. The following guidelines can be helpful:

(a) Any crack found in a tank, no matter how small, demands immediate action to relieve the stress in the tank by venting, flaring, or transferring the contents of the tank.
(b) Cracks in fillet welds (i.e., those used to attach brackets or reinforcement plates) are not critical unless a crack extends into tank metal.
(c) When a crack is in conjunction with a dent, score, or gouge, the tank should be unloaded as soon as possible before moving it.

(d) Consider the pressure of the commodity and evaluate the potential for a pressure rise.

(b) Score, gouge, wheel burn, rail burn

Scores and gouges are evaluated in the following manner, using the depth of the indentation as a guideline:

(a) Longitudinal scores are of greatest concern; however, circumferential (hoop) scores must be evaluated as well.
(b) Scores or gouges crossing a weld with removal of the filler metal are of little concern.
(c) Longitudinal scores or gouges that cross a weld and damage the heat-affected zone are potentially critical; therefore, the contents of the tank should be transferred immediately by experienced personnel.
(d) When the internal pressure exceeds one half of the allowable internal pressure listed for the tank, tanks having scores or gouges should be unloaded in place by experienced personnel.
(e) Wheel burns do not induce a high probability of failure.
(f) For loaded tank cars with a wheel burn, the following action should be taken:

1. With a wheel burn less than $^1/_8$ in. (3.2 mm), the tank can be transported, not in ordinary train service, to the closest loading/unloading facility, and the tank emptied
2. With a wheel burn $^1/_8$ in. (3.2 mm) or greater, the tank should be unloaded as soon as possible without further transportation.

(g) When there is no liquid behind the point of the wheel burn to cool the tank shell, the rubbing of the wheel tends to heat and deform the metal much more than on a loaded car.
(h) For a wheel burn on an empty tank car, the following steps should be taken:

1. For a wheel burn less than $^1/_4$ in. (6.35 mm), the car should be sent to a shop for repair.
2. For a wheel burn $^1/_4$ in. (6.35 mm) or greater, the internal pressure should be reduced by flaring or venting any remaining contents to not over 10 psi (69 kPa) before being sent to the shop.

(i) All rail burns are serious and require that the contents be transferred to another tank car or cargo tank before the car is transported from the site.
(j) For a tank with a gouge, the following steps should be taken:

1. For a gouge less than $^1/_8$ in. (3.2 mm) deep, the tank can be uprighted and transported *a short distance* prior to transfer
2. For a gouge $^1/_8$ in. (3.2 mm) or greater, the tank should be uprighted and the contents transferred in place before being transported any distance.

(c) Puncture
(d) Flame impingement
(e) Dent

Sharp dents in the shell of the tank are the most serious, because these dents can reduce the strength of the tank significantly. Dents should be evaluated using the following guidelines:

(a) Generally, for dents in the shell of tank cars built prior to 1967, the tank should be unloaded, without moving it, given the following conditions:

1. Minimum radius of curvature of 4 in. (102 mm) or less
2. Presence of a crack anywhere
3. Dent crossing a weld
4. Presence of a score or gouge
5. Evidence of cold work

Dents with a radius of curvature more than 4 in. (102 mm) are not problems by themselves.

(b) Generally, for dents in the shell of tank cars built since 1967, the tank should be unloaded, without moving it, given the following conditions:

1. Minimum radius of curvature of 2 in. (51 mm) or less
2. Presence of a crack anywhere
3. Dent crossing a weld
4. Presence of a score or gouge
5. Evidence of cold work

Dents with a radius of curvature more than 2 in. (51 mm) are not problems by themselves.

(c) Massive dents in heads of the tank are generally not serious unless gouges or cracks are present with the dents.

Note: Reduction in tank volume due to massive denting is not a major consideration unless it is suspected that atmospheric temperature may approach the "shell full temperature" of 115°F (46°C) summer loading or 95°F (35°C) winter loading. The loss of volume due to massive denting will lower the shell full temperature a range of 3°F to 4°F (1.7°C to 2.2°C). Massive denting could reduce tank shell capacity by as much as 5 percent. If massive denting causes the volume of the tank to equal the volume of the loading, the tank may undergo hydrostatic failure.

(d) Small dents [not exceeding 12 in. (305 mm) in diameter] in heads in conjunction with cold work in the bottom of the dent are marginally safe if they show a radius of curvature less than 4 in. (102 mm) for tanks built prior to 1967 or less than 2 in. (51 mm) for tanks built since 1967. Such tanks should be unloaded in place. In any case, move the tank as little as possible and unload it promptly.

(f) Corrosion

9-2.2.10 Describe the significance of the depth of scores, gouges, wheel burns, and rail burns on tank cars in assessing tank damage.

Scores, gouges, wheel burns, and rail burns reduce the thickness of the metal in the tank, thus reducing the strength of the tank metal.

9-2.2.11 Describe the significance of scores, gouges, wheel burns, and rail burns crossing a weld on a pressure tank car in assessing tank damage.

Scores, gouges, wheel burns, and rail burns reduce the thickness of the metal in the tank, thus reducing the strength of the tank metal. This is complicated by the reduction of strength associated with damage to the "heat-affected zone."

9-2.2.12 Describe the significance of damage to the "heat affected" zone of a weld on a tank car in assessing tank damage.

Because of this change in composition in the tank metal, the ductility of the steel in this heat-affected zone is reduced. The heat-affected zone is a likely origin for cracks.

9-2.2.13 Describe the significance of a condemning dent of a tank car in assessing tank damage.

The speed at which the car is to be offloaded becomes extremely important.

9-2.2.14 Given various types of tank cars, describe the significance of pressure increases in assessing tank damage.

Should the tank be weakened, increases in pressure could overstress the tank and cause failure.

9-2.2.15 Given various types of tank cars, describe the significance of the amount of lading in the tank in assessing tank damage.

Overloaded tank cars have little, or no, room for expansion, so when exposed to thermal stress the risk for violent rupture is greater.

9-2.2.16 Describe the significance of flame impingement on a tank car.

9-3 Competencies — Planning the Response

In 4-3.1, the technician level responder is required to identify the appropriate response objectives for responders at that level. The options available are either offensive, defensive, or nonintervention. The response objectives for the technician with a tank car specialty are expanded to include highly technical, offensive operations.

Response objectives now include those objectives that can lead to final mitigation. While the responder at the technician level can stabilize a situation until "industrial experts" arrive for final and complete mitigation, the technician with a tank car specialty can become trained or certified to assist in the following work:

(a) Plan the operation:

1. Develop a list of required equipment for the selected operation
2. Prepare a plan for set-up, implementation, and shutdown of the operation
3. Prepare a site safety plan

(b) Set up the operation:

1. Hold a safety briefing
2. Position the equipment
3. Set up and activate the emergency shut-off system, if used
4. Purge the liquid and vapor hoses and test for leaks

(c) Implement the operation

(d) Shut down the operation:

1. Purge the hoses and/or piping
2. Disassemble and decontaminate the equipment
3. Secure cars

(e) Determine disposition of cars and prepare them for transportation

9-3.1 Determining the Response Options.

Given the analysis of an emergency involving tank cars, technicians with a tank car specialty shall determine the response options for each tank car involved. The technician with a tank car specialty shall be able to:

Product removal methods are outside the legitimate responsibility of the local emergency response personnel. However, oversight of their planning and implementation is within the responsibilities of local emergency response agencies.

9-3.1.1 Describe the purpose of, potential risks associated with, procedures for, equipment required to implement, and safety precautions for the following product removal techniques for tank cars:

(a) Transferring liquids and vapors

The purpose of transferring liquids and gases is often associated with removal from a damaged or potentially damaged containment vessel to one that is undamaged. The equipment will vary with the type of vessel involved and the hazardous material being transferred. Transfer procedures are generally established in advance by good industry practice. Only essential personnel, outlined, in most cases, in the overall incident management systems of the hazardous materials branch, should be involved in the process.

A transfer is the movement of the contents of a damaged or overloaded tank car into a receiving tank (e.g., a tank car, a cargo tank, an intermodal tank, or a fixed tank).

In rail transportation, transfers may be used when the following conditions exist:

(a) The tank car tank itself is sound but, due to bolster or other mechanical damage, the car cannot be safely mounted on its trucks and rerailed.
(b) The site conditions prevent rerailing the damaged tank car (e.g., the terrain does not permit use of cranes or other rerailing equipment).
(c) The tank car tank is overloaded.
(d) The damage to leaking valves and fittings cannot be repaired.
(e) The tank car tank has been damaged to the extent that it cannot be safely rerailed and moved to an appropriate unloading point.

Typically, transfers in the field are distinguished by the basic equipment used to move the contents from a damaged or overloaded tank car. Gas or liquid transfers can be accomplished in the field using one of the following methods:

(a) *Vapor compressor.* This product removal method uses a vapor compressor to move the contents of a damaged or overloaded tank car into a receiving tank (e.g., a tank car, cargo tank, or portable tank). The vapor compressor pulls the vapors from the receiving tank, compresses them, and forces them into the damaged tank car. The higher pressure in the damaged tank car pushes the liquefied gas into the receiving tank. The use of the vapor compressor will result in a pressure increase in the damaged tank car. This transfer method should be used only when an increase in pressure in the damaged tank car is acceptable.

(b) *Vapor compressor and a liquid pump.* This product removal method uses a vapor compressor and a liquid pump to move the contents of a damaged or overloaded tank car into a receiving tank (e.g., a tank car, cargo tank, or portable tank). The vapor compressor is used to accelerate the rate of transfer by withdrawing vapors from the receiving tank, compressing them, and forcing them into the damaged tank car. The higher pressure in the damaged tank car pushes the liquefied gas into the pump. The use of the vapor compressor will result in a pressure increase in the damaged tank car. This transfer method should be used only when an increase in pressure in the damaged tank car is acceptable. This method is justified when the receiving tank is a greater distance from the damaged or overloaded tank car.

(c) *Compressed air or an inert gas.* This product removal method uses a compressed gas (e.g., nitrogen or carbon dioxide) to move the contents of a damaged or overloaded tank car into a receiving tank (e.g., a tank car, cargo tank, or portable tank). The compressed gas creates a positive pressure differential in the damaged tank car that pushes the liquid into the receiving tank. Vapor from the receiving tank may have to be vented to the atmosphere or scrubbed. The use of the compressed gas will result in a pressure increase in the damaged tank car. This transfer method should be used only when an increase in pressure in the damaged tank car is acceptable. Check with the shipper to determine the compatibility of the compressed gas to be used.

(d) *Liquid pump.* This product removal method uses a liquid pump to move the contents of a damaged or overloaded tank car into a receiving tank (e.g., a tank car, cargo tank, or portable tank). The material in the damaged or overloaded tank car is then pumped into the receiving tank. The use of a liquid pump does not increase the pressure in the damaged tank car; however, if another means of creating positive pressure differential is used, a pressure increase may occur.

(e) *Vapor pressure (with or without flaring).* This product removal method uses the material's own vapor pressure to move the contents of a damaged or overloaded tank car into a receiving tank (e.g., a tank car, cargo tank, or portable tank). In addition, a vapor flare maintains the necessary positive pressure differential between the damaged or overloaded tank car and the receiving tank by burning off vapors in the receiving tank at the outlet of a flare pipe. The pressure in the receiving tank is kept as low as possible.

(b) Flaring liquids and vapors

Flaring is the controlled release and disposal of flammable materials by burning from the outlet of a flare pipe (horizontal or vertical). It is used to reduce the pressure or dispose of the residual vapors in a damaged or overloaded tank car. *Vapor flaring* is the burning of vapors of a liquefied compressed gas at the outlet of a vertical flare pipe as the vapors exit the flare pipe. *Liquid flaring* is the vaporizing of liquid product and burning of the vapors at the end of a horizontal flare pipe. A pit is used to contain any product that is not completely burned.

Flaring liquids and gases is a procedure that can be used to deplete the amount of hazardous material involved or to depressurize a vessel. It should be performed only by persons who are trained in the technique. In some cases where the burning is already underway at a vent or pressure relief valve when responders arrive, a prescribed procedure will be to allow the flaring process to continue. Determination must be made that the flaring does not present a source of ignition to other spilled flammable substances.

In rail transportation, flaring is used for the following three basic purposes:

(a) Reduce the pressure inside a tank car
(b) Dispose of vapors remaining in a tank car during or after transfer of the liquid
(c) Burn off liquid where transfer is impractical

Flaring may also be used to expedite recovery operations or as an interim method until a transfer can begin.

(c) Venting

Venting is the process of reducing the pressure in a tank by releasing liquefied compressed gas vapors into the atmosphere. This release can be direct or, in case of toxic products, indirect through an appropriate treatment system. Typically, venting is used with nonflammable gases.

Extreme care must be exercised in a venting operation and only after consultation with the shipper, carrier, or other tank car specialist.

(d) Hot and cold tapping

Hot tapping describes a situation in which welding or cutting is done on a container or piping while it contains a flammable liquid or gas. It is an emergency procedure in which circumstances necessitate the work and the contents cannot be removed prior to performance of the work. The work must be done only by those who have been trained to do such procedures.

The hot tap is a technique for providing access to the contents of a tank car when damage to the valves and fittings precludes access to the contents. Once the hot tap is completed, transfer, flaring, or venting can take place.

Hot tapping involves the welding of a threaded nozzle into an undamaged section of the tank that is in contact with the liquid. A liquid valve is attached to the nozzle. A hole is then drilled through the tank with a special drilling machine. This hot tapping (drilling) machine is equipped with seals that prevent loss of product during the drilling operation. Liquid hoses or pipe can be attached to the valve outlet.

Cold tapping is similar to hot tapping except that the attachment of the threaded nozzle to the tank is accomplished without welding and instead by strapping the nozzle plate onto the tank.

(e) Vent and burn

Vent and burn describes a highly specialized, and seldom practical, technique that involves the use of shaped charges that are designed to create an opening in a container and set fire to its contents. The purpose is to deplete the supply of contained hazardous flammable substances when other methods are unavailable.

Vent and burn is a method of removing liquefied flammable compressed gases or flammable liquids from a tank car by creating controlled openings in the tank using explosives. Explosive charges are strategically placed on the tank, one at the highest point on the tank for venting vapor and the second at the lowest point on the tank for releasing liquid. The released contents are allowed to flow into a pit for evaporation or burnoff.

Vent and burn is the last resort and is to be performed only by experienced personnel.[1]

9-3.1.2 Describe the inherent risks associated with, procedures for, equipment required to implement, and safety precautions for leak control techniques on various tank car fittings.

9-3.1.3 Describe the effect flaring or venting gas or liquid has on the pressure in the tank (flammable gas or flammable liquid product).

Flaring and venting reduce the pressure or dispose of the residual vapors in a damaged or overloaded tank car.

9-3.1.4 Describe the inherent risks associated with, procedures for, equipment required to implement, and safety precautions for lifting of tank cars.

The lifting of tank cars should be performed only by experienced personnel, such as railroad or shipper mechanical personnel or specially trained and equipped contractors.

9-3.1.5 Describe the inherent risks associated with, procedures for, and safety precautions for the following operations:

(a) Shutting off locomotives using the fuel shutoff and the battery disconnect
(b) Setting and releasing brakes on rail cars
(c) Uncoupling rail cars

The technician with a tank car specialty will perform these tasks in a manner appropriate to the rail equipment used. These tasks should be performed using appropriate personal protective equipment for the material involved and the working conditions.

9-3.1.6 Describe the hazards associated with working on railroad property during emergencies.

The Union Pacific Railroad has provided the following summary of these hazards.[2]

While working on railroad property, always take the following precautions:

- Always wear a hard hat, safety glasses, and sturdy work boots, preferably steel-toed. Tennis shoes and regular low-cut casual shoes are not acceptable.
- Wear hearing protection in situations that call for its use.
- Do not wear bright red or orange clothing on the right-of-way; train crews can confuse these colors with emergency situations.
- Stay clear of the tracks whenever possible; trains can sneak up on you undetected due to atmospheric conditions and terrain.
- When confronted with a passing train, always stand away from the track to prevent injury from flying debris or loose rigging. Also, observe the train as it passes so that you are prepared to take evasive action in the event of an emergency.
- In double track territory, never stand between tracks when a train is passing. This could place you in a precarious situation if another train suddenly appears on the other track.
- Never walk or stand on the track; rail surfaces can be extremely slippery and many rails in curves are lubricated. When you cross the rails, step over them.
- Try to maintain at least 20 ft from the rails when walking on the right-of-way. Never walk down the center of the track.
- Be prepared for the movement of cars at any time—in either direction. Stay at least 20 ft away from the ends of cars when crossing the track and never climb on, under, or between cars. Never rely solely on others to protect you from train movement—watch yourself.
- Stay away from remote-controlled switches. The switch points can move unexpectedly—with enough force to crush ballast rock!! Stay away from any other devices you are unsure of.
- Avoid pole lines within the right-of-way. These lines may carry from 500 volts to 2700 volts. Due to the terrain, sometimes these lines are located very close to the ground.
- Be careful when working around a derailment. Hazardous materials may be present, so check with the local railroad personnel before approaching.
- Equipment must never be moved across the tracks except at established road crossings and never moved across bridges or through tunnels.
- A 100-car train moving at 60 miles-per-hour can take more than one mile to stop in the event of an emergency. Never judge the distance or speed of a train by the headlight.
- Never lay metal objects across the rails. This is a safety hazard.

9-4 Competencies — Implementing the Planned Response

Most of the competencies in Section 9-4 require the actual demonstration of a task. These tasks require an in-depth knowledge of the tank car, its contents, and the specialized equipment needed to complete the task. Since these tasks must be done on actual tank cars, only a few training facilities will be able to provide practical training and/or certification.

9-4.1 Implementing the Planned Response.

Given an analysis of an emergency involving tank cars and the planned response, technicians with a tank car specialty shall implement or oversee the implementation of the selected response options safely and effectively. The technician with a tank car specialty shall be able to:

The equipment and resources necessary for demonstrating these tasks are not readily available. Requests for training for the performance of these tasks should be directed to the local shipper, carrier, or contractor personnel in the community, possibly through the Local Emergency Planning Committee.

9-4.1.1 Given a leaking manway cover plate (loose bolts), control the leak.

The technician with a tank car specialty will demonstrate the ability to choose the appropriate tools and tighten the loose bolts on a leaking manway cover plate. This task should be performed using personal protective equipment appropriate for the material involved and for the working conditions.

9-4.1.2 Given leaking packing on the following tank car fittings, control the leak:

(a) Gauging device packing nut

The technician with a tank car specialty will choose the appropriate tools and tighten the gauging device packing nut, as appropriate for the specific make of valve. This task should be performed using personal protective equipment appropriate for the material involved and for the working conditions.

(b) Liquid or vapor valve packing nut

The technician with a tank car specialty will choose the appropriate tools and tighten the liquid or vapor valve packing nuts or bolts, as appropriate for the specific make of valve. This task should be performed using personal protective equipment appropriate for the material involved and for the working conditions.

(c) Top-operated bottom outlet valve packing gland

The technician with a tank car specialty will choose the appropriate tools and tighten the packing gland on a top-operated bottom outlet valve, as appropriate for the specific make of valve. This task should be performed using personal protective equipment appropriate for the material involved and for the working conditions.

9-4.1.3 Given an open bottom outlet valve with a defective gasket in the cap, control the leak.

The technician with a tank car specialty will choose the appropriate tools, ensure that the bottom outlet valve is closed, and tighten the cap on a bottom outlet valve, as appropriate for the specific make of valve. This task should be performed using personal protective equipment appropriate for the material involved and for the working conditions.

9-4.1.4 Given a leaking top-operated bottom outlet valve, close valve completely to control leak.

The technician with a tank car specialty will close the top-operated bottom outlet valve, as appropriate for the specific make of valve. This task should be performed using personal protective equipment appropriate for the material involved and for the working conditions.

9-4.1.5 Given leaking fittings on a chlorine tank car, use the Chlorine C kit, as appropriate, to control the leak.

The technician with a tank car specialty will apply the C kit to control a leaking combination safety relief valve and leaking liquid and vapor valves on a chlorine tank car, following the instructions provided by the manufacturer of the C kit or local standard operating procedures. This task should be performed using personal protective equipment appropriate for the material involved and for the working conditions.

9-4.1.6 Given the following types of leaks on various types of tank cars, plug or patch those leaks:

(a) Puncture
(b) Irregular-shaped hole
(c) Cracks, splits, or tears

The technician with a tank car specialty will select and apply various methods of plugging and patching to control or stop leakage of the tank car's contents. This task should be performed using personal protective equipment appropriate for the material involved and for the working conditions.

9-4.1.7 Given the appropriate equipment and resources, demonstrate the following:

(a) Transferring of liquids and vapors
(b) Flaring of liquids and vapors
(c) Venting

The technician with a tank car specialty will participate as a member of a team assigned to perform product removal. These tasks should be performed using personal protective equipment appropriate for the material involved and for the working conditions.

9-4.1.8 Given the appropriate resources, perform the following tasks:

(a) Shut off locomotives using the fuel shutoff and the battery disconnect
(b) Set and release brakes on rail cars
(c) Uncouple rail cars

The technician with a tank car specialty will perform these tasks in a manner appropriate to the rail equipment used. These tasks should be performed using personal protective equipment appropriate for the material involved and for the working conditions.

The equipment and resources necessary for demonstrating these tasks are not readily available. Requests for training for the performance of these tasks should be directed to the railroad or shippers in the community, possibly through the Local Emergency Planning Committee.

9-4.1.9* Demonstrate bonding and grounding procedures for the transfer of flammable and combustible products from tank cars, or other products that can give off flammable gases or vapors when heated or contaminated, including the following:

Local procedures for these tasks should be written out and consistent with nationally accepted practices.

The technician with a tank car specialty will participate as a member of a team assigned to set up bonding and grounding for the transfer of tank cars. These tasks should be performed using personal protective equipment appropriate for the material involved and for the working conditions.

A-9-4.1.9 When bonding and grounding, a ground resistance tester and an ohm meter should be used. The ground resistance tester measures the earth's resistance to a ground rod, and the ohm meter measures the resistance of the connections to ensure electrical continuity. One ground rod might not be enough; more may have to be driven and connected to the first to ensure a good ground. Resistance varies with types of soils.

(a) Selection of proper equipment
(b) Sequence of bonding and grounding connections
(c) Proper testing of bonding and grounding connections

The technician with a tank car specialty should be able to verify (using the appropriate equipment) the following:

(a) Ground rod resistance to earth
(b) Connections between ground rod and tank car
(c) Connections between ground rod and main ground rod and ground cable

9-4.1.10 Given a simulated flammable liquid spill from a tank car, describe the procedures for site safety and fire control during cleanup and removal operations.

The technician with a tank car specialty will describe the procedures for site safety and fire control during cleanup and removal operations when confronted with a flammable liquid leak from an intermodal tank. These tasks should be performed using personal protective equipment appropriate for the material involved and for the working conditions.

References Cited in Commentary

1. *Transportation Test (Technology) Center, Field Product Removal Methods for Tank Cars,* Association of American Railroads for the Federal Railroad Administration, Office of Research and Development, 1995.
2. Union Pacific Railroad, *Participant's Manual: Tank Car Safety Course,* April 1997.

CHAPTER 10

Competencies for the Technician with a Cargo Tank Specialty

10-1 General

10-1.1 Introduction.

Technicians with a cargo tank specialty shall be trained to meet all competencies of the first responder awareness, operational, and hazardous materials technician levels and the competencies of this chapter. The technician with a cargo tank specialty also shall receive any additional training to meet applicable United States Department of Transportation (DOT), United States Environmental Protection Agency (EPA), Occupational Safety and Health Administration (OSHA), and other appropriate state, local, or provincial occupational health and safety regulatory requirements.

In the 1987 edition of NFPA 472, one of the competencies required for the hazardous materials specialist (incorporated into the hazardous materials technician in 1992) was merely to "describe" specific techniques. In the commentary on that competency, Martin F. Henry wrote the following: "The task is generally performed by people with particular expertise and responsibility for the operation, under the supervision and control of responders." The specific techniques listed in that competency were transferring liquids and gases, flaring liquids and gases, hot tapping, and venting and burning.

Now in this new Chapter 10 of NFPA 472, it is required that competency in performing these tasks be demonstrated. For example, 10-4.1.4 reads: "Given the following product transfer and recovery equipment, demonstrate the safe and correct application and use of each of the following:

(a) Portable pumps (air, electrical, gasoline/diesel)
(b) Vehicles with power-take-off (PTO) driven pumps
(c) Pressure transfer
(d) Vacuum trucks"

The new specialty levels introduced in Chapters 9, 10, and 11 of this 1997 edition of NFPA 472 cover extremely hazardous and highly skilled operations that have not had any standardized training or certification previously. The technician with a tank car specialty, the technician with a cargo tank specialty, and the technician with an intermodal tank specialty are levels that are above OSHA's technician and specialist levels and are not defined by the present OSHA regulations (Title 29, *Code of Federal Regulations*, Part 1910.120). For a comparison of NFPA 472 and OSHA 1910.120, see Chapter 9, Table 9.1.

10-1.2 Definition.

Technicians with a cargo tank specialty are those persons who provide support to the hazardous materials technician, provide oversight for product removal and movement of damaged cargo tanks, and act as a liaison between technicians and other outside resources. These technicians are expected to use specialized chemical-protective clothing and specialized control equipment.

10-1.3 Goals.

The goal of this chapter shall be to provide the technician with a cargo tank specialty with the knowledge and skills to perform the following tasks safely. In addition to being competent at the technician level, the technician with a cargo tank specialty shall be able to:

(a) Analyze a hazardous materials incident involving cargo tanks to determine the magnitude of the problem in terms of outcomes by completing the following tasks:

1. Determine the type and extent of damage to cargo tanks
2. Predict the likely behavior of cargo tanks and their contents in an emergency

(b) Plan a response for an emergency involving cargo tanks within the capabilities and competencies of available personnel, personal protective equipment, and control equipment by determining the response options (offensive, defensive, and nonintervention) for a hazardous materials emergency involving cargo tanks

(c) Implement the planned response to a hazardous materials incident involving cargo tanks

10-1.4 Mandating of Competencies.

This standard does not mandate that hazardous materials response teams performing offensive operations on cargo tanks have technicians with a cargo tank specialty. Technicians operating within the bounds of their training as listed in Chapter 4 of this standard are able to intervene in cargo tank incidents. However, if a hazardous materials response team desires to train some or all its technicians to have in-depth knowledge of cargo tanks, this chapter sets out the required competencies.

The committee wanted to be perfectly clear that existing and new responders at the hazardous materials technician level can still perform basic offensive operations on cargo tank trucks that they have always been qualified to do. This new specialty level covers those highly technical skills and knowledge primarily needed for conducting product removal and transfer operations. For example, the skills required by the competency in 10-4.1.5 are skills that the technician normally does not possess. A hazardous materials response team may have a few members trained to this level or can request that the shipper, carrier, or an environmental contractor bring someone with this specialty to the scene. Programs covering these competencies are already in place at a number of hazardous materials training centers, including the Association of American Railroads Transportation Test Center (AAR/TTC), the California Specialized Training Institute, and the New Jersey Office of Emergency Management—Hazardous Materials Emergency Response Program.

The committee wants to be clear that this specialty level is not mandated for any hazardous materials response team or its members. Arrangements to request assistance are perfectly appropriate in these situations.

10-2 Competencies — Analyzing the Incident

10-2.1 Determining the Type and Extent of Damage to Cargo Tanks.

Given examples of damaged cargo tanks, technicians with a cargo tank specialty shall describe the type and extent of damage to each cargo tank and its fittings. The technician with a cargo tank specialty shall be able to:

10-2.1.1 Given the specification mark for a cargo tank and the appropriate reference materials, describe the tank's basic construction and features.

In this document, cargo tank trucks are grouped into the following five categories:

(a) MC-306/DOT-406 cargo tanks are commonly used to transport liquid petroleum products at atmospheric pressures. Since 1995, all cargo tanks in this service must be built to the DOT-406 specification. These are nonpressurized (atmospheric pressure) tanks, with maximum working pressures of 3 psig to 5 psig (21 kPa to 34 kPa). Most of these cargo tanks are not insulated and have a capacity between 7500 gal and 10,000 gal (28,387 L and 37,850 L).

(b) MC-307/DOT-407 cargo tanks are commonly used to transport flammable and combustible liquids, mild corrosives, and chemicals with a vapor pressure of 18 psi at 100°F (37.8°C) or greater, but not more than 40 psi at 170°F (76.7°C). Since 1995, all cargo tanks in this service must be built to the DOT-407 specification. Tank capacities range up to 7000 gal (26,495 L).

(c) MC-312/DOT-412 cargo tanks are commonly used to transport high-density liquids and strong corrosives, such as nitric and sulfuric acid. Since 1995, all cargo tanks in this service must be built to the DOT-412 specification. Tank design pressures range from 35 psi to 50 psi (241 kPa to 345 kPa), with maximum capacities of approximately 5000 gal to 6000 gal (18,925 L to 22,710 L).

(d) MC-331 cargo tanks are pressurized containers commonly used for the transportation of liquefied and compressed gases. Design pressures range from 100 psi to 500 psi (690 kPa to 3448 kPa), with capacities ranging from 2500 gal to 11,500 gal (9463 L to 43,528 L).

(e) MC-338 cargo tanks are commonly used to transport cryogenic liquids, such as liquid nitrogen and liquid helium. These are a tank-within-a-tank design, with a typical working pressure of 100 psig (690 kPa). Inner tank pressures can range from 23.5 psi to 500 psi (162 kPa to 3448 kPa) depending on the product being transported. Tank capacities range from 5000 gal to 14,000 gal (18,925 L to 52,990 L).

Under federal law, a cargo tank constructed to DOT specifications must have a certification plate mounted on the cargo tank. On truck and trailer units, the certification plate will be mounted on the left front of the tank. Tanks constructed prior to 1985 will have the specification plate mounted on the right front of the tank.

The certification plate provides the DOT container specification number, date of manufacture and test, shell material, container pressure ratings, number of compartments and their capacity, and maximum product load.

Some cargo tanks are designed to multiple container specifications, which allows them to transport more than one commodity. Common multipurpose configurations are the combination MC-306/DOT-406/MC-307/DOT-407 unit and the MC-307/DOT-407/MC-312/DOT-412 unit. In addition to the manufacturer's specification plate, these cargo tanks have a second "multipurpose" plate which identifies the specification under which the cargo tank is operated. These plates are color-coded, as are the fittings that are added to make the cargo tank to meet the respective specifications. Color codes are as follows:

(a) MC-306/DOT-406 plate and fittings = red
(b) MC-307/DOT-407 plate and fittings = green
(c) MC-312/DOT-412 plate and fittings = yellow
(d) Nonspecification cargo tank = blue

10-2.1.2 Given examples of cargo tanks (some jacketed; some not jacketed), point out the jacketed cargo tanks.

Jacketed cargo tanks can be recognized by one or more of the following visual indicators:

(a) Flat appearance of cargo tank ends
(b) MC-307/DOT-407 cargo tanks with oval, non-circular shape
(c) Lightweight, bright or shiny aluminum outer jacket on pressurized MC-307/DOT-407 or MC-312/DOT-412 cargo tanks
(d) Rough, relatively narrow welds

10-2.1.3 Given examples of the following types of cargo tank damage, identify the type of damage in each example:

(a) Crack

A crack is a narrow split or break in the container metal that may penetrate through the container metal. Cracks are typically associated with dents and rail burns. Cracks typically occur in tension areas, not compression areas, and can cause failure because they can grow under stress.

(b) Scrape, score, gouge, or loss of metal

A score is a reduction in the thickness of the container shell. It is an indentation in the container made by a relatively blunt object. A score is characterized by the relocation of the container or weld metal in such a way that the metal is pushed aside along the track of contact with the blunt object.

A gouge is a reduction in the thickness of the container. It is an indentation in the shell made by a sharp, chisel-like object. A gouge is characterized by the cutting and complete removal of the container or weld metal along the track of contact.

A street burn is a deformation in the shell of a cargo tank. It is actually a long dent that is inherently flat. A street burn is generally caused by a container overturning and sliding some distance along a cement or asphalt road.

(c) Puncture
(d) Dent
(e) Flame impingement
(f) Corrosion (internal/external)

A puncture is a hole in the tank. A dent is a deformation of the container metal caused by impact with a relatively blunt object. When a sharp radius of curvature is associated with the dent, the possibility of cracking exists. Flame impingement is flame striking on the surface of the tank, either in the liquid space or the vapor space. Corrosion is pitting of the tank metal, thus reducing the thickness and, possibly, the strength of the tank metal.

10-2.1.4 Given simulated damage to an MC-331 cargo tank, determine the extent of damage to the heat-affected zone.

The heat-affected zone is an area in the metal next to the actual weld. This zone is less ductile than either the weld or the metal due to the effect of the welding process. The heat-affected zone is vulnerable to cracks.

10-2.1.5* Given an MC-331 cargo tank containing a liquefied gas, determine the amount of liquid in the tank.

MC-331 measuring devices include the following:

(a) Magnetic float gauge with a rotary dial or rotogauge that indicates quantity, by percentage, loaded in the tank
(b) Fixed-level gauge that indicates the specific quantity

A-10-2.1.5 See A-9-2.1.16.

Other methods for determining the amount of liquid include shipping papers, the presence of a frost line, the use of touch to feel for the colder liquid level, and the use of heat sensors.

10-2.1.6 Given an MC-306/DOT-406, MC-307/DOT-407, and MC-312/DOT-412 cargo tank, point out and explain the design, construction, and operation of each of the following safety devices:

(a) Internal safety valve or external valve with accident protection, including method of activation (air, cable, hydraulic)

Internal safety valves sit "inside" the tank to protect the valve against mechanical stress and accident damage. They are commonly found on MC-306/DOT-406 and MC-307/DOT-407 cargo tanks.

External valves with accident protection sit outside of the tank and are surrounded with a metal framing to protect the valve against mechanical stress and accident damage. They are found on some MC-307/DOT-407 and MC-312/DOT-412 cargo tanks.

(b) Shear-type breakaway piping

Internal safety valves will have a "shear cut" section of piping, within 4 in. (102 mm) of the tank shell, designed to break under mechanical stress. This shear cut reduces the thickness of the piping by approximately 20 percent. If an accident causes stress at the shear point, the piping should fail at the shear point while the internal valve remains intact within the compartment.

(c) Emergency remote shutoff device

Emergency remote shutoff devices, when actuated, automatically close all internal safety valves. They are primarily designed for use during product transfer operations when personnel cannot safely reach the discharge outlets and controls. These devices will always be found at the left front of the cargo tank and may, in some instances, also be found at the right rear.

(d) Pressure and vacuum relief protection devices

Both normal and emergency relief protection is required on all cargo tanks. Common pressure relief devices include relief valves, breather vents, fusible plugs and caps, frangible discs, and pressure vents. Vacuum relief protection is designed to protect the integrity of the tank container during offloading operations.

(e) Dome cover design

Dome cover and manhole assembly designs will vary with the type of liquid cargo tank (i.e., MC-306/DOT-406 vs. MC-312/DOT-412). There will generally be one dome cover for each compartment; however, in some instances a compartment may have more than one dome cover.

Manhole assemblies for MC-306/DOT-406 cargo tanks will usually incorporate other devices, such as the dome cover opening, fusible plug, and overfill sensor.

10-2.1.7 Given an MC-331 and MC-338 cargo tank, point out and explain the design, construction, and operation of each of the following safety devices:

(a) Internal safety valve or external valve with accident protection, including method of activation (air, cable, hydraulic)

Internal safety valves sit "inside" the tank to protect the valve against mechanical stress and accident damage.

External valves with accident protection sit outside of the tank and are surrounded with a metal framing to protect the valve against mechanical stress and accident damage.

(b) Excess flow valve

Excess flow valves are designed to almost completely shut off the flow of product when the discharge valve is sheered off and the flow rate increases.

(c) Fusible link and nut assemblies

In the event of a spill fire in or around a cargo tank, fusible links or nut assemblies will melt, releasing cable tension or air pressure and allowing the internal safety valve to automatically close. Fusible devices are required to actuate at temperatures not greater than 250°F (120°C).

(d) Emergency remote shutoff device

Emergency remote shutoff devices, when actuated, automatically close all internal safety valves. They are primarily designed for use during product transfer operations when personnel cannot safely reach the discharge outlets and controls. These devices will always be found at the left front of the cargo tank, and may, in some instances, also be found at the right rear.

(e) Pressure relief protection devices

MC-331 cargo tanks are protected with spring-loaded pressure relief devices located along the top centerline of the container.

MC-338 cargo tanks are a tank-within-a-tank design and have relief protection for both the inner tank and the outer tank. A combination of spring-loaded pressure relief devices and rupture discs are used.

10-2.1.8 Given an MC-306/DOT-406 cargo tank, identify and describe the following normal methods of loading and unloading:

(a) Top loading

Top loading is primarily used for the transfer of combustible liquids and low vapor pressure products (e.g., fuel oil), especially in rural areas. A fill stem tube is inserted into each compartment via the dome cover and product is then transferred.

(b) Bottom loading

Bottom loading is the most prevalent method for the transfer of flammable liquids, including gasoline. Product is loaded into each compartment through its respective bottom discharge piping and internal safety valve. Bottom loading is a "closed system" in which no vapors are released into the environment.

(c) Vapor recovery system

Vapor recovery systems are used to collect the product vapors generated as part of the transfer process. Although vapor recovery is an inherent part of bottom loading, it may also be found on top-loading operations.

Each compartment has a vent connected to the vapor recovery piping system. These vents are connected either mechanically or pneumatically to each compartment's internal safety valve. When the internal valve is opened, the vent will also open automatically. This provides both vacuum and pressure protection during transfer operations. As product is transferred, the vapors are collected into the vapor collection header on the cargo tank and then piped to either a vapor condensing unit or a burner.

When the cargo tank is offloaded, vapors are returned to the cargo tank through a 3-in. (76-mm) vapor line. Vapor recovery piping and connections will often be marked by an orange color code.

10-2.1.9 Given the following types of cargo tank trucks and tube trailer, identify and describe the normal methods of loading and unloading:

(a) MC-307/DOT-407
(b) MC-312/DOT-412
(c) MC-331
(d) MC-338
(e) Compressed gas tube trailer

10-2.1.10 Describe the normal and emergency methods of activation for the following types of cargo tank truck valve systems:

All internal safety valves rely on either air or hydraulic pressure or mechanical force to place the valve into the open position. If this pressure or force is removed, the internal safety valve will automatically close.

Emergency methods for activating the internal safety valve include use of the emergency remote shut-off device(s) and the activation of fusible devices in a fire situation. In a rollover situation, internal safety valves can also be manually opened; the method of activation will vary with the type of valve and its method of actuation.

(a) Air

Air-actuated valves are found on all types of cargo tanks. On some cargo tanks, normal activation of the internal safety valve may be a two-step process comprised of the opening of a master air control valve and the opening of the respective compartment valve.

(b) Cable

Cable-actuated valves are found on all types of cargo tanks. Activation of a control handle will move the respective internal safety valve. If tension is released on the cable, such as when a fusible device is actuated, the internal safety valve will automatically close.

A secondary safeguard found on MC-306/DOT-406 cargo tanks with cable-actuated systems is to close the compartment door on the right side of the tank where all internal valve controls are located. When the door is pushed closed, all internal safety control valve handles will be forced to the vertical, or closed, position.

(c) Hydraulic

Hydraulic-actuated valves are found on MC-307/DOT-407 and MC-312/DOT-412 cargo tanks. A hydraulic control unit is located near the discharge valves; in order to actuate the internal valve, the operator must increase the hydraulic system pressure through the use of a hand pump and open the respective internal safety valve. If hydraulic pressure is lost, the internal safety valve(s) will automatically close.

10-2.1.11 Given a cargo tank involved in an emergency, identify the factors to be evaluated as part of the cargo tank damage assessment process, including the following:

(a) Type of cargo tank (MC or DOT specification)
(b) Pressurized or nonpressurized
(c) Number of compartments
(d) Type of tank metal (e.g., aluminum vs. stainless steel)
(e) Nature of the emergency (e.g., rollover, vehicle accident, struck by object, etc.)
(f) Container stress applied to the cargo tank
(g) Type and nature of tank damage (e.g., puncture, dome cover leak, valve failure, etc.)
(h) Amount of product both released and remaining in the cargo tank

10-2.2 Predicting the Likely Behavior of the Cargo Tank and Its Contents.

Technicians with a cargo tank specialty shall predict the likely behavior of the cargo tank and its contents. The technician with a cargo tank specialty shall be able to:

These competencies build on the competencies of the hazardous materials technician. The hazardous materials technician with a cargo tank specialty will have expertise in predicting the likely behavior of the cargo tank and its contents. In some cases, a private sector specialist employee A may also have these same skills and knowledge, but only for the specific cargo tank truck and chemical used by his or her company. For example, an employee of an oil company may be the resident expert on cargo tank trucks that carry gasoline and fuel oils. If the appropriate training or certification has been completed, this person can operate at the same level as the technician with a cargo tank specialty, but only for the cargo tanks used by the oil company.

10-2.2.1 Given the following types of cargo tanks (including a tube trailer), describe the likely breach/release mechanisms:

(a) MC-306/DOT-406 cargo tanks
(b) MC-307/DOT-407 cargo tanks
(c) MC-312/DOT-412 cargo tanks
(d) MC-331 cargo tanks
(e) MC-338 cargo tanks
(f) Compressed gas tube trailer

The technician with a cargo tank specialty should be able to discuss the different types of breach, release, dispersion characteristics, contact potential, and hazards for various stress conditions on these types of cargo tanks.

10-2.2.2 Describe the difference in types of construction materials used in cargo tanks and their significance in assessing tank damage.

MC-306/DOT-406 cargo tanks are commonly constructed of aluminum, although older MC-305 steel and stainless steel tanks built prior to 1967 may occasionally be found. In some areas, MC-306/DOT-406 cargo tanks made from fiberglass reinforced plastic (FRP) have also been tested.

MC-307/DOT-407 cargo tanks may be constructed of steel, aluminum, stainless steel, titanium, Hastaloy C, and related alloys. Most MC-307/DOT-407 cargo tanks are then insulated with fiberglass and covered by a stainless steel jacket.

MC-312/DOT-412 cargo tanks may be constructed of steel, aluminum, stainless steel, titanium, or Hastaloy C. They may also be constructed of fiberglass reinforced plastic under an exemption. In some instances, the tank may be lined with a material (e.g., rubber, plastic) that is suitable to protect the tank against chemical attack.

MC-331 cargo tanks are constructed of mild steel (NQT-nonquenched tempered) or high tensile steel (QT-quenched and tempered).

MC-338 cargo tanks are a tank-within-a-tank design similar to a thermos bottle. The inner tank is typically constructed of special steel alloys compatible with the product to be transported and capable of withstanding extremely cold temperatures. The outer container is typically steel. The space surrounding the entire inner tank is evacuated of atmosphere and insulated with a multilayered mylar film.

Compressed gas tube trailers consist of a group of stainless steel cylinders, 9 in. to 48-in. (229 mm to 1219 mm) in diameter, permanently mounted on a semitrailer.

10-2.2.3 Describe the significance of the jacket on cargo tanks in assessing tank damage.

An undamaged jacket may serve as a heat shield from radiated heat. Also, the jacket is not designed to hold the product, so mechanical damage to the jacket may not be indicative of the extent of damage to the tank itself.

10-2.2.4 Describe the significance of each of the following types of damage on different types of cargo tanks in assessing tank damage:

(a) Crack

Since it is difficult to determine when a crack is critical, accurate and timely decisions must be made. The following guidelines can be helpful.

(a) Any crack found in a tank, no matter how small, demands immediate action to relieve the stress in the cargo tank by venting, flaring, or transferring the contents of the tank.
(b) When a crack is in conjunction with a dent, score, or gouge, the cargo tank should be unloaded as soon as possible before moving it.
(c) Consider the pressure of the cargo tank contents and evaluate the potential for a pressure rise.

(b) Scrape, score, gouge, or loss of metal

Scores and gouges are evaluated in the following manner, using the depth of the indentation as a guideline.

(a) Longitudinal scores are of greatest concern; however, circumferential (hoop) scores must be evaluated as well.
(b) Scores or gouges crossing a weld with removal of the filler metal are of little concern.
(c) Longitudinal scores or gouges that cross a weld and damage the heat-affected zone are potentially critical; therefore, the contents of the cargo tank should be transferred immediately by experienced personnel.
(d) When the internal pressure exceeds one half of the allowable internal pressure listed for the tank, cargo tanks having scores or gouges should be unloaded in place by experienced personnel.

(c) Puncture
(d) Dent

Sharp dents in the shell of the cargo tank are the most serious because these dents can reduce the strength of the tank significantly. Dents should be evaluated using the following guidelines.

(a) Dents with a sharp radius may develop cracks. Cracks usually develop on the convex side of a dent, usually inside of the cargo tank where they cannot be readily detected.
(b) Sharp dents in a cargo tank shell can significantly reduce the strength of a tank.
(c) Cargo tanks with dents should be offloaded in place if the following conditions exist:

1. Presence of a crack anywhere within the dent
2. Evidence of the dent crossing a weld
3. Presence of a score or gouge
4. Evidence of cold work

(e) Flame impingement

The following points should be noted when evaluating flame impingement:

(a) Should the tank also be weakened due to mechanical stress, the increase of internal pressure created by the thermal stress of flame impingement could quickly overstress the tank and cause early failure of the cargo tank.

(b) Applying cooling water streams onto the outer shell of an MC-338 cryogenic liquid cargo tank is ineffective because of the tank's heavy insulation. In addition, water may freeze and block safety relief devices.

(f) Corrosion (internal/external)

10-2.2.5 Given simulated damage to the heat-affected zone on an MC-331 cargo tank, describe the significance of the damage in assessing tank damage.

Because of this change in composition in the tank metal, the ductility of the steel in this heat-affected zone is reduced. The heat-affected zone is a likely origin for cracks.

10-3 Competencies — Planning the Response

In 4-3.1, the technician level responder is required to identify the appropriate response objectives for responders at that level. The options available are either offensive, defensive, or nonintervention. The response objectives for the technician with a cargo tank specialty are expanded to include highly technical, offensive operations.

Response objectives now include those objectives that can lead to final transfer and recovery, uprighting, and mitigation. While the responder at the technician level can stabilize the situation until "industrial experts" arrive for final and complete mitigation, the technician with a cargo tank specialty can become trained or certified to do the following work.

(a) Plan the operation:

1. Prepare a plan for set-up, implementation, and termination of the operation
2. Develop and acquire the equipment necessary for the selected operation
3. Prepare a site safety plan

(b) Set up the operation:

1. Hold a safety briefing
2. Position the resources and equipment
3. Set up and activate the emergency shut-off system, if appropriate
4. Purge the liquid/vapor transfer hoses and test for leaks

(c) Implement product transfer and recovery operations
(d) Terminate product transfer and recovery operations:

1. Purge the hoses and/or piping
2. Disassemble and decontaminate the equipment
3. Secure cargo tank

(e) Implement uprighting operations
(f) Determine disposition of the cargo tank and prepare for transportation

10-3.1 Determining the Response Options.

Given the analysis of an emergency involving cargo tanks, technicians with a cargo tank specialty shall determine the response options for each cargo tank involved. The technician with a cargo tank specialty shall be able to:

10-3.1.1 Given an incident involving a cargo tank, describe the methods, procedures, risks, safety precautions, and equipment that are required to implement spill and leak control procedures.

This competency builds on the competencies of the hazardous materials technician.

Product removal methods may be outside the legitimate responsibility of the local emergency response personnel. However, oversight of their planning and implementation is within the responsibilities of local emergency response agencies.

10-3.1.2 Given an overturned cargo tank, describe the factors to be evaluated for uprighting, including the following:

Tank truck manufacturers advise against attempts to upright an MC-306/DOT-406 cargo tank while it contains any product. For other types of cargo tanks, a detailed hazard and risk assessment must be conducted. Evaluation criteria are outlined in 10-3.1.2(a) through (g).

(a) Type of cargo tank and material of construction

(b) Condition and weight of the cargo tank
(c) Type and nature of stress applied to the cargo tank
(d) Preferred lifting points
(e) Selection of lifting straps and/or air bags
(f) Lifting capabilities of wreckers and cranes
(g) Site safety precautions

10-4 Competencies — Implementing the Planned Response

10-4.1 Implementing the Planned Response.

Given an analysis of an emergency involving a cargo tank and the planned response, technicians with a cargo tank specialty shall implement or oversee the implementation of the selected response options safely and effectively. The technician with a cargo tank specialty shall be able to:

The equipment and resources necessary for demonstrating these tasks may not be readily available. Requests for training for the performance of these tasks should be directed to the local shipper, carrier, or contractor personnel in the community, possibly through the Local Emergency Planning Committee.

10-4.1.1 Demonstrate the methods for containing the following leaks on liquid cargo tanks (e.g., MC-306/DOT-406, MC-307/DOT-407, and MC-312/DOT-412):

(a) Puncture

The technician with a cargo tank specialty will select and apply various methods of plugging and patching to control or stop leakage of the contents. This task should be performed using appropriate personal protective equipment for the material involved and the working conditions.

(b) Irregular-shaped hole

The technician with a cargo tank specialty will select and apply various methods of plugging and patching to control or stop leakage of the contents. This task should be performed using appropriate personal protective equipment for the material involved and the working conditions.

(c) Split or tear

The technician with a cargo tank specialty will select and apply various methods of plugging and patching to control or stop leakage of the contents. This task should be performed using appropriate personal protective equipment for the material involved and the working conditions.

(d) Dome cover leak

The technician with a cargo tank specialty will select and apply various methods to control or stop leakage from the dome cover of a liquid cargo tank. This task should be performed using appropriate personal protective equipment for the material involved and the working conditions.

(e) Valves and piping

The technician with a cargo tank specialty will select and apply various methods to isolate, control, or stop leakage of the contents from valves and piping. This task should be performed using appropriate personal protective equipment for the material involved and the working conditions.

(f) Pressure relief devices (e.g., vents, burst disc, etc.)

The technician with a cargo tank specialty will select and apply various methods to control or stop leakage of the contents from pressure relief devices. This task should be performed using appropriate personal protective equipment for the material involved and the working conditions.

10-4.1.2 Describe the methods for containing the following leaks in MC-331 and MC-338 cargo tanks:

The technician with a cargo tank specialty will evaluate tactical options and provide an appropriate method to control the release of contents. The technician with a cargo tank specialty should also describe the appropriate personal protective equipment required for the material involved.

(a) Crack
(b) Failure of safety relief device (e.g., relief valve, burst disc, etc.)
(c) Piping failure

10-4.1.3* Demonstrate bonding and grounding procedures for the transfer of flammable and combustible products from cargo tanks, or other products that can give off flammable gases or vapors when heated or contaminated, including the following:

Local procedures for these tasks should be written out and consistent with nationally accepted practices.

The technician with a cargo tank specialty will participate as a member of a team assigned to set up bonding and grounding for the transfer of product from a cargo tank. These tasks should be performed using appropriate personal protective equipment for the material involved and the working conditions.

(a) Selection of proper equipment
(b) Sequence of bonding and grounding connections
(c) Proper testing of bonding and grounding connections

When bonding and grounding, a ground resistance tester and an ohm meter should be used. The ground resistance tester measures the earth's resistance to a ground rod, and the ohm meter measures the resistance of the connections to ensure electrical continuity. One ground rod might not be enough; more may have to be driven and connected to the first to ensure a good ground. Resistance varies with types of soils.

The technician with a cargo tank truck specialty should be able to verify (using the appropriate equipment) the following:

(a) Ground rod resistance to earth
(b) Connections between ground rod and tank car
(c) Connections between ground rod and main ground rod and ground cable

(See Supplement 13 for more information on this topic.)

A-10-4.1.3 See A-9-4.1.9.

10-4.1.4 Given the following product transfer and recovery equipment, demonstrate the safe and correct application and use of each of the following:

The purpose of transferring liquids and gases is often associated with removal from a damaged or potentially damaged containment vessel to one that is undamaged. The equipment will vary with the type of vessel involved and the hazardous material being transferred. Transfer procedures are generally established in advance by good industry practice. Only essential personnel, outlined, in most cases, in the overall incident management system of the hazardous materials branch, should be involved in the process.

A transfer is the movement of the contents of a damaged or overloaded cargo tank into a receiving tank (e.g., a tank car, cargo tank, intermodal tank, or fixed tank).

In highway transportation, transfers may be used when any of the following conditions exist:

(a) Site conditions prevent uprighting the damaged cargo tank car (e.g., the terrain does not permit use of cranes)
(b) Damage to leaking valves and fittings cannot be repaired
(c) Tank is sound, but cannot be safely moved
(d) Cargo tank has been damaged to the extent that it cannot be safely uprighted

Generally, cargo tank transfers should only be performed when the following conditions exist:

(a) Site safety precautions are in-place
(b) Delayed container rupture is not likely
(c) Required valves are accessible and functioning
(d) Tank is in a position that allows for the transfer
(e) Appropriate receiving tank is available
(f) Transfer equipment is available
(g) Experienced personnel are on-site to perform the transfer
(h) All ignition sources are removed and/or controlled
(i) Appropriate personal protective equipment is used

(a) Portable pumps (air, electrical, gasoline/diesel)

This product removal method uses a liquid pump to move the contents of a damaged or overloaded cargo tank into a receiving tank (e.g., a tank car, cargo tank, or portable tank). The material in the damaged or overloaded cargo tank is then pumped into the receiving tank. The use of a liquid pump does not increase the pressure in the damaged cargo tank; however, if another means of creating positive pressure differential is used, a pressure increase may occur.

In evaluating the use of portable and power-take-off (PTO) driven pumps, consideration should be given to the following factors:

(a) Materials of construction. Although not as critical with hydrocarbon products, both the pump and associated hoses, valves, and gaskets must be compatible with the product(s) involved. Product contamination may also be a concern.
(b) Power rating and pressure capacity of the pump, including lift and flow capabilities.
(c) Energy source and sparking potential of the pump. Gasoline, diesel, and electrical pumps must be explosion-proof and should only be used as a last resort.
(d) Grounding and bonding requirements.

(b) Vehicles with power-take-off (PTO) driven pumps

See commentary for 10-4.1.4(a).

(c) Pressure transfer

There are several options for accomplishing a pressure transfer, including the following:

(a) Compressed air or an inert gas:

This product removal method uses a compressed gas (e.g., nitrogen or carbon dioxide) to move the contents of a damaged or overloaded cargo tank into a receiving tank (e.g., a tank car, cargo tank, or portable tank). The compressed gas creates a positive pressure differential in the damaged cargo tank that pushes the liquid into the receiving tank. Vapor from the receiving tank may have to be vented to the atmosphere or scrubbed. The use of the compressed gas will result in a pressure increase in the damaged cargo tank. This transfer method should be used only when an increase in pressure in the damaged cargo tank is acceptable. Check with the shipper to determine the compatibility of the compressed gas to be used.

(b) Vapor pressure (with or without flaring):

This product removal method uses the material's own vapor pressure to move the contents of a damaged or overloaded cargo tank into a receiving tank (e.g., a tank car, cargo tank, or portable tank). In addition, a vapor flare maintains the necessary positive pressure differential between the damaged or overloaded cargo tank and the receiving tank by burning off vapors in the receiving tank at the outlet of a flare pipe. The pressure in the receiving tank is kept as low as possible.

(c) Vapor compressor:

This product removal method uses a vapor compressor to move the contents of a damaged or overloaded pressurized cargo tank (e.g., MC-331, MC-338) into a receiving tank (e.g., a tank car, cargo tank, or portable tank). The vapor compressor pulls the vapors from the receiving tank, compresses them, and forces them into the damaged cargo tank. The higher pressure in the damaged cargo tank pushes the liquefied gas into the receiving tank. The use of the vapor compressor will result in a pressure increase in the damaged cargo tank. This transfer method should be used only when an increase in pressure in the damaged cargo tank is acceptable.

(d) Vapor compressor and a liquid pump:

This product removal method uses a vapor compressor and a liquid pump to move the contents of a damaged or overloaded pressurized cargo tank (e.g., MC-331, MC-338) into a receiving tank (e.g., a tank car, cargo tank, or portable tank). The vapor compressor is used to accelerate the rate of transfer by withdrawing vapors from the receiving tank, compressing them, and forcing them into the damaged cargo tank. The higher pressure in the damaged cargo tank pushes the liquefied gas into the pump. The use of the vapor compressor will result in a pressure increase in the damaged cargo tank. This transfer method should be used only when an increase in pressure in the damaged cargo tank is acceptable. This method is justified when the receiving tank is a greater distance from the damaged or overloaded cargo tank.

(d) Vacuum trucks

Vacuum trucks are an efficient and expeditious tool for recovering flammable and combustible liquids. However, the vacuum truck is not inherently safe, as the air surrounding the vacuum pump exhaust can become saturated with flammable vapors.

To minimize this flammability hazard, the following safety procedures should be used:

(a) The vacuum truck should be located upwind of any transfer point
(b) An exhaust hose of sufficient length should be used to direct the flammable vapors to an area free from hazards and personnel, considering wind direction and velocity, terrain, exposures, etc.
(c) Continuous air monitoring of the area should be conducted
(d) Ensure that the materials being loaded are compatible with materials previously loaded and that mixing will not present a hazard
(e) Adequate venting must always be provided

10-4.1.5 Given a simulated overturned MC-306/DOT-406 cargo tank, demonstrate the safe and proper procedures for the following methods of product removal and transfer:

The technician with a cargo tank specialty will participate as a member of a team assigned to perform product removal and transfer. These tasks should be performed using appropriate personal protective equipment for the material involved and the working conditions. Additional information on these methods of product removal can be found in the reference book *Gasoline Tank Truck Emergencies: Guidelines and Procedures.*[1]

(a) Drilling
(b) Unloading lines
(c) Vapor recovery lines
(d) Internal safety valve

10-4.1.6 Given a simulated overturned MC-307/DOT-407 cargo tank, demonstrate the safe and proper procedures for product removal and transfer.

The technician with a cargo tank specialty will participate as a member of a team assigned to perform product removal and transfer. These tasks should be performed using appropriate personal protective equipment for the material involved and the working conditions.

10-4.1.7 Given a simulated overturned MC-331 cargo tank, demonstrate the safe and proper procedures for product removal and transfer.

The technician with a cargo tank specialty will participate as a member of a team assigned to perform product removal and transfer. These tasks should be performed using appropriate personal protective equipment for the material involved and the working conditions.

10-4.1.8 Given the necessary resources, demonstrate the flaring of an MC-331 flammable gas cargo tank.

The technician with a cargo tank specialty will participate as a member of a team assigned to perform flaring operations. Flaring tasks should be performed using appropriate personal protective equipment for the material involved and the working conditions.

Flaring liquids and gases is a procedure that can be used to deplete the amount of hazardous material involved or to depressurize a vessel. It should be performed only by persons who are trained in the technique. In some cases, where the burning is already underway at a vent or pressure relief valve when responders arrive, a prescribed procedure will be to allow the flaring process to continue. Determination must be made that the flaring does not present a source of ignition to other spilled flammable substances.

Flaring is the controlled release and disposal of flammable materials by burning from the outlet of a flare pipe (horizontal or vertical). It is used to reduce the pressure or dispose of the residual vapors in a damaged or overloaded tank car.

Flaring is used for the following three basic purposes:

(a) Reduce the pressure inside a cargo tank
(b) Dispose of vapors remaining in a pressurized cargo tank during or after transfer of the liquid
(c) Burn off liquid where transfer is impractical

Flaring may also be used to expedite recovery operations or as an interim method until a transfer can begin.

Vapor flaring is the burning of the vapors of a liquefied compressed gas at the outlet of a vertical flare pipe as the vapors exit the flare pipe.

Liquid flaring is the vaporizing of a liquid product and burning of the vapors at the end of a horizontal flare pipe. A pit is used to contain any product that is not completely burned.

10-4.1.9 Given a simulated flammable liquid spill from a cargo tank, describe the procedures for site safety and fire control during cleanup and removal operations.

In their textbook, *Gasoline Tank Truck Emergencies: Guidelines and Procedures,* Hildebrand and Noll state that, "Product removal operations cannot commence until after the incident site is stabilized. Again, stabilization means that all fires have been extinguished and ignition sources controlled, all spills have been confined, and the entire spill area has been foamed down and cleaned up as necessary. The incident scene should be continuously monitored."[2]

Specific site safety considerations that should be addressed include the following:

(a) Only a minimum number of properly trained and protected personnel should be allowed in the immediate hazard area.

(b) Air monitoring is continuously being conducted throughout the incident.

(c) Backup crews with a minimum of 11/2-in. (38-mm) foam handlines and at least two 20 lb to 30 lb dry chemical fire extinguishers are in place to protect all personnel involved in the offloading and uprighting operation. Some organizations will use a minimum of two foam handlines, placing one foam handline on each side of the cargo tank for maximum protection.

(d) A foam blanket should be applied, as necessary, throughout the incident. Just because a foam blanket is visible on the spill does not ensure adequate vapor suppression.

(e) Always have an escape signal and path for personnel working in the immediate hazard area.

(f) Ensure that all personnel remain alert.

References Cited in Commentary

1. Michael S. Hildebrand and Gregory G. Noll, *Handling Gasoline Tank Truck Emergencies: Guidelines and Procedures,* Fire Protection Publications, Stillwater, OK, 1991.
2. Ibid.

CHAPTER 11

Competencies for the Technician with an Intermodal Tank Specialty

11-1 General

11-1.1 Introduction.

Technicians with an intermodal tank specialty shall be trained to meet all competencies of the first responder awareness, operational, and hazardous materials technician levels and the competencies of this chapter. The technician with an intermodal tank specialty also shall receive any additional training to meet applicable United States Department of Transportation (DOT), United States Environmental Protection Agency (EPA), Occupational Safety and Health Administration (OSHA), and other appropriate state, local, or provincial occupational health and safety regulatory requirements.

In the 1987 edition of NFPA 472, one of the competencies required for the hazardous materials specialist (incorporated into the hazardous materials technician in 1992) was merely to "describe" specific techniques. In the commentary on that competency, Martin F. Henry wrote the following: "The task is generally performed by people with particular expertise and responsibility for the operation, under the supervision and control of responders." The specific techniques listed in that competency were transferring liquids and gases, flaring liquids and gases, hot tapping, and venting and burning.

Now in this new Chapter 11 of NFPA 472, it is now required that competency in performing these tasks be demonstrated. For example, 11-4.1.6 reads, "Given the following product transfer and recovery equipment, demonstrate the safe and correct application and use of the following:

(a) Portable pumps (air, electrical, gasoline/diesel)
(b) Vehicles with power-take-off (PTO) driven pumps
(c) Pressure transfer
(d) Vacuum trucks"

The new specialty levels introduced in Chapters 9, 10, and 11 of this 1997 edition of NFPA 472 cover extremely hazardous and highly skilled operations that have not had any standardized training or certification previously. The technician with a tank car specialty, the technician with a cargo tank specialty, and the technician with an intermodal tank specialty are levels that are above OSHA's technician and specialist levels and are not defined by the present OSHA regulations (Title 29, *Code of Federal Regulations,* Part 1910.120).

11-1.2 Definition.

Technicians with an intermodal tank specialty are those persons who provide support to the hazardous materials technician, provide oversight for product removal and movement of damaged intermodal tanks, and act as a liaison between technicians and other outside resources. These technicians are expected to use specialized chemical-protective clothing and specialized control equipment.

11-1.3 Goals.

The goal of this chapter shall be to provide the technician with an intermodal tank specialty with the knowledge and skills to perform the following tasks safely. In addition to being competent at the technician level, the technician with an intermodal tank specialty shall be able to:

(a) Analyze a hazardous materials incident involving an intermodal tank to determine the magnitude of the problem in terms of outcomes by completing the following tasks:

1. Determine the type and extent of damage to an intermodal tank
2. Predict the likely behavior of an intermodal tank and its contents in an emergency

(b) Plan a response for an emergency involving an intermodal tank within the capabilities and competencies of available personnel, personal protective equipment, and control equipment by determining the response options (offensive, defensive, and nonintervention) for a hazardous materials emergency involving intermodal tanks

(c) Implement the planned response to a hazardous materials incident involving intermodal tanks

11-1.4 Mandating of Competencies.

This standard does not mandate that hazardous materials response teams performing offensive operations on intermodal tanks have technicians with an intermodal tank specialty. Technicians operating within the bounds of their training as listed in Chapter 4 of this standard are able to intervene in intermodal tank incidents. However, if a hazardous materials response team desires to train some or all its technicians to have in-depth knowledge of intermodal tanks, this chapter sets out the required competencies.

The committee wanted to be perfectly clear that existing and new responders at the hazardous materials technician level can still perform operations on intermodal tanks that they have always been qualified to do. This new specialty level covers those highly technical skills and knowledge needed only rarely in a major accident, skills that the technician normally does not possess. A hazardous materials response team may have a few members trained to this level or a request can be made to the railroad, manufacturer, or shipper to bring someone with this specialty to the scene. Because of the relative newness of this level, it is unrealistic to expect to see responders with either the training or certification necessary to achieve this specialty level in the near future.

The committee wants to be clear that this specialty level is not mandated for any hazardous materials response team or its members. Arrangements to request assistance are perfectly appropriate in these situations and are encouraged.

11-2 Competencies — Analyzing the Incident

These competencies are a good example of the difference between the technician level and the intermodal tank specialty level. The competency in 4-2.3.4 for the technician level states, "Identify the types of damage that a pressure container could incur." This knowledge can be learned from a lecture, reviewing graphics, or studying reference sources. Competencies for the technician with an intermodal tank specialty require hands-on training with a "damaged intermodal tank." The technician with an intermodal tank specialty should have an intimate, detailed knowledge of intermodal tank cars.

There are competencies for the technician with an intermodal tank specialty that can use "simulated damage" equipment or tanks and they are specifically noted, such as in 11-2.1.10.

11-2.1 Determining the Type and Extent of Damage to Intermodal Tanks.

Given examples of damaged intermodal tanks, technicians with an intermodal tank specialty shall describe the type and extent of damage to each intermodal tank and its fittings. The technician with an intermodal tank specialty shall be able to:

The intermodal tank is generally built as a cylinder enclosed at the ends by heads. Other tank shapes (rectangular tanks) and configurations (tube modules) are rare. Tanks with multiple compartments are also rare. The intermodal tank's capacity ordinarily does not exceed 6340 gal (about 24,000 L), but can go as high as 7130 gal (about 27,000 L).

In NFPA 472, intermodal tanks are grouped into the following four types:

(a) Non-pressure intermodal tanks, called intermodal portable tanks or IM portable tanks, comprise over 90 percent of the total number of tank containers. They generally transport liquid and solid materials at maximum allowable working pressures (MAWP) of up to 100 psig (6.8 bar). Tanks are tested to 1.5 times the MAWP. In the United States, the following two groups of nonpressure intermodal tanks are common:

1. IM-101 intermodal tanks are built to withstand MAWPs from 25.4 psig (1.75 bar) to 100 psig (6.8 bar). They may transport both nonhazardous and hazardous materials (including toxic, corrosive, and flammable materials with flash points below 32°F [0°C]). Internationally, an IM-101 intermodal tank is called an IMO Type 1 tank container.
2. IM-102 intermodal tanks are designed to withstand lower MAWPs 14.5 psig (1.0 bar) up to 25.4 psig (1.75 bar). They transport materials like whiskey, alcohols, some corrosives, pesticides, insecticides, resins, industrial solvents, and flammables (flash points between 32°F and 140°F [0°C and 60°C]). More commonly, they transport nonregulated materials like food-grade commodities. Internationally, an IM-102 intermodal tank is basically equivalent to the IMO Type 2 tank container.

(b) Pressure tank containers, known as DOT Specification 51 intermodal tanks, are less common in transport. They are designed to handle internal pressures ranging from 100 psig (6.8 bar) to 500 psig (34.0 bar) and generally transport gases liquefied under pressure, like LP-Gas and anhydrous ammonia. They may also carry liquids such as motor fuel anti-knock compound or aluminum alkyls. Internationally, they are called IMO Type 5 tank containers.

(c) Cryogenic tank containers carry refrigerated liquid gases, like argon, oxygen, and helium. Internationally, they are called IMO Type 7 tank containers.

(d) Tube modules transport gases in high pressure specification 3T cylinders tested to 3000 psi or 5000 psi and are permanently mounted within an ISO frame.

11-2.1.1 Given the specification mark for an intermodal tank and the appropriate reference materials, describe the tank's basic construction and features.

The design, construction, and use of intermodal tanks must conform to the strict standards and regulations of many agencies, both in the United States and abroad. Markings on the intermodal tank indicate the standards to which the tank was built.

Intermodal tanks must meet the design, construction, and safety standards set forth by the U.S. Department of Transportation (DOT). Tanks meeting these standards will have the specification markings or an exemption number displayed on both sides, generally near the tank's reporting marks (initials) and number.

Examples of specification markings found include the following:

(a) IM 101
(b) IM 102
(c) Specification 51

Exemptions from the regulations are authorized for packages, containers, and the preparation and offering of hazardous materials for shipment. In these cases, the outside of the package must be plainly and durably marked "DOT-E" in 2-in. (51-mm) letters and numerals, followed by the number assigned, for example, DOT-E8623.

For interchange purposes in rail transportation, tank containers should conform to the requirements of Section 600, "Specification for Acceptability of Tank Containers," found in the Association of American Railroad's (AAR) *Specification for Tank Cars.*[1]

Tanks meeting these requirements will display the "AAR 600" marking in 2-in. (51-mm) letters on both sides near the tank's reporting marks (initials) and numbers.

The European Agreement Concerning Transport of Dangerous Goods by Truck (ADR) and the European Agreement Concerning Transport of Dangerous Goods by Rail (RID) are used in Europe for the movement of intermodal tanks. ADR/RID markings may remain when the tank is transported in the United States.

11-2.1.2 Given examples of intermodal tanks (some jacketed; some not jacketed), point out the jacketed intermodal tanks.

The technician with an intermodal tank specialty will be able to identify those intermodal tanks with jackets.

11-2.1.3 Given examples of various intermodal tanks, point out and explain the design and purpose of each of the following intermodal tank components, when present:

(a) Supporting frame

The supporting frame of an intermodal tank protects the tank and provides for stacking, lifting, and securing the tank. It also supports the walkways and ladders.

The most common supporting frame size for intermodal tanks is 20 ft × 8 or 8 ½ ft × 8 or 9 ½ ft (6.1 m × 2.4 or 2.6 m × 2.4 or 2.9 m). Except for some half-height intermodal tanks, which are 35 ft (10.7 m) long, very few tanks longer than 20 ft (6.1 m) are used in the United States. The exception seems to be cryogenic intermodal tanks typically found in highway transportation.

There are two basic supporting frames: the box type, which encloses the tank in a cage-like framework, and the beam type, which uses frame structures only at the ends of the tank.

(b) Corner casting

Supporting frames for all intermodal containers, including intermodal tanks, are built with standard corner fittings called corner castings. They are used to secure the tank and to lift it with standard container handling equipment. Corner castings must conform to ISO Standards.

(c) Insulation

Insulation is used to moderate the effects of temperature on the commodity. Mineral wool, fiberglass, polyurethanefoam, and polystyrene foam are used as insulating materials. Insulation is usually 3 in. to 4 in. (76 mm to 102 mm) thick.

(d) Jacket

Insulation is always covered with a jacket (called cladding) with flashing to make it weathertight. Jackets are made of metal, at least 0.03937 in. (1 mm) thick, or an equivalent thickness of plastic, reinforced with either glass or fiber.

(e) Heater coils (steam/electric)
(f) Refrigeration unit

A refrigeration unit on an intermodal tank is used to moderate the temperature of the commodity during transportation. Steam or electric heating may also be found on some intermodal tanks, especially those where the commodity must be heated during transportation or unloading.

(g) Data plate

A corrosion-resistant data plate provides additional technical, approval, and operational data. The data plate is permanently attached to the tank or frame.

11-2.1.4 Given examples of various fittings arrangements for pressure, nonpressure, and cryogenic intermodal tanks, point out and explain the design, construction, and operation of each of the following fittings, when present:

(a) Spill box

On nonpressure intermodal tanks, the top fittings are surrounded by a spill box which protects the tank's shell from spillage. Spilled material, as well as rainwater, in the spill box drains away through one or more small open pipes.

(b) Manhole cover

A manhole is located on top of the tank, at the center, to allow for access into the tank. It is secured by six or eight wing nuts on a hinged and bolted lid fitted with a replacement gasket.

(c) Air line connection

An air line connection, located on the tank's top, can be used for pressure unloading, vapor return, and blanketing the contents with an inert gas. The airline connection may be flanged or have a valve attached.

(d) Top outlet

Top loading valves are attached to a removable eduction pipe (called a dip leg, dip tube, or siphon tube) running into the tank.

(e) Bottom outlet valve

When the tank container is intended to carry hazardous materials, two externally operated, bottom outlet valves are required. Bottom outlet valves, located on the discharge end of the tank, are connected in a series with a replacement gasket between them.

A liquidtight closure on the external bottom outlet valve is also required. This closure may be a blind flange (required on international shipments), a screw cap, or a cam-lock cap attached to the external valve.

(f) Thermometer

Some intermodal tanks have a built-in thermometer to measure the temperature of the commodity inside.

(g) Pressure gauge

Some intermodal tanks have one or more pressure gauges to measure the pressure inside the tank.

(h) Gauging device

A dipstick may be inside the manhole. It is used in conjunction with a calibration chart, known as a strapping chart, to measure the amount of commodity in the tank.

(i) Liquid or vapor valve

Intermodal tanks may have valves for loading and unloading liquids and vapors depending on the characteristics of the commodity being transported.

(j) Sample valve

The sample valve provides for taking a sample of the commodity.

(k) Thermometer well

The thermometer well is a fitting on a pressure intermodal tank where the temperature of the commodity can be determined when a thermometer is placed into the well.

11-2.1.5 Given examples of various safety devices for pressure, nonpressure, and cryogenic intermodal tanks, point out and explain the design, construction, and operation of each of the following safety devices, when present:

(a) Safety relief valve

Safety relief valves are pressure relief devices with the valve held closed by one or more springs. When pressure in the safety relief valve exceeds the safety relief valve setting, the valve opens. The valve recloses when the tank pressure is reduced below the safety relief valve setting.

A combination pressure/vacuum relief valve is generally found in pairs on nonpressure intermodal tanks. The valve protects the tank from both overpressure and vacuum. In many cases, the relief valve will have a rupture disc located between the safety relief valve spring and the commodity to protect the spring. The valve may also have a pressure gauge to determine if the disc is ruptured.

(b) Regulator valve

Regulator valves are devices to control the release of vapors from the tank when the contents become heated.

(c) Rupture disc

Safety vents are pressure relief devices that use a frangible disc, also called a rupture disc, to seal the vent opening. This disc is designed to rupture at a predetermined pressure to relieve internal pressure. Once ruptured, the safety vent does not reclose.

Rupture discs are made of metal (lead is no longer authorized by the AAR), plastic, rubber, or a combination of metal, plastic, and rubber. Safety vents are used primarily on nonpressure tank cars, but may not be used with flammable liquids and poisons.

(d) Fusible link/nut assemblies

Fusible links or nuts may be found on cable-actuated remote control shutoff devices. Upon melting, the release of cable tension will close the valve.

(e) Emergency remote shutoff device

In an emergency, the internal valve (foot valve) can be shut off from a remote location. As you face the discharge end of the tank, the emergency shutoff device will be on the right-hand side, near the far end.

(f) Excess flow valve

Excess flow valves may be attached inside the tank between the manway cover plate and the eduction line. They almost completely cut off the flow of product when the valve is sheered off in an accident. They operate by either product flow or, when the car is overturned, by gravity. Under normal conditions, gravity keeps the excess flow valves open, but higher flow rates, associated with the valve being sheered off, or a break in the hose closes them. When the tank car is turned over, gravity closes the valves.

11-2.1.6 Given the following types of intermodal tank damage, identify the type of damage in each example and explain its significance.

(a) Crack

A crack is a narrow split or break in the container metal that can penetrate through the metal of the container. Cracks are typically associated with dents.

(b) Puncture

A puncture is a hole in the tank.

(c) Dent

A dent is a deformation of the container metal. It is caused by impact with a relatively blunt object. When a sharp radius of curvature is associated with the dent, the possibility of cracking exists.

(d) Flame impingement

Impingement is flame striking the surface of the tank, either in the liquid space or the vapor space.

(e) Corrosion (internal/external)

The effects of corrosion may reduce the thickness of the tank, thus weakening the tank.

(f) Metal loss (gouge/score)

A score is a reduction in the thickness of the container shell. It is an indentation in the container made by a relatively blunt object. A score is characterized by the relocation of the container or weld metal where the metal is pushed aside along the track of contact with the blunt object.

A gouge is a reduction in the thickness of the container. It is an indentation in the shell made by a sharp, chisel-like object. A gouge is characterized by the cutting and complete removal of the container or weld metal along the track of contact.

11-2.1.7 Given three examples of damage to the framework of intermodal tanks, describe the damage in each example and explain its significance in the risk analysis process.

The technician with an intermodal tank specialty will describe the extent of damage to the supporting frame. Also, the technician will explain the significance of the damage to the continued transportation of the commodity and the tank.

11-2.1.8 Given an intermodal tank involved in an emergency, identify the factors to be evaluated as part of the intermodal tank damage assessment process, including the following:

(a) Type of intermodal tank
(b) Pressurized or nonpressurized
(c) Number of compartments
(d) Type of tank metal
(e) Nature of the emergency
(f) Container stress applied to the intermodal tank
(g) Type and nature of tank damage
(h) Amount of product both released and remaining in the intermodal tank

The technician with an intermodal tank specialty will be able to collect the information/data in 11-2.1.8 on a given intermodal tank involved in an emergency. Where necessary for safety reasons, this task should be performed using appropriate personal protective equipment for the material involved and the working conditions.

11-2.1.9* Given a pressure intermodal tank containing a liquefied gas, determine the amount of liquid in the tank.

A-11-2.1.9 Methods for determining the amount of liquid include the use of gauges, shipping papers, the presence of frost line, the use of touch or feel for the colder liquid level, and the use of heat sensors.

The technician with an intermodal tank specialty will use various types of gauging devices to determine the innage (amount of liquid) or outage (amount of vapor space) in an intermodal tank.

11-2.1.10* Given simulated damage to a pressure intermodal tank, determine the extent of damage to the heat-affected zone.

A-11-2.1.10 See A-9-2.1.11.

Because of this change in composition in the tank metal, the ductility of the steel in this heat-affected zone is reduced. The heat-affected zone is a likely origin for cracks.

11-2.2 Predicting the Likely Behavior of the Intermodal Tank and Its Contents.

Technicians with an intermodal tank specialty shall predict the likely behavior of the intermodal tank and its contents. The technician with an intermodal tank specialty shall be able to:

Again, these competencies build on the competencies of the hazardous materials technician. The hazardous materials technician with an intermodal tank specialty will be an expert in predicting the likely behavior of the intermodal tank and its contents. In some cases, a private sector specialist employee A may also have these same skills and knowledge, but only for a specific intermodal tank and chemical. For example, an employee of a petrochemical enterprise may be the resident expert on intermodal tanks that carry a flammable gas. If the appropriate training or certification has been completed, this person can operate at the same level as the technician with an intermodal tank specialty, but only for the intermodal tank(s) used by the petrochemical company.

11-2.2.1 Given the following types of intermodal tanks, describe the likely breach/release mechanisms:

(a) IMO Type 1/IM-101
(b) IMO Type 2/IM-102
(c) IMO Type 5/DOT-51
(d) DOT-56
(e) DOT-57
(f) DOT-60
(g) Cryogenic (IMO Type 7)

The technician with an intermodal tank specialty will describe the various types of breach/release mechanisms for the various types of intermodal tanks.

The basis for this competency comes from past experience with intermodal tanks as found in various publications.

11-2.2.2 Describe the difference in types of construction materials used in intermodal tanks relative to assessing tank damage.

Ninety (90) percent or more of intermodal tanks are built of stainless steel; almost all of the rest are built of mild steel. Stainless steel is used because of its excellent properties in cold temperatures. Aluminum and magnesium alloy tanks are built, but they cannot be used in water transportation.

Minimum head and shell thickness is measured in terms of "equivalent thickness in mild steel" after forming. For stainless steel tanks, the minimum thickness is just under $\frac{1}{8}$ in. (3.2 mm) for nonregulated materials and just under $\frac{3}{16}$ in. (4.8 mm) for regulated materials. For steel tanks, the minimum thickness is $\frac{1}{4}$ in. (6.35 mm) for nonregulated materials and $\frac{3}{8}$ in. (9.5 mm) for regulated materials.

Most tanks are built according to the pressure vessel standards of the American Society of Mechanical Engineers (ASME), with the welds X-rayed. Welds on carbon steel tanks are post-weld stress relieved.

The shipper or the intermodal tank manufacturer is an excellent source of technical information on the stressing of the tank.

11-3 Competencies — Planning the Response

In 4-3.1, the technician level responder is required to identify the appropriate response objectives for responders at that level. The options available are either offensive, defensive, or nonintervention. The response objectives for the technician with an intermodal tank specialty are expanded to include highly technical offensive operations.

Response objectives now include those objectives that can lead to final mitigation. The hazardous materials technician can only stabilize a situation until "experts" arrive for final and complete mitigation.

The competencies outlined in Section 11-3 all carry with them an inherent danger. Since most of these operations are rarely done at an actual incident, the technician with an intermodal tank specialty should give a detailed briefing to the hazardous materials branch safety officer and branch officer, as well as to the incident commander, before starting any operations.

Table 11.1 describes the skills required for handling intermodal tank problems as outlined in the competencies in Section 11-3.

11-3.1 Determining the Response Options.

Given the analysis of an emergency involving intermodal tanks, technicians with an intermodal tank specialty shall determine the response options for each intermodal tank

Table 11.1 Handling Intermodal Tank Problems

Problem	Objectives	Actions	Methods
• Leaking fittings – Not secure – Wear – Damage	• Stop release; forward to destination	• Close • Tighten • Replace part • Repair • Replace	
	• Stop release; forward for further action	• Cap • Repair after empty • Replace after empty	
• Overloaded tank	• Reduce load; forward to destination	• Product removal – Fixed facility – Field	• Transfer
• Tank damage or structure damage	• Offload; forward for further action	• Product removal – Field	• Transfer • Flare • Vent
	• Reduce internal pressure	• Product removal – Field	• Transfer • Flare • Vent
		• Gain access to product	• Hot tap • Cold tap

Source: Union Pacific Railroad, *Participant's Manual: Tank Car Safety Course,* April 1997.

involved. The technician with an intermodal tank specialty shall be able to:

11-3.1.1 Describe the purpose of, potential risks associated with, procedures for, equipment required to implement, and safety precautions for the following product removal techniques for intermodal tanks:

Product removal methods are outside the legitimate responsibility of the local emergency response personnel. However, oversight of their planning and implementation is within the responsibilities of local emergency response agencies.

Local procedures for these tasks should be written out and consistent with nationally accepted practices.

(a) Transferring liquids and vapors (pressure/pump)

The purpose of transferring liquids and gases is often associated with removal from a damaged or potentially damaged container to one that is undamaged. The equipment will vary with the type of container involved and the hazardous material being transferred. Transfer procedures are generally established in advance by good industry practice. Only essential personnel, outlined, in most cases, in the overall incident management system of the hazardous materials branch, should be involved in the process.

A transfer is the movement of the contents of a damaged or overloaded intermodal tank into a receiving tank (e.g., a tank car, cargo tank, intermodal tank, or fixed tank).

(b) Hot tapping

Hot tapping describes a situation in which welding or cutting is done on a container or piping while it contains a flammable liquid or gas. It is an emergency procedure where circumstances necessitate the work and where the contents cannot be removed prior to performance of the work. The work must be done only by those who have been trained to do such procedures.

The hot tap is a technique for providing access to the contents of an intermodal tank when damage to the valves and fittings precludes access to the contents. Once the hot tap is completed, transfer, flaring, or venting can take place.

Hot tapping involves the welding of a threaded nozzle into an undamaged section of the tank that is in contact with the liquid. A liquid valve is attached to the nozzle. A hole is then drilled through the tank with a special drilling machine. This hot tapping (drilling) machine is equipped with seals that prevent loss of product during the drilling operation. Liquid hoses or pipe can be attached to the valve outlet.

(c) Flaring liquids and vapors

Flaring liquids and gases is a procedure that can be used to deplete the amount of hazardous material involved or to depressurize a vessel. It should be performed only by persons who are trained in the technique. In some cases, where the burning is already underway at a vent or pressure relief valve when responders arrive, a prescribed procedure will be to allow the flaring process to continue. Determination must be made that the flaring does not present a source of ignition to other spilled flammable substances.

Flaring is the controlled release and disposal of flammable materials by burning from the outlet of a flare pipe (horizontal or vertical). It is used to reduce the pressure or dispose of the residual vapors in a damaged or overloaded intermodal tank.

11-3.1.2 Describe the purpose of, procedures for, and risks associated with controlling leaks from various fittings on intermodal tanks, including equipment needed and safety precautions.

The technician with an intermodal tank specialty will describe these items before attempting to make repairs within their level of training.

11-4 Competencies — Implementing the Planned Response

Most of the competencies in Section 11-4 require the actual demonstration of a task. These tasks require an in-depth knowledge of the intermodal tank, its contents, and the specialized equipment needed to complete the task. Since these tasks must be done on actual intermodal tanks, only a few training facilities will be able to provide practical training and/or certification.

11-4.1 Implementing the Planned Response.

Given an analysis of an emergency involving intermodal tanks and the planned response, technicians with an intermodal tank specialty shall implement or oversee the implementation of the selected response options safely and effectively. The technician with an intermodal tank specialty shall be able to:

Since some of these tasks require specialized resources that are not commonly available to local emergency response personnel, repairs beyond those indicated with each competency should be left to those with the specialized resources and training.

Equipment and resources for these tasks are not readily available; therefore, requests for training on how to perform these tasks should be directed to the local shipper, carrier, or contractor personnel in the community, possibly through the Local Emergency Planning Committee.

11-4.1.1 Given leaks from the following fittings on intermodal tanks, control the leaks using proper methods and procedures.

(a) Manway cover
(b) Bottom outlet
(c) Liquid/vapor valve
(d) Safety relief device
(e) Tank

The technician with an intermodal tank specialty will select and apply appropriate procedures and/or various methods of plugging and patching to control or stop leakage of the commodity. These tasks should be performed using appropriate personal protective equipment for the commodity involved and the working conditions.

11-4.1.2 Demonstrate proper procedures for the following types of emergency product removal:

(a) Gas/liquid transfer (pressure/pump)
(b) Flaring
(c) Venting

All product removal methods are considered outside the legitimate responsibility of the local emergency responder; however, oversight of the planning and implementation of these methods is within the realm of responsibility of local emergency response agencies. Remember, protecting yourself and the community are your primary responsibilities.

Local procedures for these tasks should be written out and consistent with nationally accepted practices.

The technician with an intermodal tank specialty will participate as a member of a team assigned to perform product removal. These tasks should be performed using appropriate personal protective equipment for the material involved and the working conditions.

11-4.1.3* Demonstrate bonding and grounding procedures for the transfer of flammable and combustible products from an intermodal tank, or other products that can give off flammable gases or vapors when heated or contaminated, including the following:

Local procedures for these tasks should be written out and consistent with nationally accepted practices.

The technician with an intermodal tank specialty will participate as a member of a team assigned to set up bonding and grounding for the transfer of intermodal tanks. These tasks should be performed using appropriate personal protective equipment for the material involved and the working conditions.

(a) Selection of proper equipment
(b) Sequence of bonding and grounding connections
(c) Proper testing of bonding and grounding connections

The technician with an intermodal tank specialty should be able to verify (using the appropriate equipment) the following:

(a) Ground rod resistance to earth
(b) Connections between ground rod and intermodal tank
(c) Connections between ground rod and main ground rod and ground cable

A-11-4.1.3 See A-9-4.1.9.

11-4.1.4 Demonstrate the methods for containing the following leaks on liquid intermodal tanks (e.g., IM-101 and IM-102):

(a) Puncture
(b) Irregular-shaped hole
(c) Split or tear
(d) Dome cover leak
(e) Valves and piping
(f) Pressure relief devices (e.g., vents, burst disc, etc.)

The technician with an intermodal tank specialty will select and apply appropriate procedures and/or various methods of plugging and patching to control or stop leakage of the commodity. These tasks should be performed using appropriate personal protective equipment for the commodity involved and the working conditions.

11-4.1.5 Describe the methods for containing the following leaks in pressure intermodal tanks:

(a) Crack
(b) Failure of safety relief device (e.g., relief valve, burst disc, etc.)
(c) Piping failure

The technician with an intermodal tank specialty will select and apply appropriate procedures and/or various methods of plugging and patching to control or stop leakage of the commodity. These tasks should be performed using appropriate personal protective equipment for the commodity involved and the working conditions.

11-4.1.6 Given the following product transfer and recovery equipment, demonstrate the safe and correct application and use of the following:

(a) Portable pumps (air, electrical, gasoline/diesel)
(b) Vehicles with power-take-off (PTO) driven pumps
(c) Pressure transfer
(d) Vacuum trucks

The technician with an intermodal tank specialty will participate as a member of a team assigned to perform product removal. These tasks should be performed using appropriate personal protective equipment for the material involved and the working conditions.

11-4.1.7* Given a simulated overturned liquid intermodal tank, demonstrate the safe and proper procedures for product removal and transfer.

The key word in this competency is "demonstrate." The competency listed in 4-2.4.2 for the hazardous materials technician requires only the ability to "identify." The technician with an intermodal tank specialty will become competent in actually performing the operation.

The technician with an intermodal tank specialty will participate as a member of a team assigned to perform product removal. These tasks should be performed using appropriate personal protective equipment for the material involved and the working conditions.

A-11-4.1.7 See A-9-4.1.9.

11-4.1.8* Given a simulated overturned pressure intermodal tank, demonstrate the safe and proper procedures for product removal and transfer.

The technician with an intermodal tank specialty will participate as a member of a team assigned to perform product removal. These tasks should be performed using appropriate personal protective equipment for the material involved and the working conditions.

A-11-4.1.8 See A-9-4.1.9.

11-4.1.9* Given the necessary resources, demonstrate the flaring of a pressure flammable gas intermodal tank.

The technician with an intermodal tank specialty will participate as a member of a team assigned to perform product removal. These tasks should be performed using appropriate personal protective equipment for the material involved and the working conditions.

A-11-4.1.9 See A-9-4.1.9.

11-4-1.10 Given a simulated flammable liquid spill from an intermodal tank, describe the procedures for site safety and fire control during cleanup and removal operations.

The technician with an intermodal tank specialty will describe the procedures for site safety and fire control during cleanup and removal operations when confronted with a flammable liquid leak from an intermodal tank. These tasks should be performed using appropriate personal protective equipment for the material involved and the working conditions.

Reference Cited in Commentary

1. Association of American Railroads, *Specification for Tank Cars.*

CHAPTER 12

Referenced Publications

12-1

The following documents or portions thereof are referenced within this standard as mandatory requirements and shall be considered part of the requirements of this standard. The edition indicated for each referenced mandatory document is the current edition as of the date of the NFPA issuance of this standard. Some of these mandatory documents might also be referenced in this standard for specific informational purposes and, therefore, are also listed in Appendix D.

12-1.1 NFPA Publications.

National Fire Protection Association, 1 Batterymarch Park, P.O. Box 9101, Quincy, MA 02269-9101.

NFPA 704, *Standard System for the Identification of the Hazards of Materials for Emergency Response*, 1996 edition.

NFPA 1561, *Standard on Fire Department Incident Management System*, 1995 edition.

NFPA 1991, *Standard on Vapor-Protective Suits for Hazardous Chemical Emergencies*, 1994 edition.

NFPA 1992, *Standard on Liquid Splash-Protective Suits for Hazardous Chemical Emergencies*, 1994 edition.

12-1.2 Other Publications.

12-1.2.1 U.S. Government Publications. U.S. Government Printing Office, Superintendent of Documents, Washington, DC 20402.

Title 29, *Code of Federal Regulations*, Part 1910.120.

North American Emergency Response Guidebook, U.S. Department of Transportation, 1996 edition.

APPENDIX A

The material contained in Appendix A of this standard is not part of the requirements of the *Code* but is included for informational purposes only. For the convenience of readers, in this handbook the Appendix A material is interspersed among the verbiage of Chapters 1 through 11 and, therefore, is not repeated here.

APPENDIX B

Competencies for the Technician with a Flammable Liquids Bulk Storage Specialty

This appendix is not a part of the requirements of this NFPA document but is included for informational purposes only.

B-1 General

B-1.1 Introduction.

Technicians with a flammable liquids bulk storage specialty should meet all requirements of the first responder awareness, operational, and hazardous materials technician levels and the competencies of this Appendix. The technician with a flammable liquids bulk storage specialty also should receive additional training to meet applicable United States Environmental Protection Agency (EPA), Occupational Safety and Health Administration (OSHA), and other appropriate state, local, or provincial occupational health and safety regulatory requirements.

B-1.2 Definition.

Technicians with a flammable liquids bulk storage specialty are those persons who, in incidents involving bulk flammable liquid storage tanks, provide support to the hazardous materials technician and other personnel, provide strategical and tactical recommendations to the on-scene incident commander, provide oversight for fire control and product removal operations, and act as a liaison between technicians, fire fighting personnel, and other outside resources. These technicians are expected to use appropriate personal protective clothing and specialized fire, leak, and spill control equipment.

B-1.3 Goal.

The goal of this Appendix is to provide the technicians with a flammable liquids bulk storage specialty with the knowledge and skills to perform the following tasks safely. In addition to being competent at the technician levels, the technician with a flammable liquids bulk storage specialty should be able to:

(a) Analyze an incident involving a bulk flammable liquid storage tank to determine the magnitude of the problem by completing the following tasks:

1. Determine the type and extent of damage to the bulk liquid storage tank
2. Predict the likely behavior of the bulk liquid storage tank and its contents in an incident

(b) Plan a response for an incident involving a flammable liquid bulk storage tank within the capabilities and competencies of available personnel, personal protective equipment, and control equipment by completing the following tasks:

1. Determine the response options (offensive, defensive, and nonintervention) for a hazardous materials incident involving flammable liquid bulk storage tanks
2. Ensure that the options are within the capabilities and competencies of available personnel, personal protective equipment, and control equipment

(c) Implement the planned response to a hazardous materials incident involving a flammable liquid bulk storage tank

B-1.4 Mandating of Competencies.

This standard does not mandate that hazardous materials response teams performing offensive operations on flammable liquids bulk storage tanks have technicians with a flammable liquids bulk storage specialty. Technicians operating within the bounds of their training as listed in Chapter 4 of this standard are able to intervene in flammable liquids bulk storage incidents. However, if a hazardous materials response team desires to train some or all its technicians to have in-depth knowledge of flammable liquids bulk storage facilities, this Appendix sets out the recommended competencies.

B-2 Competencies — Analyzing the Incident

B-2.1 Determining the Type and Extent of Damage to the Bulk Storage Tank.

Given examples of storage tank incidents, technicians with a flammable liquids bulk storage specialty should describe the type of storage tank, and the type and extent of damage to the tank and its associated piping and fittings. The technician with a flammable liquids bulk storage specialty should be able to:

B-2.1.1 Given examples of various flammable liquid bulk storage operations, identify and describe the procedures for the normal movement and transfer of product(s) into and out of the facility and storage tanks.

Examples should be based upon local or regional facilities and could include marketing terminals, pipeline operations and terminals, refineries, and bulk storage facilities.

B-2.1.2 Given examples of the following atmospheric pressure bulk liquid storage tanks, describe the tank's design and construction features, and types of products commonly found.

(a) Cone roof tank
(b) Open (external) floating roof tank
(c) Open floating roof tank with a geodesic dome external roof
(d) Covered (internal) floating roof tank

According to NFPA 30, *Flammable and Combustible Liquids Code,* atmospheric tanks are defined as storage tanks operating at pressures from atmospheric to 0.5 psig. The floating roof on an open floating roof tank can be a pan roof or a pontoon floating roof, while the floating roof on a covered floating roof tank can be constructed of aluminum, steel or fiberglass, or a pontoon floating roof.

B-2.1.3 Given examples of the following types of low pressure horizontal and vertical bulk liquid storage tanks, describe the tank's uses and design and construction features.

(a) Horizontal tank
(b) Dome roof tank

According to NFPA 30, *Flammable and Combustible Liquids Code,* low pressure tanks are defined as storage tanks operating at pressures from 0.5 psig but not more than 15 psig.

B-2.1.4 Given examples of various atmospheric and low pressure bulk liquid storage tanks, describe the design and purpose of each of the following storage tank components, when present:

(a) Tank shell material of construction
(b) Type of roof and material of construction
(c) Primary and secondary roof seals (as applicable)
(d) Incident venting/pressure relief devices
(e) Tank valves
(f) Tank gauging devices
(g) Tank overfill device
(h) Secondary containment methods (as applicable)
(i) Tank piping and piping supports
(j) Fixed or semi-fixed fire protection system

B-2.1.5 Given three examples of primary and secondary spill confinement measures, describe the design, construction, and incident response considerations associated with each method provided.

B-2.2 Predicting the Likely Behavior of the Bulk Storage Tank and Contents.

Technicians with a flammable liquids bulk storage specialty should predict the likely behavior of the tank and its contents. The technician with a flammable liquids bulk storage specialty should be able to:

B-2.2.1 Given examples of different types of bulk flammable liquid storage tank facilities, identify the impact of the following fire and safety features on the behavior of the products during an incident, when present:

(a) Tank spacing
(b) Product spillage and control (impoundment and diking)
(c) Tank venting and flaring systems
(d) Transfer and product movement capabilities
(e) Monitoring and detection systems
(f) Fire protection systems

B-2.2.2 Given a flammable liquid bulk storage tank involved in a fire, identify the factors to be evaluated as part of the risk assessment process, including the following:

(a) Type of storage tank
(b) Product involved
(c) Amount of product within the storage tank
(d) Nature of the incident (e.g., seal fire, tank overfill, full-surface fire, etc.)
(e) Tank spacing and exposures
(f) Fixed or semi-fixed fire protection systems present

B-2.2.3 Given three types of incidents involving flammable liquid bulk storage tanks, describe the likely fire and spill behavior for each incident.

Examples of fire and spill incidents could include tank overfills, seal fires on floating roof tanks, floating roof with a sunk internal roof, tank or piping failures, full surface fire, etc.

B-2.2.4 Describe the causes, hazards, and methods of handling the following conditions as they relate to fires involving flammable liquid bulk storage tanks:

(a) Frothover
(b) Slopover
(c) Boilover

For additional information, see NFPA 30, *Flammable and Combustible Liquids Code* and API 2021, *Guide for Fighting Fires In and Around Flammable and Combustible Atmospheric Petroleum Storage Tanks*.

B-3 Competencies — Planning the Response

B-3.1 Determining the Response Options.

Given an analysis of an incident involving flammable liquid storage tanks, technicians with a flammable liquids bulk storage specialty should determine response options for the storage tank involved. The technician with a flammable liquids bulk storage specialty should be able to:

B-3.1.1 Describe the factors to be evaluated in evaluating and selecting Class B fire fighting foam concentrates for use on flammable liquids.

B-3.1.2 Describe the factors to be considered for the portable application of Class B fire fighting foam concentrates for the following types of incidents:

(a) Flammable liquid spill (no fire)
(b) Flammable liquid spill (with fire)
(c) Flammable liquid storage tank fire

B-3.1.3 Given examples of different types of flammable liquid bulk storage tanks, identify and describe the application, use, and limitations of the types of fixed and semi-fixed fire protection systems that can be used, including the following:

(a) Foam chambers
(b) Catenary systems
(c) Subsurface injection system
(d) Fixed foam monitors
(e) Foam/water sprinkler systems

B-3.1.4 Describe the hazards, safety procedures, and tactical guidelines for handling an accumulated (in-depth) flammable liquid-spill fire.

B-3.1.5 Describe the hazards, safety procedures, and tactical guidelines for handling product/water drainage and runoff problems that can be created at a flammable liquid bulk storage tank fire.

B-3.1.6 Describe the hazards, safety procedures, and tactical guidelines for handling a flammable liquid bulk storage tank with a sunken floating roof.

B-3.1.7 Given a flammable liquid storage tank fire, describe the methods and associated safety considerations for extinguishing the following types of fires by using portable application devices:

(a) Pressure vent fire
(b) Seal fire on an open floating roof tank
(c) Seal fire on an internal floating roof tank
(d) Full-surface fire on an internal floating roof tank
(e) Full-surface fire on an external floating roof tank
(f) Dike fire
(g) Pipeline manifold fire

B-3.1.8 Given the size, dimensions, and products involved for a flammable liquid-spill fire, determine the following:

(a) Appropriate extinguishing agent
(b) Appropriate application method (both portable and fixed system application)
(c) Appropriate application rate and duration
(d) Required amount of Class B foam concentrate and required amount of water
(e) Volume and rate of application of water for cooling exposed tanks

For additional information, see NFPA 11, *Standard for Low-Expansion Foam*.

B-3.1.9 Given the size, dimensions, and product involved for a flammable liquid storage tank fire, determine the following:

(a) Appropriate extinguishing agent
(b) Appropriate application method (both portable and fixed system application)
(c) Appropriate application rate and duration
(d) Required amount of Class B foam concentrate and required amount of water
(e) Volume and rate of application of water for cooling involved and exposed tanks

For additional information, see NFPA 11, *Standard for Low-Expansion Foam*.

B-3.1.10 Given the size, dimensions, and product involved for a fire involving a single flammable liquid bulk storage tank and its dike area, determine the following:

(a) Appropriate extinguishing agent
(b) Appropriate application method (both portable and fixed system application)
(c) Appropriate application rate and duration
(d) Required amount of Class B foam concentrate and required amount of water
(e) Volume and rate of application of water for cooling involved and exposed tanks

For additional information, see NFPA 11, *Standard for Low-Expansion Foam*.

B-3.1.11 Given the size, dimensions, and product involved for multiple flammable liquid storage tanks burning within a common dike area, determine the following:

(a) Appropriate extinguishing agent

(b) Appropriate application method (both portable and fixed system application)
(c) Appropriate application rate and duration
(d) Amount of Class B foam concentrate and water required
(e) Volume and rate of application of water for cooling involved and exposed tanks

For additional information, see NFPA 11, *Standard for Low-Expansion Foam*.

B-4 Competencies — Implementing the Planned Response

B-4.1 Implementing the Planned Response.

Given an analysis of an incident involving flammable liquid storage tanks, technicians with a flammable liquids bulk storage specialty should implement or oversee the implementation of the selected response options safely and effectively. The technician with a flammable liquids bulk storage specialty should be able to:

B-4.1.1 Given a simulated flammable liquid fire, demonstrate the safe and effective methods for extinguishing the following types of fires by using portable application devices:

(a) Valve and/or flange fire
(b) Pump fire (horizontal or vertical)
(c) Pressure vent fire
(d) Large spill fire
(e) Storage tank fire

B-4.1.2 Given a simulated incident involving a three-dimensional flammable liquid fire, demonstrate the safe and effective method for controlling the fire by using portable application devices.

B-4.1.3 Demonstrate bonding and grounding procedures for the transfer of flammable liquids, including the following:

(a) Selection of proper equipment
(b) Sequence of bonding and grounding connections
(c) Proper testing of bonding and grounding connections

B-4.1.4 Given a simulated flammable liquid spill from a bulk storage tank or pipeline, describe the procedures for site safety and fire control during cleanup and removal operations.

APPENDIX C

Competencies for the Technician with a Flammable Gases Bulk Storage Specialty

This appendix is not a part of the requirements of this NFPA document but is included for informational purposes only.

C-1 General

C-1.1 Introduction.

Technicians with a flammable gases bulk storage specialty should meet all requirements of the first responder awareness, operational, and hazardous materials technician levels and the competencies of this Appendix. The technician with a flammable gases bulk storage specialty also should receive additional training to meet applicable United States Environmental Protection Agency (EPA), Occupational Safety and Health Administration (OSHA), and other appropriate state, local, or provincial occupational health and safety regulatory requirements.

C-1.2 Definition.

Technicians with a flammable gases bulk storage specialty are those persons who, in incidents involving bulk flammable gas storage tanks, provide support to the hazardous materials technician and other personnel, provide strategical and tactical recommendations to the on-scene incident commander, provide oversight for fire control and product removal operations, and act as a liaison between technicians, fire fighting personnel, and other outside resources. These technicians are expected to use appropriate personal protective clothing and specialized fire, leak, and spill control equipment.

C-1.3 Goal.

The goal of this Appendix is to provide the technicians with a flammable gases bulk storage specialty with the knowledge and skills to perform the following tasks safely. In addition to being competent at the technician levels, the technician with a flammable gases bulk storage specialty should be able to:

(a) Analyze an incident involving a bulk flammable gas storage tank to determine the magnitude of the problem by completing the following tasks:

1. Determine the type and extent of damage to the bulk storage tank
2. Predict the likely behavior of the bulk storage tank and its contents in an incident

(b) Plan a response for an incident involving a flammable gas bulk storage tank within the capabilities and competencies of available personnel, personal protective equipment, and control equipment by completing the following tasks:

1. Determine the response options (offensive, defensive, and nonintervention) for a hazardous materials incident involving flammable gas bulk storage tanks
2. Ensure that the options are within the capabilities and competencies of available personnel, personal protective equipment, and control equipment

(c) Implement the planned response to a hazardous materials incident involving a flammable gas bulk storage tank

C-1.4 Mandating of Competencies.

This standard does not mandate that hazardous materials response teams performing offensive operations on flammable gas bulk storage tanks have technicians with a flammable gases bulk storage specialty. Technicians operating within the bounds of their training as listed in Chapter 4 of this standard are able to intervene in flammable gas bulk storage incidents. However, if a hazardous materials response team desires to train some or all its technicians to have in-depth knowledge of flammable gas bulk storage facilities, this Appendix sets out the recommended competencies.

C-2 Competencies — Analyzing the Incident

C-2.1 Determining the Type and Extent of Damage to the Bulk Storage Tank.

Given examples of storage tank incidents, technicians with a flammable gases bulk storage specialty should describe the type of storage tank and extent of damage to the tank and its associated piping and fittings. The technician with a flammable gases bulk storage specialty should be able to:

C-2.1.1 Given examples of various flammable gas bulk storage operations, identify and describe the procedures for the normal movement and transfer of product(s) into and out of the facility storage tanks.

Examples should be based upon local or regional facilities and could include marketing terminals, pipeline operations and terminals, refineries, bulk storage facilities, and underground storage caverns.

C-2.1.2 Given examples of the following types of high pressure bulk gas storage tanks, describe the tank's uses and design and construction features.

(a) Horizontal (bullet) tank
(b) Spherical tank

Additional information on the design and construction of high pressure bulk gas storage tanks can be referenced from NFPA 58, *Standard for the Storage and Handling of Liquefied Petroleum Gases,* and API 2510-A, *Fire Protection Considerations for the Design and Operation of Liquefied Petroleum Gas (LPG) Storage Facilities.*

C-2.1.3 Given examples of various high pressure bulk gas storage tanks, point out and explain the design and purpose of each of the following storage tank components and fittings, when present:

(a) Liquid valve and vapor valve
(b) Safety relief valve
(c) Gauging device
(d) Tank piping and piping supports
(e) Fixed or semi-fixed fire protection system

C-2.2 Predicting the Likely Behavior of the Bulk Storage Tank and Contents.

Technicians with a flammable gases bulk storage specialty should predict the likely behavior of the tank and its contents. The technician with a flammable gases bulk storage specialty should be able to:

C-2.2.1 Given examples of different types of bulk flammable gas storage tank facilities, identify the impact of the following fire and safety features on the behavior of the products during an incident, when present.

(a) Tank spacing
(b) Product spillage and control (impoundment and diking)
(c) Tank venting and flaring systems
(d) Transfer and product movement capabilities
(e) Monitoring and detection systems
(f) Fire protection systems

C-2.2.2 Given examples of different types of flammable gas bulk storage tanks, identify and describe the application, use, and limitations of the types of fixed and semi-fixed fire protection systems that can be used, including the following:

(a) Water spray systems
(b) Fixed foam monitors
(c) Fixed hydrocarbon monitoring systems

C-2.2.3 Given a flammable gas bulk storage tank and its associated piping, describe the likely breach/release mechanisms and fire scenarios.

C-3 Competencies — Planning the Response

C-3.1 Determining the Response Options.

Given an analysis of an emergency involving flammable gas storage tanks, technicians with a flammable gases bulk storage specialty should determine response options for the storage tank involved. The technician with a flammable gases bulk storage specialty should be able to:

C-3.1.1 Describe the hazards, safety, and tactical considerations required for the following types of flammable gas incidents:

(a) Flammable vapor release (no fire)
(b) Flammable vapor release (with fire)
(c) Liquefied flammable gas release (no fire)
(d) Liquefied flammable gas release (with fire)

C-3.1.2 Given a flammable gas storage tank with a liquid leak from the safety relief valve, describe the hazards, safety, and tactical considerations for controlling this type of leak.

C-3.1.3 Given a flammable gas fire from an elevated structure (e.g., tower or column), describe the hazards, safety, and tactical considerations for controlling this type of leak.

C-3.1.4 Describe the purpose of, potential risks associated with, procedures for, equipment required to implement, and safety precautions for the following product removal techniques:

(a) Transfer of liquids and vapors
(b) Flaring of liquids and vapors
(c) Venting
(d) Hot and cold tapping

C-3.1.5 Describe the effect flaring or venting of gas or liquid has on the pressure in the tank (flammable gas or flammable liquid product).

C-3.1.6 Describe the hazards, safety procedures, and tactical guidelines for handling product/water drainage and runoff problems that can be created at a flammable gas bulk storage facility incident.

C-4 Competencies — Implementing the Planned Response

C-4.1 Implementing the Planned Response.

Given an analysis of an emergency involving flammable gas bulk storage tanks, technicians with a flammable gases bulk storage specialty should implement or oversee the implementation of the selected response options safely and effectively. The technician with a flammable gases bulk storage specialty should be able to:

C-4.1.1 Given a simulated flammable gas incident, demonstrate the safe and effective method for controlling the following types of emergencies by using portable application devices:

(a) Unignited vapor release
(b) Valve and/or flange vapor release (no fire)
(c) Valve and/or flange fire
(d) Pump fire (horizontal or vertical)

C-4.1.2 Given a simulated incident involving the simultaneous release of both flammable liquids and flammable gases, demonstrate the safe and effective method for controlling the following types of emergencies by using portable application devices:

(a) Unignited vapor release
(b) Flange fire
(c) Pump seal fire

C-4.1.3 Demonstrate bonding and grounding procedures for the transfer of flammable gases, including the following:

(a) Selection of proper equipment
(b) Sequence of bonding and grounding connections
(c) Proper testing of bonding and grounding connections

C-4.1.4 Given a simulated flammable gas incident from a bulk storage tank or pipeline, describe the procedures for site safety and fire control during cleanup and removal operations.

APPENDIX D

Referenced Publications

D-1

The following documents or portions thereof are referenced within this standard for informational purposes only and are thus not considered part of the requirements of this standard unless also listed in Chapter 12. The edition indicated here for each reference is the current edition as of the date of the NFPA issuance of this standard.

D-1.1 NFPA Publications.

National Fire Protection Association, 1 Batterymarch Park, P.O. Box 9101, Quincy, MA 02269-9101.

NFPA 11, *Standard for Low-Expansion Foam*, 1994 edition.
NFPA 30, *Flammable and Combustible Liquids Code*, 1996 edition.
NFPA 58, *Standard for the Storage and Handling of Liquefied Petroleum Gases*, 1995 edition.
NFPA 471, *Recommended Practice for Responding to Hazardous Materials Incidents*, 1997 edition.
NFPA 473, *Standard for Competencies for EMS Personnel Responding to Hazardous Materials Incidents*, 1997 edition.
NFPA 1561, *Standard on Fire Department Incident Management System*, 1995 edition.
NFPA 1991, *Standard on Vapor-Protective Suits for Hazardous Chemical Emergencies*, 1994 edition.
NFPA 1992, *Standard on Liquid Splash-Protective Suits for Hazardous Chemical Emergencies*, 1994 edition.
NFPA 1993, *Standard on Support Function Protective Clothing for Hazardous Chemical Operations*, 1994 edition.

D-1.2 Other Publications.

D-1.2.1 API Publications. American Petroleum Institute, 2101 L Street, NW, Washington, DC 20037.

API 2021, *Guide for Fighting Fires In and Around Flammable and Combustible Liquid Atmospheric Petroleum Storage Tanks*, 1991.
API 2510-A, *Fire Protection Considerations for the Design and Operation of Liquefied Petroleum Gas (LPG) Storage Facilities*, 1989.

D-1.2.2 Chemical Manufacturers Association Publications. Chemical Manufacturers Association, 1300 Wilson Blvd., Arlington, VA 22209.

Packaging for Transporting Hazardous and Non-Hazardous Materials, June 1989 edition.
Recommended Terms for Personal Protective Equipment, 1985.

D-1.2.3 National Fire Academy Publication. National Fire Academy, Federal Emergency Management Agency, Emmitsburg, MD 21727.

Hazardous Materials Incident Analysis, 1984.

D-1.2.4 National Response Team Publication. National Response Team, National Oil and Hazardous Substances Contingency Plan, Washington, DC 20593.

NRT-1, *Hazardous Materials Emergency Planning Guide*, 1987.

D-1.2.5 U.S. Government Publications. U.S. Government Printing Office, Superintendent of Documents, Washington, DC 20402.

Title 29, *Code of Federal Regulations*, Parts 1910.119 – 1910.120.
Title 40, *Code of Federal Regulations*, Part 261.33.
Title 40, *Code of Federal Regulations*, Part 302.
Title 40, *Code of Federal Regulations*, Part 355.
Title 49, *Code of Federal Regulations*, Parts 170–179.

D-1.2.6 Miscellaneous Publications.

Benner, Ludwig, Jr., *A Textbook for Use in the Study of Hazardous Materials Emergencies*, 2nd edition, Lufred Industries, Inc., Oakton, VA, 1978.
Noll, Gregory G., et al., *Hazardous Materials, Managing the Incident*, 2nd edition, Fire Protection Publications, Stillwater, OK, 1995.

NIOSH/OSHA/USCG/EPA *Occupational Safety and Health Guidance Manual for Hazardous Waste Site Activities*, October 1985.

Wright, Charles J., "Managing the Hazardous Materials Incident," *Fire Protection Handbook*, 18th edition, National Fire Protection Association, Quincy, MA, 1997.

EPA, *Standard Operating Safety Guides*, June 1992.

Maslansky, Carol J. and Stephen P., "Air Monitoring Instrumentation," New York, NY, Van Nostrand Reinhold, 1993.

Grey, Gerald L., et al., *Hazardous Materials/Waste Handling for the Emergency Responder*, Fire Engineering Publications, New York, NY, 1989.

Tentative Interim Amendment for NFPA 472

The NFPA Hazardous Materials Response Personnel Committee at its *Report on Comments* meeting (Fall 1996) discussed the newly recognized threat posed by intentional releases of hazardous materials due to acts of terrorism or other criminal activity. Although it was acknowledged that many of the techniques and equipment to control these incidents are very similar to a normal hazardous materials incident, the indicators of a potential problem are often very different.

Traditionally, responders have been trained to identify hazardous materials based on occupancy location, container shapes, markings, and color. However, in the case of terrorist incidents, the responsible parties do not want anyone to be able to recognize that hazardous materials are present. Similarly, the presence of hazardous materials may be unknown in more routine occurrences where illegal manufacturing, storage, disposal, and transportation of such materials may be taking place (for example, in an unlicensed auto body repair shop).

The NFPA Hazardous Materials Response Personnel Committee appointed a task group to author additions to the NFPA 472 standard to specifically address these new hazardous materials threats. The TIA process was chosen since NFPA 472 had just finished its current revision cycle and would not be entering a regular revision cycle for several years. This TIA was finalized with the help of several representatives from federal agencies such as the FBI; U.S. Army Edgewood Research, Development, and Engineering Center; National Fire Academy, FEMA; U.S. Army Technical Escort Unit; U.S. Department of Energy, U.S. Marine Corps, Chemical/Biological Incident Response Force; and U.S. Army Medical Research Institute of Infectious Diseases. These agencies have many years of experience from the study and research into military uses and defenses for these chemical, biological, and nuclear threats.

The additional training objectives listed in the text of this TIA should not be seen as stand-alone competencies, but are intended to be additional items added to the base knowledge of the different levels outlined in NFPA 472. The field of hazardous materials response, especially in the chemical and biological arena, is an ever evolving field of knowledge.

Tentative Interim Amendment

NFPA 472

Professional Competence of Responders to Hazardous Materials Incidents

1997 Edition

Reference: Chapters 2, 3, 4 and 5
TIA 97-1 (NFPA 472)

Pursuant to Section 4 of the NFPA Regulations Governing Committee Projects, the National Fire Protection Association has issued the following Tentative Interim Amendment to NFPA 472, *Standard for Professional Competence of Responders to Hazardous Materials Incidents*, 1997 edition. The TIA was processed by the Hazardous Materials Response Personnel Committee, and was issued by the Standards Council on April 3, 1997, with an effective date of April 23, 1997.

A Tentative Interim Amendment is tentative because it has not been processed through the entire standards-making procedures. It is interim because it is effective only between editions of the standard. A TIA automatically becomes a proposal of the proponent for the next edition of the standard; as such, it then is subject to all of the procedures of the standards-making process.

(continues)

1. *Add the following new paragraphs to read:*

2-2.1.13* Identify types of locations that could become targets for criminal or terrorist activity using hazardous materials.

A-2-2.1.13 The following are some examples of potential criminal or terrorist targets:

(a) Public assembly
(b) Public buildings
(c) Mass transit systems
(d) Places with high economic impact
(e) Telecommunications facilities
(f) Places with historical or symbolic significance

This new material addresses the need for competency regarding chemical and biological weapon use. One may not give much thought to the possibility of a terrorist incident when called to treat a medical emergency at a rock concert, but if the information you receive indicates numerous casualties of unknown causes, you should be aware of the possibility and take measures to reduce any exposure to responders.

2-2.1.14* Identify at least 4 indicators of possible criminal or terrorist activity involving hazardous materials.

A-2-2.1.14 The following are some examples of indicators of possible criminal or terrorist activity:

(a) The presence of hazardous materials or laboratory equipment that is not relevant to the occupancy
(b) Intentional release of hazardous materials
(c) Unexplained patterns of sudden onset illnesses or deaths
(d) Unusual odors or tastes
(e) Unexplained signs of skin, eye, or airway irritation
(f) Unusual security, locks, bars on windows, covered windows, and barbed wire
(g) Unexplained vapor clouds, mists, and plumes
(h) Victims twitching, tightness in chest, sweating, pin-point pupils (miosos), runny nose (rhinorrhea), and nausea and vomiting

This list of possible items or situations should alert the responder to take additional precautions to avoid possible contamination.

2-4.1.6* Identify the specific actions necessary when an incident is suspected to involve criminal or terrorist activity.

A-2-4.1.6 The following are some examples of actions required to be taken:

(a) Communicate the suspicion during the notification process
(b) Isolate potentially exposed people
(c) Document the initial observation

The notification and isolation process is used to protect all responders when a criminal or terrorist incident may be involved. The awareness responder needs to document observations for use by law enforcement officials in the case of an illegal act.

3-2.1.6* Identify at least 3 additional hazards that could be associated with an incident involving criminal or terrorist activity.

A-3-2.1.6 The following are some example of hazards:

(a) Secondary events intended to incapacitate emergency responders
(b) Armed resistance
(c) Use of weapons
(d) Booby traps
(e) Secondary contamination from handling patients

Responders may need to first assess the risk of further criminal or terrorist activity at the scene before proceeding.

3-2.2.6 Identify the type of assistance provided by the federal defense authorities, such as Defense Logistics Agency and U.S. Army Operations Center, with respect to criminal or terrorist activities involving hazardous materials.

Assistance from Defense Logistics Agency and U.S. Army Operations Center can include trained personnel, monitoring equipment, medical treatment, and antidotes. The *North American Emergency Response Guidebook* contains the telephone numbers for these agencies.

3-2.2.6.1 Identify the procedure for contacting federal defense authorities as specified in the local emergency response plan (ERP) or the organization's standard operating procedures (SOP).

3-2.3.9* Given the following types of warfare agents, identify the corresponding DOT hazard class and division:

(a) Nerve agents
(b) Vesicants (blister agents)
(c) Blood agents
(d) Choking agents
(e) Irritants (riot control agents)
(f) Biological agents and toxins

A-3-2.3.9 Some examples of hazard class are as follows:

	DOT Hazard Class
(a) Nerve agents	
Tabun (GA)	6.1
Sarin (GB)	6.1
Soman (GD)	6.1
V agent (VX)	6.1
(b) Vesicants (blister agents)	
Mustard (H)	6.1
Distilled mustard (HD)	6.1
Nitrogen mustard (HN)	6.1
Lewisite (L)	6.1
(c) Blood agents	
Hydrogen cyanide (AC)	6.1
Cyanogen chloride (CK)	2.3
(d) Choking agents	
Chlorine (CL)	2.3
Phosgene (CG)	2.3
(e) Irritants	
CS	6.1
CR	6.1
CN	6.1
OC	2.2 (subsequent risk 6.1)
(f) Biological agents and toxins	
Anthrax	6.2
Mycotoxin	6.1 or 6.2
Plague	6.2
Tularemia	6.2

The list of these potential chemical warfare agents is provided to put them in perspective with other hazardous materials.

3-3.4.5 Describe the procedure listed in the local emergency response plan or the organization's standard operating procedures for decontamination of a large number of people exposed to hazardous materials.

An area must be designated immediately, then cordoned off, and all contaminated persons directed to the controlled area. If this is not done expeditiously, contaminated persons will leave the scene and may infect other people, places, and things. Also, they may seek medical attention from sources not prepared to provide proper care since the details of their exposure will not be known.

3-4.4.6 Describe procedures, such as those listed in the local emergency response plan or the organization's standard operating procedures, to preserve evidence at hazardous materials incidents involving suspected criminal or terrorist acts.

The collection of criminal evidence has a more rigorous test for acceptance in a court of law than in civil or regulator law procedures. In most cases, this means preserving evidence until it can be collected by law enforcement officials such as is done at the scene of a possible arson fire. Although hazardous materials response personnel have been called to the scenes of incidents that constitute potential violations of environmental regulations, the preservation of criminal evidence has not been addressed before now.

4-2.1.1.7 For each of the following, describe a method that can be used to detect them:

(a) Nerve agents
(b) Vesicants (blister agents)
(c) Biological agents and toxins
(d) Irritants (riot control agents)

Technicians need to be able to identify chemical and biological agents in addition to other hazardous materials. Different methods and monitoring equipment are required to identify or classify unknown chemical or biological materials because in most cases there will be no other way to identify the agent.

4-2.3.1.4 Demonstrate a method for collecting samples of the following:

(a) Liquid
(b) Solid
(c) Gas

In many cases, the hazardous materials response team will not have the appropriate monitoring equipment to identify the agent. The techniques for collecting liquid, solid, and gas samples are critical to identification of the material when the sample is analyzed at a laboratory.

4-3.5.6 Identify the procedures, equipment, and safety precautions for collecting legal evidence at hazardous materials incidents.

Proper procedures must be used to collect evidence where there is the possibility of a crime having been committed.

5-2.2.7* Describe the health risks associated with the following:

(a) Nerve agents
(b) Vesicants (blister agents)

(continues)

Once the health risks are known, the incident command has a better idea on how to estimate the outcomes from a specific exposure. This is absolutely necessary in both treating contaminated persons and protecting responders.

(c) Blood agents
(d) Choking agents
(e) Biological agents and toxins
(f) Irritants (riot control agents)

A-5-2.2.7 Some examples are as follows:

Common Name	NFPA 704	Military Abbreviation	PEL/TWA mg/m^3	LD_{50} ($mg\ min/m^3$)
(a) Nerve agents				
Sarin	411	GB	0.0001	70
Soman	411	GD	0.00003	70
Tabun	421	GA	0.0001	133
V agent	411	VX	0.00001	10 (percutaneous) 30 (vapor)
(b) Vesicants (blister agents)				
Mustard	411	H, HD	0.003	1500
Lewisite	411	L	0.003	1000–1500
(e) Biological agents and toxins		**Days/Latency**	**Fatal**	
Anthrax		1–5	Yes	
Botulism		2–3	Yes	
Cholera		2–5	Yes	
Encephalitis		2–5	Yes	
Plague		1–3	Yes	
Tularemia		1–10	Yes	

5-3.3.5 Identify the limitations of military chemical/biological protective clothing.

The protective clothing used by the hazardous materials responder is designed and constructed to afford close to 100% protection when used properly. The protective clothing used by the military incorporates several considerations not compatible with this assumption. Military clothing is lightweight, inexpensive, and very flexible, and does not provide the same level of protection.

5-6.4.6 Identify the procedures required for legal documentation and chain of custody/continuity described in the organization's standard operating procedures or the local emergency response plan.

2. *Revise the following paragraphs to read as follows:*

2-4.2 Initiating the Notification Process. Given either a facility or transportation scenario involving hazardous materials, regardless of the presence of criminal or terrorist activities, the first responder at the awareness level shall identify the appropriate initial notifications to be made and how to make them, consistent with the local emergency response plan or the organization's standard operating procedures.

3-4.1.6 Identify the items to be considered in a safety briefing prior to allowing personnel to work at the following:

(a) Hazardous materials incident
(b)* Hazardous materials incident involving criminal or terrorist activities.

There are distinct differences between a hazardous materials incident and such an incident involving criminals or terrorists. The differences include secondary events intended to incapacitate emergency responders, the use of intentionally unknown agents, armed resistance, and secondary contamination from contaminated persons who may have left the scene.

A-3-4.1.6(b) See A-3.2.1.6.

4-2.2.2 Describe the following terms and explain their significance in the risk assessment process:

(a) Acid, caustic
(b) Air reactivity
(c) Biological agents and toxins
(d) Boiling point
(e) Catalyst
(f) Chemical interactions
(g) Chemical reactivity
(h) Compound, mixture
(i) Concentration
(j) Corrosivity (pH)
(k) Critical temperatures and pressure

(l) Expansion ratio
(m) Flammable (explosive) range (LEL & UEL)
(n) Fire point
(o) Flash point
(p) Halogenated hydrocarbon
(q) Ignition (autoignition) temperature
(r) Inhibitor
(s) Instability
(t) Ionic and covalent compounds
(u) Irritants (riot control agents)
(v) Maximum safe storage temperature (MSST)
(w) Melting point/freezing point
(x) Miscibility
(y) Nerve agents
(z) Organic and inorganic
(aa) Oxidation potential
(bb) pH
(cc) Physical state (solid, liquid, gas)
(dd) Polymerization
(ee) Radioactivity
(ff) Saturated, unsaturated, and aromatic hydrocarbons
(gg) Self-accelerating decomposition temperature (SADT)
(hh) Solution, slurry
(ii) Specific gravity
(jj) Strength
(kk) Sublimation
(ll) Temperature of product
(mm) Toxic products of combustion
(nn) Vapor density
(oo) Vapor pressure
(pp) Vesicants (blister agents)
(qq) Viscosity
(rr) Volatility
(ss) Water reactivity
(tt) Water solubility

5-3.4.3 Given the local emergency response plan and/or the organization's standard operating procedures, identify which agency will perform the following:

(a) Receive the initial notification
(b) Provide secondary notification and activation of response agencies
(c) Make ongoing assessments of the situation
(d) Command on-scene personnel (incident management system)
(e) Coordinate support and mutual aid
(f) Provide law enforcement and on-scene security (crowd control)
(g) Provide traffic control and rerouting
(h) Provide resources for public safety protective action (evacuation or shelter in-place)
(i) Provide fire suppression services when appropriate
(j) Provide on-scene medical assistance (ambulance) and medical treatment (hospital)
(k) Provide public notification (warning)
(l) Provide public information (news media statements)
(m) Provide on-scene communications support
(n) Provide emergency on-scene decontamination when appropriate
(o) Provide operational-level hazard control services
(p) Provide technician-level hazard mitigation services

(continues)

(q) Provide environmental remedial action ("cleanup") services
(r) Provide environmental monitoring
(s) Implement on-site accountability
(t) Provide on-site responder identification
(u) Provide command post security
(v) Provide crime scene investigation
(w) Provide evidence collection and sampling

PART THREE

NFPA 473

Standard for Competencies for EMS Personnel Responding to Hazardous Materials Incidents, 1997 Edition, with Commentary

Following the development of NFPA 471 and NFPA 472, the Hazardous Materials Response Personnel Committee undertook the development of this Standard relating to the roles and responsibilities of EMS personnel at hazardous materials incidents. In this 1997 edition, the committee identifies the levels of competence required of emergency medical services (EMS) personnel who respond to hazardous materials incidents, specifically for basic life support and advanced life support personnel in the prehospital setting.

The text of the Standard is printed in black, and the commentary and its accompanying art captions, tables, and charts are printed in an easy-to-read blue ink.

CHAPTER 1

Administration

1-1 Scope

This standard identifies the levels of competence required of emergency medical services (EMS) personnel who respond to hazardous materials incidents. It specifically covers the requirements for basic life support and advanced life support personnel in the prehospital setting.

Every effort was made to ensure that the needs and operations of the various types of emergency medical services (EMS) systems were considered in developing this standard. As a result, this document can be applied to emergency medical services associated with fire departments, third services, private ambulance services, and industrial emergency medical services. The competencies described can be achieved by both career and volunteer personnel.

The standard is based on an analysis of the tasks EMS personnel perform at hazardous materials incidents. After these tasks were identified, the competencies necessary for their performance were developed. These competencies can serve as the basis for developing EMS hazardous materials training and certification programs.

After many revisions of the draft for this standard, it became apparent that EMS responders to hazardous materials incidents should be classified on two levels. To avoid confusion with the titles of other hazardous materials responders, these levels will be referred to as EMS Level I and EMS Level II.

1-2* Purpose

The purpose of this standard is to specify minimum requirements of competence and to enhance the safety and protection of response personnel and all components of the emergency medical services system. It is not the intent of this standard to restrict any jurisdiction from exceeding these minimum requirements. (*See Appendix B.*)

The primary objective of response to hazardous materials incidents is to save lives and prevent injuries of both the public and the responders. Hazardous materials incidents often involve victims who need treatment and transportation to medical facilities. The management of these EMS operations and hazardous materials patients differs from the management of other medical operations. For example, EMS personnel may have to work in protective clothing, deal with potential secondary contamination, and treat injuries or illnesses that have unfamiliar medical care protocols. This standard provides information on the knowledge and skills necessary to conduct safe and effective EMS operations.

A-1-2 The competency requirements for EMS personnel contained herein have been prepared to reduce the numbers of accidents, exposures, and injuries resulting from hazardous materials incidents.

1-3 Definitions

Advanced Life Support (ALS).

Emergency Medical Technician-Paramedic (EMT-P). An individual who has successfully completed a course of instruction that meets or exceeds the requirements of the U.S. Department of Transportation National Standard EMT-Paramedic Curriculum and who holds an EMT-P certification from the authority having jurisdiction.

Emergency Medical Technician-Intermediate (EMT-I). (This category can include EMT-Cardiac.) An individual who has completed a course of instruction that includes selected modules of the U.S. Department of Transportation

National Standard EMT-Paramedic Curriculum and who holds an intermediate level EMT-I or EMT-C certification from the authority having jurisdiction.

EMT-P and EMT-I are nationally recognized classifications of advanced life support providers. The length of their training and the procedures they perform at each level vary from state to state and sometimes from jurisdiction to jurisdiction within states. The U.S. Department of Transportation standard curricula serve as the basis for the majority of EMS training programs.

Authority Having Jurisdiction.* The organization, office, or individual responsible for approving equipment, an installation, or a procedure.

A-1-3 Authority Having Jurisdiction. The phrase "authority having jurisdiction" is used in NFPA documents in a broad manner, since jurisdictions and approval agencies vary, as do their responsibilities. Where public safety is primary, the authority having jurisdiction may be a federal, state, local, or other regional department or individual such as a fire chief; fire marshal; chief of a fire prevention bureau, labor department, or health department; building official; electrical inspector; or others having statutory authority. For insurance purposes, an insurance inspection department, rating bureau, or other insurance company representative may be the authority having jurisdiction. In many circumstances, the property owner or his or her designated agent assumes the role of the authority having jurisdiction; at government installations, the commanding officer or departmental official may be the authority having jurisdiction.

Since this document addresses the broad concept of hazardous materials, there may be many authorities exercising jurisdiction. These can include the manufacturer, the shipper, state/federal government, and the local community response authorities.

In this document, the authority having jurisdiction (AHJ) for purposes of patient care and protocols includes the local medical control authority. In some areas, the local medical control authority, rather than a regulatory agency, may be the designated AHJ.

Basic Life Support (BLS).

*Emergency Medical Technician-Ambulance (EMT-A).** An individual who has completed a specified EMT-A course developed by the U.S. Department of Transportation and who holds an EMT-A certification from the authority having jurisdiction.

*Emergency Care First Responder (ECFR).** An individual who has successfully completed the specified Emergency Care First Responder course developed by the U.S. Department of Transportation and who holds an ECFR certification from the authority having jurisdiction.

A-1-3 Basic Life Support (BLS). *Emergency Medical Technician-Ambulance (EMT-A).* This level in some jurisdictions may be recognized as EMT-Basic (EMT-B).

Emergency Care First Responder (ECFR). In Canada, the terminology used is Emergency Medical Assistant-1 (EMA-1), Emergency Medical Assistant-2 (EMA-2), and Emergency Medical Assistant-3 (EMA-3).

Cold Zone. The control zone of a hazardous materials incident that contains the command post and such other support functions as are deemed necessary to control the incident. This zone is also referred to as the clean zone or support zone in other documents.

It might appear that there is no outer boundary to the cold zone, but this is not the case. One might equate the outer boundary at a hazardous materials incident with the fire lines that are established at a major fire or other public emergency. Under most circumstances, the public at large would not have access to the cold zone.

Competence. The possession of knowledge, skills, and judgment needed to perform indicated objectives satisfactorily.

While knowledge and skills can be measured, judgment is not as easily evaluated. Nonetheless, education and training and actual experience gained in the field, or gained secondhand by studying field experiences from actual incidents, can help to improve a responder's decision-making ability. Because the outcome of an incident is determined by the decisions made by those handling the response, the need for proper and adequate training is paramount.

Components of EMS System. The parts of a comprehensive plan to treat an individual in need of emergency medical care following an illness or injury. These components include the following:

(a) First responders
(b) Emergency dispatching
(c) EMS agency response
(d) Hospital emergency departments
(e) Specialized care facilities

The provision of emergency medical care is generally a coordinated effort among personnel from several different agencies. Each will have a particular role to play in the pre-hospital care, transportation, and hospital management of those who have been exposed to hazardous materials.

Confinement. Those procedures taken to keep a material, once released, in a defined or local area.

Contaminant. A hazardous material that physically remains on or in people, animals, the environment, or equipment, thereby creating a continuing risk of direct injury or a risk of exposure.

Inherent in the definition of contaminant is the concept that the toxic or harmful material is present where it should not be and can be transmitted to other areas or persons. Injuries from contaminants may be external, such as those caused by corrosives, cryogenics, and flammable liquids; or internal, such as those caused by asphyxiate carcinogens, irritant chemicals, and poisons. Radiation exposure can cause both external and internal injury. Some substances that are harmless on their own can become hazardous materials when exposed to heat or when accidentally combined with another chemical. Early identification of the hazardous substances involved at the scene is paramount to instituting effective, appropriate treatment. When the substance is not identified, the type of injury rather than its exact cause may dictate the initial treatment offered.

Control. The procedures, techniques, and methods used in the mitigation of a hazardous materials incident, including containment, extinguishment, and confinement.

The word *control* can be used interchangeably with the word *mitigation*. Every measure taken to control a hazardous materials incident is part of the mitigation process. Limiting the degree and spread of contamination, by whatever measure, is also part of the control or mitigation process.

Control Zones. Areas at a hazardous materials incident that are designated based on safety and the degree of hazard. Many terms are used to describe the zones involved in a hazardous materials incident. For purposes of this standard, these zones shall be defined as the hot, warm, and cold zones.

Other terms commonly used include *site control zones* and *work zones*. The committee chose to use basic terms such as *hot, warm,* and *cold* because the words are simple and easily understood and they clearly suggest the nature of the situation one would expect to encounter in an area so designated.

Decontamination (Contamination Reduction). The physical and/or chemical process of reducing and preventing the spread of contamination from persons and equipment involved in a hazardous materials incident.

Broadly speaking, decontamination includes actions taken at an incident that serve to reduce or even prevent contamination of equipment or personnel at an incident. Good decontamination practices should incorporate and emphasize the notion of prevention as a first step. (Decontamination is described in detail in Chapter 7 of NFPA 471 in this handbook. In addition, a step-by-step decontamination procedure is described in Supplement 10.)

Decontamination Area. The area, usually located within the warm zone, where decontamination takes place.

The purpose of a decontamination area is to reduce the likelihood that contamination will spread to the cold zone and beyond. Therefore, the "decon area" is usually located in the warm zone (decontamination corridor) because that is the transition area between the clean, or uncontaminated, area and the hot zone. *(See Figure 1.1.)*

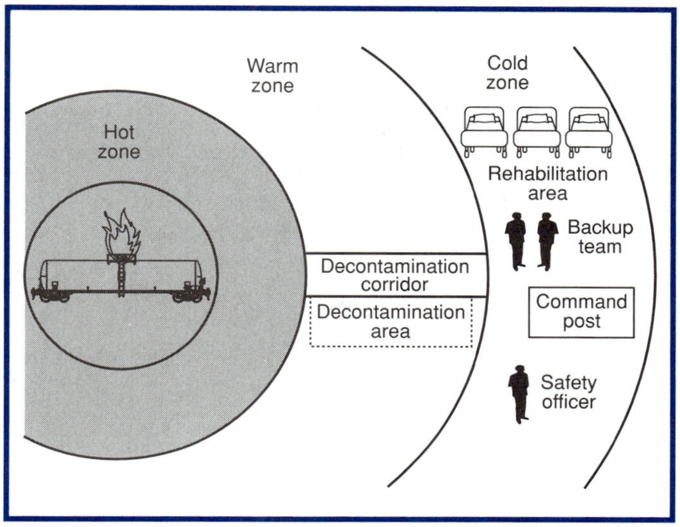

***Figure 1.1** The warm zone is known as the decontamination corridor because it is the transition area between the clean, or uncontaminated, area and the contaminated hot zone.*

Demonstrate. To show by actual performance. This performance can be supplemented by simulation, explanation, illustration, or a combination of these.

Describe. To explain verbally or in writing using standard terms recognized in the hazardous materials response community.

Gross Decontamination. The initial phase of the decontamination process during which the amount of surface contaminant is significantly reduced. This phase can include mechanical removal and initial rinsing.

Decontamination can be a multiphase process. In certain situations, only partial removal of contaminants is achieved. Gross decontamination, the first phase of the process, usually removes 80 percent to 90 percent of the contaminants. The final complete decontamination of victims would take place in a holding area established by responders.

Hazard/Hazardous. Capable of posing an unreasonable risk to health, safety, or the environment; capable of doing harm.

Hazardous Materials.* A substance (solid, liquid, or gas) capable of creating harm to people, property, and the environment.

Class/Division. The general category of hazard assigned to a hazardous material under the DOT regulations. The division is a subdivision of a hazard class.

Class 1 (Explosives)

Division 1.1—Explosives with a mass explosion hazard

Division 1.2—Explosives with a projection hazard

Division 1.3—Explosives with predominantly a fire hazard

Division 1.4—Explosives with no significant blast hazard

Division 1.5—Very insensitive explosives

Division 1.6—Extremely insensitive explosives

Class 2

Division 2.1—Flammable gas

Division 2.2—Nonflammable, nonpoisonous compressed gas

Division 2.3—Poison gas

Division 2.4—Corrosive gas (Canadian designation)

Class 3 (Flammable Liquid)

Division 3.1—Flammable liquids, flashpoint <0°F

Division 3.2—Flammable liquids, flashpoint 0°F and above but <73°F

Division 3.3—Flammable liquids, flashpoint 73°F and up to 141°F

Combustible Liquid

Class 4

Division 4.1—Flammable solid

Division 4.2—Spontaneously combustible material

Division 4.3—Dangerous when wet material

Class 5

Division 5.1—Oxidizer

Division 5.2—Organic peroxide

Class 6

Division 6.1—Poisonous material

Division 6.2—Infectious material

Class 7 (Radioactive material)

Class 8 (Corrosive material)

Class 9 (Miscellaneous hazardous material)

ORM-D material

A-1-3 Hazardous Materials. There are many definitions and descriptive names being used for the term hazardous materials, each of which depends on the nature of the problem being addressed.

Unfortunately, there is no one list or definition that covers everything. The United States agencies involved, as well as state and local governments, have different purposes for regulating hazardous materials that, under certain circumstances, pose a risk to the public or the environment.

(a) *Hazardous Materials.* The United States Department of Transportation (DOT) uses the term *hazardous materials,* which covers eight hazard classes, some of which have subcategories called classification, and a ninth class covering other regulated materials (ORM). DOT includes in its regulations hazardous substances and hazardous wastes as an ORM-E, both of which are regulated by the Environmental Protection Agency (EPA), if their inherent properties would not otherwise be covered.

(b) *Hazardous Substances.* EPA uses the term *hazardous substances* for the chemicals that, if released into the environment above a certain amount, must be reported and, depending on the threat to the environment, for which federal assistance in handling the incident can be authorized. A list of the hazardous substances is published in Title 40, *Code of Federal Regulations,* Part 302, Table 302.4.

(c) *Extremely Hazardous Substances.* EPA uses the term *extremely hazardous substances* for chemicals that must be reported to the appropriate authorities if released above the threshold reporting quantity. Each substance has a threshold reporting quantity. The list of extremely hazardous substances is identified in Title III of Superfund Amendments and Reauthorization Act (SARA) of 1986 (Title 40, *Code of Federal Regulations,* Part 355).

(d) *Toxic Chemicals.* EPA uses the term *toxic chemicals* for chemicals whose total emissions or releases must be reported annually by owners and operators of certain facilities that manufacture, process, or otherwise use a listed toxic chemical. The list of toxic chemicals is identified in Title III of SARA.

(e) *Hazardous Wastes.* EPA uses the term *hazardous wastes* for chemicals that are regulated under the Resource, Conservation and Recovery Act (Title 40, *Code of Federal Regulations,* Part 261.33). Hazardous wastes in transportation are regulated by DOT (Title 49, *Code of Federal Regulations,* Parts 170–179).

(f) *Hazardous Chemicals.* The United States Occupational Safety and Health Administration (OSHA) uses the term *hazardous chemicals* to denote any chemical that would be a risk to employees if exposed in the workplace. Hazardous chemicals cover a broader group of chemicals than the other chemical lists.

(g) *Hazardous Substances.* OSHA uses the term hazardous substances in Title 29, *Code of Federal Regulations,*

Part 1910.120, which resulted from Title I of SARA and covers emergency response. OSHA uses the term differently than EPA. Hazardous substances, as used by OSHA, cover every chemical regulated by both DOT and EPA.

Hazardous Materials Response Team. The hazardous materials response team is an organized group of trained response personnel, operating under an emergency response plan and appropriate standard operating procedures, who handle and control actual or potential leaks or spills of hazardous materials requiring possible close approach to the material. The team members respond to releases or potential releases of hazardous materials for the purpose of control or stabilization of the incident.

A hazardous materials response team may include responders from only one agency or responders from various agencies and/or disciplines. EMS providers, for example, might come from a separate organization, but they should be seamlessly integrated into the team. All members of the response team must follow a single operating procedure and have an organizational structure recognized by all of the responders. Most importantly, all of the team members must train together on a regular basis. As stated earlier, not all personnel on the team need to be trained to the same level. However, the duties and responsibilities of each member must be commensurate with his or her level of training. For example, if the incident calls for operations to control a hazardous materials release and to work in specialized chemical protective clothing, these functions should only be attempted by hazardous materials technicians or private sector specialist employees Level A.

High Temperature-Protective Clothing. Protective clothing designed to protect the wearer from short-term high temperature exposures. This type of clothing is usually of limited use in dealing with chemical commodities.

Specialized high temperature clothing is designed to provide protection from convective and conductive heat, in accordance with the performance requirements in NFPA 1971, *Standard on Protective Ensemble for Structural Fire Fighting,*[1] and from high levels of radiant heat for limited exposures. NFPA 1976, *Standard on Protective Clothing for Proximity Fire Fighting,*[2] provides performance criteria for proximity suits. These suits include a one- or two-piece overgarment with hood, gloves, and, often, boot covers of an aluminized or cotton fabric. Fire entry suits are a specialized protective clothing type designed to protect the wearer against abnormally high temperatures for a brief exposure of two or three minutes.

Hot Zone. The area immediately surrounding a hazardous materials incident, which extends far enough to prevent adverse effects from hazardous materials releases to personnel outside the zone. This zone is also referred to as the exclusion zone or restricted zone in other documents.

The hot zone is the area where contamination does or could take place. It is also the area where cleanup operations are performed. The boundary between the hot zone and the warm zone should be clearly indicated by some physical means, such as lines, hazard tape, or equipment barriers. Movement of personnel from one zone to another must be tightly regulated and supervised to minimize contamination. The designation and monitoring of access points allows for greater control of movement from zone to zone. *(See Figure 1.2.)*

Identify. To select or indicate verbally or in writing using standard terms to establish the identity of; the fact of being the same as the one described.

Incident. An emergency involving the release or potential release of a hazardous material, with or without fire.

There is a wide difference of opinion as to what constitutes a hazardous materials incident when fire is involved. At one extreme are those who would like to categorize every fire as a hazardous materials incident because every fire produces toxic products of combustion that are clearly hazardous. A second, and more

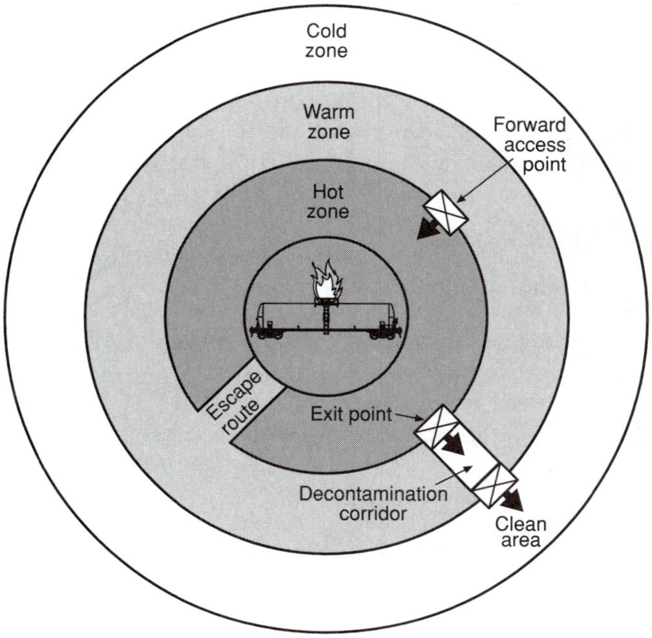

***Figure 1.2** Movement of personnel from one zone to another must be tightly regulated and supervised to minimize contamination. The designation and oversight of access points allows for greater control of movement from zone to zone.*

preferred, approach is to limit the definition to the actual involvement in fire of a recognized hazardous material, such as gasoline.

Frequently, however, the line between the two positions is blurred. Is a fire in a fuel storage tank a fire, or should it be classified as a hazardous materials incident? The answer may vary from one agency to another. A fire department might list it as a fire, for example, while an environmental agency might see it as a hazardous materials incident. Several other examples can be used to illustrate the problem, which should not be taken lightly. There are many more complicating factors involved in operating at a designated hazardous materials incident than there are in operating at a fire. If the incident involves hazardous materials, for example, then the regulatory rules of OSHA and EPA must be followed.

Incident Commander. The person responsible for all decisions relating to the management of the incident. The incident commander is in charge of the incident site. This term is equivalent to the on-scene incident commander.

The incident commander is responsible for the overall control of operations. Where multiple agencies are likely to be involved (generally the case when hazardous materials are involved), the roles and responsibilities of the various agencies should be clarified ahead of time. At the scene, the actual command may change from one person to another as the incident develops and becomes more complex. Some incident management systems provide for a "unified command" when multiple agencies are involved. How the system is structured is less important than the fact that there is a system for command and control, that everyone involved is aware of their role, and that training exercises have been conducted to work out any problems.

See NFPA 472, Chapter 5, in this handbook for more detail on incident command structure.

Incident Management System. An organized system of roles, responsibilities, and standard operating procedures used to manage emergency operations, as described in NFPA 1561, *Standard on Fire Department Incident Management System*. Such systems are often referred to as "Incident Command Systems."

An effective incident management system is one of the most important aspects of operating safely during an emergency. NFPA 1561, *Standard on Fire Department Incident Management System,*[3] provides an excellent guide for developing an effective incident management system and clearly addresses the components that must be included for personnel to operate at an incident in an organized and safe manner.

Local Area. A geographic area that includes the defined response area and receiving facilities for an EMS agency.

An EMS system is an organization or group of agencies that provides emergency medical services within a defined geographic area. This area may be a single municipality, or it may include several municipalities or an entire county or region. For the purposes of this document, the term *local area* can be used to refer to both the recognized response area and mutual assistance areas.

Local Emergency Planning Committee (LEPC). (As mandated by SARA Title III.) Includes elected state and local officials, police, fire, civil defense, public health professionals, environmental, hospital, and transportation officials as well as representatives of facilities, community groups, and the media.

The LEPC must develop and maintain a current hazardous materials response plan for the area it covers. This plan designates the responsibilities that EMS personnel are to undertake during hazardous materials emergencies.

Medical Control. The physician providing direction for patient care activities in the prehospital setting.

The medical control physician in charge can be at the scene or can direct EMS responders at the scene by radio or other means of communication. Medical control protocol can also be written in advance to be followed at the scene by first responders. Written medical control protocol can be superseded by actual contact with the medical control as the incident unfolds.

Medical Surveillance. The ongoing process of medical evaluation of hazardous materials response team members and public safety personnel who respond to a hazardous materials incident.

Objective. A goal that is achieved through the attainment of a skill, knowledge, or both, that can be observed or measured.

Personal Protective Equipment. The equipment provided to shield or isolate a person from the chemical, physical, and thermal hazards that can be encountered at a hazardous materials incident. Personal protective equipment includes both personal protective clothing and respiratory protection. Adequate personal protective equipment should protect the respiratory system, skin, eyes, face, hands, feet, head, body, and hearing.

The purpose of personal protective equipment is to protect the responder from anticipated hazards at the scene. Although protective equipment has improved substantially in recent years, the nature of the hazards to which emergency personnel must respond has become much more complex. Responders must be adequately trained to use, care for, and select appropriate personal protective equipment. Protective equipment will not prevent injuries or illness if improperly used.

See NFPA 471 and NFPA 472 and Supplement 3 of this handbook for more information on the selection and care of protective clothing.

Protective Clothing. Equipment designed to protect the wearer from the heat and/or hazardous materials that might contact the skin or eyes. Protective clothing is divided into the following three types:

(a) Chemical-protective clothing

1. Liquid splash-protective clothing
2. Vapor-protective clothing

(b) High temperature-protective clothing
(c) Structural fire fighting protective clothing

Protocol. A series of sequential steps describing the precise patient treatment.

Region. A geographic area that includes the local and neighboring jurisdiction for an EMS agency.

Respiratory Protection. Equipment designed to protect the wearer from the inhalation of contaminants. Respiratory protection is divided into the following three types:

(a) Positive pressure self-contained breathing apparatus
(b) Positive pressure air line respirators
(c) Air purifying respirators

Inhaling toxic gases and other airborne contaminants is a principal cause of serious injury to responders; therefore respiratory protection at the scene of a hazardous materials incident is of the utmost importance.

A positive pressure self-contained breathing apparatus (SCBA) has positive pressure inside the facepiece during both inhalation and exhalation. SCBA are respirators that supply a breathable atmosphere that is either carried in or generated by the apparatus and is independent of the ambient environment.

A positive pressure air line respirator supplies air in positive pressure, during both inhalation and exhalation, from a source located at some distance from the user and connected to the user by an air line hose.

An air purifying respirator does not have a separate air supply; rather, it passes ambient air through a filtering device before the user inhales it. These respirators are designed and tested for specific agent(s) and must not be worn in areas with low oxygen content.

See NFPA 471, Chapter 5, in this handbook for additional information.

Safely. To perform the objective without injury to self or others, property, or the environment.

Secondary Contamination.* The transfer of contaminants to personnel or equipment outside the hot zone.

A-1-3 Secondary Contamination. A substance is considered to pose a serious risk of secondary contamination if it is likely to be carried on equipment, clothing, skin, or hair in sufficient quantities to be capable of harming personnel outside of the hot zone.

Shall. Indicates a mandatory requirement.

Should. Indicates a recommendation or that which is advised but not required.

Termination. That portion of incident management in which personnel are involved in documenting safety procedures, site operations, hazards faced, and lessons learned from the incident. Termination is divided into three phases: debriefing the incident, post-incident analysis, and critiquing the incident.

Debriefing the incident involves collecting all the pertinent information regarding the nature of the incident and all the emergency actions and operations performed at the scene. The collected information is then evaluated in a post-incident analysis. Critiquing an incident provides all responders with an opportunity to review the valuable "lessons learned" in a specific incident to enhance the success of future hazardous materials operations.

Understanding. The process of gaining or developing the meaning of various types of materials or knowledge.

Warm Zone. The area where personnel and equipment decontamination and hot zone support takes place. It includes control points for access corridor and thus assists in reducing the spread of contamination. This is also referred to as the decontamination, contamination reduction, or limited access zone in other documents.

One purpose of the warm zone is to reduce the likelihood of contaminating the cold zone and beyond. Persons entering the warm zone from the cold zone must wear appropriate personal protective equipment.

A decontamination corridor within the warm zone is a defined path between the hot zone and the cold zone where personnel and equipment are decontaminated. At very large incidents, several access corridors may be needed. The access corridors must be tightly controlled and supervised to regulate movement between the zones. *(See Figures 1.3(a) and 1.3(b).)*

Figure 1.3(a) *At a recent chemical incident caused by terrorists at B'nai Brith headquarters in Washington, DC, the decon corridor (shown at top center) in the warm zone and the cold zone (in the foreground) are clearly visible. (Photo by Susan Walsh/AP Worldwide)*

Figure 1.3(b) *A plastic curtain offers some privacy for the 113 office workers who had to be decontaminated at a terrorist incident in Washington, DC. Two workers became ill during the incident. (Photo by Susan Walsh/AP Worldwide)*

References Cited in Commentary

1. NFPA 1971, *Standard on Protective Ensemble for Structural Fire Fighting,* National Fire Protection Association, Quincy, MA, 1997.
2. NFPA 1976, *Standard on Protective Clothing for Proximity Fire Fighting,* National Fire Protection Association, Quincy, MA, 1992.
3. NFPA 1561, *Standard on Fire Department Incident Management System,* National Fire Protection Association, Quincy, MA, 1995.

CHAPTER 2

Competencies for EMS/HM Level I Responders

2-1 General

2-1.1 Introduction.

All EMS personnel at EMS/HM Level I, in addition to their BLS or ALS certification, shall be trained to meet at least the first responder awareness level as defined in NFPA 472, *Standard for Professional Competence of Responders to Hazardous Materials Incidents*, and all competencies of this chapter.

2-1.2* Definition.

EMS personnel at EMS/HM Level I are those persons who, in the course of their normal duties, might be called on to perform patient care activities in the cold zone at a hazardous materials incident. EMS/HM Level I responders shall provide care only to those individuals who no longer pose a significant risk of secondary contamination.

A-2-1.2 See Appendix D.

Unlike the EMS Level II responders (defined in Chapter 1 and further described in Chapter 3), EMS/HM Level I responders work only in the cold zone during a hazardous materials incident. These workers do not don chemical-protective clothing and respiratory equipment. Ideally, before reaching EMS/HM Level I responders, victims will have undergone "field decontamination" and have a reduced risk of passing contaminants on to others.

2-1.3 Goal.

The goal of the competencies at EMS/HM Level I shall be to provide the individual with the knowledge and skills necessary to safely deliver emergency medical care in the cold zone. Therefore the EMS/HM Level I responder shall be able to:

Hazardous materials incidents differ from other situations in which EMS personnel provide patient care in the following ways:

(a) These situations require greater coordination with other response personnel;
(b) The EMS provider does not effect rescue (unless he or she is also a Hazardous Materials Technician); and
(c) The incident generally takes considerably more time than most incidents to which EMS personnel respond because of the time needed to decontaminate the patient and protect the transport vehicle and EMS personnel from secondary contamination.

All these factors are contrary to the usual practice of EMS providers. For example, in most situations rapid treatment and transportation is emphasized. In hazardous materials incidents, it takes time to rescue the patient from the hot zone (hazardous materials rescuers' response times are generally longer and they must don a Level A vapor protection suit and self-contained breathing apparatus before entering the hot zone), to decontaminate the patient, and to transfer the patient from the rescuer to the EMS provider. EMS providers may find the waiting or their inability to effect rescue personally stressful. Once an individual is contaminated, however, he or she can contaminate others, so field stabilization of a patient within the hot zone by hazardous materials technicians should take place before patient care is begun in the cold zone.

(a) Analyze a hazardous materials emergency to determine what risks are present to the provider and the patient by completing the following tasks:

Sometimes, when EMS workers arrive at a scene, the hazardous material has still not been fully identified. Patient decontamination and treatment by workers in the hot and warm zones is then likely to be aimed at a general kind of hazard class, based on signs and symptoms observed at the scene and circumstances of the incident reported by witnesses and foreseen by the hazardous materials incident plan for that site. Workers in the cold zone will need to evaluate each arriving victim to ensure that decontamination efforts in the hot and warm zones have been successful and that secondary decontamination is not a factor.

1. Determine the hazards present to the Level I responder and the patient in a hazardous materials incident

The responder must be able to determine from clues presented during dispatch, response, and approach whether a hazardous material is present at the scene and whether that product poses a risk to the patient and, in turn, the responder. Operators or witnesses, placards, the normal occupancy of the building at the scene (such as a chemical storage building), the type of containers involved, and the presence of fires or explosions are a few typical indicators of the presence of a hazardous material.

2. Assess the patient to determine the risk of secondary contamination

Patients exposed to a hazardous material may pose a risk of secondary contamination to others who come in contact with them. From their knowledge of toxic exposure, patient assessment and treatment, and decontamination procedures, responders must be able to determine what actions are necessary to prepare patients to be treated and transported safely. In many cases, treatment will have to wait until the hazardous materials technicians decontaminate and transfer the victim to the cold zone.

(b) Plan a response to provide the appropriate level of emergency medical care to persons involved in hazardous materials incidents by completing the following tasks:

Once responders have determined that there is a risk of hazardous materials involvement, they must be able to plan the actions necessary to request the help needed to rescue, decontaminate, care for, and transport the hazardous materials victim. The plan should also identify the level of protection for EMS personnel, preparation of supplies and vehicles for transport, and level of prehospital treatment. This EMS plan becomes one part of the overall plan prepared by the hazardous materials technician or incident commander. The current medical protocols and/or the input from medical control should be the foundation for the medical treatment part of the plan.

1. Describe the role of the Level I responder in a hazardous materials incident

This standard cautions against overstepping an individual's level of responsibility as assigned in the EMS response plan. To be most effective and safe, Level I responders must clearly understand their duties and responsibilities as a part of a planned response to a hazardous materials incident in the community and how their responsibilities mesh within the framework of the overall plan for medical services.

2. Plan a response to provide the appropriate level of emergency medical care in a hazardous materials incident

To ensure that patients exposed to hazardous materials receive the appropriate care, the Level I responder must know the procedures for acquiring the needed information to treat patients with specific exposures. The responder who is familiar with treatment procedures will have all the necessary supplies and equipment ready to safely assess, care for, and transport the patient.

3. Determine if the personal protective equipment provided is appropriate

Responders at this level have a very limited ability to protect themselves from the risks of exposure. Their clothing will provide only limited splash protection to the skin and offer very little respiratory protection. This knowledge should convince responders to make sure they know what decontamination procedures must be performed so that they are not exposed or contaminated.

4. Determine if the equipment and supplies provided are adequate

Certain supplies and equipment must be available on the ambulance *(see Table 2.1)* to care for the victim of a hazardous materials exposure. The Level I responder must be able to evaluate the situation and the patient's condition and determine specifically what is needed to care for the patient on the scene and during transport. If the responder determines that the supplies and equipment are inadequate, he or she must know how to request additional resources quickly.

The various supply and equipment needs of EMS/HM Level I responders for each incident type anticipated should be listed in the EMS plan. Ideally, such a plan should be available to those at the scene along with check lists and blank patient record forms. Workers at the scene should also be able to request additional assistance or equipment as necessary once more information becomes available and individual patient needs can be considered.

(c) Implement the planned response by completing the following tasks:

The responders' ability to analyze and plan the response will determine how effectively they will treat

Table 2.1 EMS Vehicle Equipment for Hazardous Materials Incidents

- Binoculars to assess scene from a safe distance.
- Plastic, preferably clear, trash bags (3 mil or 4 mil) to isolate and dispose of contaminated articles and toxic vomitus.
- Plastic sheeting to cover floor of ambulance in the rare case where a contaminated victim must be transported, or if the victim might vomit ingested toxic material.
- A large supply of oxygen to treat breathing problems caused by exposure to hazardous materials (more than is usually carried).
- A large washbasin, bucket, or plastic wastebasket which can be lined with a trash bag to collect contaminated eye wash water or vomitus.
- Disposable plastic-coated blankets (or "chucks") to soak up and isolate liquids from a decontaminated patient. Use these for absorbing toxic vomitus.
- Disposable gowns and slippers for patients who must remove contaminated clothes at the scene and for EMS personnel (long sleeve gowns) to cover outer clothes.
- Disposable surgical or examination gloves.
- Surgical or other paper masks.
- Waterproof disposable shoe covers.
- Splash goggles or face shields to protect EMS personnel from splashes while they work on the patient.
- Inexpensive stethoscopes, blood pressure cuffs, and other gear which can be discarded if contaminated.
- Isotonic saline and IV tubing for eye irrigation.
- A bag valve mask (BVM) or similar device in lieu of mouth-to-mouth respiration. (Pocket masks are NOT acceptable.)
- Liquid soap for washing off oily contaminants.
- Epsom salts for soaking hydrofluoric acid burns.
- Shears or sharp knife for removing clothing from victim.
- Copy of the *1996 North American Emergency Response Guidebook*, published by the U.S. Department of Transportation, a copy of these protocols, and other appropriate medical management protocols.

Source: Based on a list prepared by the Contra Costa/Solano County Joint Emergency Medical Services Hazardous Materials Response Program.[1]

and transport the patient(s). It is vital that care be taken in preparing the patient, not only to minimize the risk of secondary contamination to the responder, but also to minimize the amount of effort needed to decontaminate personnel and equipment after the incident.

1. Perform the necessary preparations for receiving the hazardous materials patient and preventing secondary contamination

Preparing to receive a hazardous materials patient is quite different from routine EMS actions. These preparations are time consuming, but they are done while other personnel on the scene prepare to rescue, evacuate, and decontaminate the patient. Adequate preparation of the personnel and the ambulance or transporting vehicle generally takes 20 to 30 minutes. Some hazardous materials teams keep one or more reserve ambulances completely stripped of all equipment to be used to transport victims of hazardous materials incidents. *(See Figure 2.1.)*

2. Treat the hazardous materials patient

Assessment and treatment of a hazardous materials victim will depend on numerous factors associated with the incident, the exposure, and the patient's condition. These factors include the following:

(a) The contaminating substance

***Figure 2.1** Ambulances should be specially prepared for transporting contaminated patients. Otherwise, expensive medical equipment that becomes contaminated may have to be disposed.*

(b) The duration of contamination
(c) Additional patient injuries or medical concerns (such as a heart condition, allergic reactions, or other chronic health conditions)

Most basic patient assessment techniques rely on the responder's senses of sight, touch, hearing, and smell. Unfortunately, personal protective equipment worn by the Level I EMS/HM responder, such as chemical splash protection suits and gloves, can diminish these senses and hinder the responder's ability to assess a patient's condition. Because contaminants may remain on the patient, responders may also have to alter their treatment procedures. Care during transport will primarily be supportive according to the patient's symptoms.

3. Transport the patient as appropriate

The normal protocol for notifying the health care facility should be used to ensure that the facility personnel are prepared and that they will be able to treat the hazardous materials patient. Selecting the appropriate vehicle in which to transport the patient or patients to that health care facility is important not only to the victim, but also to the emergency services in the response area. Communities in many parts of the country have a limited number of ambulances. Since a hazardous materials incident will require a lengthy time commitment, the responder must be aware of any alternate means of transportation that can be safely used for patients. Alternatives may include other emergency response units, such as command vehicles or reserve ambulances, and buses for multiple victims.

Some EMS providers and hazardous materials response teams keep reserve ambulances that are stripped of all equipment for the specific use of transporting contaminated patients. Generally, medical equipment and supplies used on an ambulance cannot be decontaminated and would otherwise have to be discarded.

Equally important to how a patient will be transported is determining which facility will receive the patient. With the guidance of the community plan, medical control will coordinate where each patient will be taken. For some large-scale incidents, medical control will notify the EMS hazardous materials branch of the capacity of each facility and a triage system will dispatch each patient to the appropriate facility. In some jurisdictions, specialty facilities will be assigned to handle hazardous materials victims, while other jurisdictions will allow all hospitals and medical care facilities to receive and treat these patients. The Joint Commission on the Accreditation of Healthcare Organizations (JCAHO) requires hospitals to have the equipment necessary to care for victims of chemical exposures. The JCAHO standards have been in place for a number of years; however, their existence does not ensure that a hospital's equipment or treatment will be adequate. Prehospital providers must get to know the medical facilities in their communities, and the best way to do this is to communicate with personnel at the facility before an incident occurs and to test the hospital's capabilities along with their own.

(d) Terminate the incident

Post-incident, or terminating, activities are especially important in hazardous materials incidents because each incident is unique. Post-incident activities generally include the following:

(a) Assisting in the debriefing
(b) Participating in the incident critique
(c) Completing all reports and narrative of actions taken

The best time to complete reports and document actions is as soon as possible after finishing the incident. These tend to be the most accurate and complete reports. If an appreciable amount of time passes before the reports are finished, many of the details may be lost from the responder's memory. Responders must recognize that post-incident activities are important not only to them but to patient follow-up and successful management of future incidents, as well.

2-2 Competencies—Analyzing the Hazardous Materials Incident

2-2.1

Given an emergency involving hazardous materials, the Level I responder shall determine the hazards to the responder and the patient in that situation. The Level I responder shall be able to:

Once EMS/HM Level I responders realize that an incident involves a hazardous material, they must be able to evaluate the conditions of the incident and the environment, know what resources are available to help assess and evaluate the risk, and interpret the information obtained from medical resources.

(a) Assess the nature and severity of the incident (size-up) as they pertain to EMS responsibilities at a hazardous materials incident with evaluation of available resources and a request for any needed assistance

For EMS responders, "size-up" consists not only of the observations they make that will help them determine the nature and severity of the incident, but also of the factors pertinent to EMS operations such as number, location, and potential injuries of victims. Many of these observations can be completed from a safe distance using binoculars.

Assessing the severity of the incident begins at dispatch. It is vital that dispatchers screen all calls carefully to obtain any information that may indicate whether a hazardous material is involved in an incident. Dispatchers should follow protocols that include questions that will allow them to gather the appropriate information.

Some incidents are actually dispatched as hazardous materials incidents. When this occurs, the EMS responder can research the product en route to assess the risk it presents. More often, however, responders are not aware that a hazardous material is involved until they reach the scene or sometime after their initial arrival. *(See 2-2.1 of NFPA 472 concerning detecting the presence of hazardous materials at the first responder awareness level.)* Any call to a high-risk occupancy or location such as a garden shop or plant nursery, farm fertilizer storage, pool equipment store, or chemical plant should immediately arouse the responder's suspicions. Responders should also suspect potential hazardous materials involvement at any truck or train accident in which cargo is spilled or disturbed.

Certain types of dispatches should automatically alert the EMS responder to the possibility that a hazardous material may be the cause of a patient's distress. These include "unconscious person" and "trouble breathing" calls and calls that involve several patients with the same problem. These situations are frequently caused by a product in the environment that may also pose a danger to the responder.

EMS responders should carry the current edition of *North American Emergency Response Guidebook*[2] and a pair of binoculars in their ambulances, at the very least. When responders suspect a hazardous material, they can use the binoculars to make observations from a safe distance, preferably up-wind, and refer to the NAERG to identify the product involved and assess the danger it presents. These techniques are taught at the first responder awareness level.

(b) Evaluate the environmental factors as they affect patient care

Environmental factors must be considered for two reasons. First, the physical environment of the area in which the incident occurs may determine to some extent the severity of the exposure. If the exposure occurs in an open area, for example, the product will disperse and its effects on the patient will not be as severe as they would have been if the exposure had occurred in an enclosed area. Second, the weather may have an impact. For example, when it is cold and a protected decontamination area is not available, decontamination procedures may cause injuries from cold-weather exposures.

(c) Identify the information resources available and how to access the following:

1. Poison Control Center

Responders can call poison control centers directly from the scene, go through medical control, or rely on the incident command to acquire the medical information, depending on the local plan. Poison control centers can provide detailed information regarding a patient's symptoms and the prescribed treatment. Often, poison control centers will coordinate the flow of medical information between the field and the receiving hospital.

Not all poison control centers have the same capabilities. EMS personnel are advised to coordinate with their local and regional poison control centers in the planning stage so that they will be able to support the field personnel during an incident.

2. Medical control
3. Material safety data sheets
4. Reference guidebooks

Not only should ambulances carry the latest edition of the *North American Emergency Response Guidebook,* they should also carry EMS hazardous materials guides such as the following for reference:

(a) *Emergency Care for Hazardous Materials Exposure,* by Bronstein and Currance[3]
(b) *Hazardous Materials Injuries: A Handbook for Pre-Hospital Care,* by Stutz et al.[4]

These reference books are designed to provide access to general guidelines on subjects such as potential hazards, protective clothing, handling fires, evacuation, and medical advice. In most cases, more specific guidance and chemical information will be needed to enter the hot zone and mitigate the incident.

5. Hazardous materials data bases

Several hazardous materials data bases currently available on computer provide detailed health and treatment information. If these data bases are not available at the scene, responders may call poison control and other such centers for the information. Examples of hazardous materials data bases include MEDITEXT, OHMTATDS, TOMAS, and TOXNET.

6. Technical information centers (CHEMTREC, NRC, etc.)
7. Technical specialists

EMS personnel should be able to consult, either directly or through their communications center, with a chemist, an occupational health specialist, or some other individual who can give them the information they need to care for patients on the scene. These technical specialists may also prove valuable at the hospital, where the patient may have to undergo more definitive treatment. Lists of technical specialists should be developed during the planning of hazardous materials responses and be accessible during emergency incidents.

8. Agency for Toxic Substances and Disease Registry (ATSDR)

Responders can reach the Agency for Toxic Substances and Disease Registry (ATSDR) 24 hours a day. These contacts should be made by, or through, the EMS branch command or the incident commander. ATSDR will provide health-related support, including on-site assistance if necessary, in hazardous materials emergencies.

(d) Given a pesticide label, identify and explain the significance of the following:

1. Name of pesticide
2. Signal word
3. EPA registration number
4. Precautionary statement
5. Hazard statement
6. Active ingredient

Seeing containers such as barrels or other types of packages with warning labels at an incident site should alert responders to the type of contamination to which a patient has been exposed. EMS personnel must understand the significance of the various parts of a container label to help identify the specific type of hazardous material.

A pesticide label, for example, can provide valuable information to EMS personnel. The name of the pesticide is usually displayed prominently on the label. Also displayed are signal words. The primary signal words used are "DANGER" and "WARNING." "DANGER," accompanied by a skull and crossbones and the word "POISON" printed in red, indicates highly toxic pesticides. "WARNING" indicates moderately toxic pesticides. The word "CAUTION" is used to identify low-toxicity materials.

The product's EPA registration number is usually printed in smaller letters on the front of the package label. Like the product name, the number ensures positive identification of the pesticide. When seeking additional expert advice, the responder must know the product name, its chemical or common name, or the EPA registration number.

Precautionary statements indicating the dangers the product presents to humans, animals, and the environment also appear on the label. The hazards statement lists the physical and chemical hazards of the substance and its ingredients, which are described as active or inert. Active ingredients must be listed by their chemical names; a common name is sometimes also listed.

Whenever possible, the label and the container should be properly wrapped and taken to the hospital or to an isolated area where the responder can access the information displayed on them.

2-2.2

Given a hazardous materials incident with a patient(s), the Level I responder shall determine the risk of secondary contamination. The Level I responder shall be able to:

Assessing a patient to determine the risk of secondary contamination will involve analysis of the patient's exposure to the product. The responder will have to determine the type of exposure, how much of the product the patient was exposed to, how many times the exposure occurred, and how long ago the exposure occurred.

Assessment will also include determining how much decontamination must be done to lower the risk of secondary contamination.

(a) Explain the basic toxicological principles relative to assessment and treatment of victims exposed to hazardous materials, including the following:

To determine the risk to both patient and rescuer, the EMS care provider must understand some basic toxicological principles.

1. Acute and delayed toxicity

Acute toxicity refers to the sudden, severe onset of symptoms due to an exposure. The effects of delayed toxicity may not develop for hours or longer after an exposure; in some instances, such as biological exposures, symptoms may not appear until three or more days after the exposure.

2. Routes of exposure to toxic materials

The routes of exposure, sometimes referred to as routes of entry, include the following:

(a) *Inhalation.* The process by which irritants or toxins enter the body through the nose, mouth, and lungs as a result of the respiratory process.
(b) *Ingestion.* The process of consuming contaminated food or water.
(c) *Absorption.* The process by which hazardous materials are absorbed into the body through the skin.

(d) *Injection.* The process by which a toxic substance is introduced directly into the blood by a needle, cannula or some other mechanical means. Contaminants entering the bloodstream through an open wound can be considered to be injected.

3. Local and systemic effects

Local effects are those in which a toxic substance comes in direct contact with the skin or other tissue. Systemic effects are the effects a toxic product has on either the entire body or on a specific system or organ.

4. Dose response as it relates to risk assessment

The chemical, biological, or radiological dose relationship refers to the response produced in the human body. It is a cause/effect relationship. The magnitude of the body's response will depend on the concentration and duration at the site, the concentration of the material itself, and the dose administered.

5.* Synergistic effects

A-2-2.2(a)5 As defined in Webster's Dictionary, the word *synergism* means "a cooperative action of discrete agencies such that the total effect is greater than the sum of the effects taken independently." In the context of hazardous materials, it is important to remember that the signs and symptoms of a given chemical are generally standard for that particular chemical. But when two or more chemicals are involved, the resultant signs and symptoms from an exposure may be dramatically different than what the EMS provider anticipates.

6. Health hazard as determined by assessing toxicity, exposure, and dose

Toxicity, exposure, and dose must all be analyzed to understand the risk a product will have on both the patient and the rescuer.

(b) Describe how the chemical contamination of patients alters the principles of triage in hazardous materials incidents

The hazardous materials entry team begins the initial triage of patients in the hot zone. Because time and resources are generally limited, patients are not triaged in the normal method. Ambulatory patients usually walk to the patient holding and/or decontamination area by themselves, while nonambulatory patients are removed from the hot zone based on the seriousness of their injuries and their location. The first patients removed are usually the first encountered. Once the patients are in the decontamination area, the amount of contamination they have suffered and their condition will determine the extent of decontamination performed. Actual medical triage is not performed until the patients have been transferred from the decontamination area to the cold zone.

(c) Explain the need for patient decontamination procedures at hazardous materials incidents

Patients must be decontaminated at the site of the hazardous materials incident to reduce their exposure to the hazardous material and to reduce the chance of secondary contamination of emergency response personnel, including the EMS provider. It must also be done to prevent the spread of contaminants to other areas and personnel. Decontamination activities are normally performed by hazardous materials technicians. In some cases, first responders at the operations level will complete decontamination of victims under the supervision of a technician. The location of the decontamination area and the duration of the decontamination procedures depend on various factors, such as the incident, the chemical, and the patient's condition.

(d) Describe how the potential for secondary contamination determines the extent of patient decontamination required

A great many chemicals are extremely toxic only in the high concentrations found in the immediate exposure area, but pose little or no risk to those outside the hot zone. Alternatively, some small amounts of specific chemicals may produce relatively little acute toxicity immediately, but are suspected of causing long-term problems such as cancer or other chronic diseases and are thus considered to pose a greater risk of secondary contamination. These factors must be considered when analyzing the potential for secondary contamination and the extent to which a patient must be decontaminated. Patients exposed to substances that pose little or no risk to persons outside the hot zone will require decontamination only to remove the substance. Those who have been exposed to substances that pose a risk of secondary contamination will have to undergo a more thorough decontamination process. Contaminants that cannot be removed must be contained to protect the rescuers.

(e) Describe the way that personnel, personal protective clothing, apparatus, tools, and equipment become contaminated and the importance and limitations of decontamination procedures

Personnel, personal protective clothing, apparatus, tools, and equipment may become contaminated if they come in direct contact with hazardous substances or with the run-off from water used to extinguish a fire, smoke, or vapors associated with hazardous materials incidents. These contaminants must be removed as soon as possible to keep them from injuring those who use these items. Decontamination is the time-consuming, labor-intensive process of removing such contaminants using various methods and solutions. One of the problems with decontamination is that the contaminating substances often cannot be seen, making it difficult to determine when they have been removed. In some cases, hazardous materials response teams are equipped with monitoring instruments that technicians can use to detect contaminants.

(f) Explain the decontamination procedures as defined by the authority having jurisdiction for patients, personnel, personal protective equipment, and apparatus at hazardous materials incidents

Each jurisdiction should develop separate procedures for decontaminating personnel, patients, equipment, and apparatus. It is important that EMS/HM Level I responders be familiar with all of these procedures so that they understand the decontamination process their patients will undergo and the process they themselves will have to undergo should they become contaminated.

2-3 Competencies—Planning the Response

2-3.1

Given a plan of action by the incident commander, the Level I responder shall describe their role in a hazardous materials incident as identified in the local emergency response plan or organization's standard operating procedures, including the following:

Level I responders must understand their local emergency response plan and their own organization's standard operating procedures for a hazardous materials incident. It is vital that these responders understand their roles and responsibilities so that there is no confusion when they are given a plan of action by an incident commander. Supplement 11 offers one example of medical standard operating procedures for a hazardous materials incident. As a test, Level I responders may want to compare their roles in their departments' standard operating procedures with that described in the supplement.

(a) Describe the emergency medical component for the hazardous materials incident response plan as developed by the authority having jurisdiction

The hazardous materials incident response plan developed by the authority having jurisdiction should do the following:

(a) Detail the responsibilities of the EMS response agencies
(b) Detail the role of the various levels of EMS responders
(c) Identify where EMS falls in the incident command structure
(d) List the interactions required of EMS with other agencies on the scene
(e) Describe the relationship between the prehospital and the hospital component in caring for chemically contaminated patients

(b) State the Level I responder's role within the hazardous materials response plan as developed by the authority having jurisdiction

The local hazardous materials response plan developed by the authorities having jurisdiction should define the EMS Level I responder's role as being the patient care provider in the cold zone.

(c) State the Level I responder's role within the hazardous materials incident management system

Level I responders should be assigned a role within the treatment, triage, or transportation branches of the hazardous materials incident management system. They will function in these sectors in the cold zone, providing patient care.

2-3.2

Given a hazardous materials incident, the Level I responder shall be able to plan a response to provide the appropriate level of emergency medical care, including the standard operating procedures for the medical management of persons exposed to hazardous materials, as specified by the authority having jurisdiction.

If they understand their roles in a hazardous materials response, Level I responders working at an incident or participating in a simulation should be able to develop a plan for patient care specific to that incident. Local jurisdictions should develop standard operating procedures for the medical management of persons exposed to hazardous materials. These procedures should include the following:

(a) Assessment of the hazardous materials victim
(b) Treatment
(c) Communications
(d) Transportation (including mode of transport and hospital determination)

Supplement 9 provides a sample of a plan that includes these considerations.

2-3.3

Given the name of the hazardous material and the type, duration, and extent of exposure and decontamination process, the Level I responder shall determine if available personal protective clothing and equipment are appropriate to implement the planned response. The Level I responder shall be able to:

Using the information available on the hazardous material involved in an incident, EMS/HM Level I responders should be able to determine whether their personal protective clothing will provide them with the protection required in accordance with their standard operating procedures.

(a) Describe the application, use, and limitations of the following:

1. Street clothing and work uniforms

Street clothing and work uniforms provide the least, if any, protection against hazardous materials exposures.

2. Structural fire fighting protective clothing

Structural fire fighting protective clothing is designed to protect fire fighters against adverse environmental conditions during structural fire fighting. These conditions include high temperatures, steam, hot water, and falling objects. This type of protective clothing is not designed for most hazardous materials exposures and will provide only limited protection from exposure in some cases and none at all in others.

3. Respiratory protective equipment

The most commonly available types of respiratory protection equipment include the following:

(a) Positive pressure SCBA, which can be used in a toxic atmosphere if the air supply lasts long enough to complete the assignment. Its disadvantages include its weight, limited duration, and bulk, which may interfere with performance.
(b) Positive pressure supplied air line respirators that provide a long duration of air and are lightweight, provided the hose does not impair the responder's mobility and is limited to 300 feet (91.5 m) and the air line is not damaged or obstructed.
(c) Air purifying respirators, which can be used with certain gases and vapors if the specific product is known. They should not be the respirator of choice where the following conditions exist:

1. Oxygen deficiency
2. IDLH concentrations of a specific substance
3. Entry into unventilated or confined spaces
4. Presence or potential presence of unidentified contaminants
5. Contaminant concentrations are unknown or exceed designated maximum use concentrations
6. Identified gases or vapors have inadequate warning properties

4. Chemical-protective clothing

Chemical-protective clothing is designed to protect the wearer's skin and eyes from direct chemical contact; most chemical-protective clothing will not provide thermal protection. Chemical-protective clothing is made from materials compatible with specific chemicals and groups of chemicals. No single material will protect against all chemicals or mixture of chemicals.

See NFPA 471 and NFPA 472 in this handbook for additional information on protective clothing selection and maintenance.

2-3.4

Given a simulated hazardous materials incident, the Level I responder shall determine if available equipment and supplies are appropriate to implement the planned response. The Level I responder shall be able to describe the equipment and supplies available to the Level I responder for the care and transportation of the hazardous materials incident patient.

The following equipment and supplies are recommended as the minimum necessary for the EMS/HM Level I responder at the scene of a hazardous materials incident:

(a) General ambulance and patient care supplies including the following:

1. Binoculars
2. Hazardous materials EMS references
3. Disposable patient care equipment, such as bag mask units, blood pressure cuffs, stokes basket, backboard with securing devices, cleaning supplies, irrigating water, patient washing supplies, yellow waste bags, patient-covering disposable sheets, Tyvek® suits, body bags, and disaster pouches
4. Clean plastic sheets and bags along with duct tape to cover equipment, floors, and walls

(b) Personal protection supplies including the following:

1. Splash suit
2. Gloves, both inner and outer
3. Boots
4. Hard hat
5. Goggles
6. Mask
7. Duct tape
8. Valuables bag
9. Clean uniform, scrubs

2-4 Competencies—Implementing the Planned Response

2-4.1

Given a plan for providing patient care at a hazardous materials incident, the Level I responder shall be able to perform the preparations necessary to receive the patient for treatment and transport. The Level I responder shall be able to:

While efforts are being made to evacuate patients from the hot zone, EMS personnel must prepare themselves and their vehicles to receive them. This is an important part of EMS activities on the scene because it is vital to their own safety, as well as the safety of others. Supplies, equipment, and the ambulance itself must be prepared so that hazardous materials exposure to the ambulance is limited and the ambulance can be readily cleaned and returned to service.

(a) List the information that needs to be communicated to the Medical Control/Receiving facility regarding the hazardous materials incident, including the following:

As soon as a hazardous materials incident is known to exist and patients are known to be involved, the medical control receiving facility should be notified so that facility personnel can initiate the hospital's hazardous materials response plans.

1. Type and nature of the incident

Vital information that needs to be communicated to the medical control receiving facility includes the following:

(a) The number of patients involved and if there is a likelihood that a large number of victims have been exposed (for example, a hazardous materials incident at a college laboratory or a shopping center)
(b) Age and sex of the patient and any obvious signs and symptoms or field assessment results of the individual patient(s) identified
(c) Obvious patient injuries in order of priority
(d) Duration of exposure
(e) Hazardous material(s) and concentration
(f) Whether the incident occurred at a fixed facility or a transportation incident
(g) Whether there was a fire and explosion or merely a spill or leak
(h) Extent of the incident
(i) Obvious warning signs, such as container labels that may yield additional information vital to treatment and whether that information or labeling will be available for transport

2. Chemical involved and its physical state

This will allow the hospital time to research the potential health care risks and treatments.

3. Number of potential patients

The hospital needs this information to determine whether additional staffing will be needed and whether the facility can handle the potential increase in patients. In many situations, the hospital may have to activate its disaster plan to accommodate a large influx of patients or request patients be taken to other hospitals.

(b) Describe the procedure for preparing the vehicle and equipment for the patient

Several steps are involved in preparing a vehicle and equipment for patients including the following:

(a) All supplies must be removed from cabinets and kits. Items needed to prepare the ambulance and personnel should be removed from storage areas. Any dressings, medications, and irrigation supplies that will be needed should also be removed. Supplies should be removed from kits, and kits should be secured.
(b) The inside walls and floor of the vehicle should be draped with a plastic covering to protect the inside of the ambulance, and all cabinets should be sealed. Various commercial kits and large plastic sheets or bags can be used to prepare the inside of the vehicle.
(c) Equipment that is not disposable should be wrapped in clear plastic.
(d) The mattress should be removed from the stretcher so that the backboard can be placed on it. The backboard should be covered with several disposable sheets or with a Tyvek® bag to receive the patient.

(c) Demonstrate the proper donning, doffing, usage, and limitations of all personal protective equipment provided to the Level I responder by the authority having jurisdiction for use in their hazardous materials response activities

Personal protective clothing for EMS personnel is identified as Level C protection and includes splash protection clothing and gloves. EMS personnel should be able to demonstrate the preparations necessary for properly donning, doffing, and using their personal protective equipment. Before they don this equipment, each member of the team should be assessed for fitness. In addition, each responder's vital signs should be taken and hydrating fluids should be given.

The steps for donning the protective clothing include the following:

(a) Removing jewelry and leather goods and placing them in a property bag in a secured area on the ambulance
(b) Applying the first layer of gloves, followed by the splash suit
(c) Putting on the boots, securing the seam with duct tape, and putting on a mask and goggles, making sure that none of the skin around the face is exposed
(d) Putting on the second layer of gloves and having duct tape applied by another responder to secure the seam between the glove and the suit

This is the minimum protection for the EMS/HM Level I responder who will be transporting patients who have undergone gross decontamination in the field.

(d) Describe the concept of patient transfer from the incident site to the decontamination area and then to the treatment area

Once the nonambulatory patient has completed decontamination, EMS personnel should bring their stretcher to the exit from the decontamination corridor. The patient will be transferred from the backboard or stretcher used for decontamination to the clean backboard on the ambulance stretcher.

2-4.2

Given a patient from a hazardous materials incident, the Level I responder shall provide patient care consistent with the planned response and the organization's standard operating procedures. The Level I responder shall be able to:

Each organization must ensure that it has effective standard operating procedures, including medical procedures, to care for patients who may be involved in incidents anticipated in its response area.

(a) Describe how chemical contamination alters the assessment and care of the hazardous materials patient

Chemical contamination alters the assessment of patients in the following ways:

(a) The history the patient gives may not be as reliable as it is for most patients because hazardous materials may induce confusion, amnesia, delirium, seizures, or coma.
(b) The history of the patient's exposure must also be obtained and include the following information:
    - The product to which the patient was exposed
    - Type of exposure
    - Concentration, quantity, and duration of the exposure
    - Number of times exposure occurred
    - Whether the patient's reaction was acute or chronic
    - The length of time that has passed since the incident occurred
    - The patient's activities since being exposed
(c) Associated injuries become very important, since they may affect the toxic substance's interaction with the body.

Physical assessment is important, especially if the patient's history is unreliable or unavailable. This initial assessment is done by the entry team in the hot zone. The next assessment is performed by the decontamination team (with Level II EMS workers if available), and the last assessment is done by EMS personnel in the cold zone.

Assessment is often limited due to the amount of protection the EMS responder must wear. The protective clothing can dull the senses that would normally be used for patient assessment.

Open wounds, such as fractures or cuts from broken glass or metal container shards, present special challenges in medical care at hazardous materials incidents because they offer an opportunity for external contaminants to breach the skin/blood barriers. Stabilizing the patient, reducing bleeding, and other normal EMS treatments may be reprioritized by medical control to focus on first reducing the risk of internal contamination.

In most cases, the initial treatment of the patient offered at the scene or en route to a medical facility is primarily aimed at relieving symptoms as appropriate and stabilizing vital signs. When the specific contaminating product is known and an antidote exists and is available at the scene, the antidote may be given in the field or later in treatment as directed by medical control. Locations where workers routinely run a higher probability of exposure to specific chemicals or substances, such as manufacturing or chemical facilities, may have antidotes available as part of their initial response SOPs. These private sector resources may or may not be used, depending on the responder's plan, the organization's SOPs, and the discretion of medical control.

(b) List the common signs and symptoms and describe the EMS treatment protocols for the following:

1. Corrosives (e.g., acid, alkali)
2. Pulmonary irritants (e.g., ammonia, chlorine)
3. Pesticides (e.g., organophosphates, carbamates)

4. Chemical asphyxiants (e.g., cyanide, carbon monoxide)
5. Hydrocarbon solvents (e.g., xylene, methylene chloride)

Table 2.2 gives examples of treatment protocols for the five categories of irritants given in the *Code*.

Table 2.2 Chemical Contaminants, Symptoms, and EMS Protocols

Corrosives

Common Signs and Symptoms

Eyes: pain, photophobia, tearing, blepharospasm, decreased visual acuity

Skin (generally resemble thermal burns): pain, tenderness, edema, erythema, sloughing, discoloration of skin

Respiratory (pain involving nose, mouth, throat, and chest): dysphagia, weakness, coughing, syncope, hoarseness, dizziness, dyspnea, wheezing, rales, or rhonchi

Associated findings include tachycardia, tachypnea, and cyanosis

Gastrointestinal: chest pain, pain, drooling, muffled or slurred speech, dysphagia, oropharyngeal burns, abdominal tenderness, abdominal pain, vomiting (sometimes with blood)

Systemic toxicity: Symptoms of metabolic acidosis with injection of acids coma, bradycardia, hypotension, weakness, excited behavior, tremor, lethargy, ataxia, and nystagmus

EMS Treatment Protocols

1. Decontaminate patient.
2. Evaluate and support ABCs (airway, breathing, and circulation).
3. Provide hi-flow oxygen.
4. Attach to cardiac monitor.
5. Provide aerosolized bronchodilators for wheezing.
6. Continuously flush affected skin and eyes with copious amounts of water or saline.
7. DO NOT induce vomiting with ingestion.

Pulmonary Irritants

Common Signs and Symptoms: cough, airway edema, bronchoconstriction, difficulty breathing, hoarseness/stridor, fatigue, pulmonary edema, respiratory arrest, cyanosis, changes in or decreased level of consciousness, increased mucus secretions, chest pain

EMS Treatment Protocols

1. Decontaminate patient.
2. Evaluate and support ABCs.
3. Administer oxygen as per local protocol.
4. Attach cardiac monitor if clinically indicated.
5. Continuously flush affected skin and eyes with copious amounts of water or saline.
6. DO NOT induce vomiting with ingestion. Immediately dilute with one (1) glass of water or milk.

Table 2.2 (Continued)

Pesticides

Common Signs and Symptoms: muscarinic effects (easy-to-remember mnemonics)—salivation, lacrimation, tremor, urination, defecation, miosis, gastrointestinal, bradycardia, emesis, diarrhea

Central nervous system: headache, anxiety, respiratory depression, seizures

EMS Treatment Protocols

1. Decontaminate patient.
2. Evaluate and support ABCs.
3. Attach to cardiac monitor.
4. If patient is symptomatic due to organophosphate poisoning, administer atropine according to local medical protocol.
5. DO NOT induce vomiting with ingestion. If available, administer activated charcoal.
6. Continuously flush affected parts and eyes with copious amounts of water or saline.

Chemical Asphyxiants

Common Signs and Symptoms (depends on product and may be immediate or delayed): anxiety, headache, hyperventilation, dizziness, muscle weakness, chest pain, dyspnea, syncope, seizures, coma

EMS Treatment Protocols

1. Decontaminate patient.
2. Evaluate and support ABCs.
3. Administer oxygen according to local protocol.
4. Attach to cardiac monitor.
5. Support blood pressure as needed according to local protocol.
6. Continuously flush affected skin and eyes with copious amounts of water or saline.

Hydrocarbon Solvents

Common Signs and Symptoms: skin irritation, dizziness, chemical conjunctivitis, weakness, headache, coma, drowsiness, chest pain, cough, tachyarrythmias, stupor, respiratory depression, pulmonary edema

EMS Treatment Protocols

1. Decontaminate patient.
2. Evaluate and support ABCs.
3. Administer oxygen as indicated by local medical protocols.
4. Attach to cardiac monitor.
5. If patient is complaining of skin or eye irritation, continuously flush skin or eyes with copious amounts of water or saline.
6. DO NOT induce vomiting. Dilute with one (1) glass of water and give activated charcoal if available.
7. Avoid epinephrine, bronchodilators, terbutaline, and other beta-adrenergic agents.

(c) Explain the potential risk with invasive procedures for hazardous materials patients

Invasive procedures are performed only in life-threatening situations or when the patient is extremely unstable in the hot or warm zones. The danger with invasive procedures is the risk of external contaminants entering the patient's bloodstream and spreading rapidly throughout the body. In some rare situations, it may be appropriate to use some form of gross or emergency decontamination and then start invasive procedures. At a minimum, the victim should be removed to the warm zone and the EMS provider should be an EMS/HM Level II responder.

(d) Demonstrate the ability to perform the following EMS functions within the incident management system during incidents involving multiple hazardous materials patients:

1.* EMS control

A-2-4.2(d)1 EMS control activities at a hazardous materials incident include, but are not limited to, the following:

(a) Identification of EMS needs, including appropriate level of protection for EMS personnel and equipment, resources for patient care, and decontamination of patient and EMS personnel
(b) Securing of resources to meet EMS needs
(c) Assignment of personnel, in the cold zone, to coordinate triage, treatment, disposition, and transport as required
(d) Assignment of appropriately trained personnel to perform medical monitoring and other EMS support functions for hazardous materials response personnel in the cold zone
(e) Assignment of appropriately trained personnel to provide patient care, assist with patient decontamination, and perform any other EMS support functions, as may be required in the warm zone

2. Triage
3. Treatment
4. Disposition and transportation

The following are some of the duties and responsibilities of personnel serving in the EMS functions in the incident management system.

(a) EMS control *[See A-2-4.2(d)(1).]*
(b) Triage

1. Establish triage area.
2. Sort and prioritize patients.
3. Reevaluate patients as necessary.
4. Deliver patients from decontamination area to treatment area.

(c) Treatment

1. Communicate with triage personnel.
2. Determine needs and locate treatment area.
3. Request personnel and supplies.
4. Process and treat patients.

(d) Disposition and transportation

1. Establish work area and communications.
2. Coordinate activities between treatment and transportation.
3. Contact hospital and advise of patients and conditions.
4. Coordinate with medical control for distributing patients.
5. Establish evacuation plan.
6. Request resources needed.

2-4.3

Given a patient from a hazardous materials incident, the Level I responder shall transport the patient as specified in the local emergency response plan and the organization's standard operating procedures. The Level I responder shall be able to:

The transportation of patients from hazardous materials incidents will differ from the normal transportation process. Because EMS personnel are dressed in protective clothing and the patient is wrapped to contain any residual contaminants, the amount of interaction with the patient will be more limited than in a usual transport situation. The anxiety level of the patient should also be taken into consideration. A special effort should be made to inform the patient of his or her treatment, to explain the need for the protective clothing of the EMS providers, and to outline decontamination procedures. Hazardous materials patients are generally not given a secondary assessment or secondary treatment (splinting, etc.) during transport.

(a) Identify the capabilities of the medical facilities available in the local area to receive hazardous materials patients

The local response plan should indicate the capabilities of all the medical facilities in the given area. In consultation with medical control, the responder will decide which facility should receive the patient from the incident. If there are a number of patients, the responder should determine whether they should be transported to one facility or distributed among several.

(b) Identify the acceptable vehicles available to transport hazardous materials patients from the treatment area to a receiving facility

Based on the local operating procedures, the EMS providers, in coordination with their supervisors, will determine whether ambulances are the appropriate mode of transportation for patients. *(See Figure 2.2.)* Alternate means of transportation include command vehicles and buses, if there are several patients. In determining which vehicles to use, the responder must consider the local and state laws addressing patient transportation as well as the condition and clinical needs of the individual patients to be transported.

(c) List the pertinent information that needs to be communicated to the receiving facility, including the following:

1. Estimated time of arrival
2. Age/sex
3. Patient condition/chief complaint
4. Associated injuries
5. Routes, extent, and duration of chemical exposure
6. Pertinent medical history
7. Signs and symptoms
8. Vital signs
9. Treatment, including decontamination and patient response
10. Pertinent chemical characteristics

Once the patient is in the care of the Level I responder, it is important that the responder obtain the patient history information listed in 2-4.3(c) and relay it to the hospital in sequence. This information will help the hospital staff prepare to treat the patient.

(d) Describe the actions necessary for the coordinated delivery of hazardous materials incidents patients to a receiving facility

In communicating with the hospital, EMS personnel should determine where in the hospital the patient is to be delivered. Hospital personnel should meet the ambulance at the designated site and transfer the patient from the ambulance stretcher to the hospital litter. Many facilities that have trauma centers also have a specific decontamination area or clean room in which patients who have been exposed to contaminants are once again evaluated and given further decontamination if necessary. This area is often accessed through a separate entrance away from the hospital proper to further reduce the risk of secondary contamination.

Figure 2.2 *While air transport is a logical choice for people who have suffered serious injuries in auto accidents, it is rarely chosen for victims of hazardous materials contamination because any contaminants on the patient may become airborne during the flight. (Photo courtesy LifeFlight, Worcester, MA)*

(e) Explain the special hazards associated with air transportation of patients exposed to hazardous materials

Any decision to transport the patient by helicopter or fixed-wing aircraft should be carefully weighed against the risk to the air crew. Contaminants may still be on the patient, and these contaminants could cause the flight crew to become ill and crash the aircraft.

When definitive decontamination has been completed, air transportation may be an option. Precautions must be taken to ensure that no contaminants from the scene are carried aboard the aircraft. This includes the patient's clothing and valuables, and gastrointestinal specimens.

2-5 Competencies—Terminating the Incident

2-5.1

Upon termination of the hazardous materials incident, the Level I responder shall complete the reporting, documentation, and EMS termination activities as required by the local emergency response plan or the organization's standard operating procedures. The Level I responder shall be able to:

When the patient has been transferred to the care of the hospital staff, the EMS personnel must clean and decontaminate the transporting vehicle and complete the appropriate personal decontamination. They must then complete the appropriate patient records, including incident and exposure reports.

(a) List the information to be gathered regarding the exposure of the patient and the EMS provider and describe the proper reporting procedures, including the following:

1. Product information
2. Routes, extent, and duration of exposure
3. Actions taken to limit exposure and contamination
4. Treatment rendered
5. Patient condition and disposition

Each EMS organization and program has a standard incident report that requires specific patient information. These reports generally have a comment or narrative area in which to list information about the product, the exposure, and the incident activities. Patient care information should also be completed, as it will be needed to develop an appropriate patient care plan.

(b) Identify situations that can necessitate critical incident stress debriefing intervention

Because hazardous materials incidents may last a long time and result in personal injury and mass casualties, they produce additional stress not encountered in the "usual" emergency incident. The increased likelihood of psychological stress may warrant a critical incident defusing and possibly a debriefing. Factors that may indicate the need for a debriefing include the injury or death of emergency responders; the injury or death of children; major trauma, especially dismemberment; and mass casualties.

(c) Describe the EMS provider's role in the post-incident critique

Since significant hazardous materials incidents do not occur frequently, it is important to critique each incident. The critique should include operational, as well as hospital, personnel. The EMS provider should participate, explaining what worked well and what didn't, what supplies were needed and were not available, and what procedures may have to be revised based on the experience.

References Cited in Commentary

1. Contra Costa/Solano County Joint Emergency Medical Services Hazardous Materials Response Program.
2. U.S. DOT, *1996 North American Emergency Response Guidebook.*
3. Alvin C. Bronstein, M.D., FACEP and Phillip L. Currance, EMT-P, *Emergency Care for Hazardous Materials Exposure,* 2nd ed., Mosby Lifeline, St. Louis, 1994.
4. Douglas R. Stutz, Robert C. Ricks, and Michael F. Olsen, *Hazardous Materials Injuries: A Handbook for Pre-Hospital Care,* Bradford Communications Corp., Greenbelt, MD, 1982.

CHAPTER 3

Competencies for EMS/ HM Level II Responders

3-1 General

3-1.1 Introduction.

All personnel at EMS/HM Level II shall be certified to the EMT-A level or higher and shall meet all competencies for EMS/HM Level I in addition to all the competencies of this chapter.

Personnel at EMS/HM Level II require a higher level of EMS certification than EMS/HM Level I personnel. While this standard sets its minimum at the EMT-A level, the emergency medical care that EMT-A level workers can deliver in most states is limited. Based on the fact that this is a national standard and that some areas of the country do not have EMS personnel above the level of EMT-A, the committee realized that they had to provide for the functions required by this level. However, EMT-Cardiac, EMT-Intermediate, or EMT-Paramedic are preferred if available.

This section also includes several hazardous materials competencies from NFPA 472 above the first responder awareness level. It was felt these were needed because the responder must be able to make an analysis to formulate plans that are to be carried out by other EMS personnel and be able to operate in the warm zone.

3-1.2 Definition.

Personnel at EMS/HM Level II are those persons who, in the course of their normal activities, might be called upon to perform patient care activities in the warm zone at hazardous materials incidents. EMS/HM Level II responder personnel might be required to provide care to those individuals who still pose a significant risk of secondary contamination. In addition, personnel at this level shall be able to coordinate EMS activities at a hazardous materials incident and provide medical support for hazardous materials response personnel.

Personnel at this level may come into direct contact with patients in the warm zone. EMS personnel must be able to work while in protective clothing and to effectively complete decontamination of patients as part of initial patient care and assessment, in the event that only emergency or gross decontamination was accomplished. These EMS workers may also be required to perform assessments of other responders within the warm zone including those who have been exposed in the hot zone.

3-1.3 Goal.

The goal of the competencies at EMS/HM Level II shall be to provide the Level II responder with the knowledge and skills necessary to perform and/or coordinate patient care activities and medical support of hazardous materials response personnel in the warm zone. Therefore the Level II responder shall be able to:

The EMS/HM Level II responder, as an integral part of the hazardous materials response team, must operate within the guidelines of the response plan and under the supervision of the incident command system at each specific incident. Protocols or direct communications with medical control will detail the medical care that must be performed.

(a) Analyze a hazardous materials incident to determine the magnitude of the problem in terms of outcomes by completing the following tasks:

1. Determine the hazards present to the Level II responder and the patient in a hazardous materials incident

EMS/HM Level II responders working in the warm zone are more likely to be exposed to contamination than Level I responders working in the cold zone. Therefore, Level II responders must be familiar with standard precautions to minimize contamination and be able to recognize signs and symptoms of toxicity while working in the warm zone.

Level II responders can come into face-to-face contact with contaminated individuals in the warm zone. Guided by their own observations of the patients and other information available to them, Level II responders must be able to assess their patients to determine the contamination severity, if secondary contamination has occurred and, if so, what type of additional decontamination measures are necessary.

2. Assess the patient to determine the patient care needs and the risk of secondary contamination

In addition to patient care of exposed victims, EMS responders in the warm zone must be able to support other responders and to assist these workers in case of toxic exposure or injury. In some plans, warm zone EMS workers are also responsible for periodic medical monitoring of responders entering and leaving the hot zone or for overseeing the procedure for responders leaving the warm zone to enter the cold zone.

(b) Plan a response to provide the appropriate level of emergency medical care to persons involved in hazardous materials incidents and to provide medical support to hazardous materials response personnel by completing the following tasks:

Once the Level II responder is able to analyze the incident and project possible outcomes, the responder must develop a plan to coordinate the EMS aspects of the overall hazardous materials response plan. This plan must include provisions for medical treatment of victims and support of the hazardous materials responders.

1. Describe the role of the Level II responder in a hazardous materials incident

The Level II responder may be assigned to one or more functions at a hazardous materials incident, including EMS control, patient decontamination, and medical surveillance/monitoring.

2. Plan a response to provide the appropriate level of emergency medical care in a hazardous materials incident

The Level II responder must develop the emergency care plan to be implemented by Level I and Level II responders. This plan must cover the treatment and transportation of the victims from the warm zone to the hospital or other health care facility.

3. Determine if the personal protective equipment provided to EMS personnel is appropriate

Upon arrival at the scene, the Level II responder must be able to use information about the hazardous material(s) to help anticipate the likely patient care needs at the incident scene. In addition, this information should suggest the necessary level of protective clothing and equipment required for responders. If the appropriate equipment is not available, or if the Level II worker is not trained in the appropriate protective equipment, the responder should inform the medical branch officer or the incident commander at the scene prior to entering the warm zone. In some cases, personnel with a higher level of training who are certified for working while in a Level A suit may be needed to provide patient care or decontamination.

(c) Implement the planned response by completing the following tasks:

All hazardous materials incident planning should include an EMS component that involves Level II workers who are able to deliver more extensive patient care in the field and supervise appropriate decontamination procedures for patients and workers prior to transport to a medical facility.

1. Perform the necessary preparations for receiving the patient

Depending on the local emergency plan, Level II responders working in the warm zone may be required to wear higher levels of personal protective clothing. In these situations, they must provide a clean isolated area in which to treat their patients while protecting themselves and their equipment.

2. Perform necessary treatment to the hazardous materials patient

In certain situations, patients brought to the warm zone will require some emergency medical care to control bleeding or other life threatening conditions before decontamination efforts begin or while they are in progress. At minimum, gross or emergency decontamination techniques should be performed before any medical treatments are started. Actually giving care or directly supervising the care is the duty of the Level II responder.

3. Coordinate and manage the EMS component of the hazardous materials incident

At the scene, Level II workers, by virtue of their higher level of training, may be called upon to supervise the hazardous materials branch and the work of Level I responders in the cold zone.

4. Perform medical support of hazardous materials incident response personnel

A Level II responder must also provide medical support to the hazardous materials response personnel.

Because hazardous materials personnel are at significant risk of becoming patients themselves, it is necessary to ensure their health and safety. In most cases, medical guidelines and work time limits will have been established for those in Level A and Level B protective gear working in the hot and warm zones. Level II EMS workers may be called upon to perform or supervise pre-suit evaluations of responders, medical evaluations of workers throughout the incident, and decontamination procedures. Some plans may also call for EMS supervision of rest periods and other rehabilitative services, such as ensuring the responders have appropriate fluid replacement breaks and cool down areas for rest.

Supplement 11 describes how these activities fit into the overall EMS response plan.

(d) Terminate the incident

Since Level II responders serve in a supervisory and coordinating role, they have more responsibilities during the termination phase. This includes providing critical incident stress debriefings, defusing, critiques, and making appropriate recommendations to the incident commander. These activities should be performed as soon as possible after the incident has been placed under control. Keeping notes, if practical, during the progress of the incident can ensure that valuable information will not be lost.

3-2 Competencies—Analyzing the Hazardous Materials Incident

Since the Level II responder is responsible for the EMS part of the response plan on which the outcome for both patients and responders depends, it is important that the responder knows enough about hazardous materials to analyze the incident and effectively estimate the risks.

3-2.1

Given an emergency involving hazardous materials, the Level II responder shall determine the hazards to the responders and the patient in that situation. The Level II responder shall be able to:

(a) Define the following chemical and physical properties and describe their importance in the risk assessment process:

These terms are commonly used to describe the physical and chemical properties of a hazardous material. The responder can use this data to predict the behavior of the hazardous material once it is outside its container. For example, knowing that propane gas (a flammable gas) has a weight heavier than air will alert the responder to potential ignition sources at or below the level of the leak.

1. Boiling point

Boiling point is the temperature at which the transition from liquid to gas occurs. At this temperature, the vapor pressure of a liquid equals the surrounding atmospheric pressure so that the liquid rapidly becomes a vapor.

2. Flammable (explosive) limits

A material's *flammable* or *explosive range* is the difference between its upper and lower flammable limits. The lower flammable limit (LFL) is the minimum concentration of vapor to air below which a flame will not propagate in the presence of an ignition source. The upper flammable limit (UFL) is the maximum vapor-to-air concentration above which a flame will not propagate. If a vapor-to-air mixture is below the LFL, it is described as being "too lean" to burn; if it is above the UFL, it is "too rich" to burn. When the vapor-to-air ratio is somewhere between the LFL and the UFL, fires and explosions can occur, and the mixture is said to be in the flammable range. The flammable range for gasoline is 1.4 percent to 7.6 percent and the flammable range for carbon monoxide is 12.5 percent to 74 percent. It is important that the responder be aware of the range as well as the LFL.

If the responder suspects or knows that flammable vapors are present, it is important that they determine the concentration of vapor in air. Combustible gas instruments are used for this purpose.

3. Flash point

The *flash point* of a liquid is the minimum temperature at which it gives off vapor in sufficient concentration to form an ignitable mixture with air. A liquid's flash point is the primary property or characteristic used to determine its relative degree of flammability. Since it is the vapors of flammable liquids that burn, vapor generation is a primary factor in determining the liquid's fire hazard.

4. Ignition temperature

Ignition temperature and *auto-ignition temperature* are interchangeable terms. The ignition temperature of a substance, whether solid, liquid, or gaseous, is the minimum temperature required to cause self-sustained combustion in the absence of any source of ignition. The responder should regard assigned ignition temperatures as approximations.

Ignition temperatures can be quite high, especially in relation to a liquid's flash point. For example, the flash point of gasoline is –45°F (–43°C), while its ignition temperature is well over 500°F (260°C).

5. Specific gravity

Specific gravity is the ratio of the weight of a volume of liquid or solid to the weight of an equal volume of water, with the gravity of water being 1.0. A substance with a specific gravity of less than 1.0 will float on water.

6. Vapor density

Vapor density measures the weight of a given vapor as compared with an equal volume of air, with air having a value of 1.0. A vapor density greater than 1.0 indicates it is heavier than air; a value less than 1.0 indicates it is lighter.

Vapor density can be important to the responder, since it will determine the behavior of free vapor at the scene of a liquid spill or gas release.

7. Vapor pressure

Vapor pressure is the pressure exerted on the inside of a closed container by the vapor in the space above the liquid in the container. Products with high vapor pressures are more volatile.

Vapor pressure is measured in mm of mercury. The vapor pressure of water is 21 mm mercury, and that of chlorine is 4,800 mm mercury.

8. Water solubility

Water solubility, or the degree to which a substance is soluble in water, can be useful in determining effective extinguishing agents and methods. Response personnel should consider the property of solubility along with that of specific gravity.

(b) Define the following terms:

Again, a good understanding of these terms will help the responder determine how to protect and treat the patient.

1. Alpha radiation

Alpha radiation involves the alpha particle, a positively charged particle emitted by some radioactive materials. It is less penetrating than beta and gamma radiation and is not considered dangerous unless ingested. If ingested, alpha radiation will attack internal organs.

2. Beta radiation

Beta radiation involves the beta particle, which is much smaller but more penetrating than the alpha particle. Beta particles can damage skin tissue, and they can damage internal organs if they enter the body. Full-protective clothing, including positive pressure self-contained breathing apparatus, will protect against most beta radiation.

3. Gamma radiation

Gamma radiation is especially harmful since it has great penetrating power. Gamma rays are a form of ionizing radiation with high energy that travels at the speed of light. It can cause skin burns and can severely injure internal organs. Protective clothing is inadequate in preventing gamma radiation from harming the body.

(c) Define the following toxicological terms and explain their use in the risk assessment process:

If the hazardous material can be positively identified, then the following information will help the responder determine the likely adverse effects to any victims and the level of protection needed for the responders themselves.

1. Threshold limit value (TLV-TWA)

TLV-TWA is the maximum concentration, averaged over 8 hours, to which a healthy adult can be repeatedly exposed for 8 hours per day, 40 hours per week.

2. Lethal concentration and doses ($LD_{50}/100$)

The LC_{50} is the median lethal concentration of an inhalable hazardous material. It is defined as the concentration of a material in air that, on the basis of laboratory tests (inhalation route), is expected to kill 50 percent of a group of test animals when administered in a specific time period.

The LD_{50} of a substance is a single dose that will cause the death of 50 percent of a group of test animals exposed to it by any route other than inhalation. Since these experiments, for obvious reasons, are never performed on humans, animals are chosen that will reportedly experience the same effects that a human being would experience.

3. Parts per million/billion (ppm/ppb)

The values used to establish the exposure limits above are quantified in *parts per million* or *parts per billion.* A good reference to remember is that 1 percent equals 10,000 ppm, 1 percent equals 1,000 ppb. So if you obtain a reading from a sampling instrument of 0.5 percent, that is equivalent to 5,000 ppm, or 500 ppb. If you then determine the TLV is 7,500 ppm, you can relate the reading from the instrument to determine the degree of hazard.

4. Immediately dangerous to life and health (IDLH)

IDLH is the maximum level to which a healthy worker can be exposed for 30 minutes and escape without suffering irreversible health effects or impairment. If at all possible, exposure to this level should be avoided. If that is not possible, responders must wear positive pressure self-contained breathing apparatus or a positive pressure supplied-air respirator with an auxiliary escape system. This limit is established by OSHA and NIOSH.

5. Permissible exposure limit (PEL)

Permissible exposure limit (PEL) is a term OSHA uses in its health standards covering exposures to hazardous chemicals. It is similar to the TLV-TWA established by the American Conference of Governmental Industrial Hygienists (ACGIH). PEL, which generally relates to legally enforceable TLV limits, is the maximum concentration, averaged over 8 hours, to which 95 percent of healthy adults can be repeatedly exposed for 8 hours per day, 40 hours per week.

6. Short-term exposure limit (TLV-STEL)

TLV-STEL is the maximum average concentration, averaged over a 15-minute period, to which healthy adults can be safely exposed for up to 15 minutes continuously. Exposure should not occur more than four times a day with at least 1 hour between exposures.

7. Ceiling level (TLV-C)

TLV-C is the maximum concentration to which a healthy adult can be exposed without risk of injury. It is comparable to the IDLH, and exposures to higher concentrations should not occur.

(d) Given a specific hazardous material and using the information sources available to the Level II responder, demonstrate extracting appropriate information about the physical characteristics and chemical properties, hazards, and suggested medical response considerations for that material

Responders must know which references and/or online data bases provide the information necessary to determine the health effects of the hazardous materials involved in an incident to establish the medical treatment that can be used to combat them, in consultation with medical control. They must also understand which properties have an impact on a patient's reactions and on the care the patient must receive.

3-2.2

Given a hazardous materials incident with a patient(s), the Level II responder shall assess the patient and conditions to determine the risk of secondary contamination. The Level II responder shall be able to:

The Level II responder can apply the information from reference sources on the product to the information he or she obtains while assessing the patient to determine the risk of secondary contamination to others. For example, if a patient states that he was completely covered by a particular hazardous material and reference sources indicate that the material is very difficult to remove once it has contaminated the skin, the chance of secondary exposure is slight since the material will not dislodge easily. However, if the responder must touch the patient to provide medical care, the contaminate may be transferred by actual physical contact.

(a) Identify sources of technical information for the performance of patient decontamination

Sources of information include EMS reference books, the poison control center, EMS/HM data systems, and the ATSDR. Telephone numbers for voice and data communications for some of these sources should be part of the EMS team's resources.

(b) Identify the factors that influence the decision of when and where to treat the patient and the extent of patient care, including the following:

Triage assessment of patients in the warm zone is one of the most important duties of the Level II responder. In some cases, complete decontamination procedures must take second place to the treatment of other life threatening injuries, such as serious bleeding. Routine decontamination procedures can cause further injury to the patient by spreading contaminants from their skin into open wounds, or can spread contaminants to others.

Triage information needs to be communicated to medical control and to other EMS workers at the scene, as appropriate, and throughout the patient transport process.

1. Hazardous material toxicity

The more toxic the product and the longer the exposure period, the faster it should be removed from the patient and the more serious the patient's condition may be.

2. Patient condition

The patient may be in critical condition due to factors other than the hazardous materials exposure; exposures are often associated with other medical problems or trauma, such as cardiovascular incidents, diabetic or other medical illnesses, and shock. If the patient's condition is unstable, the time between decontamination and the implementation of life-saving treatment may have to be as short as possible.

3. Availability of decontamination

Some jurisdictions can provide complete patient decontamination in the field year round, but this is more the exception than the rule. In most areas, resources are only available to deal with gross contaminants by mechanical removal, disrobing, and a thorough rinsing with water. Definitive decontamination, which consists of a thorough soaping and rinsing, generally must be performed in a sheltered environment or at a medical facility.

3-3 Competencies—Planning the Response

3-3.1

Given a plan of action by the incident commander, the Level II responder shall describe his or her role in a hazardous materials incident as identified in the local emergency response plan or the organization's standard operating procedures. The Level II responder shall be able to describe the importance of coordination between various agencies at the scene of hazardous materials incidents.

The local emergency response plan should define the duties and responsibilities of EMS/HM responders at each level. Jurisdictions can use this standard as a guide to updating their own plans if these plans do not currently contain this information.

The Level II EMS/HM responder should perform the following functions:

(a) Coordinate the delivery of emergency medical services with the incident commander
(b) Maintain communications with the incident commander
(c) Establish and maintain communications with EMS personnel at the scene and at medical control
(d) Establish EMS control operations and direct the administration of all EMS operations, in accordance with the local SOPs
(e) Make provisions for the appropriate level of personal protection for the EMS responders
(f) Advise the incident commander whether additional personnel or resources are needed to implement the EMS medical care plan
(g) Establish and coordinate patient contamination control operations, in accordance with the local SOPs
(h) Ensure that patients receive the appropriate emergency medical care according to the incident's emergency medical plan
(i) Ensure the efficient transport and transfer of patients to a designated medical facility
(j) Make provisions for the ongoing medical surveillance of hazardous materials response personnel

To perform their duties and responsibilities, Level II responders must coordinate with personnel representing the numerous agencies on the scene of a hazardous materials incident. These include both emergency response agencies and support agencies, such as the health department, environmental agencies, emergency management agencies, the police and fire departments, and disaster response teams.

By coordinating with these agencies, EMS personnel will have the resources they need to perform their functions safely. It will also prevent duplication of effort and ensure effective on-scene operations.

3-3.2

Given a hazardous materials incident, the Level II responder shall plan a response to provide the appropriate level of emergency medical care to persons involved in hazardous materials incidents and to provide medical support to hazardous materials response personnel. The Level II responder shall be able to:

Developing a plan of response for the EMS component is one of the most important functions of the Level II responder, since the flow of EMS operations depends on this plan. To assist the Level II responder, each organization should have a standard format outlining the plan to serve as a guide at each incident. This will ensure that important items are not missed.

(a) Given a simulated hazardous materials incident, assess the problem and formulate and implement a plan including the following:

The functions listed are an integral part of the EMS response at a hazardous materials incident. Each can and should be broken down into components and itemized on a checklist so they can be addressed for each incident. At any major hazardous materials incident, at least one EMS responder should be assigned to supervise each of these functions.

See Supplement 11.

1. EMS control activities
2. EMS component of an incident management system
3. Medical monitoring of personnel utilizing chemical-protective and high temperature-protective clothing
4. Triage of hazardous materials victims
5. Medical treatment for chemically contaminated individuals
6. Product and exposure information gathering and documentation

(b) Describe the importance of pre-emergency planning relating to specific sites

The response plans for any hazardous materials incident should specify in general terms the placement of the following areas:

(a) Staging of ambulances
(b) Triage and treatment sites
(c) Patient and personnel decontamination areas
(d) Medical surveillance

(c) Describe the hazards and precautions to be observed when approaching a hazardous materials incident

When approaching a hazardous materials incident, EMS responders should take the following precautions:

(a) Look for environmental clues that indicate the presence of a hazardous material.
(b) Approach the scene from uphill and upwind.
(c) Stop and use binoculars to observe the incident before approaching.
(d) Be careful not to drive through any run-off or spill.

(d) Describe the considerations associated with the placement, location, and setup of the patient decontamination site

The patient decontamination site should be:

(a) Near the exit from the hot zone to minimize the spread of contaminants
(b) Located in an area that could contain any contaminated run-off
(c) Protected from any adverse weather conditions and provide the patient with privacy, if possible
(d) Located with the response team's decontamination area, if it does not interfere with the decontamination process

(e) Explain the advantages and limitations of the following techniques of decontamination and how they are or are not applicable to patient decontamination:

1. Absorption
2. Chemical degradation
3. Dilution
4. Isolation

See Table 3.1 for a comparison of the various decontamination techniques.

(f) Describe when it would be prudent to pull back from a hazardous materials incident

When an incident threatens to escalate or changing conditions increase the risk to personnel, responders should consider pulling back from the incident and relocating operations. Generally, this is a decision made by the incident commander.

3-3.3

Given the name of the hazardous material and the type, duration, and extent of exposure, the Level II responder shall determine if the protective clothing and equipment available to EMS personnel is appropriate to implement the planned response. The Level II responder shall be able to:

(a) Identify the advantages and dangers of search and rescue missions at hazardous materials incidents

A search and rescue mission with appropriate personnel protective equipment (PPE) may disclose the existence and location of victims and result in their rescue. However, it may also place the rescuer in a dangerous situation. This task, therefore, is normally completed by responders at the technician level.

Table 3.1 Decontamination Techniques: Advantages and Disadvantages

Decontamination Techniques	Advantages	Disadvantages	Patient Application
Absorption	Easily applied; nonreactive with the product; best for water-reactive products; and makes liquids easy to pick up	Generally expensive; materials are not rendered harmless; must be bagged and treated as hazardous waste; generally effective only for flat surfaces	Limited, although certain pads can be used to absorb product from the skin if water cannot be used for flushing
Chemical Degradation	Renders the product neutral or harmless	Generally produces exothermic reaction, which may burn skin; exact product may not be known; or there may be a mixture of chemicals	Is impractical for patient use because it produces heat in neutralizing the product
Dilution	Water is readily available; can be applied rapidly; lowers the concentration of the product and may render it harmless	Run-off must be contained; may be water-reactive	Most common and generally effective means of patient decontamination
Isolation	Does not require supplies, only a separate area	Does nothing to negate the effects of any contaminants	Does nothing to treat or mitigate contaminants

(b) Identify the advantages and hazards associated with the rescue, extrication, and removal of a victim from a hazardous materials incident

The advantage of rescuing, extricating, and removing a patient from a hazardous materials incident is that it may save the patient's life. However, the risks to rescuers are significant. The time available for a rescue is limited by the responders' air supply needs, and it is often difficult for an entry team, which usually consists of only two or three persons, to immobilize and extricate a patient safely. For example, in a situation where there are multiple victims from a terrorist incident, hazardous materials technicians may simply drag victims from the contaminated area to the decontamination area without performing any medical treatment. These patients must then be decontaminated before any medical treatment can begin. The number of victims and the conditions at the incident scene dictate the actions taken to rescue victims. These actions must protect responders while rescuing those victims that have a chance for survival.

(c) Describe the types, application, use, and limitations of protective clothing used by EMS personnel at hazardous materials incidents

The personal protection available to EMS personnel generally provides the minimal chemical protection. Level I responders who work in the cold zone have splash protection for exposed skin surfaces and, generally, minimal respiratory protection.

Level II responders should be familiar with all of the various levels of protection used by responders who work in the warm zone, including Level C and Level B personal protective equipment (PPE) and self-contained breathing apparatus (SCBA).

(d) Demonstrate how to interpret a chemical compatibility chart for chemical-protective clothing

Because the competency calls for a demonstration of ability, the Level II responder must be familiar with the different charts available from the protective clothing manufacturer or other chemical protection references and be able to interpret the information on the charts as it applies to the selection of PPE and other gear necessary for the incident at hand.

3-4 Competencies—Implementing the Planned Response

3-4.1

Given a plan for providing patient care at a hazardous materials incident, the Level II responder shall perform the preparations necessary to receive the patient for treatment and transport. The Level II responder shall be able to demonstrate the proper donning, doffing, and usage of all personal protective equipment provided to the Level II responder by the authority having jurisdiction.

Since the Level II responder works in the warm zone, he or she must be able to select the appropriate level of PPE and be able to don and doff it efficiently.

3-4.2

At the scene of a hazardous materials incident, the Level II responder shall be able to provide or coordinate the patient care. The Level II responder shall be able to:

Because the Level II responder may be the first EMS person to reach the patient, the responder must be able to implement the necessary care-for-life support in coordination with decontamination and other activities taking place in the warm zone. In cases where patients are critically ill or injured, the Level II responder will need to prioritize each patient's need for treatment, transport, and decontamination appropriately and be able to direct others in carrying out the necessary procedures in a timely fashion.

(a) Given a simulated hazardous materials incident and using local available resources, demonstrate the implementation of the patient decontamination procedure (*see Appendix E*)

(b) Explain the principles of emergency decontamination and its application for critically ill patients

There are two situations to consider. The first is the severity of the patient's condition as a result of the exposure to a hazardous material, and the second is a critical illness or injury that is not a result of the exposure.

Where the patient's primary condition is hazardous material exposure, it is vital that as much of the contaminant as possible be removed from the victim as rapidly as possible. In this situation, gross decontamination procedures will be adequate until complete decontamination can be accomplished later.

Where the patient's primary injury or condition is not a result of the exposure, life support can be applied while the product is being removed, or removal may be delayed while responders attempt to stabilize the patient's condition while in the warm zone. The EMS providers must be in appropriate PPE during treatment of these victims.

(c) Demonstrate the ability to coordinate patient care activities, including treatment, disposition, and transportation of patients

The responder must be able to demonstrate an ability to coordinate the activities necessary for effective patient care.

3-4.3

Given a simulated hazardous materials incident, the Level II responder shall be able to demonstrate the ability to establish and manage the EMS component of an incident management system.

During a simulation, the Level II responder must demonstrate the ability to coordinate the functions associated with any of the EMS components in the incident management system. This includes EMS control and the duties of triage officer, treatment officer, disposition and transportation officer, and safety officer.

3-4.4

Given a simulated hazardous materials incident, the Level II responder shall perform medical support of hazardous materials incident response personnel. The Level II responder shall be able to:

The Level II responder should be able to explain and supervise the medical support for hazardous materials response personnel.

(a) Explain the components of pre-entry and post-entry assessment, including the following:

1. Vital signs

These include temperature, pulse, respiration (rate and character), and blood pressure.

2. Body weight

Fluid loss is best measured in the field by measuring the responder's pre- and post-entry body weights.

3. General health

An idea of responders' general health can be obtained by observing their physical appearance and asking specific questions about their well-being. Those who are recovering from an illness or feel "under the weather" should not be allowed to serve in any level of personal protective equipment but a work uniform. See Chapter 8 of NFPA 471 in this handbook for more details on fitness for responders who must wear protective clothing.

4. Neurological status

A responder's neurological status must be assessed to determine baseline functioning. Changes in neurological status are early indicators of physical or mental stress, dehydration, or exposure to toxic products. Slurred speech, staggered walking, or incoherent behavior are signs that a responder's medical condition should be evaluated.

5. Electrocardiographic rhythm strip, if available

The pre-entry strip provides a baseline reading to compare to the post-entry strip.

(b) Explain the following factors and how they influence heat stress for hazardous materials response personnel:

1. Hydration

This is probably the most important factor for working effectively in the heat that is retained in protective clothing. Response personnel must be prehydrated, and replacement fluids must be administered after entry to effect a rapid recovery. A plan for providing fluid replacement at the scene is described in detail in Supplement 11.

2. Physical fitness

The degree of a responder's physical fitness is directly related to the ability to work for any length of time in heat stress conditions. There is a direct correlation between the aerobic fitness of a responder and his or her ability to work efficiently while using a self-contained breathing apparatus (SCBA). A person in good physical condition can work for up to 30 minutes in a 30-minute SCBA, while a person that does not exercise may only be able to work for 10 minutes before running out of air.

3. Environmental factors

Extreme heat or cold will make it more difficult for personnel to function in PPE. Heat increases the heat stress inherent in wearing PPE, and extreme cold exacerbates the difficulty of maneuvering in PPE. Cold reduces the flexibility of the PPE fabrics, which is especially troublesome when trying to perform activities wearing gloves.

4. Activity levels

The amount and type of work to be performed can produce various levels of heat exhaustion and must be considered when determining entry times. Increased work and the loss of body fluids will result in reduced entry times.

5. Level of PPE

The higher the level of PPE required for protection from the contaminants at the scene, the more heat stress responders will suffer and the more difficult they will find it to move.

6. Duration of entry

Entry must be timed to ensure an adequate air supply is left for decontamination. The entry time may have to be further limited during extremely hot weather because of heat stress and tasks that require high levels of physical exertion.

(c) Explain the medical monitoring protocols and demonstrate medical monitoring procedures for personnel at the scene of a hazardous materials incident

Medical monitoring is described in detail in Chapter 8 of NFPA 471 in this handbook. Table 3.2 offers a brief outline of medical monitoring concerns and considerations.

(d) Describe the criteria for site selection of a medical monitoring station

The medical monitoring site should be near the dressing area but away from noise and commotion, if possible. If the baseline readings are to be accurate, personnel must be assessed in a quiet environment.

(e) Demonstrate the ability to set up and operate a medical monitoring station

The Level II responder must be able to select an appropriate site and establish a medical monitoring station with the supplies and equipment necessary to perform assessments and keep accurate records. The responder must also demonstrate an ability to supervise the station so that medical support is accomplished in a timely manner and does not delay dressing and entry.

(f) Demonstrate the ability to interpret and analyze data obtained from medical monitoring of hazardous materials response personnel

The Level II responder must be able to review a reading and determine whether it is within the normal or safe limits for entry. The guidelines in Chapter 8 of NFPA 471 in this handbook should be used as the acceptable limits for entry clearance.

(g) Given a simulated hazardous materials incident, demonstrate proper documentation of medical monitoring

Each organization must have an established recordkeeping system to document pre- and post-entry physical findings. The Level II responder is responsible for ensuring that these records are properly completed and available for use throughout the incident response.

3-5 Competencies—Terminating the Incident

3-5.1

Upon termination of the hazardous materials incident, the Level II responder shall complete the reporting, documentation, and EMS termination activities as required by the local emergency response plan or the organization's standard operating procedures. The Level II responder shall be able to:

(a)* Describe the information regarding incident EMS activities that needs to be relayed through the chain of command to the incident commander

A-3-5.1(a) The type of information that should be made available to the incident commander would include, but not necessarily be limited to, the following:

(a) Patients

1. Number
2. Condition
3. Disposition

(b) Hazardous materials response personnel

1. Number of personnel screened
2. Adverse reactions noted
3. Personnel transported for further treatment
4. Completed records
5. Recommended medical, physical, and psychological needs for immediate rehabilitation
6. Recommended medical surveillance follow-up

(c) Availability of EMS personnel and equipment

The Level II responder should check to see that all personnel and equipment have been adequately decontaminated at the scene and readied for a return to service.

The responder also should contact the medical facilities that received patients to determine whether they need any additional information about the patients or the circumstances of the incident. In addition, the responder must collect the information required to complete the incident and exposure records and determine whether a critical incident stress debriefing is needed, based on the evaluation of the incident.

(b) Describe the activities required in terminating the EMS component of a hazardous materials incident

(c) Describe the process and demonstrate the ability to conduct the EMS portion of an incident critique

Where hazardous materials incidents occur infrequently, each incident should be critiqued. In areas where response teams are very busy, a critique is only necessary for incidents of long duration and when numerous agencies are involved.

Critiques often carry negative connotations because they may become finger-pointing sessions if not conducted properly. To be successful, the critique facilitator should take the following steps:

(a) Assign specific presentations on each aspect of the incident.

Table 3.2 Components of Medical Monitoring

Pre-Entrance Examination	Monitoring During Entry	Post-Entry Monitoring	Monitoring Protocol
Vital Signs including the following: (a) Blood pressure (b) Pulse (c) Respiratory rate (d) Temperature (e) EKG rhythm strip (10 seconds), if available **Skin Evaluation,** including any sign of: (a) Rashes (b) Open sores/wounds **Mental Status** The individual should be alert and oriented to time and place, have clear speech and a normal gait, and be able to respond appropriately to the situation. **Medical History** Should include recent information about the following: (a) Medications, including over the counter, taken within the past 72 hours (b) Alcohol consumption within the past 24 hours (c) Any new medical treatment or diagnosis made within the past two weeks (d) Symptoms of fever, nausea, vomiting, diarrhea, or cough within the past 72 hours (e) Weight (f) Hydration: has consumed 16 ounces of water or diluted activity drink	(a) Changes in gait, speech, or behavior that require entry personnel to undergo immediate decontamination, doffing of protective clothing, and assessment should be monitored. (b) If entry personnel complain of chest pain, dizziness, shortness of breath, weakness, nausea, or headache, they should undergo immediate decontamination, doffing of protective clothing, and assessment.	**Monitoring** should include the following: (a) History—any symptoms of hazardous materials exposure, environmental exposure, or cardiovascular collapse (b) Vital signs including the following: blood pressure, pulse, respiratory rate, temperature, EKG (if available) (c) Weight (d) Skin evaluation (e) Mental status **Follow-up** should include the following: (a) Repeat monitoring of vital signs every 5–10 minutes until they return to less than 85 percent of maximum pulse rate. If at 10 minutes the signs have not returned to within 10 percent of baseline, perform orthostatic vital signs. (b) Determine from medical control what information regarding latent reactions/symptoms should be communicated to response personnel. (c) If any of the following symptoms are present, contact medical control for direction and preparation for possible transport to a medical facility: 1. Body weight loss of greater than 3 percent or positive orthostatic (pulse increase of 20 beats per minute or systolic blood pressure decrease by 20 mm of Hg at two minutes standing) 2. Greater than 85 percent maximum pulse at 10 minutes 3. Temperature greater than 101°F (oral) or 102°F (core) 4. Nausea, vomiting, diarrhea, altered mental status, or respiratory, cardiac, or dermatologic complaints	(a) Rest time for all personnel should equal at least minimum suit time. Individuals may require additional time for oral rehydration. All personnel should be informed of signs and symptoms to watch for. (b) If the team member is not within 10 percent of baseline within 10 minutes, orthostatic vital signs should be taken. (c) If personnel experience greater than 3 percent body weight loss (4 ½ pounds in a 150-pound person); positive orthostatic (pulse increases by 20 beats per minute or systolic blood pressure decreases by 20 mm of Hg at two minutes standing); greater than 85 percent of maximum pulse at 10 minutes; temperature greater than 101°F (oral) or 102°F (core); nausea, altered mental status, or any other symptoms, the following treatment should be performed: 1. Intravenous fluids hydration with Ringers Lactate or Normal Saline at rate (usually wide open) to get pulse less than 100 beats per minute, systolic blood pressure greater than 110 mm of Hg 2. Administration of oxygen 4 L to 6 L per minute via nasal cannula, may increase as needed 3. Consultation of reference protocols or medical control for treatment of specific symptoms/types of exposure

Note: See Chapter 8 of NFPA 471 in this handbook for a complete discussion of medical monitoring.

(b) Prepare maps, tapes, and drawings of the site so those involved can visualize the incident. If pictures and videos are available, they should be used.
(c) Develop and follow an agenda to ensure that all the facts are presented and that recommendations can be developed for revising procedures or protocols.
(d) After the conclusion of the critique, prepare and distribute a written report so that everyone can benefit from the "lessons learned."

(d) Explain the process of making revisions to EMS operating procedures and response capabilities as a result of information learned

Each organization and jurisdiction should have a process by which the recommendations resulting from incident critiques can be circulated. Level II responders should be familiar with and be able to use the mechanism in their jurisdiction.

CHAPTER 4

Referenced Publications

4-1

The following documents or portions thereof are referenced within this standard as mandatory requirements and shall be considered part of the requirements of this standard. The edition indicated for each referenced mandatory document is the current edition as of the date of the NFPA issuance of this standard. Some of these mandatory documents might also be referenced in this standard for specific informational purposes and, therefore, are also listed in Appendix F.

4-1.1 NFPA Publications.

National Fire Protection Association, 1 Batterymarch Park, P.O. Box 9101, Quincy, MA 02269-9101.

NFPA 472, *Standard for Professional Competence of Responders to Hazardous Materials Incidents,* 1997 edition.

NFPA 1561, *Standard on Fire Department Incident Management System,* 1995 edition.

APPENDIX A

The material contained in Appendix A of this standard is not part of the requirements of the *Code* but is included for informational purposes only. For the convenience of readers, in this handbook the Appendix A material is interspersed among the verbiage of Chapters 1 through 3 and, therefore, is not repeated here.

APPENDIX B

Training

This appendix is not a part of the requirements of this NFPA document but is included for informational purposes only.

B-1 General

The Emergency Medical Services (EMS) personnel responding to hazardous materials incidents should be trained and should receive regular continuing education to maintain competency in three areas: emergency medical technology, hazardous materials, and specialized topics approved by the authority having jurisdiction.

B-1.1 EMS Training.

Recognized U.S. DOT, state, regional, or local training curricula should constitute the entry level EMS preparation for continuing hazardous materials training. At a hazardous materials incident it is desirable that all EMS BLS provider personnel be trained to the U.S. DOT EMT-A level or equivalent.

B-1.2 Hazardous Materials Training.

The foundation for EMS response to a hazardous materials incident should be the competencies described in NFPA 472, *Standard for Professional Competence of Responders to Hazardous Materials Incidents*.

B-1.3 Specialized Training.

Following completion of approved EMS training and appropriate level of hazardous materials instruction described in this standard, the authority having jurisdiction should stipulate additional specialized instruction that the EMS personnel responding to hazardous materials incidents must complete.

B-2 Training Plan

B-2.1

The authority having jurisdiction should develop a formal training plan and provide a program to train EMS personnel to the level being utilized.

B-2.2

A training plan should be developed and contain guidelines for the following functional categories:

(a) Program management
(b) Content development
(c) Instructor competencies
(d) Technical specialist competencies

B-2.3

The training plan should be criteria-based to maintain a consistent quality of curriculum and instruction.

B-2.4

The training plan should specify entry knowledge and skill levels, training, and refresher training for both students and instructors.

B-2.5

The training plan should define evaluation criteria for successful completion of knowledge and skill objectives of the training program.

B-2.6

The training plan should provide for supervised field experience for EMS hazardous materials responder and EMS hazardous materials coordinator training levels.

B-3 Training Program

The training program should be a comprehensive competency-based guideline of the implementation and presentation of the required subject material. As a minimum it should address the areas discussed in this section.

B-3.1 Program Manager.

B-3.1.1 The program manager should have the authority and responsibility for the overall implementation of the program.

B-3.1.2 The program manager should be able to demonstrate knowledge of the following:

(a) The content of NFPA 472, *Standard for Professional Competence of Responders to Hazardous Materials Incidents;* NFPA 471, *Recommended Practice for Responding to Hazardous Materials Incidents;* and this standard
(b) EMS delivery systems
(c) Budgeting and financial planning
(d) Processes used to develop instructional materials

B-3.1.3 The program manager should demonstrate the skill and ability to perform the following tasks:

(a) Coordinate the training program
(b) Evaluate program effectiveness
(c) Identify instructors and technical specialists

B-3.2 Content.

The content of the training program should include the competencies of this standard as a minimum.

B-3.3 Evaluation.

In recognition of the need for technically sound curricula and instruction to meet the competencies outlined in this standard, careful evaluation of all instructors' training, background, and experience should be made.

B-3.3.1 The authority having jurisdiction should ensure that the training program meets the needs of the local area.

B-3.3.2 The program manager should ensure that the training program meets the needs of the hazardous materials response team and the EMS providers.

B-4 Instruction

The need exists for technically sound curricula and delivery to meet the competencies outlined in this standard.

B-4.1 Instructors.

The instructor should

(a) Have mastery of the material he/she presents
(b) Have an understanding of the training program objectives
(c) Have the ability to teach and evaluate

B-4.2 Technical Specialist.

The technical specialist is a person who has technical expertise and practical knowledge in a specific area. This category is intended to support training activities by allowing individuals not otherwise qualified at the instructor level to present an essential segment for which they do have expertise.

B-4.3 Final Evaluation.

Upon completion of the training program, the student should demonstrate competency in all prescribed content areas. This evaluation should include written and practical testing as specified by the program manager and instructors.

APPENDIX C

Recommended Support Resources

This appendix is not a part of the requirements of this NFPA document but is included for informational purposes only.

C-1 General

Emergency medical service personnel who respond to hazardous materials incidents must operate within a network of support resources. This appendix addresses the general classes of these resources and presents a recommended minimum level of support necessary for adequate emergency medical response.

C-2 Poison Control Centers (PCC)

C-2.1 Goal.

In addition to providing support to the general hazardous materials response, the goal of the Poison Control Center is to provide the emergency medical personnel who respond to hazardous materials incidents with medical guidance, information, and advice during incidents involving toxic chemical releases and associated injuries. The PCC should regularly participate in the following activities together with the EMS component of the hazardous materials incident response.

C-2.1.1 Preplanning Assistance. Poison Control Centers should provide preplanning assistance, including the following:

(a) Training
(b) EMS hazardous materials standard operating procedures review
(c) EMS reference materials

C-2.1.2 Technical Advice. Poison Control Centers should have the ability to coordinate decontamination, treatment, and transportation of injured persons. The PCC should be available to the EMS personnel who respond to hazardous materials incidents for emergency consultation around the clock and during the normal working hours for nonemergency consultation. Poison Control Centers should be capable of providing advice regarding the following areas:

(a) Identity of ingredients
(b) Toxicity of substances involved and symptoms and signs of exposure
(c) Recommended level of protective clothing
(d) Potential for secondary contamination
(e) Recommended decontamination procedures
(f) Specific treatment and/or antidotes

C-2.1.3 Data Bases. The PCC should supervise and review the EMS data bases used during hazardous materials incident response.

C-2.1.4 Medical Surveillance. The PCC should provide support for the following:

(a) Surveillance quality assurance program design
(b) Surveillance Q/A program review
(c) Medical follow-up activities

C-3 Chemical Injury Treatment Centers

C-3.1 Goal.

The emergency medical responders to hazardous materials incidents should transfer chemically injured patients to facilities having adequate chemical injury treatment capability. All such facilities should have a minimum level of competency to receive chemically injured patients, including the following provisions.

C-3.1.1 Patient Decontamination Capabilities. Facilities should have the following resources in order to perform patient decontamination:

(a) Decontamination area
(b) Proper ventilation system
(c) Restricted access
(d) Runoff containment

C-3.1.2 Facilities should provide a cadre of trained in-house hazardous materials incident injury treatment personnel.

C-3.1.3 Chemical injury treatment centers should have on hand personal protective clothing for hospital personnel that may treat hazardous materials patients.

C-3.1.4 All treatment centers should have formal hazardous materials incident response procedures directed to EMS providers and hospital personnel.

C-4 Communications

The network of emergency medical response resources to hazardous materials incidents should be linked by an adequate communication system within the incident command post. The following components are suggested as a minimum.

C-4.1 Radiotelephone.

All mobile and fixed EMS components should be able to coordinate EMS hazardous materials incident response via at least one dedicated frequency. All fixed facilities shall have r-f emergency power capability for at least one radio channel.

C-4.2 Telephone Service.

There should be telephone service within the Medical Section/Division; preferably a cellular telephone.

C-4.3 Computer.

All components of the EMS hazardous materials incident response system should have an orientation to and direct or indirect access to computerized chemical data bases, computerized preplans, and computerized operational command and control.

C-4.3.1 Fixed Installation. Computer generated information should be readily available to field and clinical EMS hazardous materials response personnel via at least two of the following:

(a) Verbal transmission
(b) Fax transmission
(c) Modem transmission

C-4.3.2 Mobile. On-scene EMS response personnel should have immediate direct access to a field computerized highly toxic hazardous materials data base and computerized command and control information.

C-4.4 Other Resources.

Additional response resources available to hazardous materials incidents include the following:

(a) CHEMTREC (CMA)
(b) ATSDR (HHS)
(c) Private resources

APPENDIX D

Medical Treatment Considerations

This appendix is not a part of the requirements of this NFPA document but is included for informational purposes only.

D-1

The assessment and prehospital care of patients who are involved in hazardous materials incidents, and who are potentially chemically contaminated, should include the following steps:

(a) The safety of the EMS provider should be provided for by securing the scene, ensuring appropriate decontamination of the patient, and protecting against exposure to communicable diseases and hazardous materials.
(b) The patient's airway should be secure and regularly monitored.
(c) The patient's breathing should be monitored and assisted when necessary.
(d) Supplemental oxygen should be administered if the surrounding environment safely permits.
(e) Bleeding should be controlled. This may be accomplished by the application of pressure bandages. Lower extremity bleeding may be controlled through the use of pneumatic anti-shock garments.
(f) When trauma may have involved cervical spine injury, an appropriate stabilization, immobilization collar should be applied.
(g) Cardiopulmonary resuscitation should be performed, if indicated.
(h) In general, avoid all prophylactic invasive procedures unless required by life-threatening conditions. This includes the establishment of intravenous lines.
(i) Direct medical control should be established.

The authority having jurisdiction should ensure that a written prehospital medical standard operating procedures protocol is in place to provide direction to EMS personnel who respond to hazardous materials incidents.

APPENDIX E

Patient Decontamination

This appendix is not a part of the requirements of this NFPA document but is included for informational purposes only.

E-1

Patient decontamination, if required, should be carried out in the warm zone by properly trained personnel wearing appropriate chemical-protective clothing and respiratory equipment.

Protocol(s) should be written to address the following:

(a) Determination of the potential for secondary contamination and the necessity for, and extent of, decontamination
(b) Selection of appropriate personal protective equipment to be worn by personnel in the warm zone who are assisting with or performing decontamination
(c) Decontamination of patients when the exposure is to an unidentified gas, liquid, or solid material
(d) Emergency decontamination of patients with critical injuries and illness requiring immediate patient care or transport

APPENDIX F

Referenced Publications

F-1

The following documents or portions thereof are referenced within this standard for informational purposes only and are thus not considered part of the requirements of this standard unless also listed in Chapter 4. The edition indicated here for each reference is the current edition as of the date of the NFPA issuance of this standard.

F-1.1 NFPA Publications.

National Fire Protection Association, 1 Batterymarch Park, P.O. Box 9101, Quincy, MA 02269-9101.

NFPA 471, *Recommended Practice for Responding to Hazardous Materials Incidents*, 1997 edition.

NFPA 472, *Standard for Professional Competence of Responders to Hazardous Materials Incidents*, 1997 edition.

F-1.2 Other Publications.

F-1.2.1 U.S. Government Publications. U.S. Government Printing Office, Superintendent of Documents, Washington, DC 20402.

Title 29, *Code of Federal Regulations*, Part 1910.120, 1995.

Title 40, *Code of Federal Regulations*, Part 261.33, 1994.

Title 40, *Code of Federal Regulations*, Part 302, 1994.

Title 40, *Code of Federal Regulations*, Part 355, 1994.

Title 49, *Code of Federal Regulations*, Parts 170–179, 1995.

F-2

The following documents are not referenced within this standard, but may be useful to the reader.

Poisoning and Drug Overdose, Kent R. Olson, M.D., ed, Appleton & Lange, Norwalk, CT, 1990.

Borak, Jonathan, Michael Callan, and William Abbott. *Hazardous Materials Exposure, Emergency Response and Patient Care,* Prentice Hall, Englewood Cliffs, NJ, 1991.

Bronstein, Alvin C., and Phillip L. Currance. *Emergency Care for Hazardous Materials Exposure*, 2nd ed., Mosby Lifeline, St. Louis, 1994.

PART FOUR

Supplements

The fourteen supplements included in this section of the *Hazardous Materials Response Handbook* provide additional information about key areas of concern for hazardous materials responders. They are not part of the official NFPA documents or the commentary presented in the previous sections of this book. A number of these supplements have been written by recognized experts in the fields they cover, and all provide in-depth coverage of various specialized areas.

1. Justifying a Haz Mat Team
2. Hazardous Materials Emergency Response: Cost Recovery Options for Local Governments
3. Selection of Chemical Protective Clothing Using NFPA Standards
4. Computer Resources for Hazardous Materials Responders
5. Haz Mat Teams in Transition: Regionalizing the Haz Mat Response in Massachusetts
6. Hazardous Materials Emergency Planning Guide
7. Beginning the Hazard Analysis Process
8. NY Fire Department Hazardous Materials Emergency Response Plan: An Overview
9. City of Sacramento/Sacramento Fire Department Hazardous Materials Emergency Response Plan, 1997
10. Guidelines for Decontamination of Fire Fighters and Their Equipment Following Hazardous Materials Incidents
11. EMS Sector Standard Operating Procedures
12. Preparing for a Hazardous Materials Accident: The Hospital Perspective
13. Grounding and Bonding Applications for Emergency Responders
14. Emergency Response to Incidents Involving Chemical and Biological Warfare Agents

SUPPLEMENT 1

Justifying a Haz Mat Team

L. Charles Smeby, Jr.

Editor's Note: This supplement identifies major areas of concern for a community forming a new or evaluating an existing hazardous materials response team. In it, we describe the expense, the minimum staffing and training requirements, and other considerations—including sources of alternative response for communities that are unable to justify the cost of team readiness and training.

INTRODUCTION

Hazardous materials response requires a rethinking of many of the traditional approaches the fire service has relied on in fire fighting and rescue work. The speed with which an incident is approached, the level of pre-incident planning required, and the dependence on specialists from other fields including the private sector differ radically from the standard operating procedures required in fire fighting. Rethinking extends to the heart of hazardous materials team planning and justification and leads us to ask, Does every community need a hazardous materials response team of its own?

The past two decades have witnessed an explosion in the numbers of hazardous materials teams created in the public sector. In most cases, these teams are under the jurisdiction and command of the fire department. Since these teams have formed, however, many communities have found that they are used rarely, if at all. For example, the fire department of New York City is recognized as the busiest in the United States. Yet, according to *Firehouse Magazine,* its hazardous materials–related runs total less than 1 percent of the overall run count each year. In New York City, this amounts to approximately 1044 runs. In smaller municipalities, a single call per year is not unusual.

According to incident records collected from state and local jurisdictions over the past several years and discussions with members of various operational teams, hazardous materials releases account for 0.5 percent to 1.0 percent of a local jurisdiction's fire calls. Approximately 50 percent of these incidents involve very small quantities (less than 55 gallons) of hazardous materials, and 75 percent of these incidents occur at fixed facilities where the material is routinely stored and used.

In the face of few calls, limited opportunity to test their training, and increased need to broaden their experience and knowledge in the field, haz mat teams become discouraged and burned out. The increased demand for training, often coupled with budget constraints, can reduce the team head count to less than optimum levels. Department chiefs with few haz mat–related runs to their credit have difficulty justifying the continuing cost of training equipment and investment in new technologies and equipment that keep a team at the highest state of readiness for any potential emergency.

In the initial rush to create haz mat teams everywhere, we were not able to accurately evaluate the basic premise that every community needs its own team or teams. Everyone, including the experts consulted for the previous edition of this handbook, supported the creation of more teams. With this edition, we are stepping back and offering the critical questions commanders should ask when justifying the creation of new and support of existing haz mat teams.

COMMUNITY CRITERIA

As with many municipal functions, community criteria demand the operation of specific municipal services such as fire and police departments. Many smaller communities, however, have no police department of their own, since coverage of this service is provided from a county or state organization or as part of a regional service alliance. Evaluation of any municipal function, then, will depend on many factors.

Evaluating the continued need for a haz mat team begins with a profile of the community. Are there sufficient hazardous materials risks within the municipality or region covered by the team? This information can be reviewed in several ways, beginning with the call history for the community. How many haz mat–related runs were made in the past five years (or less, depending on the team's inception date), and were these runs all in one or two categories? For example, if the community has few manufacturing or industrial sites that carry risks of incidents in the transportation, storage, or manufacture of products using hazardous materials, then the justification of a potential catastrophic incident can be discounted. If, on the other hand, there is a major roadway with a high risk of trucking accidents or a major railroad spur within its borders, it can be determined whether related incidents met expectations of predicted risks.

Any changes within the community profile also need to be considered. For example, has a large employer made any significant changes in its facility, shifting from administration to manufacturing or reducing the work force in response to shifting markets? The prepared response planner will call the company's security director or plant manager to learn whether and how these changes will impact an existing haz mat response plan. Because response needs are tied in many cases to the day to day operations of local users of hazardous materials, response plans need to be constantly reevaluated, in the face of experience within the response area and with the changing needs of the community. Tracking these changes over time allows planners to predict, with some degree of certainty, how these changes will affect the incident numbers.

Once the incident numbers and profiles are obtained, a planner needs to look at how the various incidents were handled. Were private sector technicians called in to mitigate the incidents, or were they handled entirely by the public sector team? Was this common to all of the incidents handled, to some, or to only a few? If private sector technicians, provided by shippers or manufacturers, assisted on a majority of the hazardous materials calls, can these responders be relied on to respond in the future? For example, consider a community with few Level A spill risks but within its borders a major rail spur that generated four calls in the past two years. The planner would determine whether the railroad provided hazardous materials technicians to mitigate the incidents, leaving the community haz mat team with the responsibility of evacuation or rescue and containment of the incident area. If this was the case, it is possible that the community could rely on the private sector for Level A coverage of these incidents (or another team from a nearby fire department) and maintain local readiness for lower levels of response. If a reliable responder unit that has been called in the past is available, then team justification may hinge on the availability of this other response resource in the future.

COST

Cost is one of the primary reasons that many communities have consolidated their teams into regional or district haz mat response units. Given that a hazardous materials response team should consist of approximately 20 members in order to provide coverage on a 24-hour basis, over holidays and weekends, and while some team members are in training, staffing costs, as well as the cost of training and equipment, are major expenses.

Hazardous materials response experts William J. Keffer and Alan Cummings, in the last edition of this handbook, said that the suggested composition for a small local team would contain the following disciplines or special capabilities:

- Three to six fire service personnel
- Two representatives of the local health authority (local health department, poison control, or medical personnel)
- A minimum of one law enforcement representative (to coordinate local law enforcement agencies, scene security, and evacuation planning)

- Two to four industry or academic personnel for special advice and assistance
- A minimum of one sponsoring agency administration person for legal management of storage and disposal

These experts stressed that the team members "should have ample opportunity to train, cross-train, and practice haz mat skills in a variety of response and control exercises, especially hands-on simulations."

The rationale for the team composition just suggested is based on observation and experience. Jurisdictions should combine considerations for storage and disposal, along with regulatory compliance, into the system before they begin to contemplate response actions. In most jurisdictions the fire service personnel become the first entity notified and the first on scene. Successful hazardous materials incident management is also dependent on competent and timely investigations by law enforcement; evaluation of hazardous material recovery, recycling, or disposal pursuant to environmental regulations; and determination of public and team member health and safety by health professionals.

According to Keffer and Cummings, if a community or facility plans for a 10-person haz mat team (requiring that 20 members be assigned), a team can be developed and maintained for about $33,350 per year (exclusive of salaries or overtime to cover vacancies and assuming that SCBA gear is already owned and maintained in sufficient numbers to provide for each team member).

Although these experts agree that such a team would present an effective response posture and provide mitigation and personnel safety for more than 90 percent of all incidents likely to occur in an average community, they recommended that, for complete hazardous materials mitigation service, it will be necessary to make arrangements for other agencies to respond when needed. Initial expenditures (for the first year of team operation) would break down as follows:

Comprehensive physical exams at about $575 each	$11,500
Out-of-service training (2 weeks)	4,600
Communications for non-fire service (pagers)	4,600
Reference resource books and programs	2,300
Personal protective gear	6,900
Mitigation and screening supplies	3,450
Total	$33,350

Items such as transportation, in-service training, and premium pay have not been costed. Properly managed small programs generally rely on vehicles readily

Table S1-1 Cost Chart for Basic Personal Protective Clothing

Item	Cost	Source
Coverall, Tyvek or Polypropylene	$2 to $4.50 each	Local safety equipment supplier
Coverall, Saranex or CPE	$10 to $25 each	
Acid suit coverall, PVC/nylon	$35 to $65 each	
Multilayer encapsulating suits	$45 to $200 each	
Surgical gloves, vinyl	$3 to $4.50 per box of 100	
Vinyl outer gloves	$12 to $16 per dozen pairs (case)	
PVC-lined outer gloves	$16 to $23 per dozen pairs	
Neoprene-lined outer gloves	$25 to $40 per dozen pairs	
Buna-nitrile–coated outer gloves	$23 to $27 per dozen pairs	
PVA outer gloves	$95 to $115 per dozen pairs	
Butyl outer gloves	$14 to $25 per dozen pairs	
Chemical overboots	$18 to $25 per pair	
Safety goggles	$4 to $7 each	
Duct tape	$1.50 to $6 per roll	Local hardware supplier
Large plastic bags	$4 to $8 per box	Local hardware or safety supplier
North American Emergency Response Guidebook	$4 each	U.S. Department of Transportation, U.S. Government Book Store, local safety supplier, local emergency management agency

available within a municipality. In-service training needs will vary with local exposure potential. In subsequent years, the $33,350 would be spent in a variable manner, depending on the needs of the individual community for both equipment and training.

Table S1-1 offers a general guide to the cost of required personal protective equipment. These costs will vary by region, by distributors and manufacturers, and the volume of purchases. They are based on figures offered by Keffer and Cummings and have been adjusted for inflation.

Finally, the cost of the mitigation itself must be considered, along with the likelihood that costs can be recovered or other funding sources can be obtained. To analyze unknown costs, several questions should be considered. What percentage of costs have been recovered in the past? How much has been spent on the recovery effort, and how long was the lag between the money spent on mitigation and the recovery of those costs? If the department cannot afford to maintain the team at the appropriate level, regionalizing (described in Supplement 5) or disbanding the team may need to be considered. (Supplement 2 offers additional cost recovery information.)

OTHER ONGOING CONSIDERATIONS

The kinds of training opportunities available in a community will affect cost, as well as team member motivation and commitment. The availability of hands-on drills and field training with team members and with those of any teams likely to be called in on mutual aid is important. However, the organization of drills and training sessions requires a lot of coordination and networking within the community and with the public and private sectors. This time must be considered as part of the work hours of the team leadership and command structure.

CONCLUSIONS

The experience of a hazardous materials team is its most valuable resource. If a team has little field experience, its field work is shaped only by the controlled conditions of drills and training sessions. Despite the best intentions, these efforts will fall short of the hands-on learning of actual incidents. In communities with limited run numbers related to hazardous materials, local or regional mutual aid partnerships can be effective ways to provide appropriate levels of protection while reducing individual community costs.

SUPPLEMENT 2

Hazardous Materials Emergency Response: Cost Recovery Options for Local Governments

Editor's Note: This supplement is drawn from a more detailed publication of the same title, produced in 1996 by the Urban Energy and Transportation Corporation, Local Transportation and Technology Institutional Project, and reprinted here with our thanks. For more information about this project and to obtain a copy of the full report, with its state-by-state summary information, please contact George Ruberg, UETC Program Manager, 22 Maple Street, Wheeling, WV 26003.

INTRODUCTION

While transportation incidents involving hazardous materials are rare compared to the total of all traffic incidents, the potential consequences of a release of these materials can be severe. In almost all cases, local fire and law enforcement personnel are usually the first officials on the scene of a haz mat transportation accident.

Although usually the responsibility for the costs of cleaning up these spills rests with the materials carrier, or another responsible party, local governments often incur significant emergency response costs long before liability can be determined by a court or other authority. The costs for a single incident can be staggering for small communities especially when the responsible party is unwilling or unable to pay the costs of cleanup.

This report summarizes federal programs that are in place to help local governments cope with cost recovery problems. The document also lists selected approaches that states have taken, either in implementing federal programs or in enacting separate legislation to achieve response and recovery goals by other means. Finally, this report analyzes liability issues for a separate category of haz mat incidents—those involving radioactive materials—that has been largely excluded from the main body of environmental regulations and describes how various federal statutes and programs govern management and response related to these special materials.

This report will be revised periodically, and will be updated as amended statutes and programmatic developments require.[1] While the researchers have made every effort to ensure that the information contained herein is correct and up-to-date, regulations frequently change, and actual implementation of state programs is sometimes quite different from that described in statutes. Reader comments and suggestions for improving the usefulness of this document are welcome.

STATUTORY FRAMEWORK: FEDERAL PROGRAMS

Federal Laws Governing Emergency Response

The first broad federal statute that provided for comprehensive oversight of hazardous materials management was the Resource Conservation and Recovery Act (RCRA), enacted in 1976. Before passage of the act, up to 90 percent of all hazardous wastes in the country may have been disposed of improperly.[2]

The RCRA did not address chemical spills, and in 1980 Congress enacted the Comprehensive Environmental Response, Compensation and Liability Act (CERCLA) to "plug holes left by RCRA."[3] The National Oil and Hazardous Substances Pollution Contingency Plan, or NCP, is the primary regulation that outlines the roles and responsibilities of federal agencies and describes how state and local jurisdictions participate in responding to hazardous substance releases. The NCP is codified at 40 CFR part 300.[4]

CERCLA authorizes the Environmental Protection Agency (EPA) to take direct action or compel responsible parties to respond to emergencies involving hazardous materials. As amended by the Superfund Amendments and Authorization Act of 1986 (SARA), the act provides $8.5 billion in funding to pay for cleanup when the potentially responsible parties cannot be identified or are insolvent. SARA Title III, the Emergency Planning and Community Right-to-Know Act (EPCRA), requires emergency planning structures at state and local levels of government, and requires notification of releases of hazardous materials.[5] Accidents involving petroleum products such as oil are expressly excluded from the scope of CERCLA.[6] Section 105 of the act authorizes "removal actions," which are defined as "short-term, emergency responses."[7]

Role of States and Localities under CERCLA

Many states participate in nearly every aspect of the CERCLA program, including enforcement, removal actions, and remedial activities.[8] Under the CERCLA framework, states and localities may act as lead agencies for cleanup. Federally recognized Native American tribes are basically treated as states for purposes of enforcement and program involvement. States and tribes may enter into cooperative agreements with EPA to become the lead agency for cleanup, after which they may recover costs from responsible parties.[9]

EPA's Local Government Reimbursement Program

As originally enacted, CERCLA did not provide specifically for local government reimbursement for emergency response cost recovery. Localities that tried to recover in tort against potentially responsible parties often encountered problems because as a general rule of common law, governments responding to accidents had a "pre-existing governmental duty to act" to respond to such incidents.[10] In enacting the 1986 Superfund law, Congress acknowledged the potential unfairness of asking local governments to pay for complex environmental response actions involving hazardous materials, particularly in the case of a transportation incident originating from a distant facility that provides no local tax revenues.

Congress intends that local governments continue to bear some share of expenses for providing temporary emergency measures. However, Congress recognized that in the past, conducting such response activities has placed a significant financial burden on some local governments . . . . [Superfund] can provide some financial relief (limited to $25,000 per single response) to local governments most seriously affected by costs above and beyond those incurred routinely and traditionally.[11]

EPA's Local Governments Reimbursement (LGR) program reimburses local governments for the costs of responding to a release (or a threatened release) of hazardous substances. The program is intended to serve as a "safety net" for those local governments that do not have funds available for emergency response activities. Participation in the LGR program is limited to any general purpose unit of local government and federally recognized tribes. Long-term remedial actions are not addressed under CERCLA Section 123, the section authorizing the program; only temporary emergency response activities may be reimbursed, and routine fire fighting or other response activities are also not covered. Some expenses that have been reimbursed have included disposable materials and supplies, rental or leasing of equipment, special technical services and laboratory costs, services and supplies purchased for an evacuation of (unbudgeted) overtime, and the decontamination of equipment.[12]

In order to be eligible, local governments must notify EPA or the National Response Center at (1-800-424-8802) within 24 hours of the incident. The LGR has application packets that must be submitted in order to receive reimbursement; in the application, the local government must demonstrate that:

1. Emergency response funds have not been budgeted;
2. State reimbursement funds are unavailable;
3. Local government insurance does not cover the incident; and
4. Attempts have been made to recover costs from the party responsible for the incident.

Local governments also must be participants in the Local Emergency Planning Committee (LEPC) process delineated in EPCRA.[13] To date, local governments have received over $900,000 from the LGR program, and several incidents have involved transportation accidents.[14] For more information, contact the LGR Hotline at 1-800-431-9209.

Federal Facilities and CERCLA

Federal facilities owned by the Departments of Defense, Interior, and Energy are regulated by CERCLA just like private facilities.[15] However, Section 111(e) of CERCLA prohibits Superfund monies from being used to clean up federal facilities sites. Cleanup plans for contamination at federal facilities are governed by Interagency Agreements, or IAGs, between EPA, the landlord department, and the state (if it is willing to be a party).[16]

Radioactive Materials and the Price–Anderson Act

The level of insurance coverage that carriers must have when transporting radioactive materials varies according to the mode and amount of materials being shipped. For example, carriers of highway route controlled quantity (HRCQ) materials must have $5 million in insurance coverage available in the event of an accident.[17] For catastrophic accidents involving nuclear materials, the Price–Anderson Act (as amended) provides liability coverage of up to $8.96 billion.[18] In order to claim damages under the Act, an "extraordinary nuclear occurrence," or ENO, must have occurred. The claimant must prove only that the incident occurred and that the damages suffered were caused by the incident.[19] It should be noted that, although the statute has been amended significantly to protect those who might be injured in a radiological disaster, the statute was originally designed to indemnify contractors and others who were involved in the nuclear industry.[20] Considering the relatively small amounts and hazard levels of radioactive materials that are transported around the country, the chances that an incident involving radioactive materials would create an ENO are vanishingly small.

COMPARISON OF STATE REGULATORY STRUCTURES

Most statutes contemplate that local units of government will serve as the first line of defense in the event of a transportation accident involving hazardous materials; the level of oversight and direction by the state, however, varies widely. Similarly, there is a broad range of complexity in the statutory structures of state codes that address hazardous materials emergency response cost recovery issues. Some states, such as Idaho, Missouri, and North Carolina, provide detailed listings of the types of expenses that are reimbursable, including equipment. Other states simply refer to "necessary and reasonable" costs. The majority of statutes recognize that only unusual or extraordinary costs resulting from the nature of the hazardous material are reimbursable, where they can be recovered at all.

The statutory language of thirty-one states enables some type of payment to local governments for hazardous materials emergency response before proceeding against parties that may be liable for an incident. Nine other states will undertake a claim against a potentially responsible party on behalf of a locality, but do not reimburse the locality beforehand. Significantly, twelve states require that the local government secure some form of state-level approval before undertaking hazardous materials response actions; activity undertaken before obtaining approval may not be reimbursable. Several states place a cap on the amount that can be recovered per incident.

Fifteen state statutes expressly authorize local governments to bill liable parties directly, or to proceed against them in court. Two states provide an alternative dispute resolution process for localities and potentially responsible parties that cannot agree on issues of liability; the parties may elect binding arbitration instead of proceeding in court and incurring related costs.

Table S2-1 compares state regulatory structures and some of the cost recovery issues that they address.

CONCLUSION

State and local governments have differing perspectives on whether statutes that spell out specific cost recovery options are useful and desirable. Obviously, much depends on the historical relationship of the two levels of government and how well they can work together to protect public health and safety. While state legislatures place a high premium on state–local cooperation in emergency planning and response, some are understandably concerned about state revenues being applied for localized needs that may be more appropriately funded through local taxes.

Hazardous materials transportation incidents, as stated above, frequently happen long distances away from their place of origin or destination, and fees and taxes levied on these materials are not incorporated into the community's tax base; effective cost recovery following an accident is therefore essential. Local officials who want to see state programs modified should stress the additional, incremental, or extraordinary

Table S2-1 Comparison of State Statutory Structures

DO THE STATE STATUTES . . .	AL	AK	AZ	AR	CA	CO	CT	DE	DC	FL	GA	HI	ID	IL	IN	IA	KS	KY	LA	ME	MD	MA	MI	MN	MS
Expressly permit the state to reimburse localities before proceeding against responsible parties?		Y			Y	Y	Y	Y		Y	Y	Y	Y	Y	Y	Y	Y	Y	Y		Y	Y	Y	Y	Y
Expressly permit the state to undertake a claim on behalf of locality?						Y		Y		Y			Y	Y			Y	Y	Y				Y		
Require localities to secure state authorization before Incurring reimbursable costs?		Y					Y				Y				Y	Y	Y	Y	Y		Y				Y
Place a cap on the amount of costs that are reimbursable from a single incident?														Y		Y							Y		
Authorize direct billing of the responsible party or litigation brought by the locality?			Y		Y	Y			Y			Y			Y						Y	Y		Y	
Expressly provide for alternative dispute resolution between localities and the responsible party?																									

	MO	MT	NB	NV	NH	NJ	NM	NY	NC	ND	OH	OK	OR	PA	RI	SC	SD	TN	TX	UT	VT	VA	WA	WV	WI	WY
Expressly permit the state to reimburse localities before proceeding against responsible parties?	Y		Y	Y	Y			Y	Y	Y		Y	Y	Y			Y				Y	Y	Y	Y	Y	
Expressly permit the state to undertake a claim on behalf of locality?				Y				Y	Y				Y				Y				Y	Y		Y		
Require localities to secure state authorization before incurring reimbursable costs?								Y	Y		Y						Y				Y	Y		Y		
Place a cap on the amount of costs that are reimbursable from a single incident?									Y			Y		Y												
Authorize direct billing of the responsible party or litigation brought by the locality?	Y			Y	Y	Y				Y	Y		Y	Y				Y		Y				Y	Y	
Expressly provide for alternative dispute resolution between localities and the responsible party?						Y								Y												

costs resulting from hazardous materials emergency response that fall upon communities, as differentiated from "normal" law enforcement and fire protection.

A critical issue in the hazardous materials emergency response involves timing of notifications. Many states require prior notification and authorization from the state before a locality may undertake an involved cleanup. If such notifications are not made promptly, a locality may find itself shut off from potential remedies offered by the state. Similarly, EPA requires notification of an incident within 24 hours to make a locality eligible for reimbursement under CERCLA Section 123.

Local government officials should be thoroughly aware of the statutory structures, implementing procedures, and regulatory requirements regarding such responses, as early communication may determine whether or not the cost will ultimately be borne by the locality.

References

1. Note on origin, scope and methodology of this report: The issue of emergency response cost recovery for local governments was the subject of much discussion at a Local Government Network workshop sponsored by UETC in Idaho Falls, Idaho in early 1995. Participants wanted to learn more about how federal programs help in this area, and how states either implement such programs or "plug" perceived holes in program coverage. This report does not address the many local ordinances that have been passed by municipalities around the country. Information for this report was gathered from a variety of on-line information resources, including the Hazardous Materials Information exchange (HMIX) and the National Conference of State Legislature's Transportation Legislative DataBase (TLDB). The support of these projects is gratefully acknowledged, and responsibility for any inaccuracies is entirely that of the authors.
2. Findlay, Roger W., and Farber, Daniel A., Environmental Law in a Nutshell, 231 (1992).
3. Gramling, George F., III and Earl, William L., Cleaning Up After Federal and State Pollution Programs: Local Government Hazardous Waste Regulation, 17 Stetson L. Rev. 639 (Summer 1988).
4. Reimbursement to Local Governments for Emergency Response to Hazardous Substance Releases, 58 Fed. Reg. 10, 4817 (1993).
5. U.S. Environmental Protection Agency, Office of Solid Waste and Emergency Response, Technical Innovation Office, CERCLA/Superfund Orientation Manual. EPA/542/R-92/005 (October 1992), II-5.
6. CERCLA provides for response to hazardous substance emergencies and the cleanup of existing sites. See Roger W. Findlay and Daniel A. Farber, Environmental Law in a Nutshell, 241 (1992).
7. Ibid. at 241.
8. Ibid., Note 5 at VIII-1.
9. Ibid., Note 6 at 243.
10. McIntyre, David, Tortfeasor Liability for Disaster Response Costs: Accounting for the True Cost of Accidents, 55 Fordham L. Rev. 1001, 1005 (May 1987).
11. Reimbursement to Local Governments for Emergency Response to Hazardous Substance Releases, 58 Fed. Reg. 10, 4817.
12. Presentation by Ms. Lisa Boynton, Project Manager, Environmental Protection Agency, Local Government Reimbursement Project, before the UETC National Conference, Baltimore, April 18, 1996.
13. U.S. Environmental Protection Agency, Office of Solid Waste and Emergency Response, Local Government Relief: EPA Provides Federal Funds for Emergency Response Activities (discussion paper).
14. Interview with Richard Douglas, Research Assistant, ICF Incorporated, August 15, 1995 (Mr. Douglas is staff support contractor for EPA's Local Government Reimbursement Hotline).
15. U.S. Environmental Protection Agency, Office of Solid Waste and Emergency Response, Technical Innovation Office, CERCLA/Superfund Orientation Manual. EPA/542/R-92/005 (October 1992), IX-1.
16. Ibid. at IX-1.
17. U.S. Department of Energy, Transporting Radioactive Materials Q&A: Answers to Your Questions, April 1993, 20.
18. Presentation of Susan Klein, DOE Office of General Counsel, at the Transportation External Coordination Working Group Meeting in Charlotte, North Carolina, January 17, 1995. Ms. Klein also added that after the incident at Three Mile Island, the NRC set up offices to process claims under Price–Anderson. However, the amount of claims submitted never exceeded the initial insurance limit ($160 million).
19. Berkovitz, Dan M., "Price-Anderson Act: Model Compensation Legislation?—The Sixty-Three Million Dollar Question," 13 Harv. Envtl. L. Rev. 1.
20. Ibid. at 10.

SUPPLEMENT 3

Selection of Chemical Protective Clothing Using NFPA Standards

Jeffrey O. Stull, International Personnel Protection, Inc.

Editor's Note: One of the most important concerns for a hazardous materials response team is the selection of chemical protective clothing. A team must purchase clothing that is appropriate to the potential exposures they are likely to encounter at incidents in their response area. In this supplement, Jeff Stull, an expert on CPC design, construction, and selection criteria, describes the key considerations in choosing the right garments, with information drawn from his experience and from several NFPA standards dealing with the performance of CPC.

INTRODUCTION

Chemical protective clothing comes in a variety of shapes, colors, and sizes. Manufacturers of chemical protective clothing are constantly developing and offering new products or new features on existing products. While product documentation has improved, claims for increased performance are not always readily apparent. End users are faced with a myriad of choices of encapsulating and splash suits at a wide range of performance and cost. With all of these choices, response organizations sometimes have a difficult time sorting out products in the marketplace. Choosing the appropriate chemical protective suit requires a general understanding of these products, knowledge of factors important in their selection, and knowledge of the standards governing their performance.

GENERAL UNDERSTANDING OF PRODUCTS

Chemical Protective Ensembles

Chemical protective suits are part of an ensemble of personnel protective equipment (PPE). As defined by the U.S. Environmental Protection Agency (EPA), ensembles consist of protective suits, a self-contained breathing apparatus (SCBA) or combination SCBA and supplied air respirator, chemically resistant gloves and boots, hard hats, communications equipment, cooling devices, and various types of undergarments *(see Table S3-1 and Figures S3-1–S3-3).*

Although the EPA levels of protection describe what the ensemble should look like, little guidance is offered for how the ensemble should perform. It is vital that the ensemble elements work together to provide the intended level of protection. This means that items should fit together (provide good interfaces) and offer consistent performance for the wearer's entire body. Unfortunately, duct tape is often used in an attempt to correct ill-fitting suits and poorly designed interfaces.

Chemical protective suits should be considered a system, consisting of the base material, seams, closures, and the overall suit design. Often, attention is paid only to the base material, neglecting other parts of the suit that have a significant impact on the suit's

Table S3-1 EPA Levels of Protection

Level	Equipment	Protection Provided	Should Be Used When	Limiting Criteria
A	Recommended: • Pressure-demand, full-facepiece SCBA or pressure-demand, supplied-air respirator with escape SCBA • Fully-encapsulating chemical-resistant suit • Inner chemical-resistant gloves • Chemical-resistant safety boots/shoes • Two-way radio communications Optional: • Cooling unit • Coveralls • Long cotton underwear • Hard hat • Disposable gloves and boot covers	The highest available level of respiratory, skin, and eye protection	• The chemical substance has been identified and requires the highest level of protection for skin, eyes, and the respiratory system based on either: • measured (or potential for) high concentration of atmospheric vapors, gases, or particulates, or • site operations and work functions involving a high potential for splash, immersion, or exposure to unexpected vapors, gases, or particulates of materials that are harmful to skin or capable of being absorbed through the intact skin • Substances with a high degree of hazard to the skin are known or suspected to be present, and skin contact is possible • Operations must be conducted in confined, poorly ventilated areas until the absence of conditions requiring Level A protection is determined	Fully encapsulating suit material must be compatible with the substances involved
B	Recommended: • Pressure-demand, full-facepiece SCBA or pressure-demand supplied-air respirator with escape SCBA • Chemical-resistant clothing (overalls and long-sleeved jacket; hooded, one- or two-piece chemical splash suit; disposable chemical-resistant one-piece suit) • Inner and outer chemical-resistant gloves • Chemical-resistant safety boots/shoes • Hard hat • Two-way radio communications Optional: • Coveralls • Disposable boot covers • Face shield • Long cotton underwear	The same level of respiratory protection but less skin protection than Level A It is the minimum level recommended for initial site entries until the hazards have been further identified	• The type and atmospheric concentration of substances have been identified and require a high level of respiratory protection, but less skin protection. This involves atmospheres: • with IDLH concentrations of specific substances that do not represent a severe skin hazard; or • that do not meet the criteria for use of air purifying respirators • Atmosphere contains less than 19.5 percent oxygen • Presence of incompletely identified vapors or gases is indicated by direct-reading organic vapor detection instrument, but vapors and gases are not suspected of containing high levels of chemicals harmful to skin or capable of being absorbed through the intact skin	• Use only when the vapor or gases present are not suspected of containing high concentrations of chemicals that are harmful to skin or capable of being absorbed through the intact skin • Use only when it is highly unlikely that the work being done will generate either high concentrations of vapors, gases, or particulates or splashes of material that will affect exposed skin

Table S3-1 (continued)

Level	Equipment	Protection Provided	Should Be Used When	Limiting Criteria
C	Recommended: • Full facepiece, air-purifying, canister-equipped respirator • Chemical-resistant clothing (overalls and long-sleeved jacket; hooded, one- or two-piece chemical splash suit; disposable chemical-resistant one-piece suit) • Inner and outer chemical-resistant gloves • Chemical-resistant safety boots/shoes • Hard hat • Two-way radio communications Optional: • Coveralls • Disposable boot covers • Face shield • Escape mask • Long cotton underwear	The same level of skin protection as Level B, but a lower level of respiratory protection	• The atmospheric contaminants, liquid splashes, or other direct contact will not adversely affect any exposed skin • The types of air contaminants have been identified, concentrations have been measured, and a canister is available that can remove the contaminant • All criteria for the use of air-purifying respirators are met	• Atmospheric concentration of chemicals must not exceed IDLH levels • The atmosphere must contain at least 19.5 percent oxygen
D	Recommended: • Coveralls • Safety boots/shoes • Safety glasses or chemical splash goggles • Hard hat Optional: • Gloves • Escape mask • Face shield	No respiratory protection Minimal skin protection	• The atmosphere contains no known hazard • Work functions preclude splashes, immersion, or the potential for unexpected inhalation of, or contact with, hazardous levels of any chemicals	• This level should not be worn in the exclusion zone • The atmosphere must contain at least 19.5 percent oxygen

effectiveness. For example, the barrier characteristics of the best material in the market can be diminished when put into a design that is awkward to wear and has poor quality seams. Therefore, all aspects of suit design are important in the choice of a chemical protective suit, not simply the base material and its chemical resistance properties as generally promoted in the marketplace. The following are examples of other desirable attributes:

- Seams should offer chemical resistance consistent with base material.
- Closures, the weak link of the system, should be protected in a manner that keeps liquid (splashes) from reaching the inside of the clothing.
- Suits should be designed to be easily donned and to minimize impairment of wearer movement, field of vision, dexterity, and tactility.

For the most part, this sort of information can only come from direct inspections or trials with potential products and from asking manufacturers for data they normally do not provide. In addition, it would be helpful to contact other purchasers and users to get their observations and experiences.

Risk Assessment

The choice of chemical protective clothing must be based on first completing a risk assessment. There are two types of risk assessments that will aid in selecting PPE for purchase or use—those performed on the general, expected situations that response teams encounter and assessments that are performed for a specific hazard. In each case, the risk assessment should consist of the following steps:

Figure S3-1 This responder is wearing A-level chemical protective clothing. The configuration of this encapsulating suit affords the wearer two levels of face protection. The SCBA worn by this responder is visible under the outer layer of the suit. (Photo by Mark C. Ide courtesy of Lt. Hansen of the Bedford, MA, Fire Department)

Figure S3-2 This responder is wearing Level B protective clothing for specific situations that require less protection from heat and chemical permeation. Note the duct tape used to provide a better seal between the sack suit legs and the boots. (Photo courtesy of Henrik G. de Gyor)

- Identifying the hazards present
- Estimating the likelihood of exposure
- Understanding the consequences of exposure
- Determining the risk

A simple model for conducting a risk assessment is shown in Table S3-2. In this model, the likelihood of exposure and the consequences of exposure are estimated for each expected hazard. Risk is determined by multiplying the exposure likelihood by the exposure consequences. In this way, risks associated with specific hazards can be determined and ranked to ascertain protection and clothing performance needs.

The hazards alone need not be the determining factor for choosing PPE; rather it is the potential for exposure that should govern selection of chemical protective clothing. For example, there are risk differences when dealing with a gallon of toluene versus dealing with a tank car full of the chemical. Underprotection should be avoided to prevent exposure, but overprotection can be just as dangerous. It can lead to injury through heat stress and hinder the wearer from safely performing the needed tasks. Contingencies must be planned for, but there should also be a sense of realism when it comes to suit selection.

Figure S3-3 This responder in Level C protective clothing is protected against chemical or other liquid splashes but has little to no protection that would permit entry into the hot zone. Note how the suit is one piece, eliminating gaps between pants and jacket. The pull-down face shield on the hat affords additional splash protection. (Photo by Mark C. Ide courtesy of Lt. Hansen of the Bedford, MA, Fire Department)

Table S3-2 Risk Assessment Areas for Selection of Chemical Protective Clothing

	Body Area Affected					
Hazard Area	**Full Body**	**Resp. System**	**Head Area**	**Torso**	**Arms/ Hands**	**Legs/ Feet**
Chemical vapor inhalation						
Chemical vapor skin absorption						
Chemical liquid skin contact						
Chemical ingestion						
Falling objects						
Flying debris						
Sharp objects						
Rough surfaces						
Slippery surfaces						
Extreme cold						
High heat						
Flame exposure						
Chemical flash fire						
Static discharge						
Electrical shock						
Poor visibility						
Falling from height						
Falling into water						
Cold stress						
Heat stress						
Mobility restriction						
Dexterity restriction						
Vision restriction						
Hearing restriction						

SELECTION FACTORS

A number of factors should be collectively considered when selecting chemical protective clothing:

- Overall suit integrity
- Material chemical resistance
- Material strength and physical hazard resistance
- Overall suit design
- Service life
- Cost

Overall Suit Integrity

While material permeation resistance is important, other material and clothing characteristics should not be overlooked. Suit integrity, for example, should be carefully examined. Encapsulating suits are easily tested for gastight integrity using pressure (inflation) testing. The pressure or inflation test evaluates the encapsulating suit for pinholes and other leaks. While this test is simple to perform, it does not evaluate the entire suit since exhaust valves are closed off. Pressure testing is recommended when receiving new suits and as a periodic test of suit condition.

Splash suits are rarely given this same attention. These suits should provide liquidtight integrity by keeping liquids off the wearer's skin or clothing. Even though most coated or laminated materials successfully offer this performance, seams, closures, and interface areas may not. These areas must be protected in order for the entire suit and ensemble to function properly under liquid exposure situations. It is possible to evaluate liquidtight integrity by using simple techniques that challenge critical areas with liquid spray and then examine the suit's interior or inner garment for evidence of penetrating liquid. This form of testing is useful to evaluate how different parts of the liquid protective ensemble work together.

Material Chemical Resistance

The most commonly used factor for selecting chemical protective clothing is permeation resistance data on the base clothing material. Chemical protective clothing resistance may be evaluated in three ways:

1. Degradation resistance
2. Penetration resistance
3. Permeation resistance

Degradation Resistance. This evaluation involves a determination of chemical effects on specific clothing material properties. In degradation resistance testing, specimens of clothing material are typically placed in contact with the test chemical for a relatively long period. Material degradation is determined in terms of visible changes, weight gain or loss, or changes in one or more material properties (such as strength). Most often, chemical degradation resistance information takes the form of qualitative ratings, which ranks material performance on a five or more part scale. These ratings most frequently are provided for glove or footwear materials but usually do not appear for garments.

Penetration Resistance. This evaluation determines how well protective clothing materials prevent the flow of liquid. Test results are reported as either pass or fail. Materials pass the test when they show no visible penetration after a given test exposure period (usually one hour). Any visible liquid on the interior of the clothing material constitutes a failure. Most coated or laminated clothing easily passes this test unless the chemical degrades the material and causes a hole. As a consequence, penetration resistance testing is most often used for breathable materials, seams, and closures.

Permeation Resistance. Permeation occurs on a submicroscopic level where chemical molecules pass through the protective clothing material. Permeation resistance testing involves measuring breakthrough time and the rate the chemical passes through the material. Breakthrough time represents the time when chemical is first detected permeating the material and the permeation rate serves as a measure for how quickly the chemical passes through the material. Because permeation resistance testing involves a very sensitive determination of clothing material barrier effectiveness, it is the preferred measurement for chemical resistance among protective clothing manufacturers. In practice, end users typically choose clothing materials that have breakthrough times longer than the expected maximum exposure time.

Material Physical Properties

Some manufacturers are beginning to present physical property data in their marketing literature as indications of material strength and durability. Commonly reported physical properties include the following:

- Tensile or breaking strength
- Burst strength
- Tear resistance
- Cut resistance (gloves and footwear)
- Puncture resistance (gloves and footwear)
- Flex durability
- Abrasion resistance
- Flame resistance

Unfortunately, unless end users are familiar with this type of data, the information may not be understood.

Physical properties are best used for comparing the relative strength or durability of different materials, provided the same test is used on all the materials compared. To understand physical properties, the end user must be able to compare the result on a new material with the result on a material that he or she has experience with. Physical failure of suits in the field may not always be attributable to material strength, but in fact be the result of a poor design or improper fit.

Design Features

Design features affecting wearer function, fit, and comfort are difficult to measure and most often subjective but are still an important part of the selection process. The best way to evaluate suit design is through trial wearings. These trials need to include tasks that replicate the same types of movements and stresses that would be placed on suits during actual use. Through this type of evaluation, end users can determine how the suit impacts their ability to perform work. The following are examples of relevant design features:

- Location and length of the closure
- Position and size of the visor
- Available suit, glove, and footwear sizes

These features dramatically affect user functioning. In particular, glove systems have been found to decrease dexterity and cause hand function problems. *(See Figure S3-4.)* Sizing is important because manufacturers offer these suits in a number of different sizes. Accommodating particularly large or small people can be difficult with a limited number of sizes. Chemical protective clothing does not have to fit poorly.

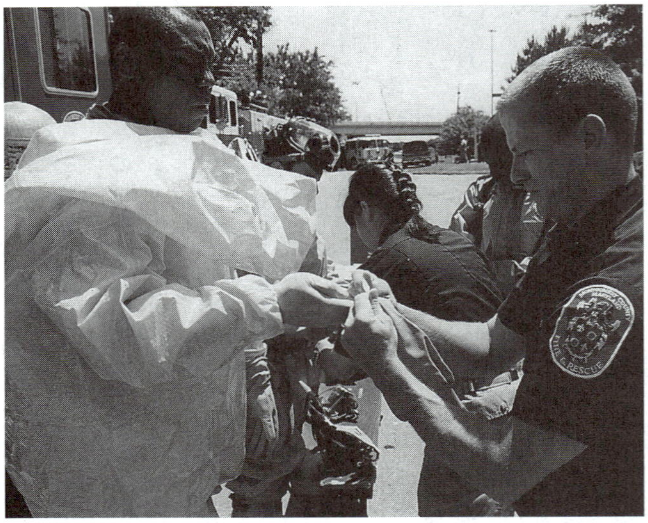

Figure S3-4 Gloves remain a problem for most hazardous materials responders. Currently, most responders use double or triple gloving techniques to compensate for a limited size range and material selection. However, using this multiglove technique is not without its tradeoffs including limited dexterity (e.g., difficulty using meter button controls). Some responders carry a small pencil stub or other disposable tool taped to their suit sleeves to help press small meter buttons with accuracy. (Photo courtesy of Henrik G. de Gyor)

Service Life

Service life is a complicated issue. In general, most users perceive inexpensive, lightweight plastic-based products as less durable and disposable, and relatively more expensive, heavy, rubber-based products as reusable. The service life of a product is actually based on its life cycle cost, durability, and ease of decontamination. Life cycle cost includes all costs associated with the use of the product including the initial purchase, maintenance, decontamination, storage, and disposal costs. While purchase costs may be the principal cost for product use, disposal costs are taking on greater significance. Durability is best assessed by determining how well the suit maintains its original condition for providing protection to the wearer. This can be assessed by measuring product chemical resistance for representative products following simulated use (information generally not provided in manufacturer literature). Ease of decontamination is important too. If the product cannot be decontaminated, it becomes disposable, no matter what the initial purchase cost is.

Cost

The issue of cost cannot be dismissed. In an ideal world, we would always buy the "best" suit in the marketplace. But the fact is that organization resources are limited. While some organizations have been able to set up programs to recoup PPE costs from those responsible for the incident, this form of chemical protective suit reimbursement cannot always be relied on. Response organizations want the optimum number and types of chemical protective clothing in their inventory to minimize selection decisions and obtain the best protection for their team members. Therefore, issues of product service life are important to the cost.

UNDERSTANDING AND USING COMPREHENSIVE PERFORMANCE STANDARDS

Creation of NFPA Standards on Chemical-Protective Clothing

In 1986, a subcommittee was formed by the National Fire Protection Association to develop standards on hazardous chemical-protective clothing. The subcommittee chose to develop three standards based primarily on the needs of emergency responders:

1. NFPA 1991, *Standard on Vapor-Protective Suits for Hazardous Chemical Emergencies,* 1994 edition
2. NFPA 1992, *Standard on Liquid Splash-Protective Suits for Hazardous Chemical Emergencies,* 1994 edition
3. NFPA 1993, *Standard on Support Function Protective Garments for Hazardous Chemical Operations,* 1994 edition

Each standard provides performance-oriented requirements for a specific protective suit ensembles (including gloves for hand protection and boots for foot protection). NFPA 1991 covers protective suits that offer protection from all forms of chemicals including vapors, gases, liquids, and solids. Both NFPA 1992 and 1993 pertain to clothing that prevents wearer exposure to liquid splashes or solid chemicals. NFPA 1991 and 1992 were prepared specifically for emergency response applications with the following characteristics:

1. The hazards range in severity.
2. The physical environment varies.
3. Aspects of the response remain uncharacterized.

In contrast, NFPA 1993 addresses non-emergency applications such as waste site cleanup, industrial situations, and decontamination where the type and extent of hazards present are more commonly known.

The NFPA standards include chapters on the following subjects:

- Administration, which contains the scope, purpose, and definitions used in the standard
- Certification, which details manufacturer and third-party certification responsibilities
- Documentation requirements: information that the manufacturer must report to the end user
- Design and performance requirements, which provide specific criteria for the overall suit, suit materials, and suit components
- Test methods, which define test procedures, parameters, and results to be reported
- Referenced publications that appear in support of the text.

An appendix was also added to provide supplementary information and recommendations for users of the standard.

The NFPA standards define a hierarchy of hazard protection as shown in Table S3-3. Using this hierarchy, the committee defined protective clothing types on the basis of needed performance as demonstrated by test methods designed to measure the type of protection provided. This method associated clothing gastight integrity and material permeation resistance with vapor protection and clothing liquidtight integrity, and material penetration resistance with liquid-splash protection. These performance-based definitions were intended to replace the historical EPA levels of protection that define what clothing should look like but not how it should perform.

In addition to defining a performance hierarchy among different types of chemical protective clothing, the NFPA standards defined consistent requirements for chemical resistance and limited flame resistance for ensuring the same level of performance for all parts of the clothing ensemble.

Starting with the 1990 edition of the NFPA standards, requirements for third-party certification with specific guidelines for independent qualification and follow-up testing, quality assurance audits of manufacturer facilities, and product labeling were included.

Revisions in 1994

Revisions of all three standards were completed in 1994. The original requirements were augmented with changes identified to offer additional protection attributes for chemical protective clothing systems.

All Standards. The 1994 changes to all three standards included the following:

- Clarifying the interpretation criteria for flame resistance
- Adding physical protection requirements for the wearer's head, hands, and feet (specifically addressing hard hats, visors, gloves, and boots)
- Establishing provisions that allow recognition of individual clothing items such as gloves and boots under each standard
- Providing guidelines that dictate how manufacturers report garment sizes

NFPA 1991. The revisions to NFPA 1991 included the following:

- Expanding the chemical battery to all 21 ASTM F 1001 chemicals. (See Table S3-4; this list includes 15 liquids and 6 gases.)
- Incorporating a test to measure the suit's capacity to vent exhaust air or cooling air
- Adding a series of requirements that address areas of enhanced protection for vapor-protective suits against both chemical flash fires and exposure to liquified gases

NFPA 1992. The revisions to NFPA 1992 included the following:

- Modifying the severity of the liquidtight integrity test to a more reasonable level of performance
- Adding requirements that address areas of enhanced protection for liquid splash-protective suits against chemical flash fires

NFPA 1993. The revisions to NFPA 1993 included adding new requirements for gloves, boots, and hoods as separate items of protective clothing.

Table S3-3 Definitions of Protective Clothing Types by Performance Tests in NFPA Standards

Type of Clothing	Material Performance	Overall Clothing Performance
Vapor Protective (NFPA 1991)	Permeation resistance	Gastight integrity
Liquid-Splash Protective (NFPA 1992/1993)	Penetration resistance	Liquidtight integrity
Particulate Protective	Particulate holdout	Particulate-tight integrity

Table S3-4 Standard Chemical Batteries for Evaluating Chemical-Protective Clothing

	ASTM F 1001			
Chemical	**Liquids**	**Gases**	**NFPA 1991**	**NFPA 1992, NFPA 1993**
Acetone	X		X	X
Acetonitrile	X		X	X
Ammonia (Anhydrous)		X	X	
1,3-Butadiene		X		
Carbon Disulfide	X		X	
Chlorine		X	X	
Dichloromethane	X		X	
Diethylamine	X		X	
Dimethylformamide	X		X	X
Ethyl Acetate	X		X	X
Ethylene Oxide		X		
Hexane	X		X	X
Hydrogen Chloride		X		
Methanol	X		X	
Methyl Chloride		X		
Nitrobenzene	X		X	
Sodium Hydroxide (50% w/w)	X		X	X
Sulfuric Acid (concentrated)	X		X	X
Tetrachloroethylene	X		X	
Tetrahydrofuran	X		X	X
Toluene	X		X	

A complete summary of the test methods and performance criteria in each standard are presented in NFPA 472, Chapter 4.

As a consequence of these changes, all parts of the ensemble were addressed in terms of physical protection and durability, in addition to chemical and flame resistance as established in the 1990 edition. For example, cut, puncture, abrasion, and flex fatigue resistance requirements were added for gloves, while footwear requirements addressed sole slippage, abrasion, puncture, toe impact, and compression resistance, as well as upper footwear cut and puncture resistance. Since many suits are configured with soft booties, manufacturers became responsible for supplying or specifying outer boots to provide consistent levels of protection.

Two new areas were addressed in the standards for protection from chemical and gas flash fires. Supplemental requirements were established that allow manufacturers to demonstrate additional protection against these hazards.

Chemical flash fires were considered to represent a serious hazard to the emergency responder. By their nature, many organic chemicals pose the threat of creating flammable atmospheres, particularly in confined spaces. The sudden ignition of a flammable atmosphere creates an intense fireball that releases significant amounts of heat capable of easily igniting many forms of clothing, including those compliant with the 1990 edition of the standards. To address this level of protection, the subcommittee established requirements for clothing materials in terms of the following criteria:

- Thermal protective performance
- Radiant heat transfer resistance
- Static charge accumulation resistance

In addition, an overall test was created to simulate the environment of a flash fire. The test involves placing suited mannequins in a closed chamber, filling the chamber with propane in its flammable range, and igniting the chamber contents to produce a flash fire lasting 6–8 seconds in duration. The requirements were established only to aid escape and not entry into a flammable environment and do not provide for the suit to survive the rescue and be reusable.

In assessing clothing performance against liquified gases, requirements were added to NFPA 1991 that addressed concerns for embrittlement and subsequent cracking of suit materials that allowed chemicals to permeate or penetrate.

Products Compliant with NFPA 1991

Chemical protective suit manufacturers have used two different approaches for meeting the requirements for NFPA 1991. NFPA 1991 requires that materials provide combined chemical and flame resistance. Permeation resistance to a 21 chemical battery with breakthrough times greater than 1 hour is required for all "primary" materials in the standard. (Primary materials are defined as those used in the garment, visor, gloves, and boots.) This same level of chemical resistance performance must also be demonstrated following repeated material flexing and abrasion for garment, glove, and footwear materials. The flame resistance test requires that primary materials resist ignition when exposed to a flame for 3 seconds, and show self-extinguishing characteristics after a subsequent 12-second flame exposure. Some manufacturers have compliant products that use single-layer garment materials. These suits are typically classified as reusable because of their high initial purchase costs and relatively rugged construction. Another approach has been to use two-layer systems of plastic laminated and aluminized flame resistant textile materials. The plastic laminate-based products must include overcovers to achieve required flame and abrasion resistance performance. This feature alone has caused criticism of the standards by users who question the need for the overcover because they feel that the majority of situations where chemical protective suits are worn do not involve the potential for flame contact or chemical flash fires. They consider the overcover to be burdensome and costly for most needs. Contrary to popular belief, the NFPA standard *does not require all suits to have an overcover.* Rather, this has been the configuration that some manufacturers have chosen to meet the overall requirements of the standard. This is attested by the fact that other manufacturers have been able to meet all requirements in a single layer.

In its protective clothing and equipment standards, the NFPA considers that issues relative to "use" belong in separate documents (such as NFPA 1500, *Standard on Fire Department Occupational Safety and Health Program*). The NFPA standards provide criteria that apply to products only up to their delivery to the end user.

Products Compliant with NFPA 1992 and NFPA 1993

Like NFPA 1991, manufacturers of protective suits and garments certified to NFPA 1992 and 1993, respectively, use different approaches for materials and garment configurations. NFPA 1992 and 1993 introduce the concept of liquid penetration resistance as the qualifying test for material barrier performance. This testing requires that material prevent the passage of liquid from outside to inside surfaces. Materials will prevent *penetration,* but may still allow *permeation* of chemicals to occur. This distinction opens new opportunities for different kinds of materials. Materials that are "breathable" yet demonstrate the necessary penetration resistance can be used in NFPA 1992 compliant suits or NFPA 1993 garments. As a consequence, both coated materials and those incorporating microporous, breathable membrane films are being used in liquid-splash protective clothing.

Garment configurations have been mainly dictated by the liquidtight integrity or "shower" test used in both standards. While simple in principle, this test has been the primary stumbling block in many certification efforts. The test involves the following procedure:

- Placing the suit over a mannequin that is already dressed in a water absorptive inner garment
- Spraying surfactant-treated water at the mannequin from several low-pressure nozzles for a period of one hour
- Examining the inside of the suit and water absorptive garment for evidence of water penetration

Any liquid penetration into the garment or watermarks on the inner garment constitute failure for the suit. The test readily detects poorly constructed closure systems, seams, or other design areas capable of allowing liquid penetration. The ramification of this test is that manufacturers have had to pay close attention to integrity issues not generally considered in the past. Such practices as using conventional zippers with cover flaps, two-piece garments, or elasticized hoods no longer provide acceptable performance relative to the test method. Instead, manufacturers use encapsulating designs, "sack" suits, and visors in most liquid splash suit designs. In addition, manufacturers of NFPA 1992 compliant clothing must specify other components such as gloves and boots not traditionally included as part of their products.

Impact of the Standards in the Marketplace on Selection

Since the adoption of the NFPA standards in 1990, a number of different chemical-protective suits have been developed and certified to each NFPA standard. It is significant that each certified product involves either a new material or a novel design or both. In effect, the products that have been certified represent advances in the state-of-the-art technology from that which existed at the time the standards were first introduced. For that matter, when NFPA 1991 was prepared, there were no products that could meet all the rigorous requirements for material performance. The fact that there are now nine different products that are compliant with the standard is testament to the ability of the clothing industry to develop "better" products offering improved protection.

The requirements in the NFPA standards are very rigorous, and resulting product designs are significantly more complex than conventional products. For example, since chemical resistance requirements are applied to all the primary materials in the suit (garment, visor, gloves, and boots), all parts of the suit must have the same barrier performance. For NFPA 1991 compliant suit systems, this means that multiple glove systems must be used, which creates dexterity and interface problems. Furthermore, seams for these suits must be taped on both sides to achieve the same level of chemical resistance as the base material.

Future Changes to NFPA 1991, 1992, 1993

Each NFPA standard is subject to constant revision. Once released, all NFPA standards must be reviewed and revised at least every 5 years. This process allows for reconsideration of important requirements in each standard and allows for public proposals and comments on each new edition. This process is now under the responsibility of the Technical Committee on Hazardous Materials Protective Clothing and Equipment.

NFPA 1991, NFPA 1992, and NFPA 1993 became effective in 1990 and were revised in 1994. At the time they were promulgated, these standards represented the best efforts to develop a set of requirements that would give a minimum level of protection for different emergency response applications. Obviously, there have been a number of improvements in suit design, materials performance, and testing procedures since the committee finished its work.

In general, several issues will be considered for each standard. These changes include the following:

- Streamlining chemical resistance testing requirements for all parts of the ensemble
- Addressing more human factors areas such as overall sizing and glove system dexterity
- Adding supplemental requirements for chemical/biological warfare protection (to address counter-terrorism concerns)

In addition, to revising the three standards, the Committee is developing a new Standard on the Selection, Care, and Maintenance of Hazardous Chemical Protective Clothing. This standard is aimed at the response organization and will address the following:

- Clothing selection for purchase
- Clothing selection on scene
- Cleaning and decontamination of clothing after use
- Procedures for inspection, repair, storage, retirement, and disposal of clothing

INCORPORATING INFORMATION FOR FINAL SELECTION

End users must judiciously choose appropriate chemical protective suits based on information supplied by the manufacturer as well as their own evaluations. These suits should be certified as being compliant with the requirements of the applicable NFPA standard. While compliance with NFPA standards should only be a prerequisite, other considerations should include the following:

- Extent and availability of the chemical resistance data base to support use of the product
- Expected life cycle cost for the product in terms of cost per use
- Number of sizes that the product is available in and the range of personnel that the suit will fit adequately
- Ease of donning, doffing, and decontamination
- Impact on wearer functioning as determined in trial wearings, particularly in the areas of field of vision, hand dexterity, and overall profile
- Accommodation of other personnel protective equipment such as the SCBA, head protection, outer boots, radio systems, cooling devices, and any inner garments
- Supporting technical documentation

Response teams should make their selection decisions only after first seeing and trying out chemical protective suits, including a review of all technical and support data. Those responsible for the decisions should make choices by conferring with other teams to determine their experience and avoid relying solely on sales or manufacturer's information.

The NFPA standards are by no means all inclusive; they are not a substitute for user education and appropriate training as covered in NFPA 471 and NFPA 472. Many response organizations consider these standards are overly rigorous and as producing expensive products. Nevertheless, the NFPA standards do provide a baseline performance that has spurred the development of chemical-protective suits for improved wearer protection. When used in conjunction with user experience, the process for selecting a chemical-protective suit can become much easier.

SUPPLEMENT 4

Computer Resources for Hazardous Materials Responders

Kevin Farrell, Manager of Information Systems
Aberdeen Proving Ground Fire Department, United States Army

Editor's Note: As the world moves toward the Information Age, the Internet is becoming a vital source of information for all fields including hazardous materials response. This brief guide to current Internet resources is an excellent starting point for the hazardous materials response professional to begin or expand a regular use of the World Wide Web. As a cautionary note, we must add that the Internet is in a constant state of flux and addresses that were excellent sources may change or change content almost overnight. In preparing this handbook, we have checked each address provided carefully, but we cannot be responsible for address changes that occur during or after this printing. Please check your addresses carefully, and verify each before setting Net system bookmarks and the like.

INTRODUCTION

Within the past five years, several new technologies have come together to allow emergency response personnel to access data sources for emergency operations. This is especially true for the response to hazardous materials incidents.

With the increasing affordability of personal computers and an enormous boost in processing power per dollar spent, desktop and laptop computer systems have become commodity items. Combined with the explosion of information resources that have been made available on-line and the ease in reaching those resources, savvy emergency response personnel can look for help with almost any situation facing them today. A cellular telephone and modem-equipped computer can bring all these resources directly to the emergency scene. *(See Figure S4-1.)*

Figure S4-1 *Computer use both in pre-incident planning and in the field has become increasingly commonplace. Here, responders in Massachusetts use a computer link to CHEMTREC to identify the hazards likely to be found at the incident scene. Note that this state-of-the-art mobile command center features computers, videotaping equipment, monitoring equipment, and both radio and cellular communications systems.*

In the area of hazardous materials planning and response, CAMEO (Computer Aided Management of Emergency Operations) is still the tool of choice both for planning before an event and for identification and decision making during an event. Combined with MARPLOT and ALOHA (Aerial Location of Hazardous Atmospheres), CAMEO can be used to predict downwind movement of a hazardous materials release by creating a plume "footprint" to aid in the decision-making process at the command post.

CAMEO was designed to fit a need long before the Internet became a conduit for emergency information used in support of emergency operations and planning, and it still fits a need today. However, today there are many resources that combine with CAMEO data to assist emergency response personnel. Of course, with the volume of information available, information overload is possible. Therefore, one of the first skills any emergency manager should learn is how to use on-line search engines and other tools to perform the lookup task quickly and efficiently. Several of the larger commercial search and cataloging sites are available at no cost and can be helpful if used properly.

Commercial search engine sites such as Yahoo! (http://www.yahoo.com/), Alta Vista (http://www.altavista.com/), and Lycos (http://lycos.cs.cmu.edu/) offer a broad range of cataloged Web information. These sites can be used during emergency operations, but an emergency manager can prepare in advance by searching and saving the locations of potentially important Internet sites before they are needed in an actual situation. Table S4-1 offers a ready reference listing of all sites described in this supplement.

Other more focused sites that relate to emergency operations should be noted and updated regularly. Many of the national organizations have a presence on the Internet, such as the National Emergency Management Association (NEMA) (http://www.nemaweb.org/), National Coordinating Council on Emergency Management (NCCEM) (http://www.nccem.org/), National Institute of Urban Search and Rescue (http://www.niusr.org/), the Federal Emergency Management Agency (FEMA) (http://www.fema.gov/), and the National Fire Protection Association (http://www.nfpa.org/).

In many cases, these sites will have additional hyperlinks to other related repositories of information. Other sites have been established especially for emergency management and response personnel, and they focus on collecting links to resources of particular interest to planners or response personnel.

Information resources of specific interest to emergency response personnel include the International Association of Fire Chiefs (IAFC) (http://www.iafc.org/), the United States Fire Administration (USFA), including the National Fire Academy (NFA) (http://www.usfa.fema.gov/), the International Association of Firefighters (IAFF) (http://www.iaff.org), and the National Volunteer Fire Council (NVFC) (http://www.nvfc.org/).

Specific sites relating to hazardous materials would have to include the Chemical Manufacturers Association, home of CHEMTREC at http://www.cmahq.com/. You cannot get specific information from the on-line version of CHEMTREC, but a whole host of resources are available for specific chemical data. One such repository of on-line information relating to MSDS type information is OSHWEB located at http://turva.me.tut.fi/cgi-bin/wilma/msds. This collection of MSDS on-line hyperlinks is one of the most definitive groups of resources in one place that you will find on-line.

Other groups, such as the Emergency Information Infrastructure Partnership (http://www.emforum.org/), attempt to gather together on-line resources for emergency management and response managers to use as reference material. The EIIP site is an outgrowth of the vice president's National Information Infrastructure (NII) project to publish state, local, and federal government resources and make them available electronically.

These focus groups provide a place on the Internet for like-minded individuals to share ideas, past experiences, and the types of real-life experiences that are difficult or impossible to catalog. This type of "knowledge base" could be invaluable to an incident manager facing a problem that has never been encountered before.

Weather is another factor that is extremely important when dealing with hazardous materials incidents. Weather systems of the catastrophic type can cause hazardous materials releases, such as the destruction resulting from hurricanes, tornadoes, or torrential flooding. In other cases, weather can be just another factor to deal with when planning a course of action for an incident already in progress. Educational institutions, in concert with the National Oceanic and Atmospheric Administrations National Weather Service (NOAA NWS), http://www.nws.noaa.gov, have an enormous amount of information dealing with everything from severe storm tracking by the National Hurricane Center, Tropical Prediction Center (http://www.nhc.noaa.gov/index.html) to a listing of local and regional forecast offices at http://www.nws.fsu.edu/wwwnws.html.

Weather factors aren't the only natural hazards that either cause or contribute to hazardous materials operations. Earthquake activity is a very real threat on the West Coast, but a seismic incident in the East would probably contribute to greater death and destruction due to a general lack of experience with earthquakes in this region. The National Earthquake Information Center in Boulder, Colorado (http://gldss7.cr.usgs.gov/)

Table S4-1 Computer Resources by Subject

Topic or Specialty	Resource Title	If Internet Site/ Site Address
Planning resources	Computer Aided Management of Emergency Operations (CAMEO)	Only available as software but many Internet sites allow downloads to CAMEO. http://www.nsc.org./ehc/cameo.htm
	MARPLOT	
	Aerial Location of Hazardous Atmospheres (ALOHA)	
	National Emergency Management Association (NEMA)	http://www.nemaweb.org/
	National Coordinating Council on Emergency Management (NCCEM)	http://www.dtic.mil/defenselink/emerg/nccem.html
	National Institute of Urban Search and Rescue	http://www.emergencyservices.com/niusr/
	Federal Emergency Management Agency (FEMA)	http://www.fema.gov/
	National Fire Protection Association	http://www.nfpa.org/
Fire service	International Association of Fire Chiefs (IAFC)	http://www.iafc.org/
	International Association of Fire Fighters	http://www.iaff.org
	National Volunteer Fire Council (NVFC)	http://www.nvfc.org/
Chemicals and hazardous materials	Chemical Manufacturers Association, home of CHEMTREC	http://www.cmahq.com/>.
	OSHWEB	http://turva.me.tut.fi/cgi-bin/wilma/msds
	Center for MSDS Partnership	http://www.fpn.navy.mil
	Hazardous Chemical Data Base	ull.chemistry.uakron.edu/erd
	Emergency Information Infrastructure Partnership	http://www.emforum.org/
Weather information	National Oceanic and Atmospheric Administrations National Weather Service (NOAA NWS)	http://www.nws.noaa.gov/weather/curcond.html
	National Hurricane Center, Tropical Prediction Center	http://www.nhc.noaa.gov/index.html
Earthquake information	The National Earthquake Information Center in Boulder, Colorado	http://gldss7.cr.usgs.gov/

is operated by the U.S. Geologic Survey and can contribute information on current events as well as historical data and additional information sources.

ASSEMBLING THE TOOLS FOR INFORMATION ACCESS

Due to the nature of computer developments in hardware and software, the industry goes through a development cycle increasing the power of desktop computer technology every six to nine months. Hardware and software that is cutting edge right now will be considered pedestrian three years from now. Therefore, guidelines on what resources the fire service manager needs to access on-line must be constrained to very general terms for this document. Thankfully, the standards being used for communication on the global Internet are relatively standardized by protocol, rather than hardware design or operating system.

The standard protocol for computer systems to communicate on the Internet is known as "Transmission Control Protocol/ Internet Protocol" or more commonly as TCP/IP. Even though the protocols may sound sinister, all of the mainstream computer operating systems today "speak" and understand this standard protocol.

Any desktop or laptop computer manufactured today that can run any of the modern operating systems such as Unix, Windows 95/NT, the Macintosh OS, or MS DOS (or its variants) can become a "client" on the Internet and access the information repositories found there.

Additional software will be needed to send and receive electronic mail, such as an SMTP or POP3 mail client. Access to USENET news groups will require an NNTP news reader, and a Web browser will be required to access World Wide Web servers. However, this software can be found easily at no charge or little cost. The only other items that you will need in order to access the data located on the Internet are an Internet connection, the fastest modem you can afford, and a phone line. The Internet can be accessed through an on-line service such as America Online (http://www.aol.com/) or, better still, through one of the thousands of local Internet service providers such as those listed on CNET at http://www.cnet.com/Content/Reviews/Compare/ISP/sample.html>.

All of the providers, both local as well as national, can supply you with the connection software needed to connect your computer to their access point on the Internet via a standard communications protocol known as Point-to-Point Protocol, or PPP. Some of the regional cable television providers as well as the Regional Bell Operating Companies (RBOCs) also offer Internet access at reasonable rates. Of course, if you happen to be able to tie into your local government network, you can access the Internet at little or reduced cost as a public safety entity. The bottom line is this: Due to the relatively low cost of powerful desktop computers, free or low-cost Internet access software tools, and thousands of points of presence (POPs) to enter the world of the Internet, there is no reason not to leverage the power of the computer and the information resources of the global Internet in support of emergency operations. The data are plentiful, are easily accessed even at an emergency scene (via a wireless or direct modem link), are routinely updated, gather no dust, and require no storage like our old stack of reference books do. Today, a desktop (or laptop) computer and an Internet connection should be the first tool an emergency manager looks to for assistance in support of emergency operations.

SUPPLEMENT 5

Haz Mat Teams in Transition: Regionalizing the Haz Mat Response in Massachusetts

Editor's Note: Like many states, the initial hazardous materials response from the public sector in Massachusetts was handled by individual fire departments. Low run numbers coupled with the high costs of equipment and training, and the difficulty in recovering those costs from those responsible for haz mat releases and other haz mat incidents, convinced Massachusetts fire fighters to take another look. Here, Director Stephen Clendenin discusses the process his state used to regionalize the haz mat response and the SOP development process now unfolding. Prior to becoming director, Clendenin was a Training Coordinator for the state's haz mat response office. The draft operational SOPs are also presented in this supplement as a starting point for others working on regionalization. We are grateful for Clendenin's insights and the draft SOPs presented here.

A CONVERSATION WITH MASSACHUSETTS HAZARDOUS MATERIALS RESPONSE DIRECTOR STEPHEN CLENDENIN

For hazardous materials response authorities, the shift from a locally based, fire-service administered hazardous materials response to a more regional or statewide plan creates its own challenges. Gaining consensus among the fire service and other responding organizations, finding ways to shift response approaches to hazardous materials incidents, and recovering response costs proved to be the main concerns of Massachusetts Hazardous Materials Response Director Stephen Clendenin. Creating the standard operating procedures (SOPs) for the new regional teams is also an ongoing process, according to Clendenin, who offered his advice to those facing a similar regionalization challenge.

Clendenin was, as he describes it, in at the beginning of the process. Initially he worked with the current District 3 team, one of the original six teams in the state. As the state took over the response planning and operations to develop the regional approach, Clendenin became the training director of the state's year-old response office. In March he became acting director of the office as well.

"The entire process of regionalizing the response actually began about five years ago, at least in conversation. We knew that there were problems with individual fire departments having to respond to hazardous materials incidents—more than half of the departments in this state are call out or volunteer. In addition, we have larger cities that have their own response teams, including Boston and Springfield, where many runs are generated. This meant that those who were in smaller communities had to maintain a state of readiness for incidents that occurred, perhaps once in two years, while other areas were stretched. And costs became a major issue as the regionalization discussions went forward.

"The first goal was, I think, to build consensus within the fire service that a regional response was the way to go. Under a regional response plan, the notification of a haz mat incident goes out to specific personnel drawn from each of the fire companies and departments within the responding district. These responders have specialized training and are called out in a tiered response pattern that may or may not involve more than one region. The local fire department then is responsible for first responder operations activities only. This shifts the response pattern that the fire service has been trained to provide, which is to get into action fast and begin tackling the problem immediately. It's not that the haz mat response is slow—it's appropriate to the overall strategy. With haz mat response, it may take a team up to 60 minutes to get to the scene and to begin mitigation. The process of careful hazard identification, analysis, and appropriate response has been proved to be the most effective because you take the time up front to find the most appropriate response and to safeguard the responders and the public at large first, and mitigate second," Clendenin said.

"What was key for us in gaining consensus was that we involved everyone at the very beginning of the process. The State Fire Marshal, the Professional Fire Fighters Union, and the Massachusetts Fire Chiefs Association were very instrumental with representing the professional paid fire service, and we also had strong representation from the volunteer/on-call fire fighting community as well," Clendenin explained.

"Everyone in the process shared a number of important concerns for their home departments and personnel. The biggest of these was the liability issue. If the various departments in the eastern part of the state were going to send responders, not just one town over, but across the state, the usual reciprocity that fire departments have with mutual aid arrangements wasn't there. It's not that the responder would go to the next town over, and that their personnel would someday return the favor. Now there was a likelihood that a responder was at risk for injury and even death several towns away and chiefs questioned why they should be responsible for paying injury and death benefits to their personnel when they are injured in another jurisdiction," Clendenin said.

"It took two years, but we resolved those concerns by having the state address the liability in these cases. That helped a great deal in gaining approval for regionalization. The state also agreed to assume the training and equipment costs, so really all the fire departments were being asked was to contribute the key personnel who would be on-call for a shared response," he added.

"We also tackled the consensus question in terms of planning our response. First, we received the SOPs of other departments, states with regional and county systems, including the Prince George County, Maryland, response team and those from the federal government and the military. We also looked at the existing SOPs used by the various departments in the Commonwealth and rather than reinvent the wheel, took the plans used in the various districts and adapted them to fit the regional system. Then we gained consensus on the plan as we moved forward with it in special committees. The plans offered here are drafts. Finalizing the plans—if you want to call it that—will take probably until Fall. But, really, no plan is ever written in stone, and there has to be flexibility and a way to change the plan overall as new things are discovered or new situations arise in the field," Clendenin said. "Ideally, a plan should be reviewed every six months and measured against the experience and new technologies, training experiences, and concerns."

In each response district, Clendenin explained, there are between 30 and 70 personnel able to respond, but they are called in tiers as need is determined. In addition, each district has specialized hazardous materials response mobile units. Technical Operations Module (TOMS) includes a fully computerized tactical response operations unit *(see Figure S5-1)*. The Operational Response Unit (ORU) contains all of the appropriate protective clothing at all levels so that, should a response require the most or the least protective wear, it is available for the response team at the incident site *(see Figure S5-2)*.

As part of the public awareness process and as a way to reach out to the various affected communities and responders, according to Clendenin, the state haz mat office has provided public speakers, created a Web site, and created a series of public information documents. The office has also circulated a sheet of frequently asked questions and answers prepared by the District 2 team—Metro-Boston—and presented here.

MASSACHUSETTS HAZARDOUS MATERIALS REGIONAL RESPONSE TEAM: COMMON QUESTIONS AND ANSWERS

When should the haz mat team be activated? The team should be activated any time that a hazardous material incident is beyond the capability of your department. Examples may include an incident requiring the use of "Level A" encapsulated protective clothing, or the need for air monitoring equipment if *your department does not have these capabilities.* As a rule most fire departments train their responders to the operational level. The operational level calls for a *defensive* approach to hazardous materials incidents. Defensive actions may include establishing zones, notifying proper authorities, diking,

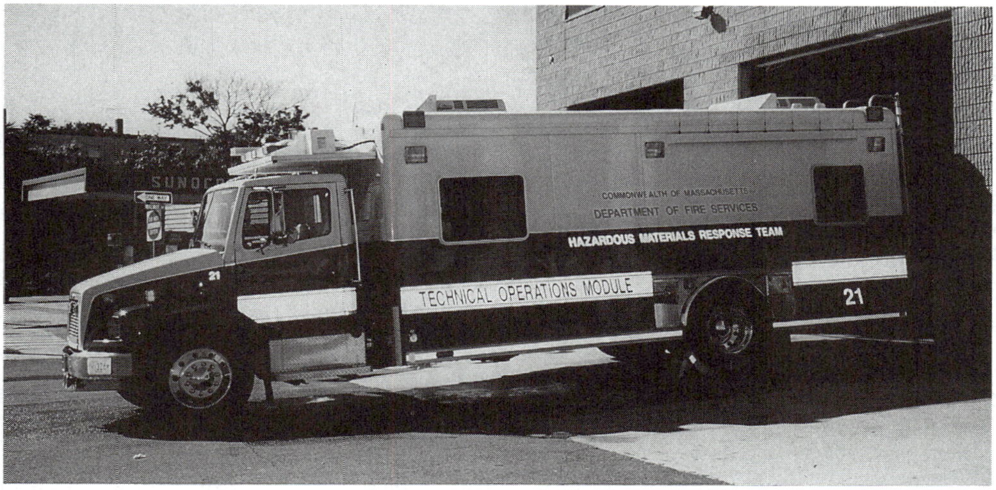

Figure S5-1 *This TOMS unit functions as a mobile command center and features a fully equipped computer center inside, with other A-level equipment storage in the exterior and interior compartments. A light panel at the front provides broadcast television quality lighting for nighttime incidents, and the television transmitter at the back gives remote command a live view of incidents through cameras mounted at the front of the vehicle.*

Figure S5-2 *Unlike the TOMS response unit, this Operational Response Unit vehicle is used at most hazardous materials incidents because it carries the majority of equipment needed in the field. Stored inside the various compartments that line both sides and the back of the unit are three levels of protective clothing; mitigation tools and equipment for plugging, patching, diking, and other kinds of containment; decontamination equipment; disposal containers; and smaller safety utilities including traffic cones, incident tape, folding chairs for rest periods for responders, additional backup radio equipment, and dozens of reference guides for field use. As on the A-unit vehicles, awnings can be unrolled and side flaps added to create a weatherproof shelter against the unit side.*

and damming. It does not include *offensive* actions, such as plugging or patching leaking vessels.

Fire departments should rely on preplanning and the use of resources, such as the North American *Emergency Response Guidebook,* whenever possible in order to determine the need for the haz mat team. If the material is identified and the *Guidebook* states that structural firefighting gear is not effective to handle this equipment, the team should be activated. If at any time the material spilled/leaked is an unknown and poses a potential threat, the team should be activated.

How do I activate the team? Once it has been determined that the team is needed by a local department, the Incident Commander can request a full team or limited response through the Metrofire Control Center. Prior to activating the team members, Metrofire will request information from the local fire department, including the following: the location of the incident; its nature (transportation, fixed facility, etc.); the name of the incident commander; material(s) involved; the location of the staging area; and whether a full or limited team response is necessary.

What will happen when the team is activated? Once the team is activated team members will be responding to that community within a very short period of time—from either their home or fire station. Generally the first team member who arrives will report to the local Incident Commander (IC) and become the team leader. As additional team members arrive, the team leader will designate the various assignments as per SOPs. If the community requesting the team has a member on the team, that member will generally be assigned as a liaison with the Incident Commander. If not, the IC will be kept abreast of any and all information the team develops and the tactics that will be necessary to mitigate the incident.

Who is in charge? The local Chief of Department as the Incident Commander or his designee is in charge of the incident and he shall be ultimately responsible for the control of the entire incident. The team shall operate under the Incident Command system, whether or not the local community is operational under the IC system. The team functions as the haz mat group within the operations branch of the Incident Command system. Strategic goals are the responsibility of the Incident Commander. The team leader shall have the authority and responsibility to establish the tactical objectives for mitigation of the incident.

Who does the team answer to? All six regional response teams are under the direction of the State Policy Board and the Executive Department of Public Safety Secretary O'Toole. The immediate supervision of the team is the Metrofire Haz Mat Committee, and each member answers to his own Chief of Department.

Who pays? Incident reimbursement is available through Metrofire. Once the incident is completed a list of team members on scene and equipment used is submitted to the Metrofire Coordinator and billed through the local department. This replacement is allowable under Massachusetts General Law (MGL), Chapter 21 E. A plan is being developed by the State Haz Mat Response Director to take over the billing process. This process will have the support of the Attorney General's Office. Once implemented, reimbursement will be automatic and the state will pursue the responsible party to collect their costs.

Why is there no "rank structure" within the team? The entire team qualified equally in the 160-hour haz mat tech course. If the team were to have a command structure, it would be difficult to predict if that command structure would respond to the incident. Every member of the entire team is trained and capable of assuming the position at an incident. The team has been trained to follow SOPs and operate under the Incident Command system. While many of the team members have vast amounts of training and experience prior to the course, the team has agreed to operate on an equal basis as haz mat techs and operate within any position on the team that may be necessary during an incident. The team does have individuals who have been picked by the members of the team to handle the administrative and training requirements of the team. Every member of the team is a member of one of the committees (equipment, training, SOP, medical). The team is also represented in each of the state's subcommittees (equipment, training, SOP, medical, vehicles).

What is a limited response and what can it do for me? To reduce costs and provide more efficient service, a smaller group level was added. The team is divided into 4- to 10-person groups—teams A, B, C, D. When a request for a limited response is received, Metrofire will notify the next group by pager. A roll call will be conducted as with a full team activation. Five or more members from a group must respond for safe operations. If less than five are able to respond, a second group will be notified and a second roll call taken.

Early in its inception the team recognized that there were incidents involving hazardous materials, some of which are encountered everyday and may not pose a serious threat to responders or citizens, but are hazardous in fact and must be handled appropriately. Limited response groups can provide technical assistance to the Incident Commander through the use of computers and other research material, and air monitoring as well. State and team SOPs still require a minimum of sixteen team members to conduct entry operations.

Why does it seem to take so long for the entry team to be operational? Based on nationally accepted standards and criteria, the team SOPs are strictly adhered to. Above all else, safety for the entry team is foremost. There may be no margin for error in dealing with some chemicals. The science and research sector must cross reference with at least three different publications/ manuals, as well as information from any other sources. Decontamination must be operational prior to entry and this procedure is also quite involved. On average the team can make entry into the exclusionary zone in less than an hour if sufficient information is available on the material(s).

Why can't the local fire fighters "suit-up" and enter the exclusionary zone? Again, national and state standards and criteria mandate that certain training and procedures must be followed before anyone may be "suited-up" and enter the hot zone. Baseline physicals are required as well as medical surveillance prior to entry and decon operations. The team has limits on members going into both entry and decon based on vitals taken. The liability that may be assumed by the Incident Commander for sending an improperly trained or non-physically fit fire fighter into a hazardous material situation could be devastating to the department, and city or town. If chemical protective clothing is necessary to mitigate an incident, there are steps taken by the team, such as testing and inspection of equipment to comply with regulations and standards. Also, the entry team must have a backup team to provide rescue if necessary and properly dressed and equipped personnel in decon. These are generally beyond the capability of the local department. While the argument may be that it is necessary to effect a rescue during the initial stages of an incident, the Incident Commander must weigh all factors and determine whether the rescuers may be jeopardized for someone that may not be rescuable.

Why is there such an extensive decon procedure? Through the team's training and the national and state standards that are mandated, decontamination is critical to safe and efficient operation and termination of the incident. The team, fire fighters, and general public are protected by this procedure. All products from the spill are contained in one area and the team is assured that all products are retained in this area for a safe exit by team members.

What does my department have to provide for the team during an incident? The team will need assistance and support in the following, but not limited to a dedicated ambulance (ALS if available) to provide medical surveillance; water supply for decon operations; hand lines manned by fire fighters; recharging of SCBA bottles (Scott 4.5); additional SCBA bottles during extended operations; electrical power and/ or lighting; and fluids for hydration and food for incidents of a long period.

Who is responsible for the delivery and return of the haz mat vehicles? The Somerville and Waltham Fire Departments have agreed to dispatch and arrange for the delivery of the vehicles to the incident if needed. The requesting community is responsible for the return of the vehicle to their respective communities. Team members may agree to return vehicles to their host departments; however, it is not their responsibility.

SOPS FOR THE COMMONWEALTH: DEPARTMENT OF FIRE SERVICES, HAZARDOUS MATERIALS, REGIONAL RESPONSE TEAM

The draft SOPs that follow are part of the full policy and procedures manual under development by the Commonwealth of Massachusetts Department of Fire Services, Hazardous Materials Response Team.[1] These consensus-driven documents were adapted from haz mat SOPs used by two of the six response districts and revised in accordance with the needs and concerns of the state's regional response team members. The SOPs do not establish a command structure within the team itself, but rather the team leaders are elected by their members. At the incident scene, the fire chief of the community involved assists the haz mat team leadership.

Mission Statement

OBJECTIVE: To clearly state the mission of the Commonwealth of Massachusetts, Department of Fire Services, Hazardous Materials Regional Response Teams.

APPLICABILITY

Department of Fire Services Divisions
Regional Steering Committee
Fire Chiefs
Response Team Members

MISSION STATEMENT
The Commonwealth of Massachusetts, Department of Fire Services, Regional Hazardous Materials Response System is established to provide specialized services

[1] For a complete copy of the SOPs for regional operations, contact the director's office at the Massachusetts Hazardous Materials Fire Services, P.O. Box 1025, State Road, Stow, MA 01775.

to the 351 communities in the Commonwealth, to enable them to protect the public, the environment, and property during incidents involving a release or potential release of hazardous materials. Regional Hazardous Material Response Teams will be strategically located to support local fire departments with technical information and specialized equipment to handle hazardous materials incidents.

Policies and Procedures Manual

OBJECTIVE: To establish an SOP, Policy and Procedures Manual of the Commonwealth of Massachusetts, Department of Fire Services, Hazardous Material Policy Board for developing and disseminating SOPs Policy, Procedures, Organizational Charts, and Information, and to prescribe the method for issuing and modifying these documents.

APPLICABILITY

Department of Fire Services Divisions
Policy Board
Regional Steering Committee
Fire Chiefs
Response Team Members

Standard Operating Procedure

1.0 DEFINITIONS

1.1 *SOP Policy and Procedures Manual:* A comprehensive collection of written Hazardous Materials Policy Board SOPs, Policies, Procedures and Organizational information which is provided to all Policy Board members, Department of Fire Services Divisions, Regional Steering Committees, Local Fire Chiefs, and Response Team personnel.

1.2 *Manual:* A short-term used in all Policies and Procedures to refer to the Policy Board's Policies and Procedures Manual.

1.3 *Directive:* A short temporary statement of policy and procedures issued by the Policy Board and/or the Director.

1.4 *RRT:* A short term used to identify the Regional Response Team.

1.5 *Information Bulletin:* A statement issued by the Director to inform RRT personnel of any matter of particular interest.

1.6 *Form:* A document issued to implement Policies and Procedures.

2.0 POLICY

2.1 The Hazardous Material Policy Board's Policies and Procedures Manual is the Official Method of disseminating Policies, Procedures, organizational structure, functions, activities and services as established by the Policy Board and the Director.

2.2 Documents in this manual include Policies and Procedures to guide and direct the Policy Board, Director, Steering Committee and RRT personnel in the performance of duty.

2.3 Documents in this manual must not supersede any part of any law, order of the Policy Board, Memorandums of Agreements between any city or Town and the Professional Firefighters of Massachusetts, or personnel regulations.

2.4 Forms issued for use as part of the implementation of a Policy or Procedure must:

A. Be assigned a title and sequential number designation to indicate the organizational area (e.g. 100-Administrative, 200-Operations, 300-Medical Surveillance! EMS, 400-Training).
B. Typed and submitted on a floppy disk to the Hazmat Office, to then be typed in Standard SOP formatting by the Hazmat Office.
C. Formatted as per [a sample attachment, not included here].

2.5 Directives must be:

A. Formatted as per [a sample attachment, not included here].
B. Numbered sequentially by year and directive number (e.g., 95-1).
C. Issued on blue paper.
D. Placed in a separate section of the Policy and Procedure Manual.
E. Include a cancellation date or canceled in writing by the Director when no longer in effect.
F. Sent to each Chief of a local fire department with Technician or Support team members and each regional steering committee.

2.6 Information Bulletins must be:

A. Formatted as per [a sample attachment, not included here].
B. Issued on yellow paper.
C. Sent to each chief of a local fire department with Technician or Support Team members and each regional steering committee.

3.0 RESPONSIBILITIES

3.1 All regional steering committees, technicians, and support team members are responsible for:

A. Familiarizing themselves with and maintaining a constant awareness of the documents contained in this manual.

B. Making suggestions for new and/or revised policies and procedures they feel are necessary.

3.2 All regional steering committees and team leaders are responsible for policy training and compliance by technicians and support team members with applicable policies and procedures.

3.3 All Policy Board Members, Regional Steering Committees, and Team Leaders must be issued a copy of each applicable policy and/or procedures issued in accordance with this policy. Each of the above must maintain their set of policies and procedures up-to-date as new documents are issued.

3.4 The Director is responsible for maintaining the official manual up-to-date at all times.

3.5 The Director is responsible for reviewing all suggestions for new or revised policies and procedures submitted and transmitting these proposals for approval as appropriate.

4.0 PROCEDURE

4.1 Any Policy Board Member, Steering Committee Member, Team Leader, Technician or Support Team Member seeing the need for the establishment or revision to, or modification of a current policy or procedure, may forward, in accordance with the procedure, set forth in this section, the suggested policy and/or procedure.

4.2 The organization shall submit a typed draft document to their team coordinator. The team coordinator will start the process for adoption of the document and keep the originator informed of the progress. If the team leader is the originator, he will submit the typed draft document to the regional steering committee.

4.3 The steering committee shall review the originator's draft document for content and need. If necessary, the draft document will be revised and then returned to the originator for review before forwarding the document to the Director and the SOP subcommittee.

4.4 After receiving the draft document from the steering committee, the SOP subcommittee will review the draft document for format, and check the document against existing documents for compatibility.

4.5 After final editing, the SOP Committee will submit the proposed SOP to the director and policy board for approval according to the following schedule.

Step 1: The SOP Subcommittee types and submits the document to the Director for his written comments. The SOP Subcommittee types and submits the document to the Team Coordinators for their written comments (14 days).

Step 2: The document is then returned to the SOP Committee for revision (30 days).

Step 3: The document is resubmitted to the Director's Office with any necessary explanations, for his review. The document will then be entered into the office computer (7 days).

Step 4: The office staff will print the document and return it to the SOP Committee for review and final corrections of format, spelling, grammatical errors, punctuation, etc. and for final approval by the SOP Committee (7 days).

Step 5: The document is then submitted to the Director for his final approval and then to the Policy Board for their approval. The document must be in the Director's office at least seven days before a Policy Board meeting, in order to be put on the agenda.

4.6 Upon approval by the Policy Board, training requirements will be identified and the document will be assigned an effective date. At the appropriate time, the document will be copied and issued to Team Members, Steering Committee Chiefs, Policy Board Members and Fire Chiefs.

5.0 GENERAL

5.1 After one year from the effective date, all documents and procedure will be reviewed by the Director, Policy Board, or SOP Committee, and revisions made as per the procedure described in Section 4.0.

5.2 Distribution of a new or revised document or page automatically cancels the existing issue of the same document or page and is identified by a new issued date or revision date.

5.3 Cancellation of documents will be done in writing and issued by the Director.

Response Team Activation: Standard Operating Procedures (201.00)

OBJECTIVE: The objective of this procedure is to define the general provisions for notification of District Haz Mat Response Team members to initiate a response to an incident.

APPLICABILITY

Department of Fire Services Divisions
Regional Steering Committee
Fire Chiefs
Response Team Members
Fire District, Control Centers
MEMA

1.0 ACTIVATION PROCEDURE

1.1 The response of the District Haz Mat Response Team is initiated by the Incident Commander of the requesting department notifying the Regional Control center for the team serving their community that they have a hazardous materials incident and request assistance of the team.

1.2 The Regional Control Center Operator will obtain the following information from the requesting community:

1.2.1 City or town.
1.2.2 Location of the incident.
1.2.3 Requesting department.
1.2.4 Callback telephone number.
1.2.5 Incident commander.
1.2.6 Nature/extent of incident, including product identification and quantity if known.
1.2.7 Assembly point for Haz Mat Team members. [See Figure S5-3, at the end of this supplement.]

1.3 The Regional Control Center Operator will then take the following actions:

1.3.1 Initiate the primary paging system.
1.3.2 The message transmitted shall be in the following form: "District (#), Tier (#), (Product), (spill, leak) at (address of incident). Team assembly point at (location of assembly point)."

Example: "District 5, Tier 2, Groups 3 & 4, Sulfuric Acid spill at 596 West Street, Thistown. Team assemble at the Grocery Mart parking lot on Main Street."

1.3.3 Confirm the Dispatch of the TOM Unit (Technical Operations Module) and the ORU (Operational Response Unit).
1.3.4 Confirm the page message was transmitted. Confirmation shall be the telephone response by one or more members within three (3) minutes.
1.3.5 If no response is received within three (3) minutes, the Regional Control Center shall initiate a second paging and activate the Backup Activation Procedure (Section 3).
1.3.6 Conduct a roll call of the communities that have not reported roll call (see 3.2.6) 15 minutes after the paging system was activated. The status of the Team members will be recorded as follows:

- Responding and ETA
- Not responding
  (sick or injured leave, unavailable)
- Undetermined

This information will be kept at the Control Center and will be relayed to the Team Leader and/or the TOM unit.

2.0 BACK-UP ACTIVATION PROCEDURE

2.1 In the event of failure of the primary paging system, the Regional Control Center shall activate the team using Fire Mutual Aid and telephone systems.

2.2 Each district team shall submit a copy of the activation procedure; to be attached to this SOP. [See Figure S5-4, at the end of this supplement.]
The procedure shall include a method to:

2.2.1 Contact on duty members as per local policy.
2.2.2 Contact off duty members as per local policy.
2.2.3 Record the status of the team members answering the activation (as in 2.3.4).
2.2.4 Relay all available information to the team members that are responding to the activation.
2.2.5 Relay to team members directions to the assembly point.
2.2.6 Report the status of the department's team members to the Regional Control Center by telephone roll call not more than 15 minutes after activation of the team.
The status of team members shall be recorded as follows:

- Responding and ETA
- Not responding
  (sick or injured leave, unavailable)
- Undetermined

2.2.7 Provide updates of the status of the department's team members not available at the time of the telephone roll call to the Regional Control Center as soon as possible.
2.2.8 Record information in the department's log as per local policy.

3.0 TEAM MEMBER DUTIES

Team members will take the following actions upon notification that the Haz Mat Team has been activated:

3.1 Determine ability to respond. No team member on sick or injury leave from their department shall respond to a Haz Mat Incident. Members are responsible at all times for their fitness for duty.

3.2 Members who have been contacted by pager will as soon as possible notify their own department and advise the dispatcher of their status (responding and ETA, not responding).

3.3 Members will record the location of the incident and the assembly point. Directions to the incident should be obtained through the primary paging system, local department, or the Control Center.

3.4 Members responding to the incident shall use good judgment and drive in accordance with all applicable laws and rules of the road.

4.0 QUARTERLY ACTIVATION DRILL

4.1 The Team Coordinator shall initiate a test of the activation procedure each quarter.

4.2 Upon notice from the Team Coordinator, the Control Center shall conduct a quarterly test of the activation procedure.

4.3 Three quarterly tests shall use the primary team paging system. One quarterly test shall be of the backup activation system. The drill will be concluded after the telephone roll call.

4.4 The Control Center operator shall follow all steps in Section 2 of this procedure.

4.5 The message format for the test shall be: Activation Test, District (#), Tier (#).

4.6 Team members shall perform all steps in Section 4 of this procedure, including a status report (Section 4.2) whether they would or would not have been able to respond to an incident at this time.

4.7 Team members shall forward to the team at the next regular drill, a critique of the activation drill, citing any problems and suggested corrective actions and improvements.

5.0 CANCELLATION OF TEAM RESPONSE

5.1 Upon notice from the Incident Commander or Haz Mat Team Leader, the response of the team may be canceled.

5.1.1 Cancellation should take place less than 30 minutes after activation.

5.2 The Incident Commander or Team Leader will notify the Control Center. The Haz Mat Team Response is not required.

5.3 Control Center will activate the paging system and broadcast a cancellation message.

5.4 Team Members will confirm receipt of message by contacting the control center by telephone.

Standard Operating Procedures for the Tiered Response (202.00)

OBJECTIVE: To define the tiered response levels of the Commonwealth of Massachusetts, Department of Fire Services, Hazardous Materials Regional Response Teams so as to provide the most efficient use of these resources and to ensure a timely response to requesting communities.

APPLICABILITY

Department of Fire Services Divisions
Regional Steering Committee
Fire Chiefs
Response Team Members
Fire District, Control Centers
MFMA

1.0 DEFINITIONS

Response Groups

1.1 All technicians shall be divided into groups of approximately 10 for activation purposes.

1.2 All Support Members shall be divided into an equal number of groups as the technicians.

1.3 The assignment of members to groups shall be the responsibility of the Steering Committee in each district. The groups shall be organized to provide efficient and timely response to requesting communities.

Response Tiers

1.4 There shall be four defined tiers of response for the Department of Fire Services, Hazardous Materials Regional Response Teams.

1.4.1 A Tier One Response is defined as hazard and risk assessment.

1.4.2 A Tier Two Response is defined as short-term operations.

1.4.3 A Tier Three Response is defined as long-term operations.

1.4.4 A Tier Four Response is defined as multiple team operations.

2.0 POLICY

2.1 A Tier One Response is defined as hazard and risk assessment.

2.1.1 A Tier One Response request would activate by pager, one (1) group of technicians of which five technicians will be assigned to the incident. The procedure to assign the five technicians will be developed by each District Steering Committee.

2.1.2 At a Tier One Response, one (1) TOM (Technical Operation Module) unit is assigned to the incident.

2.1.3 The team will be able to assist in research of materials hazards, hazard and risk analysis, and act in an advisory capacity to the Incident Commander.

2.1.4 At a Tier One Response, the duties of the Response Team include, but are not limited to, performing the functions of Team Leader, Science, Safety and Communications.

2.2 A Tier Two Response is defined as short-term operations.

2.2.1 A Tier Two Response would initially activate two (2) groups of technicians and two (2) groups of support members.

2.2.2 The Team Leader may request additional groups if the Team Leader determines that the existing response is insufficient for that incident's needs.

Example: A third group of technicians may be activated to augment the existing Tier Two Response without escalating the incident to a Tier Three Response. One (1) group of support members shall be activated along with each group of technicians activated.

2.2.3 At a Tier Two Response, one (1) TOM (Technical Operations Module) and one (1) ORU (Operational Response Unit) is assigned to the incident.

2.2.4 In addition to the capabilities described for a Tier One Response, at a Tier Two Response the operations of the Response Team would include assessment to determine the need for additional resources and equipment and limited mitigation.

2.2.5 In addition to the duties described for a Tier One Response, at a Tier Two Response the Response Team duties will include performing the functions of Medical, Entry, Logistics and Decontamination.

2.2.6 The Incident Commander may request the response of the statewide Incident Command Communications Unit (ICCU).

2.2.7 The Incident Commander may request the response of the Director's Office.

2.3 Tier Three Response is defined as long-term operations.

2.3.1 A Tier Three Response request would activate one (1) full response team, consisting of all technicians and support personnel.

2.3.2 At a Tier Three Response, one (1) TOM unit and one (1) ORU, plus one OSU (Operational Support Unit) is assigned to the incident. In districts where additional ORUs are sited, those equipment trucks may be assigned to the incident upon request of the Team Leader.

2.3.3 At a Tier Three Response, the Response Team would be capable of multiple entries, use of specialized mitigation equipment, specialized decontamination, and lengthy operations.

2.3.4 At a Tier Three Response, the Statewide Incident Command and Communications Unit (ICCU) is dispatched to the incident.

2.3.5 At a Tier Three Response, the Director's Office will respond.

2.4 A Tier Four Response is defined as Multiple Team Operations.

2.4.1 If an incident exceeds the resources of a single Response Team, additional response groups and equipment from other Hazardous Materials Regional Response Teams may be activated as needed.

SOPs for First Arriving Team Members (203.00)

OBJECTIVE: The objective of this SOP is to outline actions to be taken until the arrival of sufficient qualified personnel to fill the positions of Team Leader and Branch Officers.

APPLICABILITY

Department of Fire Services Divisions
Regional Steering Committee
Fire Chiefs
Response Team Members
MEMA

1.0 RESPONSIBILITIES: First Arriving Team Member

1.1 The first arriving member will be responsible to begin size-up and to organize in preparation for arrival of the Team Members, the TOM (Technical Operations Module) unit and the ORU (Operational Response Unit).

1.2 Consult with Incident Commander or designated local officials and select a safe area for members to park, and arrange for shuttle transportation from the parking area to the Haz Mat staging area at the scene.

1.3 Ensure the assembly point meets the criteria listed in the activation SOP and that someone from the local community is at the assembly point.

1.4 On arrival at the scene meet with the Incident Commander and designate a staging area for the Haz Mat Team.

1.5 Obtain a briefing of the incident from the Incident Commander. Complete Initial Briefing Checklist.

1.6 Initial Briefing Checklist given to the Science Branch Officer.

2.0 ATTACHMENT [See Figure S5-5, at the end of this supplement.]

2.1 First Arriving Team Member Checklist

Team Leader SOP (204.00)

OBJECTIVE: The objective of this SOP is to outline the responsibilities of the Team Leader.

APPLICABILITY
Department of Fire Services Divisions
Regional Steering Committee
Fire Chiefs
Response Team Members
MEMA

1.0 RESPONSIBILITIES

1.1 A Hazardous Materials Team Leader (Haz Mat Team Leader) shall be designated for all responses involving the Regional Response Team.

1.2 The Team Leader shall be a qualified Hazardous Materials Technician.

1.3 The First Arriving Technician shall assume the role of Team Leader.

1.4 A Technician serving as the Team Leader at an incident in his community may pass command to another technician.

1.5 The Team Leader may be transferred to another technician only once.

1.6 The Team Leader, whenever transferring command to another Technician, shall ensure that the new Team Leader is thoroughly briefed.

1.7 The Team Leader shall follow and complete the Team Leader checklist. [See Figure S5-6, at the end of this supplement.]

1.8 The Team Leader shall maintain communications with the Incident Commander and keep the IC informed of Team operations.

1.9 The Team Leader shall appoint the Branch Officers and coordinate their activities.

1.10 In consultation with Branch Officers, shall develop the Haz Mat Operations Plan. [See Figure S5-7.]

1.11 The Team Leader shall consult with Branch Officers to keep each adequately informed of operational needs.

1.12 The Team Leader shall conduct a briefing with the Incident Commander and Branch Officers to present an operational plan for the incident. This briefing will be conducted prior to Hot Zone Operations. [See Figures S5-8 and S5-9.]

1.13 The Team Leader shall coordinate with the Safety Officer to ensure that field operations are conducted safely.

1.14 The Team Leader shall ensure that all necessary records regarding the Incident are completed. [See Figure S5-10.]

Safety Branch Office SOPs (208.00)

OBJECTIVE: The objective of this SOP is to outline the roles and responsibilities of the Safety Branch Officer.

APPLICABILITY
Department of Fire Services Divisions
Regional Steering Committee
Fire Chiefs
Response Team Members
MEMA

On all Hazardous Material Team responses, the Team Leader shall assign a Safety Branch Officer.

The Safety Branch Officer is responsible for developing the site safety plan and to monitor the incident and operations to assure personal safety.

The Safety Branch Officer will work with the Incident Safety Officer appointed by the Incident Commander. The Incident Safety Officer is responsible for the welfare of all persons operating at the Incident.

1.0 RESPONSIBILITIES

The Safety Branch Officer shall:

1.1 Be a qualified Hazardous Materials Technician.

1.2 Develop and post a site safety plan.

1.3 Be positioned to be available to the Incident Command Post.

1.4 Review the local Incident Safety Officer plan to restrict entry into the site to fire department personnel and other cooperating agencies.

1.5 Follow and complete the Safety Branch Officer checklist.

1.6 Remain in constant contact with the Team Leader and the Incident Commander, and maintain an awareness of the overall operations.

1.7 Remain in contact with the local Incident Safety Officer assigned to coordinate any joint operations.

1.8 Periodically meet with branch officers and review checklists to ensure all elements of the site safety plan are met.

1.9 Correct unsafe acts or conditions through the regular line of authority.

1.10 Retain authority to halt operations in any branch if unsafe conditions are observed.

1.11 Monitor to ensure accepted practices are adhered to throughout the course of the emergency.

1.12 Anticipate safety and health hazards and prepare a plan to manage the risks.

1.13 Prepare reports for termination and post incident briefings. [See Figure S5-11.]

Medical Branch Officer SOPs (207.00)

OBJECTIVE: The objective of this SOP is to outline the roles and responsibilities of the Medical Branch Officer.

APPLICABILITY
- Department of Fire Services Divisions
- Regional Steering Committee
- Fire Chiefs
- Response Team Members
- MEMA

On all District Hazardous Materials Team responses, the Team leader shall assign a Medical Branch Officer.

1.0 RESPONSIBILITIES

The Medical Branch Officer shall:

1.1 Be a qualified Hazardous Materials Technician.

1.2 Be responsible for monitoring the medical condition of all Entry and Decon members.

1.3 In consultation with the Team Leader or Team Leader select an appropriate site to conduct medical screenings.

1.4 If necessary or desirable, employ local EMTs to perform medical screenings.

1.5 Assign and supervise personnel performing pre-entry and post-entry screenings.

1.6 Coordinate care for members injured during an incident.

1.7 Complete the Medical Branch Officer checklist [See Figure S5-12.]

1.8 Have the authority to remove any member from duty if he believes, for medical reasons, that the team member is unfit for entry operations.

1.9 Have the authority to see that any entry team member be transported to a medical facility if he deems it necessary.

1.10 Complete records of all entry and decon members.

1.11 Complete exposure records on all team members.

1.12 File all required reports.

2.0 PRE-ENTRY MEDICAL SCREENING PROCEDURE

2.1 Medical screenings are performed during an incident to:

a) Establish baseline vital signs
b) Identify individuals with potential risk

2.2 Medical monitoring is required for all personnel who will be wearing Level A, B or C protective equipment.

2.3 The following assessment must be completed and recorded:

2.3.1 Vital Signs

a) Blood pressure
b) Pulse
c) Respiratory rate
d) Temperature
e) Weight
f) FKG

2.3.2 Skin Evaluation

a) Rashes
b) Lesions
c) Open sores
d) Wounds

2.3.3 Mental Status

a) Alert, oriented to time, place, person

2.3.4 Recent Medical History

a) Medications within 72 hours
b) Alcohol consumption within 24 hours

c) Medical treatment within two weeks
d) Symptoms of fever, nausea, vomiting, diarrhea, or cough

2.4 Exclusion Criteria

- Blood Pressure. Greater than 180/105
- Pulse. Greater than 70% maximum heart rate [(220 – age) × 0.7]
- Respiration. Greater than 24 per minute
- Temperature. Greater than 99.5 or less than 97.0
- Weight. No exclusion
- EKG. Dysrhythmia not previously detected (must be cleared by Medical Control)
- Skin Evaluation. No open sores, large areas of rash, or sunburn
- Mental Status. Any altered mental state
- Medical History. Presence of nausea, vomiting, diarrhea, fever, URI, or heat exhaustion within 24 hours

New prescription medication within 2 weeks or OTC medication within 24 hours must be cleared by medical control. Heavy alcohol consumption within 24 hours or any alcohol within 2 hours.

2.5 Documentation

2.5.1 All observations shall be recorded on the "PERSONAL MEDICAL SCREENING" form.
2.5.2 The form shall be maintained by the Medical Branch Officer.

3.0 POST ENTRY MEDICAL SCREENING

3.1 After personnel have completed decontamination, they will report to the Medical Branch for post-entry screening.

3.2 The following assessment shall be completed and recorded:

3.2.1 Vital Signs

a) Blood pressure
b) Pulse
c) Respiratory rate
d) Temperature
e) Weight
f) EKG

3.2.2 Skin Evaluation
3.2.3 Mental Status

a) Alert, oriented to time, place, person

3.2.4 Medical History

Evaluation for any signs or symptoms of heat stress, cardiovascular compromise or chemical exposure.

3.3 Post-Entry Screening Procedure

3.3.1 Rest and recovery time should equal suit time plus rehydration time.
3.3.2 Repeat vital signs, monitoring every 5–10 minutes until vital signs return to 85% of baseline.
3.3.3 If at 10 minutes, the vital signs have not returned to within 10% of the baseline, perform an orthostatic BP and pulse. (Orthostatics are considered positive if the pulse increases by 20 beats/minutes, or the systolic blood pressure decreases by 20 mmHg @ 2 minutes standing.)
3.3.4 If any of the following conditions exist, contact medical control and prepare for transport to a medical facility.

a) Body weight loss greater than 3%
b) Positive orthostatics
c) Pulse greater than 85% maximum rate at 10 minutes.
d) Body temperature greater than 1010 core
e) Any altered mental status
f) Any "significant" medical complaint

3.3.5 Determine from medical control what information regarding latent reactions/symptoms should be communicated to response personnel.
3.3.6 All medical information must be documented and maintained on file. [See Figure S5-13.]

Entry Branch Officer SOPs (209.00)

OBJECTIVE: The objective of this SOP is to outline the roles and responsibilities of the Entry Branch Officer.

APPLICABILITY

Department of Fire Services Divisions
Regional Steering Committee
Fire Chiefs
Response Team Members
MEMA

On all Hazardous Material Team responses the Hazmat Team Leader shall assign an Entry Branch Officer.

The Entry Branch Officer is responsible to organize personnel and properly equip them with PPE for assignment of recon, rescue and/or mitigation tasks.

1.0 RESPONSIBILITIES

The Entry Team Officer shall:

1.1 Be a qualified Hazardous Materials Technician.

1.2 In consultation with the Team Leader and/or Team Leader Aide, select an appropriate site to stage for entry team personnel.

1.3 Follow and complete the Entry Officer Checklist.

1.4 Assign support personnel to assist entry personnel donning PPE.

1.5 Receive reports from the Safety Branch Officer.

1.6 Receive from the Science Branch Officer appropriate information about the incident.

1.7 Receive from the Science Officer status reports to prepare personnel for operations.

1.8 Make reports to the Team Leader concerning the status of entry resources. [See Figures S5-14 and S5-15.]

Decon Branch Officer SOPs (210.00)

OBJECTIVE: The objective of this SOP is to outline the roles and responsibilities of the Decon Branch Officer.

APPLICABILITY

Department of Fire Services Divisions
Regional Steering Committee
Fire Chiefs
Response Team Members
MEMA

1.0 RESPONSIBILITIES

1.1 Decontamination Branch Officer (Decon officer) will be assigned by the Team Leader on all incidents involving entry operations or when personnel may be exposed to hazardous materials.

The Decon officer shall assume the responsibility for safe and acceptable methods of decontamination for the incident.

1.2 The Decon officer shall be a qualified Hazardous Materials Technician.

1.3 After receiving his/her assignment, the Decon officer will obtain an identification vest, portable radio, and a Decon Team Checklist packet.

1.4 The Decon officer will receive from the Science Branch Officer information concerning the materials involved and appropriate decontamination methods.

2.0 DECONTAMINATION LINE SETUP

2.1 The Decon officer will identify potential locations for the Decon corridor based on the terrain and close proximity to the Hot Zone work area. Attention should be focused on locations that are uphill, flat, or slightly sloping toward the Hot Zone. The location must be as close as practical to the work area to limit travel distances by Entry personnel. Other considerations include accessibility, surface material, lighting, drains, waterways, water availability and location, and weather.

2.2 The Decon corridor will be clearly marked with traffic cones or barrier tape and be secured against entry by unauthorized personnel.

2.3 The Decon officer will receive from the Science officer the proper PPE selection for the Decon Team. The Decon Officer will then request sufficient quantities and types of the appropriate PPE from the Logistics officer.

2.4 To safely reduce the contamination of personnel and equipment, the Decon Officer will receive from the Science branch the appropriate solution (s) and methods.

2.5 The Decon corridor must be completed and all personnel in place prior to any work commencing in the hot zone. Emergency hand signals must be reviewed prior to entry in the hot zone.

3.0 DECONTAMINATION PROCEDURES

3.1 The Decon corridor must consist of a minimum of a tool drop, an emergency corridor, one gross shower, one rinse station and a PPE drop. The corridor may be expanded with as many additional stations as may be required by the nature of the incident.

3.2 The Decon officer must ensure proper procedures. The Decon procedure is outlined as follows:

3.2.1 If tools are to be reused by another entry team, they should be placed in a container or area designated as the tool drop prior to personnel entering the gross decontamination station.

3.2.2 If tools are not to be reused, they may be taken to the gross Decon station for cleaning prior to being left at the tool drop.

3.2.3 Gross Decon is accomplished by either brushing away or vacuuming dry materials, or by absorbing/adsorbing the material with some appropriate method or product. When the material is not water reactive, water or another solution may be used to dilute the materials. The objective of gross Decon is to remove the bulk of the hazardous material from the surface of PPE and tools. Measures must be taken to retain decontamination water runoff.

3.2.4 The next step is the wash/rinse station, where residual contaminants are scrubbed away with brushes and a detergent solution. Contaminants are then rinsed away with a water spray.

3.2.5 After rinsing, PPE is carefully removed and set aside for disposal or testing. Once PPE is removed, the SCBA can be removed and set aside for cleaning. Personnel will then be sent to Medical personnel.

3.2.6 The final step in the Decon process is personal showers, either on site or as soon as practical otherwise.

4.0 EMERGENCY DECONTAMINATION PROCEDURES

4.1 Emergency Decon may be needed for the following situations:

a) When PPE fails due to an accidental breach or degradation or when personnel become accidentally contaminated.
b) When personnel have been injured or are in immediate need of medical attention and have not been exposed to hazardous materials.

4.2 Emergency Decon where someone has been or is believed to have been contaminated:

4.2.1 Remove PPE from the victim and begin flushing affected body areas.
4.2.2 Remove as much contaminant as possible to prevent secondary contamination to Medical personnel.
4.2.3 Advance the injured/exposed member through the Decon line.
4.2.4 Dress the injured/exposed member in a Tyvek suit or other suitable clothing.
4.2.5 Move the injured/exposed person to a safe area for further evaluation and treatment.

4.3 Emergency Decon measures for an injury/ medical emergency where person has not been exposed or contaminated.

4.3.1 Assess the condition of the member in the suit. Does the emergency in the suit exceed the severity of the threat from exposure to the material?
4.3.2 Choose Decon line or emergency Decon corridor.
4.3.3 Follow standard decon procedures with care for injury.
4.3.4 Contact Medical Branch Officer to develop plan of care.

5.0 TERMINATION PROCEDURES

5.1 All tools must be cleaned prior to returning them to service.

5.2 All tools, equipment, and PPE contaminated beyond the Decon capabilities on site will be inventoried and placed in containers, marked, and set aside for cleaning or disposal.

5.3 All Decon pool water must be tested to determine the presence of contaminants. If contaminated, it must be secured for disposal.

5.4 All Decon Team members must decontaminate each other or themselves.

5.5 All materials used by the Decon branch during decontamination operations must be documented by the Decon officer.

5.6 Notify all branch personnel to report to the debriefing as scheduled by the Team Leader. [See Figure S5-16.]

Logistics Branch Officer (SOP 211.00)

OBJECTIVE: The objective of this SOP is to outline the roles and responsibilities of the Logistics Branch Officer.

APPLICABILITY
- Department of Fire Services Divisions
- Regional Steering Committee
- Fire Chiefs
- Response Team Members
- MEMA

On all Hazardous Materials Team responses, the Team Leader 5 assigns a Logistics Branch Officer.

The Logistics Branch Officer shall assume responsibility for procurement of resources required for hazardous materials operations and the documentation of resources and equipment utilized.

1.0 RESPONSIBILITIES

1.1 Shall be a qualified Hazardous Materials Technician.

1.2 In consultation with the Team Leader, select a site for the ORU.

1.3 In consultation with the Team Leader and the Incident Commander, select a site to stage equipment supplied by outside agencies.

1.4 Coordinate with the Team Leader and Science Branch Officer to determine the type of operation to be conducted and possible equipment needed.

1.5 Coordinate with the Liaison Officer for contact with outside agencies.

1.6 Deliver to a staging area in the warm zone all tools and equipment required for operations.

1.7 Maintain a record of all equipment and supplies issued. [See Figure S5-17.]

1.8 Account for all tools, equipment, and supplies used during the incident.

1.9 Forward to the Team Leader a list of tools, equipment and supplies that were expended and used and need to be replaced.

1.10 Assure that any equipment utilized by First Responders is appropriately decontaminated or isolated.

1.11 Coordinate with the on-scene representative from contractor's and outside agencies.

1.12 Complete the Hazardous Materials LOGISTICS Checklist. [See Figure S5-18.]

INCIDENT COMMAND ACTIVATION WORKSHEET

In the event an incident occurs in your community requiring a response by a Massachusetts Hazardous Materials Response Team call:

Control Center:	Phone#:

Before calling, please have the following information ready:

City/Town:

Location of Incident:

Requesting Department:

Person Making Call:

Callback Number(s):

Incident Commander:

Nature, Extent of Incident

Material(s) ID:	Quantity:

Fire	☐	Spill	☐	Leak	☐	Continuous Release	☐
Building	☐	Transportation	☐	Railroad	☐	Vessel	☐
Open Area	☐						

Response Tier Requested: ☐1 ☐2 ☐3 (Tier 2 is default)

Assembly Point for Team Members:

Prepare to give the Control Center:

☐ Assembly point must be easy to locate for members unfamiliar with your community. An exit ramp off a highway, major road intersection, distinct landmark or building is preferred.

☐ Station someone from your community (police, fire, etc.) to meet the responding members and provide them with detailed directions to a secure parking area.

Parking Area for Team Members ______________________________

☐ Provide shuttle transportation for team members from the parking area to the incident scene.

Figure S5-3 *Worksheet from SOP 201.00.*

CONTROL CENTER ACTIVATION WORKSHEET

Incident#:	Date of Alarm:	Time: hours

Fire Alarm Operator:

The requesting community will provide the following information:

City/Town:

Location of Incident:

Requesting Department:

Person Making Call:

Callback Number(s):

Incident Commander:

Nature, Extent of Incident

Material(s) ID: | Quantity:

Fire ☐ Spill ☐ Leak ☐ Continuous Release ☐

Building ☐ Transportation ☐ Railroad ☐ Vessel ☐

Open Area ☐

Response Tier Requested: ☐1 ☐2 ☐3 (Tier 2 is default)

Assembly Point for Team Members:

Ask the Caller to Verify that:

- ☐ Assembly point must be easy to locate for members unfamiliar with your requesting community. An exit ramp off a highway, major road intersection, distinct landmark or building is preferred.
- ☐ Station someone from your community (police, fire, etc.) to meet the responding members.
- ☐ Parking area for Team Members vehicles is established.
- ☐ Shuttle transportation from parking area to incident is arranged.

Figure S5-4 *Worksheet from SOP 201.00*

FIRST ARRIVING TEAM MEMBER

Arrival Time:

Incident#:	Date of Alarm:	Time: hours

Location:

Nature of Incident:

INITIAL BRIEFING WITH INCIDENT COMMANDER

	Designate staging area for Haz-Mat team
	Fire department in command
	Incident Commander

SITE CONTROL

	Access to scene restricted
	Isolation zones established, hazard area isolated
	Distances obtained from:
	Material(s) identified: Name ______________ Quantity ______________ Name ______________ Quantity ______________
	Defensive operations taken to confine incident: ______________ ______________ ______________ ______________ ______________
	Number injured or exposed personnel:
	Contaminated personnel in safe refuge
	Evacuation of exposures required?
	Other agencies notified: ______________ ______________ ______________

Figure S5-5 *Worksheet from SOP 203*

MASSACHUSETTS HAZARDOUS MATERIALS RESPONSE TEAM

Team Leader Checklist

Incident#:	Date of Alarm:	Time: hours
Date Operations Terminated:		Time: hours

Total Time of Alarm: ________days ________hrs ________minutes

Nature of Incident:

Location:

Incident Commander:

Team Leader: identified by vest

ASSIGN BRANCH OFFICERS

1. Science Officer:
2. Safety Officer:
3. Aide:
4. Medical Officer:
5. Logistics Officer:
6. Decon Officer:
7. Entry Officer:
8. Staff Liaison:
9. Other Staff Positions:

Figure S5-6 *Worksheet from SOP 204*

HAZARD AND RISK ASSESSMENT

Science Branch

- ☐ Materials involved
- ☐ Hazards identified
- ☐ Nature of release
- ☐ Likely harm without intervention estimated
- ☐ Are Isolation Zones (hot, warm) adequate?
- ☐ Evacuation of exposures required?
- ☐ Site description and layout
- ☐ Environmental Impacts

SAFETY

- ☐ Site safety plan complete

MEDICAL

- ☐ Rehab facilities established
- ☐ Medical monitoring established

ENTRY BRANCH

- ☐ Adequate personnel
- ☐ Entry staging/dressing area adequate
- ☐ Equipment and supplies adequate

DECONTAMINATION BRANCH

- ☐ Personnel
- ☐ Decon corridor adequate
- ☐ Equipment and supplies adequate

Figure S5-7 *Worksheet from SOP 204*

BRIEFING WITH INCIDENT COMMAND

- ☐ Fire Department Incident Commander ______________________
- ☐ Designate staging area for Hazmat Team
- ☐ Obtain situation description
    - Material(s) involved
    - Nature of spill or release
- ☐ Defensive operations to confine incident
- ☐ Contaminated personnel identified, in safe refuge

SITE MANAGEMENT

- ☐ Access to scene restricted
- ☐ Access controlled by ______________________
- ☐ Hazmat staging area designated away from Command Post area
- ☐ Site Organization Plan made

Designate areas for:

- ☐ Team Leader with Incident Commander
- ☐ Safety
- ☐ Science and Communications (TOM)
- ☐ Decon
- ☐ Entry
- ☐ Logistics; Equipment; Truck; Outside Agencies
- ☐ Medical; Rehab Area

Figure S5-8 *Worksheet from SOP 204.*

LOGISTICS BRANCH

- ☐ Adequate personnel
- ☐ Site for equipment truck
- ☐ Supplies, materials and equipment available
- ☐ Staging officer for contractor/outside agencies
- ☐ Staging area for contractors and outside agency equipment

STAFF LIAISON

- ☐ Assembly area for outside agencies
- ☐ Appropriate agencies notified
    - ☐ DEM
    - ☐ EPA
    - ☐ Manufacturer
    - ☐ Shipper
    - ☐ Consignee
    - ☐ Others

BRANCH OFFICERS BRIEFING

- ☐ All Branch Officers present
- ☐ Incident Commander present
- ☐ Outside agency representative present
- ☐ Incident profile (Science Officer)
    - ☐ Materials involved
    - ☐ Physical layout
    - ☐ Nature of release
- ☐ Options for mitigation (Science Officer)

  for each option, evaluate the following

  A. Techniques

  B. Materials and equipment

  C. Entry Team

  D. Safety considerations

Figure S5-9 *Worksheet from SOP 204.*

BRANCH OFFICERS BRIEFING (continued)

☐ Recommended mitigation plan (Science Officer)
for each option, evaluate the following
A. Techniques
B. Materials and equipment
C. Entry Team
D. Safety considerations

☐ Evaluation of Options
for each option, Branch Officers in turn evaluate the capabilities of their branch to meet the requirements

☐ Review and approve selected option

☐ Review assignments for Hazmat Team, Incident Command, Agencies, Contractors, Industry Representatives.
Outline options, courses of action, responsibilities and roles of each group. Adjust as necessary for plan.

OPERATIONS

☐ All Hazmat officers and personnel prepared for operations

☐ Notify Incident Command that operations are commencing

☐ Coordinate with Safety and Branch Officers during entry operations

☐ Monitor operations and evaluate the effectiveness of the plan.

Figure S5-9 *(Continued)*

TERMINATION

DECONTAMINATION

- ☐ All personnel decontaminated
- ☐ All tools and equipment decontaminated
- ☐ Isolate tools & equipment not decontaminated

MEDICAL

- ☐ All personnel cleared
- ☐ All members through rehab

SAFETY

- ☐ Site safety considerations for scene security

LOGISTICS

- ☐ All equipment secure or accounted for

AIDE

- ☐ All Hazmat personnel accounted for

GENERAL DEBRIEFING FOR ALL AGENCIES

- ☐ Incident Commander released Hazmat Team

HAZMAT TEAM DEBRIEFING

- ☐ Medical - signs, symptoms of exposure
- ☐ Team members check out (aide)

BRANCH OFFICER MEETING

- ☐ All documentation and Officers checklists complete
- ☐ Report submission deadline set
- ☐ Report team status to District Control

Figure S5-10 *Worksheet from SOP 204.*

SAFETY BRANCH OFFICER CHECKLIST

Incident#:	Date of Alarm:	Time: hrs
Location:		
Nature of Incident:		
Safety Officer:		identified by vest
Safety Monitors:		
1.	2.	3.

	INCIDENT PROFILE
	Received from Science Branch a description of the incident
	Chemical information
	Site layout and description
	Weather information
	Hazards to personnel
	Health effects of exposure
	Hot, warm and cold zone specifications
	From the Team Leader and the Incident Commander, obtain an overview of the incident.
	SITE SAFETY
	Hazard zones established and communicated to Incident Commander, Team Leader, and Operating personnel.
	Are hazard zones adequate for possible change in conditions?
	Identify hazardous situations associated with the incident.

Figure S5-11 *Worksheet from SOP 208.*

	SITE SAFETY (continued)
	Evaluate weather, wind direction, and speed
	Review site plan layout (should be drawn)
	Incident Command Post in safe location
	TOM and ORU in safe location
	Staging areas in safe location
	Positioning of companies and personnel evaluated
	Review incident mitigation plan
	Confirm with Medical Branch Officer; hospital identified and notified
	All personnel on site wearing proper protective clothing (safety shoes, helmet, coveralls, eye and ear protection)
	Monitor and evaluate site practices of each branch
	Recommend corrective action as necessary to prevent injury or exposure
	Monitor and evaluate site practices by other agencies
	Investigate accidents that have occurred within incident area
	Brief Incident Safety Officer
	EMERGENCY PROCEDURES
	Evacuation signal established and communicated to all personnel
	Evacuation plan, travel routes identified
	Procedure to decon and treat injured member ready
	Procedure to decon and treat exposed or contaminated member ready
	HEALTH AND SANITATION
	Rehabilitation area established and staffed
	Area protected from weather available for staging
	Washing facility set up
	Food / drink handling procedure established
	Toilet facilities available
	Shower facility available

Figure S5-11 *(Continued)*

	BRANCH OFFICERS BRIEFING
	Prepare report on branch status.
	Evaluate branch readiness for mitigation plan.
	OPERATIONS
	Personnel operating equipment are qualified and familiar with the equipment
	Arrange a "dry run" with equipment and techniques
	Safety monitor assigned for each entry team
	Entry teams briefed concerning hazards and procedures
	Hazard and procedures briefing by team leader
	TERMINATION
	Monitor site for safe work practices (routine and hazardous material)
	Prepare a report for the Incident Commander concerning safety for follow-up operations

Figure S5-11 *(Continued)*

MEDICAL BRANCH OFFICER CHECKLIST

Incident#:	Date of Alarm:	Time: hours

Location:

Nature of Incident:

Medical Officer: ☐ identified by vest

Medical Personnel:

	INCIDENT PROFILE
	Obtain from Science Branch Officer information about the materials involved and hazards to personnel.
	SITE SELECTION AND SET UP
	In consultation with the Team Leader, select a site for medical screening.
	Designate a separate treatment area for injured or exposed personnel.
	Has an ambulance been assigned exclusively to the Hazmat Team?
	Determine the desired level of EMS (basic, intermediate, paramedic).
	With the Team Leader and Incident Commander, arrange for adequate EMS resources for anticipated needs of the team, other responders and civilians.
	Identify and contact medical control at the hospital which will receive injured persons.
	Arrange for sufficient EMT's to perform pre and post entry screenings for all Decon and Entry personnel.
	Sufficient screening forms available.
	Maintain logs for all pre-entry and post entry screening.
	BRANCH OFFICERS BRIEFING
	Prepare report on branch status.
	Evaluate branch readiness for mitigation plan.

Figure S5-12 *Worksheet from SOP 207.*

	OPERATIONS
	Personnel and equipment staged to evacuate and treat injured persons.
	Monitor for changing conditions, receive updates from Science Branch.
	Prepare for post entry screenings.
	Prepare for pre-entry screening for relief personnel.
	TERMINATION
	All personnel post screenings complete.
	All personnel screening forms complete.
	Complete report of screenings.
	Complete report of on site treatment of injuries.
	Complete report of persons transported for treatment.
	Prepare report for debriefings on signs/symptoms of exposure.
	Prepare report for Incident Commander of EMS, health hazard concerns for follow-up operations.

Figure S5-12 *(Continued)*

PERSONNEL MEDICAL SCREENING

Name:	Assignment:
Recent Medical History:	
Pre-Entry EKG:	Post Entry EKG:
Weight, Pre-Entry:	Weight, Post Entry:

VITAL SIGNS

Vital Signs MAXIMUM	Blood Pressure 180/105	Pulse 70% MHR	Respirations 24	Temperature 99.5
Pre entry time:				
POST ENTRY				
Time:				
Time:				
Time:				
Time:				
Time:				

Exposure record *(nature, signs/symptoms, patient complaint, injury)*:

On scene treatment by:

Transported to a medical facility:

Referred for follow-up examination:

Figure S5-13 *Worksheet from SOP 207.*

ENTRY BRANCH OFFICER CHECKLIST

Incident#:	Date of Alarm:	Time: hrs

Location:

Nature of Incident:

Entry Officer: identified by vest

ENTRY TEAMS			
Team 1			
Support 1			
Team 2			
Support 2			
Team 3			
Support 3			
Team 4			
Support 4			

	INCIDENT PROFILE
	Briefed by Science Officer
	Material identification
	Hazards
	Nature of incident

	SITE SELECTION AND SET-UP
	In consultation with the Team Leader, select site to stage the entry teams
	Site should be protected from the weather
	Site should be close to the point of entry
	Requisition materials and supplies from logistics

Figure S5-14 *Worksheet from SOP 209.*

	BRANCH OFFICERS BRIEFING
	Prepare report on branch status.
	Evaluate branch readiness for mitigation plan.
	OPERATIONS
	Assign support personnel to each entry member
	Complete entry team checklists
	Safety Monitor assigned to each team
	Equipment checked and ready
	Anticipate need for additional entry
	Maintain at least one entry team at ready while teams are operating in the hot zone
	TERMINATION
	Ensure all entry checklists are complete and filed
	All equipment used inventoried
	All equipment returned to logistics
	All entry teams briefed by Medical Branch Officer on signs/symptoms of exposure
	All members notified of time and place of debriefing

Figure S5-14 *(Continued)*

ENTRY TEAM SAFETY CHECKLIST

(completed by Safety Monitor)

Entry Team # ______________________

A. ______________ name ______________ support

B. ______________ name ______________ support

C. ______________ name ______________ support

Safety Monitor ______________________

EQUIPMENT / ITEM	A	B	C
Dressed in jumpsuit			
Medical pre-entry screening completed			
Personal items tagged and secured			
Spare clothing tagged, moved to Decon			
Entry suit serial number Zippers, seams, stitching			
Gloves (inner and over)			
Boots			
Helmet			
SCBA Cylinder full Low air alarm PASS device Facepiece			
Communications Proper channel Equipment tested			
Safety hand signals reviewed and understood			
Hydrated (gatorade type drink, or water)			
Mitigation Plan Briefing by Science and Team Leader Objectives clear Tools and equipment ready			
Operations			
On air time			
SCBA seal check			
Suit closed, zippers, and seals checked Radio check, notify communications			
Decon Off air time			
Medical Post screening complete			
To Rehab			

Figure S5-15 *Worksheet from SOP 209.*

DECON SOLUTIONS

Decon Solution A: Solution containing 5% sodium carbonate (Na_2CO_3) and 5% trisodium phosphate (Na_3Po_4).

Decon Solution B: Solution containing 10% calcium hypochlorite ($Ca(C10_3)$.

Decon Solution C: Solution containing 5% trisodium phosphate (Na_3PO_2). This solution can also be used as a general purpose rinse.

Decon Solution D: Dilute solution of hydrochloric acid (HC1). Mix one pint of concentrated HC1 into 10 gallons of water.

Decon Solution E: Concentrated solution of Tide or other detergent and water. Mix into a paste and scrub with a brush. Rinse with water.

The following is a guideline for selecting degradation chemicals for the type of hazard identified:

1.	Inorganic acids, metal processing waste	A
2.	Heavy metal; mercury, lead, cadmium, etc.	B
3.	Pesticides, chlorinated phenols, dioxins and PCB's	B
4.	Cyanides, ammonia and other non-acidic inorganic waste	B
5.	Solvents and organic compounds such as Trichlorethylene, Chloroform and Toluene	C or A
6.	PBB's and PCB's	C or A
7.	Oily, greasy unspecified wastes not suspected to be contaminated with pesticides	C
8.	Inorganic bases, alkali and caustics wastes	D
9.	Radioactive materials	E
10.	Etiologic agents	A & B

Figure S5-16 *Worksheet from SOP 210.*

DECON CHECKLIST

Date:	Location:

	Initial Briefing from the Team Leader
	Incident Profile
	Decon solution and method
	PPE

PERSONNEL ASSIGNMENTS

Decon Officer:

Decon Personnel:

Wash/rinse ____________________
____
____
____

PPE Drop ____________________
____

Air Supply ____________________

	All personnel monitored by Medical Branch

DECON SITE SELECTION CRITERIA

	Decon are located in Warm Zone at exit from Hot Zone
	Decon area located uphill/upwind from Hot Zone
	Decon area level or sloped toward Hot Zone
	Water supply available

DECON SITE SETUP

	Area clearly marked with traffic cones and barrier tape to be secure against unauthorized entry.
	Entry and exit points marked
	Emergency corridor established and clearly marked
	Runoff containment (tarp, plastic sheeting, dikes)

Figure S5-16 *(Continued)*

	DECON SITE SETUP (continued)
	Gross Decon shower(s) setup
	Water supply established
	Arrange containment basins and pools in proper order
	Disposal containers in place for PPE and equipment drop
	Decon solutions mixed
	Brushes, hand sprayers, hoses and equipment in place
	Tool drop set up
	Spare SCBA cylinders available
	Relief personnel available
	BRANCH OFFICERS BRIEFING
	Prepare report on branch status.
	Evaluate branch readiness for mitigation plan.
	ENTRY / DECON OPERATIONS
	Decon and entry personnel briefed on hazards
	Emergency procedures and hand signals reviewed and understood
	Decon and entry personnel briefed on Decon procedures
	Decon corridor complete
	Decon personnel on air
	Monitor for adequate relief personnel
	TERMINATION
	Disposable/contaminated materials isolated, bagged and containerized
	All containers sealed, marked and isolated
	All team equipment cleaned and accounted for

Figure S5-16 *(Continued)*

EQUIPMENT LIST

	Telephone list for agencies, contractors and resources

Heavy Equipment

	Loaders
	Dump trucks
	Dumpsters
	Crane
	Forklift

Supplies

	Sand or other diking material
	Shoring or blocking materials
	Absorbent pads and booms
	Absorbent materials
	Material for chemical neutralization

Tools and Equipment

	Special tools or equipment
	Replacement for expended/damaged tools or equipment
	Protective clothing
	SCBA cylinders

Firefighting Supplies

	Dry chemical
	Foam, AFFF Polar Solvent HI-EX
	Protective clothing

Figure S5-17 *Worksheet from SOP 211.*

	Personal Needs
	Food, drinks
	Clothing
	Washing and shower facilities
	Heated or air conditioned space
	Transportation
	Sanitation

Figure S5-17 *(Continued)*

LOGISTICS BRANCH OFFICER CHECKLIST

Incident#:	Date of Alarm:	Time: hrs

Location:

Nature of Incident:

Logistics Officer: identified by vest

Logistics Personnel:

1.	2.	3.

	SITE SELECTION AND SET UP
	Consult with Team Leader.
	Select a site uphill, upwind from the hot zone.
	Locate the ORU convenient to Decon, and Entry.
	Adequate space to stage equipment.
	Mark area with barrier tape and traffic cones.
	Restrict access to ORU and equipment.
	Request adequate personnel to issue, track and inventory equipment and supplies.
	Equipment check out sheets on hand.
	Personnel assigned to distribute tools, equipment & supplies.
	STAGING
	Appoint one or more members to manage the staging of equipment supplied by contractors and outside agencies.
	Select a site separate from the ORU and Team Staging.
	Stage all local, contractor and outside agency equipment.
	Maintain a check-in list for local, contractor and outside agencies.
	Access to staged equipment restricted to logistics.

Figure S5-18 *Worksheet from SOP 211.*

BRANCH OFFICERS BRIEFING	
	Prepare report on branch status.
	Evaluate branch readiness for mitigation plan.
OPERATIONS	
	All tools, equipment and supplies checked out.
	Equipment & supply need projected and replenished.
	List of expendable supplies maintained.
TERMINATION	
	Tools, equipment and supplies accounted for.
	Missing, lost or damaged tools and equipment listed.
	Tools and equipment unable to be decontaminated listed.
	Expendable supplies list complete.
	Tools and equipment decontaminated.

Figure S5-18 *(Continued)*

SUPPLEMENT 6

Hazardous Materials Emergency Planning Guide

Editor's Note: This supplement contains excerpts from a U.S. government publication detailing the organization and planning of a community hazardous materials incident response plan. This plan was developed by the National Response Team of the National Oil and Hazardous Substances Contingency Plan, 2100 2nd Street S.W., Washington, DC 20593.

THE BACKGROUND OF THIS GUIDANCE

This Haz Mat Emergency Planning Guide has been developed cooperatively by 14 federal agencies. It is being published by the National Response Team in compliance with Section 303(f) of the "Emergency Planning and Community Right-to-Know Act of 1986," Title III of the "Superfund Amendments and Reauthorization Act of 1986" (SARA).

This guide replaces the Federal Emergency Management Agency's (FEMA) *Planning Guide and Checklist for Hazardous Materials Contingency Plans* (popularly known as FEMA-10).

This guide also incorporates material from the U.S. Environmental Protection Agency's (EPA) interim guidance for its Chemical Emergency Preparedness Program (CEPP) published late in 1985. EPA is revising and updating CEPP technical guidance materials that will include site-specific guidance, criteria for identifying extremely hazardous substances, and chemical profiles and a list of such substances. Planners should use this general planning guide in conjunction with the CEPP materials.

In recent years, the U.S. Department of Transportation (DOT) has been active in emergency planning. The Research and Special Programs Administration (RSPA) has published transportation-related reports and guides and has contributed to this general planning guide. The U.S. Coast Guard (USCG) has actively implemented planning and response requirements of the National Contingency Plan (NCP) and has contributed to this general planning guide.

The U.S. Occupational Safety and Health Administration (OSHA) and the U.S. Agency for Toxic Substances and Disease Registry (ATSDR) have assisted in preparing this general planning guide.

In addition to its FEMA-10, FEMA has developed and published a variety of planning-related materials. Of special interest here is *Guide for Development of State and Local Emergency Operations Plans* (known as CPG 1-8) that encourages communities to develop multihazard emergency operations plans (EOPs) covering all hazards facing a community (e.g., floods, earthquakes, hurricanes, as well as hazardous materials incidents). This general planning guide complements CPG 1-8 and indicates how hazardous materials planners can develop or revise a multihazard EOP. It also describes a sample outline for an emergency plan covering only hazardous materials, if a community does not have the resources to develop a multihazard EOP.

The terms *contingency plan, emergency plan,* and *emergency operations plan* are often used interchangeably, depending upon whether one is reading the NCP, CPG 1-8, or other planning guides. This guide consistently refers to *emergency plans* and *emergency planning*.

This guide will consistently use *hazardous materials* when generally referring to hazardous substances, petroleum, natural gas, synthetic gas, acutely toxic chemicals, and other toxic chemicals. Title III of SARA uses the term *extremely hazardous substances* to indicate those chemicals that could cause serious irreversible health effects from accidental releases.

1. INTRODUCTION

1.1 The Need for Hazardous Materials Emergency Planning

Major disasters like that in Bhopal, India, in December 1984, which resulted in 2000 deaths and over 200,000 injuries, are rare. Reports of hazardous materials spills and releases, however, are increasingly commonplace. Thousands of new chemicals are developed each year. Citizens and officials are concerned about accidents (e.g., highway incidents, warehouse fires, train derailments, industrial incidents) happening in their communities. Recent evidence shows that hazardous materials incidents are considered by many to be the most significant threat facing local jurisdictions.

Because of the risk of hazardous materials incidents, and because local governments will be completely on their own in the first stages of almost any hazardous materials incident, communities need to maintain a continuing preparedness capacity. A specific tangible result of being prepared is an emergency plan. Some communities might have sophisticated and detailed written plans but, if the plans have not recently been tested and revised, these communities might be less prepared than they think for a possible hazardous materials incident.

1.2 Purpose of This Guide

The purpose of this guide is to assist communities in planning for hazardous materials incidents.

"Communities" refers primarily to local jurisdictions. There are other groups of people, however, that can profitably use this guide. Rural areas with limited resources may need to plan at the county or regional level. State officials seeking to develop a state emergency plan that is closely coordinated with local plans can adapt this guidance to their purposes. Likewise, officials of chemical plants, railroad yards, and shipping and trucking companies can use this guidance to coordinate their own hazardous materials emergency planning with that of the local community.

"Hazardous materials" refers generally to hazardous substances, petroleum, natural gas, synthetic gas, acutely toxic chemicals, and other toxic chemicals. "Extremely hazardous substances" is used in Title III of the Superfund Amendments and Reauthorization Act of 1986 to refer to those chemicals that could cause serious health effects following short-term exposure from accidental releases. The U.S. Environmental Protection Agency published an initial list of 402 extremely hazardous substances for which emergency planning is required. Because this list may be revised, planners should contact EPA regional offices to obtain information. This guidance deals specifically with response to hazardous materials incidents—both at fixed facilities (manufacturing, processing, storage, and disposal) and during transportation (highways, waterways, rail, and air). Plans for responding to radiological incidents and natural emergencies such as hurricanes, floods, and earthquakes are not the focus of this guidance, although most aspects of plan development and appraisal are common to these emergencies. Communities should see NUREG 0654/FEMA-REP-1 and/or FEMA-REP-5 for assistance in radiological planning. Communities should be prepared, however, for the possibility that natural emergencies, radiological incidents, and hazardous materials incidents will cause or reinforce each other.

The objectives of this guide are as follows:

- Focus community activity on emergency preparedness and response
- Provide communities with information useful in organizing the planning task
- Furnish criteria to determine risk and to help communities decide whether they need to plan for hazardous materials incidents
- Help communities conduct planning that is consistent with their needs and capabilities
- Provide a method for continually updating a community's emergency plan

This guide will *not*

- Give a simple "fill-in-the-blanks" model plan (because each community needs an emergency plan suited to its own unique circumstances);
- Provide details on response techniques; or
- Train personnel to respond to incidents.

Community planners will need to consult other resources in addition to this guide. Related programs and materials are discussed in Section 1.5.

1.3 How to Use This Guide

This guide has been designed so it can be used easily by both those communities with little or no planning experience and those communities with extensive planning experience.

All planners should consult the decision tree in Figure S6-1 for assistance in using this guide.

1.4 Requirements for Planning

Planners should understand federal, state, and local requirements that apply to emergency planning.

1.4.1 Federal Requirements. This section discusses the principal federal planning requirements found in the National Contingency Plan; Title III of SARA; the Resource Conservation and Recovery Act; and FEMA's requirements for Emergency Operations Plans.

A. National Contingency Plan. The National Contingency Plan (NCP), required by Section 105 of the Comprehensive Environmental Response, Compensation, and Liability Act (CERCLA), calls for extensive preparedness and planning. The National Response Team (NRT), comprised of representatives of various federal government agencies with major environmental, transportation, emergency management, worker safety, and public health responsibilities, is responsible for coordi-

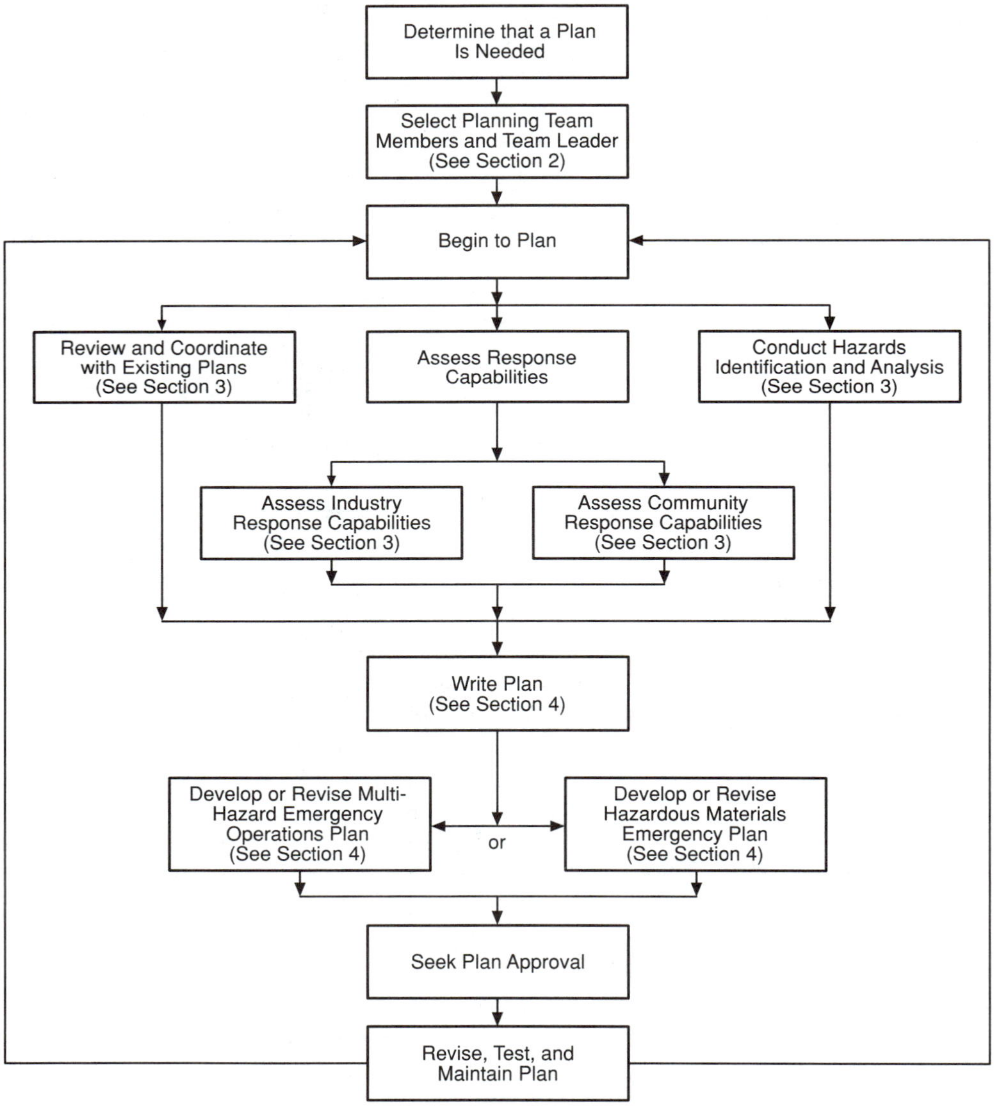

Figure S6-1 Overview of planning process.

nating federal emergency preparedness and planning on a nationwide basis.

A key element of federal support to local responders during hazardous materials transportation and fixed facility incidents is a response by U.S. Coast Guard (USCG) or Environmental Protection Agency (EPA) On-Scene Coordinators (OSCs). The OSC is the federal official predesignated to coordinate and direct federal responses and removals under the NCP. These OSCs are assisted by federal Regional Response Teams (RRTs) that are available to provide advice and support to the OSC and, through the OSC, to local responders.

Federal responses may be triggered by a report to the National Response Center (NRC), operated by the Coast Guard. Provisions of the federal Water Pollution Control Act (Clean Water Act), CERCLA ("Superfund"), and various other federal laws require persons responsible for a discharge or release to notify the NRC immediately. The NRC Duty Officer promptly relays each report to the appropriate Coast Guard or EPA OSC, depending on the location of an incident. Based on this initial report and any other information that can be obtained, the OSC makes a preliminary assessment of the need for a federal response.

B. Title III of SARA ("Superfund Amendments and Reauthorization Act of 1986"). Significant new hazardous materials emergency planning requirements are contained in Title III of SARA (also known as the "Emergency Planning and Community Right-to-Know Act of 1986"). Title III of SARA requires the establishment of state emergency response commissions, emergency planning districts, and local emergency planning committees. The governor of each state appoints a state emergency response commission whose responsibilities include: designating emergency planning districts; appointing local emergency planning committees for each district; supervising and coordinating the activities of planning committees; reviewing emergency plans; receiving chemical release notifications; and establishing procedures for receiving and processing requests from the public for information about and/or copies of emergency response plans, material safety data sheets, the list of extremely hazardous substances prepared as part of EPA's original Chemical Emergency Preparedness Program initiative *(see Section 1.5.2)*, inventory forms, and toxic chemical release forms.

C. Resource Conservation and Recovery Act. The Resource Conservation and Recovery Act (RCRA) established a framework for the proper management and disposal of all wastes. The Hazardous and Solid Waste Amendments of 1984 (HSWA) expanded the scope of the law and placed increased emphasis on waste reduction, corrective action, and treatment of hazardous wastes.

D. FEMA Emergency Operations Plan Requirements. Planning requirements for jurisdictions receiving FEMA funds are set forth in 44 CFR Part 302, effective May 12, 1986. This regulation calls for states and local governments to prepare an emergency operations plan (EOP) that conforms with the requirements for plan content contained in FEMA's CPG 1-3, CPG 1-8, and CPG 1-8A. These state and local government EOPs must identify the available personnel, equipment, facilities, supplies, and other resources in the jurisdiction, and state the method or scheme for coordinated actions to be taken by individuals and government services in the event of natural, man-made (e.g., hazardous materials), and attack-related disasters.

E. OSHA Regulations. Occupational Safety and Health Administration regulations require employers involved in hazardous waste operations to develop and implement an emergency response plan for employees. The elements of this plan must include:

1. Recognition of emergencies
2. Methods or procedures for alerting employees on site
3. Evacuation procedures and routes to places of refuge or safe distances away from the danger area
4. Means and methods for emergency medical treatment and first aid for employees
5. The line of authority for employees
6. On-site decontamination procedures
7. Site control means
8. Methods for evaluating the plan

Employers whose employees will be responding to hazardous materials emergency incidents from their regular work location or duty station (e.g., a fire department, fire brigade, or emergency medical service) must also have an emergency response plan. (See 29 CFR Part 1910.120.)

1.4.2 State and Local Requirements. Many states have adopted individual laws and regulations that address local government involvement in hazardous materials. Local authorities should investigate state requirements and programs before they initiate preparedness and planning activities. Emergency plans should include consideration of any state or local community right-to-know laws. When these laws are more demanding than the federal law, the state and local laws sometimes take precedence over the federal law.

1.5 Related Programs and Materials

Because emergency planning is a complex process involving a variety of issues and concerns, community planners should consult related public and private sector programs and materials. The following are selected examples of planning programs and materials that may be used in conjunction with this guide.

1.5.1 FEMA's Integrated Emergency Management System (CPG 1-8). FEMA's *Guide for Development of State and Local Emergency Operations Plans* (CPG 1-8) provides information for emergency management planners and for state and local government officials about FEMA's concept of emergency operations planning under the Integrated Emergency Management System (IEMS). IEMS emphasizes the integration of planning to provide for all hazards discovered in a community's hazards identification process. CPG 1-8 provides extensive guidance in the coordination, development, review, validation, and revision of EOPs *(see Section 4.2).* This guide for hazardous materials emergency planning is deliberately meant to complement CPG 1-8. It describes how a community can incorporate hazardous materials planning into an existing multihazard EOP, or how it can develop a multihazard EOP while addressing possible hazardous materials incidents.

In either case, communities should obtain a copy of CPG 1-8 from FEMA and follow its guidance carefully. All communities, even those with sophisticated multihazard EOPs, should consult this guide to ensure adequate consideration of hazardous materials issues.

1.5.2 EPA's Chemical Emergency Preparedness Program (CEPP). In June 1985, EPA announced a comprehensive strategy to deal with planning for the problem of toxins released to the air. One section of this strategy, the Chemical Emergency Preparedness Program (CEPP), was designed to address accidental releases of acutely toxic chemicals. This program has two goals: to increase community awareness of chemical hazards and to enhance state and local emergency planning for dealing with chemical accidents. Many of the CEPP goals and objectives are included in Title III of SARA *(see Section 1.4.1).* EPA's CEPP materials (including technical guidance, criteria for identifying extremely hazardous substances, chemical profiles and lists) are designed to complement this guidance and to help communities perform hazards identification and analysis. CEPP materials can be obtained by writing to EPA.

1.5.3 DOT Materials. The U.S. Department of Transportation's (DOT) *Community Teamwork* is a guide to help local communities develop a cost-effective hazardous materials transportation safety program. It discusses hazards assessment and risk analysis, the development of an emergency plan, enforcement, training, and legal authority for planning. Communities preparing an emergency plan for transportation-related hazards might use *Community Teamwork* in conjunction with this guide.

Lessons Learned is a report on seven hazardous materials safety planning projects funded by DOT. The projects included local plans for Memphis, Indianapolis, New Orleans, and Niagara County (NY); regional plans for Puget Sound and the Oakland/San Francisco Bay Area; and a state plan for Massachusetts. The *Lessons Learned* report synthesizes the actual experiences of these projects during each phase of the planning process. A major conclusion of this study was that local political leadership and support from both the executive and legislative branches are important factors throughout the planning process. This guide incorporates portions of the experiences and conclusions from *Lessons Learned.*

DOT's *Emergency Response Guidebook* provides guidance for fire fighters, police, and other emergency services personnel to help them protect themselves and the public during the initial minutes immediately following a hazardous materials incident. This widely used guidebook is keyed to the identification placards required by DOT regulations to be displayed prominently on vehicles transporting hazardous materials. All first responders should have copies of the *Emergency Response Guidebook* and know how to use it.

DOT has also published a four-volume guide for small towns and rural areas writing a hazardous materials emergency plan. DOT's objectives were to alert officials of those communities to the threat to life, property, and the environment from the transportation of hazardous materials, and to provide simplified guidance for those with little or no technical expertise. Titles of the volumes are Volume I, *A Community Model for Handling Hazardous Materials Transportation Emergencies*; Volume II, *Risk Assessment Users Manual for Small Communities and Rural Areas*; Volume III, *Risk Assessment/Vulnerability Model Validation*; and Volume IV, *Manual for Small Towns and Rural Areas to Develop a Hazardous Materials Emergency Plan.*

1.5.4 Chemical Manufacturers Association's Community Awareness and Emergency Response Program (CMA/CAER). Chemical Manufacturers Association's (CMA) Community Awareness and Emergency Response (CAER) program encourages chemical plant managers to take the initiative in cooperating with local communities to develop integrated emergency plans for responding to hazardous materials incidents. Because chemical industry representatives can be especially knowledgeable during the planning process, and because many chemical plant officials are willing and able to share equipment and personnel during response operations, community planners should seek out local CMA/CAER participants. Even if no such local initiative is in place, community planners can approach chemical plant managers or contact CMA and ask for assistance in the spirit of the CAER program.

Users of this general planning guide might also purchase and use the following three CMA/CAER publications: *Community Awareness and Emergency Response Program Handbook, Site Emergency Response Planning,* and *Community Emergency Response Exercise Program.*

2. SELECTING AND ORGANIZING THE PLANNING TEAM

2.1 Introduction

This chapter discusses the selection and organization of the team members who will coordinate hazardous materials planning. The guidance stresses that successful planning requires community involvement throughout the process. Enlisting the cooperation of all parties directly concerned with hazardous materials will improve planning, make the plan more likely to be used, and maximize the likelihood of an effective response at the time of an emergency. Experience shows that plans are not used if they are prepared by only one person or one agency. Emergency response requires trust, coordination, and cooperation among responders who need to know who is responsible for what activities, and who is capable of performing what activities. This knowledge is gained only through personal interaction. Working together in developing and updating plans is a major opportunity for cooperative interaction among responders. (As indicated in Section 1.4.1, Title III of SARA requires governors to appoint a state emergency response commission that will designate emergency planning districts and appoint local emergency planning committees for each district. The state commission might follow the guidance in this chapter when appointing planning committees.)

2.2 The Planning Team

2.2.1 Forming the Planning Team. In selecting the members of a team that will bear overall responsibility for hazardous materials planning, four considerations are most important:

- The members of the group must have the ability, commitment, authority, and resources to get the job done.
- The group must possess, or have ready access to, a wide range of expertise relating to the community, its industrial facilities and transportation systems, and the mechanics of emergency response and response planning.
- The members of the group must agree on their purpose and be able to work cooperatively with one another.
- The group must be representative of all elements of the community with a substantial interest in reducing the risks posed by hazardous materials.

A comprehensive list of potential team members is presented in Figure S6-2.

In those communities receiving FEMA funds, paid staff may already be in place for emergency operations planning and other emergency management tasks. This staff should be an obvious resource for hazardous materials planning. FEMA has two training courses for the person assigned as the planning team leader and for team members—Introduction to Emergency Management, and Emergency Planning. Another course, Hazardous Materials Contingency Planning, is an interagency "train-the-trainer" course presented cooperatively by EPA, FEMA, and other NRT agencies. Course materials and the schedule of offerings are available through state emergency management agencies.

2.2.2 Respect for All Legitimate Interests. While many individuals have a common interest in reducing the risks posed by hazardous materials, their differing economic, political, and social perspectives may cause them to favor different means of promoting safety. For example, people who live near a facility with hazardous materials are likely to be greatly concerned about avoiding any threat to their lives, and are likely to be less intensely concerned about the costs of developing accident prevention and response measures than some of the other groups involved. Others in the community are likely to be more sensitive to the costs involved, and may be anxious to avoid expenditures for unnecessarily elaborate prevention and response measures. Also, facility managers may be reluctant for proprietary reasons to disclose materials and processes beyond what is required by law.

There may also be differing views among the agencies and organizations with emergency response functions about the roles they should play in case of an incident. The local fire department, police department, emergency management agency, and public health agency are all likely to have some responsibilities in re-

Part A: Experience shows that the following individuals, groups, and agencies should participate in order for a successful plan to be developed:

- Mayor/city manager (or representative)
- County executive (or representative)/ board of supervisors
- State elected officials (or representative)
- Fire department (paid and volunteer)
- Police department
- Emergency management or civil defense agency
- Environmental agency (e.g., air and/or water pollution control agency)
- Health department
- Hospitals, emergency medical service, veterinarians, medical community
- Transportation agency (e.g., DOT, port authority, transit authority, bus company, truck or rail companies)
- Industry (e.g., chemical and transportation)
- Coast Guard/EPA representative (e.g., agency response program personnel)
- Technical experts (e.g., chemist, engineer)
- Community group representative
- Public information representative (e.g., local radio, TV, press)*

Part B: Other groups/agencies that can be included in the planning process, depending on the community's individual priorities:

- Agriculture agency
- Indian tribes within or adjacent to the affected jurisdiction
- Public works (e.g., waste disposal, water, sanitation, and roads)
- Planning department
- Other agencies (e.g., welfare, parks, and utilities)
- Municipal/county legal counsel
- Workers in local facilities
- Labor union representatives (e.g., chemical and transportation, industrial health units)
- Local business community
- Representatives from volunteer organizations (e.g., Red Cross)
- Public interest and citizens groups, environmental organizations, and representatives of affected neighborhoods
- Schools or school districts
- Key representatives from bordering cities and counties
- State representatives (governor, legislator's office, state agencies)
- Federal agency representatives (e.g., FEMA, DOT/RSPA, ATSDR, OSHA)

* Required by Title III of SARA.

Figure S6-2 *Potential members of an emergency planning team.*

sponding to an incident. However, each of these organizations might envision a very different set of responsibilities for their respective agencies for planning or for management on scene.

In organizing the community to address the problems associated with hazardous materials, it is important to bear in mind that all affected parties have a legitimate interest in the choices among planning alternatives. Therefore, strong efforts should be made to ensure that all groups with an interest in the planning process are included.

Some interest groups in the community have well-defined political identities and representation, but others may not. Government agencies, private industry, environmental groups, and trade unions at the facilities are all likely to have ready institutional access to an emergency planning process. Nearby residents, however, may lack an effective vehicle for institutional representation. Organizations that may be available to represent the residents' interests include neighborhood associations, church organizations, and ad hoc organizations formed especially to deal with the risks posed by the presence of specific hazardous materials in a neighborhood.

2.2.5 Size of Planning Team. For the planning team to function effectively, its size should be limited to a workable number. In communities with many interested parties, it will be necessary to select from among them carefully so as to ensure fair and comprehensive representation. Some individuals may feel left out of the planning process. This can be offset by providing these individuals access to the process through the various approaches noted in the following sections, such as membership on a task force or advisory council. In addition, all interested parties should have an opportunity for input during the review process.

2.3 Organizing the Planning Process

After the planning team members have been identified, a team leader must be chosen and procedures for managing the planning process must be established.

2.3.1 Selecting a Team Leader. A community initiating a hazardous materials emergency planning process may choose to appoint an individual to facilitate and lead the effort, or may appoint a planning team and have the group decide who will lead the effort. Either approach can be used. It is essential to establish clear responsibility and authority for the project. The chief executive (or whoever initiates the process) should determine which course is better suited to local circumstances. (The emergency planning committee required by Title III of SARA is to select its own chairperson.)

Regardless of how the team leader is selected, it is his or her primary responsibility to oversee the team's efforts through the entire planning process. Because the role of leader is so significant, a co-chair or back-up could also be named.

Five factors are of major importance in selecting a team leader:

- The degree of respect held for the person by groups with an interest in hazardous materials
- Availability of time and resources
- The person's history of working relationships with concerned community agencies and organizations

- The person's management and communication skills
- The person's existing responsibilities related to emergency planning, prevention, and response

2.4 Beginning to Plan

When the planning team members and their leader have been identified and a process for managing the planning tasks is in place, the team should address several interrelated tasks. These planning tasks are described in the next chapter.

3. TASKS OF THE PLANNING TEAM

3.1 Introduction

The major tasks of the planning team in completing hazardous materials planning are:

- Review of existing plans, which prevents plan overlap and inconsistency, provides useful information and ideas, and facilitates the coordination of the plan with other plans
- Hazards analysis, which includes hazards identification, vulnerability analysis, and risk analysis
- Assessment of preparedness, prevention, and response capabilities, which identifies existing prevention measures and response capabilities (including mutual aid agreements) and assesses their adequacy
- Completion of hazardous materials planning that describes the personnel, equipment, and procedures to be used in case of accidental release of a hazardous material
- Development of an ongoing program for plan implementation/maintenance, training, and exercising

(See Table S6-1.)

3.4.1 Facility Resources

What is the status of the safety plan (also referred to as an emergency or contingency plan) for the facility? Is the safety plan consistent with any community emergency plan?

Table S6-1 Sample Hazard Analysis for a Hypothetical Community

	Hazard A	Hazard B	Hazard C
1. Hazards Identification (Major Hazards)			
a. Chemical	Chlorine	Ammonia	Liquid methyl isocyanate (MIC)
b. Location	Water treatment plant	Tank truck on local interstate highway	Pesticide manufacturing plant in nearby semi-rural area
c. Quantity	2000 lb	5000 lb	5000 lb
d. Properties	Poisonous; may be fatal if inhaled. Respiratory conditions aggravated by exposure. Contact may burn skin and eyes. Corrosive. Effects may be delayed.	Poisonous; may be fatal if inhaled. Vapors irritate eyes, respiratory tract. Liquid burns skin, eyes. Liquid may cause frostbite. Effects may be delayed. Burns within certain vapor concentration limits; increased fire hazard in presence of oil, other combustibles.	Causes death by respiratory distress after inhalation. Other health effects include permanent eye damage, respiratory distress, disorientation. Explosive. Extremely flammable.
2. Vulnerability Analysis			
a. Vulnerable zone	Spill of 2000 lb chlorine from storage tank could raise concentration of chlorine gas above level of concern within 1650-ft radius.	Spill of 5000 lb ammonia from tank truck collision could raise concentration of ammonia above level of concern within 1320-ft radius.	Spill of 5000 lb MIC could raise concentration of MIC vapors above level of concern within 3300-ft radius, assuming liquid is hot when spilled, tank is not diked, MIC is at 100% concentration.
b. Population within vulnerable zone	Approximately 500 residents of nursing home; workers at small factory.	Up to 700 persons in nearby residences, commercial establishments, vehicles. Influx of visitors to forest preserve in the fall.	Up to 200 workers at plant, 1000 children in school.

Table S6-1 (continued)

	Hazard A	Hazard B	Hazard C
c. Private and public property that may be damaged	Facility equipment, vehicles, structures susceptible to damage from corrosive fumes. Community's water supply may be temporarily affected since facility is primary supplier. Mixture with fuels may cause explosion.	25 residences, 2 fast-food restaurants, 30-room motel, a truck stop, a gas station, a mini-market. Highway, nearby vehicles may be damaged by fire or explosion resulting from collision.	Runoff to a sewer may cause explosion hazard as MIC reacts violently with water.
d. Environment that may be affected	Terrestrial life.	Adjacent forest highly susceptible to fires, especially during drought.	Nearby farm animals.
3 Risk Analysis			
a. Probability of hazard occurrence	Low, because chlorine is stored in area with leak-detection equipment in 24-hour service with alarms. Protective equipment kept outside storage room.	High. Highway interchange has history of accidents due to poor visibility of exits, entrances.	Low. Facility has up-to-date containment facilities with leak detection equipment, and emergency plan for employees. Good security arrangements to deter tampering, accidents.
b. Consequences if people are exposed	High levels of chlorine gas in nursing home, factory could cause death, respiratory distress. Bedridden patients especially susceptible.	Release of vapors, subsequent fire may cause traffic accidents. Injured, trapped motorists subject to lethal vapors, possible incineration. Windblown vapors can cause respiratory distress.	If accident occurs while school is in session, children could be killed, blinded, and/or suffer chronic debilitating respiratory problems. Plant workers would be subject to similar effects.
c. Consequences for property	Possible superficial damage to equipment structures from corrosive fumes.	Repairable damage to highway. Potential destruction of nearby vehicles by fire, explosions.	Vapors may explode in confined space causing repairable property damage. Fires could cause repairable damage.
d. Consequences of environmental exposure	Possible destruction of surrounding fauna, flora.	Potential for fire damage to adjacent forest preserve due to combustible material (recoverable in the long term).	Farm animals, other fauna could die or suffer health effects necessitating their destruction or indirectly causing death.
e. Probability of simultaneous emergencies	Low	High	Low
f. Unusual environmental conditions	None	Hilly terrain prone to mists, creating adverse driving conditions.	Located in a 500-year river floor plain.

- Is there a list of potentially toxic chemicals available? What are their physical and chemical characteristics, potential for causing adverse health effects, controls, interactions with other chemicals? Has the facility complied with the community right-to-know provisions of Title III of SARA?
- Has a hazards analysis been prepared for the facility? If so, has it been updated? Has a copy been provided to the local emergency planning committee?
- What steps have been taken to reduce identified risks?
- How does the company reward good safety records?
- Have operation or storage procedures been modified to reduce the probability of a release and minimize potential effects?
- What release prevention or mitigation systems, equipment, or procedures are in place?
- What possibilities are there for safer substitutes for any acutely toxic chemicals used or stored at the facility?
- What possibilities exist for reducing the volume of the hazardous materials in use or stored at the facility?
- What additional safeguards are available to prevent accidental releases?
- What studies have been conducted by the facility to determine the feasibility of each of the following approaches for each relevant production process or operation: (a) input change, (b) product reformulation, (c) production process change, and (d) operational improvements?

- Are on-site emergency response equipment (e.g., fire-fighting equipment, personal protective equipment, communications equipment) and trained personnel available to provide on-site initial response efforts?
- What equipment (e.g., self-contained breathing apparatus, chemical suits, unmanned fire monitors, foam deployment systems, radios, beepers) is available? Is equipment available for loan or use by the community on a reimbursable basis? (Note: Respirators should not be lent to any person not properly trained in their use.) Is there emergency medical care on site?
- Are the local hospitals prepared to accept and provide care to patients who have been exposed to chemicals?
- Who is the emergency contact for the site (person's name, position, and 24-hour telephone number) and what is the chain of command during an emergency?
- Are employee evacuation plans in effect and are the employees trained to use them in the event of an emergency?
- What kinds of notification systems connect the facility and the local community emergency services (e.g., direct alarm, direct telephone hook-up, computer hook-up) to address emergencies on site?
- What is the mechanism to alert employees and the surrounding community in the event of a release at the facility?
- Is there a standard operating procedure for the personal protection of community members at the time of an emergency?
- Does the community know about the meaning of various alarms or warning systems? Are tests conducted?
- How do facility personnel coordinate with the community government and local emergency and medical services during emergencies? Is overlap avoided?
- What mutual aid agreements are in place for obtaining emergency response assistance from other industry members? With whom?
- Are there any contacts or other prearrangements in place with specialists for cleanup and removal of releases, or is this handled in-house? How much time is required for the cleanup specialists to respond?
- What will determine concentrations of released chemicals existing at the site? (Are there toxic gas detectors, explosimeters, or other detection devices positioned around the facility? Where are they located?) Are wind direction indicators positioned within the facility perimeter to determine in what direction a released chemical will travel? Where are they located?
- Is there capability for modeling vapor cloud dispersion?
- Are auxiliary power systems available to perform emergency system functions in case of power outages at the facility?
- How often is the safety plan tested and updated? When was it last tested and updated?
- Does the company participate in CHEMNET or the CAER program?
- Does the company have the capability and plans for responding to off-site emergencies? Is this limited to the company's products?

What is the safety training plan for management and employees?

- Are employees trained in the use of emergency response equipment, personal protective equipment, and emergency procedures detailed in the plant safety plan? How often is training updated?
- Are simulated emergencies conducted for training purposes? How often? How are these simulations evaluated and by whom? When was this last done? Are the local community emergency response and medical service organizations invited to participate?
- Are employees given training in methods for coordinating with local community emergency response and medical services during emergencies? How often?
- Is management given appropriate training? How frequently?
- Is there an emergency response equipment and systems inspection plan?
- Is there a method for identifying emergency response equipment problems? Describe it.
- Is there testing of on-site alarms, warning signals, and emergency response equipment? How often is this equipment tested and replaced?

3.4.2 Transporter Resources

What cargo information and response organization do ship, train, and truck operators provide at a release?

- Do transport shipping papers identify hazardous materials, their physical and chemical characteristics, control techniques, and interactions with other chemicals?
- Do transports have proper placards?
- Are there standard operating procedures (SOPs) established for release situations? Have these procedures been updated to reflect current cargo characteristics?

- Who is the emergency contact for transport operators? Is there a 24-hour emergency contact system in place? What is the transport operation's chain of command in responding to a release?

What equipment and cleanup capabilities can transport operations make available?

- What emergency response equipment is carried by each transporter (e.g., protective clothing, breathing apparatus, chemical extinguishers)?
- Do transports have first-aid equipment (e.g., dressings for chemical burns and water to rinse off toxic chemicals)?
- By what means do operators communicate with emergency response authorities?
- Do transport operations have their own emergency response units?
- What arrangements have been established with cleanup specialists for removal of a release?

What is the safety training plan for operators?

- Are operators trained in release SOPs and to use emergency response equipment? How often is training updated?
- How often are release drills conducted? Who evaluates these drills and do the evaluations become a part of an employee's file?
- Are safe driving practices addressed in operator training? What monetary or promotional incentives encourage safety in transport operation?

Is there a transport and emergency response equipment inspection plan?

- What inspections are conducted? What leak detection and equipment readiness tests are done? What is the schedule for inspections and tests?
- Are problems identified in inspections corrected? How are maintenance schedules established?

3.4.3 Community Resources

What local agencies make up the community's existing response preparedness network? Some examples include:

- Fire department
- Police/sheriff/highway patrol
- Emergency medical/paramedic service associated with local hospitals or fire and police departments
- Emergency management or civil defense agency
- Public health agency
- Environmental agency
- Public works and/or transportation departments
- Red Cross
- Other local community resources such as public housing, schools, public utilities, communications

What is the capacity and level of expertise of the community's emergency medical facilities, equipment, and personnel?

Does the community have arrangements or mutual aid agreements for assistance with other jurisdictions or organizations (e.g., other communities, counties, or states; industry; military installations; federal facilities; response organizations)? In the absence of mutual aid agreements, has the community taken liability into consideration?

What is the current status of community planning and coordination for hazardous materials emergency preparedness? Have potential overlaps in planning been avoided?

- Is there a community planning and coordination body (e.g., task force, advisory board, interagency committee)? If so, what is the defined structure and authority of the body?
- Has the community performed any assessments of existing prevention and response capabilities within its own emergency response network?
- Does the community maintain an up-to-date technical reference library of response procedures for hazardous materials?
- Have there been any training sessions, simulations, or mock incidents performed by the community in conjunction with local industry or other organizations? If so, how frequently are they conducted? When was this last done? Do they typically have simulated casualties?

Who are the specific community points of contact and what are their responsibilities in an emergency?

- List the agencies involved, the area of responsibility (e.g., emergency response, evacuation, emergency shelter, medical/health care, food distribution, control access to accident site, public/media liaison, liaison with federal and state responders, locating and manning the command center and/or emergency operating center), the name of the contact, position, 24-hour telephone number, and the chain of command.
- Is there any specific chemical or toxicological expertise available in the community, either in industry, colleges and universities, poison control centers, or on a consultant basis?

What kinds of equipment and materials are available at the local level to respond to emergencies? How can the equipment, materials, and personnel be made available to trained users at the scene of an incident?

Does the community have specialized emergency response teams to respond to hazardous materials releases?

- Have the local emergency services (fire, police, medical) had any hazardous materials training, and if so, do they have and use any specialized equipment?
- Are local hospitals able to decontaminate and treat numerous exposure victims quickly and effectively?
- Are there specialized industry response teams (e.g., CHLOREP, AAR/BOE), state/federal response teams, or contractor response teams available within or close to the community? What is the average time for them to arrive on the scene?
- Has the community sought any resources from industry to help respond to emergencies?

Is the community emergency transportation network defined?

- Does the community have specific evacuation routes designated? What are these evacuation routes? Is the general public aware of these routes?
- Are there specific access routes designated for emergency response and services personnel to reach facilities or incident sites? (In a real incident, wind direction might make certain routes unsafe.)

Does the community have other procedures for protecting citizens during emergencies (e.g., asking them to remain indoors, close windows, turn off air-conditioners, tune into local emergency radio broadcasts)?

Is there a mechanism that enables responders to exchange information or ideas during an emergency with other entities, either internal or external, to the existing organizational structure?

Does the community have a communications link with an Emergency Broadcast System (EBS) station? Is there a designated emergency communications network in the community to alert the public, update the public, and provide communications between the command center and/or emergency operating center, the incident site, and off-scene support? Is there a back-up system?

- What does the communications network involve (e.g., special radio frequency, network channel, siren, dedicated phone lines, computer hook-up)?
- Is there an up-to-date list, with telephone numbers, of radio and television stations (including cable companies) that broadcast in the area?
- Is there an up-to-date source list with a contact, position, and telephone number for technical information assistance? This can be federal (e.g., NRC, USCG CHRIS/HACS, ATSDR, OHMTADS), state, industry associations (e.g., CHEMTREC, CHLOREP, AAR/BOE, PSTN), and local industry groups (e.g., local AlChE, ASME, ASSE chapters).

Is there a source list with a contact, position, and telephone number for community resources available?

- Does the list of resources include wreck clearing, transport, cleanup, disposal, health, analytical sampling laboratories, and detoxifying agents?

Have there been any fixed facility or transportation incidents involving hazardous materials in the community? What response efforts were taken? What were the results? Have these results been evaluated?

3.5 Writing an Emergency Plan

When the team has reviewed existing plans, completed a hazards identification and analysis, and assessed its preparedness, prevention, and response capabilities, it can take steps to make serious incidents less likely. Improved warning systems, increased hazardous materials training of industry and local response personnel, and other efforts at the local level, can all make a community better prepared to live safely with hazardous materials. The team should also begin to write an emergency plan if one does not already exist, or revise existing plans to include hazardous materials. Chapter 4 describes two approaches to developing or revising an emergency plan. Chapter 5 describes elements related to hazardous materials incidents that should be included in whichever type of plan the community chooses to write.

4. DEVELOPING THE PLAN

4.1 Introduction

Most communities have some type of written plan for emergencies. These plans range from a comprehensive multihazard approach as described in FEMA's CPG 1-8 (*Guide for Development of State and Local Emergency Operations Plans*) to a single telephone roster for call-up purposes, or an action checklist. Obviously the more complete and thorough a plan is, the better prepared the community should be to deal with any emergency that occurs.

The "Emergency Planning and Community Right-to-Know Act of 1986" requires local emergency planning committees to develop local plans for emergency responses in the event of a release of an extremely hazardous substance. Those communities receiving FEMA funds are required to incorporate hazardous materials planning into their multihazard emergency operations plan (EOP). Other communities are encouraged to prepare a multihazard EOP in accordance with CPG 1-8 since it is the most comprehensive approach to emergency planning. Not every community, however, may be ready for or capable of such a comprehensive approach. Because each community must plan in light of its own situation and resources, a less exhaustive approach may

A. Introduction

1. Incident Information Summary
2. Promulgation Document
3. Legal Authority and Responsibility for Responding
4. Table of Contents
5. Abbreviations and Definitions
6. Assumptions/Planning Factors
7. Concept of Operations
   a. Governing Principles
   b. Organization Roles and Responsibilities
   c. Relationship to Other Plans
8. Instructions on Plan Use
   a. Purpose
   b. Plan Distribution
9. Record of Amendments

B. Emergency Assistance Telephone Roster

C. Response Functions*

1. Initial Notification of Response Agencies
2. Direction and Control
3. Communications (among Responders)
4. Warning Systems and Emergency Public Notification
5. Public Information/Community Relations
6. Resource Management
7. Health and Medical Services
8. Response Personnel Safety
9. Personal Protection of Citizens
   a. Indoor Protection
   b. Evacuation Procedures
   c. Other Public Protection Strategies
10. Fire and Rescue
11. Law Enforcement
12. Ongoing Incident Assessment
13. Human Services
14. Public Works
15. Others

D. Containment and Cleanup

1. Techniques for Spill Containment and Cleanup
2. Resources for Cleanup and Disposal

E. Documentation and Investigative Follow-up

F. Procedures for Testing and Updating Plan

1. Testing the Plan
2. Updating the Plan

G. Hazards Analysis (Summary)

H. References

1. Laboratory, Consultant, and Other Technical Support Resources
2. Technical Library

NOTE: Depending upon local circumstances, communities will develop some sections of the plan more extensively than other sections.

Figure S6-3 *Sample outline of a hazardous materials emergency plan.*

be the only practical, realistic way of having some type of near-term plan. Each community must choose the level of planning that is appropriate for it, based upon the types of hazards found in the community.

This chapter discusses two basic approaches to writing a plan: (1) development or revision of a hazardous materials appendix (or appendices to functional annexes) to a multihazard EOP following the approach described in FEMA's CPG 1-8, and (2) development or revision of a plan covering only hazardous materials. Each approach is discussed in more detail below.

4.2 Hazardous Materials Appendix to Multihazard EOP

The first responders (e.g., police, fire, emergency medical team) at the scene of an incident are generally the same whatever the hazard. Moreover, many emergency functions (e.g., direction and control, communications, and evacuation) vary only slightly from hazard to hazard. Procedures to be followed for warning the public of a hazardous materials incident, for example, are not that different from procedures followed in warning the public about other incidents such as a flash flood. It is possible, therefore, to avoid a great deal of unnecessary redundancy and confusion by planning for all hazards at the same time.

A multihazard EOP avoids developing separate structures, resources, and plans to deal with each type of hazard. Addressing the general aspects of all hazards first and then looking at each potential hazard individually to see if any unique aspects are involved result in efficiencies and economies in the long run. Multihazard EOPs also help ensure that plans and systems are reasonably compatible if a large-scale hazardous materials incident requires a simultaneous, coordinated response by more than one community or more than one level of government. *(See Figure S6-3.)*

A community that does not have a multihazard plan is urged to consider seriously the advantages of this integrated approach to planning. In doing so, the community may want to seek state government advice and support.

4.3 Single-Hazard Emergency Plan

If a community does not have the resources, time, or capability readily available to undertake multihazard planning, it may wish to produce a single-hazard plan addressing hazardous materials.

Figure S6-3 identifies sections of an emergency plan for hazardous materials incidents. The sample outline is not a model. It is not meant to constrain any community. Indeed, each community should seek to develop a plan that is best suited to its own circumstances, taking advantage of the sample outline where appropriate.

The type of plan envisioned in the sample outline would affect all governmental and private organizations involved in emergency response operations in a particular community. Its basic purpose would be to provide the necessary data and documentation to anticipate and coordinate the many persons and organizations that would be involved in emergency response actions. As such, the plan envisioned in this sample outline is intended neither to be a "hip-pocket" emergency response manual, nor to serve as a detailed standard operating procedures (SOPs) manual for each of the many agencies and organizations involved in emergency response actions, although it could certainly be used as a starting point for such manuals. Agencies that want to develop an SOPs manual could begin with the information contained under the appropriate function in Plan Section C of this sample outline. If it is highly probable that an organization will be involved in a hazardous materials incident response, then more highly detailed SOPs should be developed.

APPENDIX A: LIST OF ACRONYMS AND RECOGNIZED ABBREVIATIONS

AAR/BOE	Association of American Railroads/Bureau of Explosives
AIChE	American Institute of Chemical Engineers
ASCS	Agricultural Stabilization and Conservation Service
ASME	American Society of Mechanical Engineers
ASSE	American Society of Safety Engineers
ATSDR	Agency for Toxic Substances and Disease Registry (HHS)
CAER	Community Awareness and Emergency Response (CMA)
CDC	Centers for Disease Control (HHS)
CEPP	Chemical Emergency Preparedness Program
CERCLA	Comprehensive Environmental Response, Compensation, and Liability Act of 1980 (PL 96-510)
CFR	Code of Federal Regulations
CHEMNET	A mutual aid network of chemical shippers and contractors
CHEMTREC	Chemical Transportation Emergency Center
CHLOREP	A mutual aid group comprised of shippers and carriers of chlorine.
CHRIS/HACS	Chemical Hazards Response Information System/Hazard Assessment Computer System
CMA	Chemical Manufacturers Association
CPG 1-3	Federal Assistance Handbook: Emergency Management, Direction and Control Programs
CPG 1-8	*Guide for Development of State and Local Emergency Operations Plans*
CPG 1-8A	*Guide for the Review of State and Local Emergency Operations Plans*
CWA	Clean Water Act
DOC	U.S. Department of Commerce
DOD	U.S. Department of Defense
DOE	U.S. Department of Energy
DOI	U.S. Department of the Interior
DOJ	U.S. Department of Justice
DOL	U.S. Department of Labor
DOS	U.S. Department of State
DOT	U.S. Department of Transportation
EENET	Emergency Education Network (FEMA)
EMA	Emergency Management Agency
EMI	Emergency Management Institute
EOC	Emergency Operating Center
EOP	Emergency Operations Plan
EPA	U.S. Environmental Protection Agency
ERD	Emergency Response Division (EPA)
FEMA	Federal Emergency Management Agency
FEMA-REP-5	*Guidance for Developing State and Local Radiological Emergency Response Plans and Preparedness for Transportation Accidents*
FWPCA	Federal Water Pollution Control Act
HAZMAT	Hazardous Materials
HAZOP	Hazard and Operability Study
HHS	U.S. Department of Health and Human Services
ICS	Incident Command System
IEMS	Integrated Emergency Management System
LEPC	Local Emergency Planning Committee
MSDS	Material Safety Data Sheet
NACA	National Agricultural Chemicals Association

NCP	National Contingency Plan
NCRIC	National Chemical Response and Information Center (CMA)
NETC	National Emergency Training Center
NFA	National Fire Academy
NFPA	National Fire Protection Association
NIOSH	National Institute of Occupational Safety and Health
NOAA	National Oceanic and Atmospheric Administration
NRC	U.S. Nuclear Regulatory Commission; National Response Center
NRT	National Response Team
NUREG 0654/	*Criteria for Preparation and Evaluation of Radiological Emergency Response Plans*
FEMA-REP-1	*Emergency Response Plans and Preparedness in Support of Nuclear Power Plants*
OHMTADS	Oil and Hazardous Materials Technical Assistance Data System
OSC	On-Scene Coordinator
OSHA	Occupational Safety and Health Administration (DOL)
PSTN	Pesticide Safety Team Network
RCRA	Resource Conservation and Recovery Act
RQs	Reportable Quantities
RRT	Regional Response Team
RSPA	Research and Special Programs Administration (DOT)
SARA	Superfund Amendments and Reauthorization Act of 1986 (PL 99-499)
SCBA	Self-Contained Breathing Apparatus
SERC	State Emergency Response Commission
SPCC	Spill Prevention Control and Countermeasures
TSD	Treatment, Storage, and Disposal Facilities
USDA	U.S. Department of Agriculture
USGS	U.S. Geological Survey
USNRC	U.S. Nuclear Regulatory Commission

APPENDIX B: BIBLIOGRAPHY

Chemical Manufacturers Association. *Community Awareness and Emergency Response Program Handbook.* Washington, DC: CMA, 1985.

Chemical Manufacturers Association. *Community Emergency Response Exercise Program.* Washington, DC: CMA, 1986.

Chemical Manufacturers Association. *Site Emergency Response Planning.* Washington, DC: CMA, 1986.

U.S. Department of Transportation. *Community Teamwork: Working Together to Promote Hazardous Materials Transportation Safety.* Washington, DC: 1986.

U.S. Department of Transportation. *Emergency Response Guidebook.* Washington, DC: 1984.

U.S. Department of Transportation. Three-Phase/Four-Volume Report: Volume I, *A Community Model for Handling Hazardous Materials Transportation Emergencies;* Volume II, *Risk Assessment Users Manual for Small Communities and Rural Areas;* Volume III, *Risk Assessment/Vulnerability Model Validation;* and Volume IV, *Manual for Small Towns and Rural Areas to Develop a Hazardous Materials Emergency Plan.* 7/81–12/85. Document is available to the U.S. public through the National Technical Information Service, Springfield, VA 22161.

U.S. Department of Transportation and U.S. Environmental Protection Agency. *Lessons Learned from State and Local Experiences in Accident Prevention and Response Planning for Hazardous Materials Transportation.* Washington, DC: December 1985.

SUPPLEMENT 7

Beginning the Hazard Analysis Process

William J. Keffer, EPA Region VII
Alan Cummings, Dynamac Inc.

Editor's Note: The first step in preparing to deal with hazardous materials incidents is to identify the types and possible sources of accidental releases. This supplement outlines the steps a community should take to analyze those facilities that use hazardous materials and the transportation corridors that bring hazardous materials into the community. Included is an item-by-item review of a material safety data sheet and instructions on using the information presented in it. Our thanks to authors William J. Keffer and Alan Cummings for submitting this paper for inclusion as a supplement to the Hazardous Materials Response Handbook.

BACKGROUND

Several recent federal studies show that there are between 5 million and 6 million known chemicals, with this number growing at the rate of about 6000 chemicals per month. Furthermore, a recent computer review by the Chemical Abstract Service of the complete list of known chemicals indicates that a first responder might reasonably be expected to encounter any of 1.5 million of these chemicals in an emergency, with 33,000 to 63,000 of them considered hazardous. To complicate matters, these hazardous chemicals are known by 183,000 different names. Fortunately, not all of these chemicals are equally common.

The U.S. Department of Transportation (DOT) and the U.S. Environmental Protection Agency (EPA) have used several measures of toxicity and volume of production to develop a shortened list of chemicals that are considered hazardous when transported in commerce. This list contains approximately 2700 chemicals, all of which are listed in 40 CFR 172.101 and the 1996 *Emergency Response Guidebook for Hazardous Materials Incidents*.

The Occupational Safety and Health Administration (OSHA) regulates about 400 chemicals on the basis of occupational exposures. This list is found in the NIOSH (National Institute of Occupational Safety and Health) *Pocket Guide to Chemical Hazards*.

Even this abbreviated list can be intimidating to local response personnel hoping to develop a comprehensive hazard analysis for their community. Further complicating their job is the fact that, according to a study by the National Academy of Sciences, National Research Council (NRC), there is so little known about seven-eighths of the 63,000 hazardous chemicals that not even a partial assessment can be made of their health hazards. Some conclusions drawn from the NRC study are as follows:

1. *Pesticides*—Of the 3350 pesticides classified as important chemicals, information sufficient to make a

partial assessment of the health hazard is only available on about 1100 to 1200 (34 percent) of them.

2. *Drugs*—Of the 1815 drugs or drug ingredients noted, about 36 percent have enough information for a partial assessment.

3. *Food Additives*—For the 8627 food additives listed, there is partial information on 19 percent.

4. *Other Chemicals*—For the remaining 48,500 industrial chemicals, there is enough information on just 10 percent to develop a partial assessment.

These two points (the lack of a generally accepted name for chemicals considered hazardous and the lack of data for assessing the risk) create an obstacle for emergency response personnel and community officials who are charged with developing a viable, effective local hazardous materials management system. Without a contingency plan, however, based on effective and accurate hazard analysis prior to an emergency, it would be difficult and time-consuming to develop the necessary information in the midst of an emergency. In order to bring what appears to be an insurmountable task into perspective, the local response community must get involved in the hazard analysis process.

The *hazard analysis process* is the process of identifying chemicals present in the community (either at fixed facilities or passing through transportation corridors) and evaluating the hazards that the chemicals present and the vulnerability of the community and systems to the release of that chemical. A hazard analysis can be performed by any individual or small group that understands the principles of risk assessment. Risk is determined by estimating the consequences of a problem and the probability that the problem will occur.

The goal of this supplement is to provide a summary of the sources of information and some methodology for use by local agencies and hazardous materials teams to improve their understanding of the hazardous materials problem in the community. This is information that can be used in both planning and emergency response operations. This supplement will also introduce the use of the material safety data sheet (MSDS) in the hazard analysis process.

HAZARD ANALYSIS DATA SOURCES

The purpose of hazard analysis is to gather data on the locations, quantities, chemical and physical properties, and health hazards of chemicals most likely to be released in a community. This process may seem monumental from two aspects: (1) the sheer numbers of chemicals out there, and (2) the lack of information in a usable form available on these chemicals. In attempting to pare down the list to a workable size and gather data on the location and identity of the chemicals found in and being transported through the community, a variety of information sources may be used.

1. *Historical records of chemicals having the most frequent instances of release on a national level.* For example, all previous studies have shown that the most commonly released hazardous chemical is commercial vehicle fuel (gasoline). The EPA commissioned a national study[1] in 1985 to look at hazardous chemicals and the sources of their release. More recent reviews of various state and local incident report summaries verify that the figures that follow are still correct. The original survey covered 6928 incidents nationwide involving chemicals other than fuel. The source of releases study indicated that 74.8 percent were fixed facility (in-plant) incidents and 25.2 percent were in-transit incidents.

The fixed facility incidents were distributed as follows:

20.7 percent storage
19.4 percent valves and pipes
14.1 percent process
17.9 percent unknown
27.8 percent other

The in-transit incidents were distributed by mode as follows:

54.5 percent truck
14.1 percent rail
3.8 percent water
3.1 percent pipeline
2.5 percent other

Perhaps the most useful data from this national study is the information on the chemicals most commonly involved in the 6928 incidents—49.5 percent of the incidents involved only 10 chemicals:

23.0 percent polychlorinated biphenyls (PCBs)
6.5 percent sulfuric acid
3.7 percent anhydrous ammonia
3.5 percent chlorine
3.1 percent hydrochloric acid
2.6 percent sodium hydroxide
1.7 percent methanol/methyl alcohol
1.7 percent nitric acid
1.4 percent toluene
1.4 percent methyl chloride

Of the 6928 incidents, 468 involved human injury or death. The same 10 chemicals just listed accounted for 35.7 percent of the death and injury events, though not at the same rate as they occurred:

9.6 percent chlorine
6.8 percent anhydrous ammonia
5.6 percent hydrochloric acid

4.7 percent sulfuric acid
2.8 percent PCBs
2.4 percent toluene
1.9 percent sodium hydroxide
1.5 percent nitric acid
0.4 percent methyl alcohol
0.1 percent methyl chloride

When the data for occurrence and injury are viewed for chemicals like chlorine and PCBs, it is apparent that the release and injury data are different. That is, although PCBs were involved in more incidents, chlorine, when released, posed a greater threat to humans. Determining this potential for causing injury to humans is the area of hazard assessment that takes the most effort on the part of the local response community. Gathering this information in a systematic manner cannot be done in the midst of an incident.

2. *Summaries of previous incidents from emergency management and environmental response organizations at the local, state, regional, and federal levels.* For example, EPA Region VII and states in the region have comprehensive, computerized records of all reported incidents by county since 1977. These records are available to any jurisdiction on request.

3. *Local fire and police department records.* These files may disclose many incidents involving hazardous materials.

4. *Local yellow pages and the state industrial directory.* These sources will show most local fixed facilities that manufacture, store, or use chemicals. The EPA has prepared a variety of industry-specific summaries for certain commercial and industrial facilities that outline which types of hazardous chemicals may be encountered. Copies of the summaries may be obtained from EPA by calling the national RCRA (Resource Conservation and Recovery Act) Industry Hotline toll free at 800-424-9346. Additional area-specific release incident information may be obtained from the emergency response program of the EPA Regional Offices from data collected by the Oil and Hazardous Materials National Response Center.

Once the chemicals in a community have been identified in name and quantity (either for contingency planning or emergency response), there are several national data bases for evaluating the hazard, vulnerability, and risk presented by those chemicals.

Poison Control Centers. If the chemical is a consumer product, the quickest way to get comprehensive hazard information is through the regional poison control center.

Manufacturer's technical medical staff. If the chemical is an industrial bulk chemical, effective assistance is generally available from CHEMTREC (Chemical Transportation Emergency Center) through the technical medical staff of the company that manufactures the chemical. Dial 800-CMA-8200 for non-emergency situations and 800-424-9300 for emergencies.

Agency for Toxic Substances and Disease Registry (ATSDR). If the chemical is a mixture or a waste, if a second opinion is required, or if the chemical is unknown, a good source of information for public exposure risks is the agency at the Centers for Disease Control called the Agency for Toxic Substances and Disease Registry.

When contacting any of these sources, remember there is a lack of full information on health assessment for many chemicals. Answers and information from any of the sources listed may be qualified, and each local response group, as part of their contingency planning, should locate a competent medical authority to work with the response community and assist in obtaining and interpreting health effects data.

MATERIAL SAFETY DATA SHEETS (MSDSs)

The recent state and federal legislation on hazard communication, right-to-know, and mandatory local notification for certain hazardous chemicals will assist in developing pre-emergency and on-scene hazard assessments of the chemicals in the community. This legislation is bound to make the MSDS one of the best sources of information on chemical hazards. (See Figure S7-1 for an example of an MSDS.)

Personnel from the Chemical Manufacturers Association (CMA), the sponsor of CHEMTREC, have available more than one million different MSDSs and are receiving more all the time. Access to these MSDSs for research and emergency use can be arranged with CMA or through any CMA member company in your area. For most local communities, it will be necessary to work with hard copies of the MSDSs and begin with the 10 most commonly released chemicals. Later, one can add to that list based on the results of the local hazard analysis that determined additional unique or peculiar local hazards.

All local response groups have access to MSDSs by local industry, as required by SARA, Title III, so it is helpful to become familiar with them. However, remember that MSDSs may not contain a complete description; they are not a cure-all and require some systematic way to approach their use. Most MSDSs deal with information for a pure substance. Since many releases are of dilute solutions, the MSDS would overstate the hazard. In any case, becoming familiar with the type of information presented on the MSDS and how that information will be of assistance in making a hazard assessment is essential—whether for pre-emergency planning or when responding to an emergency.

```
BURDICK & JACKSON, INC.
1953 SOUTH HARVEY STREET
MUSKEGON, MI  49442  USA

                                      ACETONE

                                      REVISION DATE:  DECEMBER, 1993
                                      REVISION NO:  1

MATERIAL SAFETY DATA SHEET
--------------------------------------------------------------------------------

INFORMATION/EMERGENCY TELEPHONE NUMBER             616.726.3171
CHEMTREC TELEPHONE NUMBER                          800.424.9300
CANADIAN EMERGENCY TELEPHONE NUMBER                613.996.6666

I.   IDENTIFICATION
--------------------------------------------------------------------------------
CHEMICAL NAME:              ACETONE                MOLECULAR WEIGHT:    58.08
CHEMICAL FAMILY:            KETONE                 FORMULA:             C3H60
SYNONYMS:                   DIMETHYL KETONE
DOT PROPER SHIPPING NAME:   ACETONE
DOT HAZARD CLASS:           FLAMMABLE LIQUID, HAZARD CLASS 3, P.G. II
DOT IDENTIFICATION NUMBER:  UN1090                 CAS NUMBER:          67-64-1

II.  PHYSICAL AND CHEMICAL DATA
--------------------------------------------------------------------------------
BOILING POINT, 760 MM HG      56.29 C
VAPOR PRESSURE AT 20 C:       184.5 MM HG
% VOLATILES BY VOLUME:        CA 100
FREEZING POINT:               -94.7
VAPOR DENSITY:                2.0
SPECIFIC GRAVITY (H2O=1):     @ 20 C 0.79
EVAPORATION RATE:             (BUAC=1)  CA 12
SOLUBILITY IN WATER:          @ 20 C COMPLETE
STABILITY:                    STABLE
HAZARDOUS POLYMERIZATION:     NOT EXPECTED TO OCCUR.
APPEARANCE AND ODOR:          CLEAR, COLORLESS LIQUID WITH A PENETRATING,
                              SWEET ODOR.
CONDITIONS TO AVOID:          HEAT, SPARKS, OPEN FLAME, OPEN CONTAINERS, AND
                              POOR VENTILATION.
MATERIALS TO AVOID:           STRONG OXIDIZING AGENTS AND STRONG ACIDS AND
                              BASES.
HAZARDOUS DECOMPOSITION
PRODUCTS:                     INCOMPLETE COMBUSTION CAN GENERATE CARBON
                              MONOXIDE AND OTHER TOXIC VAPORS

III. FIRE AND EXPLOSION HAZARD DATA
================================================================================
FLASH POINT (TEST METHOD);     -18 C (TAG CLOSED CUP)
AUTO IGNITION TEMPERATURE:     465 C
FLAMMABLE LIMITS IN AIR % BY VOLUME:     LOWER LIMIT  2.6  UPPER LIMIT:  12.8
UNUSUAL FIRE AND EXPLOSION HAZARDS:      VERY VOLATILE AND EXTREMELY
                                         FLAMMABLE; MIXTURES WITH WATER
                                         CAN BE FLAMMABLE
EXTINGUISHING MEDIA:                     CARBON DIOXIDE, DRY CHEMICAL,
                                         ALCOHOL FOAM, WATER MIST OR FOG
```

Figure S7-1 *Example of a material safety data sheet.*

```
1 SPECIAL FIRE FIGHTING PROCEDURES:      WEAR FULLY PROTECTIVE CLOTHING AND
                                         SELF-CONTAINED BREATHING APPARATUS.
                                         HEAT WILL BUILD PRESSURE AND MAY
                                         RUPTURE CLOSED STORAGE CONTAINERS.
                                         KEEP FIRE-EXPOSED CONTAINERS COOL
                                         WITH WATER SPRAY.

IV. HAZARDOUS COMPONENTS
================================================================================
ACETONE                 WT. % CA 100     TLV 750 PPM          CAS NO.  67-64-1

V.  HEALTH HAZARDS
================================================================================
    OCCUPATIONAL EXPOSURE LIMITS         CONCENTRATION IMMEDIATELY
                                               DANGEROUS TO HEALTH

OSHA     TWA              750 PPM        OSHA/NIOSH           20,000 PPM
         STEL           1,000 PPM
         CEILING        NOT LISTED

ACGIH    TLV-TWA          750 PPM        ODOR THRESHOLD
         TLV-STEL       1,000 PPM        NSC                  2 PPM
                                         NIOSH                NOT LISTED

NIOSH    10-HOUR TWA      250 PPM

CARCINOGENIC DATA
ACETONE IS NOT LISTED AS A CARCINOGEN BY IARC, NTP, OSHA, OR ACGIH.

PRIMARY ROUTES OF ENTRY
ACETONE MAY EXERT ITS EFFECTS THROUGH INHALATION, SKIN ABSORPTION, AND
INGESTION.

INDUSTRIAL EXPOSURE:       ROUTE OF EXPOSURE/SIGNS AND SYMPTOMS
INHALATION:                EXPOSURE CAN CAUSE EYE, NOSE, AND THROAT
                           IRRITATION, HEADACHE, NAUSEA, DIZZINESS AND
                           NARCOSIS.

EYE CONTACT:               LIQUID AND HIGH VAPOR CONCENTRATION CAN CAUSE
                           IRRITATION.

SKIN CONTACT:              PROLONGED OR REPEATED SKIN CONTACT CAN CAUSE
                           IRRITATION AND DERMATITIS THROUGH DEFATTING OF SKIN.

INGESTION:                 SYMPTOM INFORMATION IS INADEQUATE/UNKNOWN.

EFFECTS OF OVEREXPOSURE
ACETONE IS A MILD EYE AND MUCOUS MEMBRANE IRRITANT, PRIMARY SKIN IRRITANT,
AND CENTRAL NERVOUS SYSTEM DEPRESSANT.  ACUTE EXPOSURE IRRITATES THE EYES
AND UPPER RESPIRATORY TRACT.  DIRECT SKIN CONTACT PRODUCES DERMATITIS,
CHARACTERIZED BY DRYNESS AND ERYTHEMA.  HIGH CONCENTRATIONS PRODUCE
NARCOSIS AND HYPOGLYCEMIA.

MEDICAL CONDITION AGGRAVATED BY EXPOSURE
PRECLUDE FROM EXPOSURE THOSE INDIVIDUALS SUSCEPTIBLE TO DERMATITIS.

EMERGENCY FIRST AID
INHALATION:            IMMEDIATELY REMOVE TO FRESH AIR.  IF NOT BREATHING,
                       ADMINISTER MOUTH-TO-MOUTH RESCUE BREATHING.  IF THERE
                       IS NO PULSE, ADMINISTER CARDIOPULMONARY RESUSCITATION
                       (CPR).  CONTACT PHYSICIAN IMMEDIATELY.
```

Figure S7-1 *(Continued)*

The minimum content of an MSDS is mandated by OSHA in the United States. There is a major effort underway to introduce a new 16-element international MSDS as a substitute for the traditional MSDS. Many companies have started to change to this 16-element format, which is much more user-friendly for response personnel. Each MSDS currently must contain the following sections:

1. The chemical name, chemical formula, common synonyms, chemical family, and manufacturer's name and emergency telephone number
2. Hazardous ingredients and regulatory exposure limits, if any
3. Physical data
4. Fire and explosion hazard data
5. Health hazard data
6. Reactivity data
7. Spill or leak procedures
8. Special protection information
9. Special precautions

Response and/or planning personnel are encouraged to review the MSDSs for at least the 10 most commonly released chemicals (previously listed) and gasoline. They should obtain current MSDSs from companies in their community (even though there are several sources of generic MSDSs, including some where the information is computerized) to establish and maintain good working relationships with local companies.

When reviewing these 11 MSDSs, personnel should take note of the different ways information is presented and the lack of uniform presentation, which can be confusing. Preparers are not required to use the standardized content in the format suggested by OSHA. The varying presentations give insight on the use of MSDSs and factors to be considered in interpreting them. The depth of information furnished in MSDSs varies depending on the extent of what is known about the chemical, as well as the management attitude of the company providing the information.

MSDS Section 1—Materials Identification

This section identifies the chemical by name, synonyms, and/or chemical family name(s). The manufacturer's name and emergency telephone number are listed in order to obtain additional data and assistance. In some cases preparers may choose to emphasize the health hazards, precautionary measures, and emergency contacts at the top of the MSDS.

```
1EYE CONTACT:      RINSE WITH COPIOUS AMOUNTS OF WATER FOR AT LEAST 15 MINUTES.
                   GET EMERGENCY MEDICAL ASSISTANCE.

SKIN CONTACT:      FLUSH THOROUGHLY FOR AT LEAST 15 MINUTES.  WASH AFFECTED
                   SKIN WITH SOAP AND WATER.  REMOVE CONTAMINATED CLOTHING
                   AND SHOES.  WASH CLOTHING BEFORE RE-USE, AND DISCARD
                   CONTAMINATED SHOES.  GET EMERGENCY MEDICAL ASSISTANCE.

INGESTION:         CALL LOCAL POISON CONTROL CENTER FOR ASSISTANCE.  CONTACT
                   PHYSICIAN IMMEDIATELY.  NEVER INDUCE VOMITING OR GIVE
                   ANYTHING BY MOUTH TO A VICTIM UNCONSCIOUS OR HAVING
                   CONVULSIONS.

VI. SAFETY MEASURES AND EQUIPMENT
------------------------------------------------------------------------------
VENTILATION:       ADEQUATE VENTILATION IS REQUIRED TO PROTECT PERSONNEL FROM
                   EXPOSURE TO CHEMICAL VAPORS EXCEEDING THE PEL AND TO
                   MINIMIZE FIRE HAZARDS.  THE CHOICE OF VENTILATION EQUIPMENT,
                   EITHER LOCAL OR GENERAL, WILL DEPEND ON THE CONDITIONS OF
                   USE, QUANTITY OR MATERIAL, AND OTHER OPERATING PARAMETERS.

RESPIRATORY:       USE APPROVED RESPIRATOR EQUIPMENT.  FOLLOW NIOSH AND
                   EQUIPMENT MANUFACTURER'S RECOMMENDATIONS TO DETERMINE
                   APPROPRIATE EQUIPMENT (AIR-PURIFYING, AIR-SUPPLIED, OR SELF-
                   CONTAINED BREATHING APPARATUS).

EYES:              SAFETY GLASSES ARE CONSIDERED MINIMUM PROTECTION.  GOGGLES
                   OR FACE SHIELD MAY BE NECESSARY DEPENDING ON QUANTITY OF
                   MATERIAL AND CONDITIONS OF USE.

SKIN:              PROTECTIVE GLOVES AND CLOTHING ARE RECOMMENDED.  THE
                   CHOICE OF MATERIAL MUST BE BASED ON CHEMICAL RESISTANCE AND
                   OTHER USER REQUIREMENTS.  GENERALLY, NEOPRENE OR RUBBER
                   OFFERS ACCEPTABLE CHEMICAL RESISTANCE.  INDIVIDUALS WHO ARE
                   ACUTELY AND SPECIFICALLY SENSITIVE TO ACETONE MAY REQUIRE
                   ADDITIONAL PROTECTIVE EQUIPMENT.

STORAGE;           ACETONE SHOULD BE PROTECTED FROM TEMPERATURE EXTREMES
                   AND DIRECT SUNLIGHT.  PROPER STORAGE OF ACETONE MUST BE
                   DETERMINED BASED ON OTHER MATERIALS STORED AND THEIR
                   HAZARDS AND POTENTIAL CHEMICAL INCOMPATIBILITY.  IN GENERAL,
                   ACETONE SHOULD BE STORED IN AN ACCEPTABLY PROTECTED AND
                   SECURE FLAMMABLE LIQUID STORAGE ROOM.

OTHER:             EMERGENCY EYEWASH FOUNTAINS AND SAFETY SHOWERS SHOULD BE
                   AVAILABLE IN THE VICINITY OF ANY POTENTIAL EXPOSURE.  GROUND
                   AND BOND METAL CONTAINERS TO MINIMIZE STATIC SPARKS.

VII. SPILL AND DISPOSAL DATA
------------------------------------------------------------------------------
SPILL CONTROL      PROTECT FROM IGNITION.  WEAR PROTECTIVE CLOTHING AND USE
                   APPROVED RESPIRATOR EQUIPMENT.  ABSORB SPILLED MATERIAL IN
                   AN ABSORBENT RECOMMENDED FOR SOLVENT SPILLS AND REMOVE TO
                   A SAFE LOCATION FOR DISPOSAL BY APPROVED METHODS.  IF
                   RELEASED TO THE ENVIRONMENT, COMPLY WITH ALL REGULATORY
                   NOTIFICATION REQUIREMENTS.  CERCLA REPORTABLE QUANTITY:
                   5,000 POUNDS.

1WASTE DISPOSAL:   DISPOSE OF ACETONE AS AN EPA HAZARDOUS WASTE.  CONTACT
                   STATE ENVIRONMENTAL AGENCY FOR LISTING OF LICENSED
                   HAZARDOUS WASTE

                   DISPOSAL FACILITIES AND APPLICABLE REGULATIONS.  HAZARDOUS
                   WASTE NUMBER:  U003 (IGNITABLE, TOXIC);  D001 (IGNITABLE).

HAZARD CLASSIFICATION                    CHEMICAL LISTINGS
IMMEDIATE HEALTH:   YES (IRRITANT)       EXTREMELY HAZARDOUS SUBSTANCES:  NO
DELAYED HEALTH:     NO                   CERCLA HAZARDOUS SUBSTANCES:  YES
FIRE:               YES                  TOXIC CHEMICALS:  YES
SUDDEN RELEASE:     NO
REACTIVE:           NO

ACETONE IS SUBJECT TO THE REPORTING REQUIREMENTS OF SECTION 313 OF TITLE III OF
THE SUPERFUND AMENDMENTS AND REAUTHORIZATION ACT OF 1986 (SARA) AND 40CFR
PART 372.  THIS PRODUCT DOES NOT CONTAIN ANY OTHER TOXIC CHEMICAL ABOVE 1%
CONCENTRATION OR A CARCINOGEN ABOVE 0.1% CONCENTRATION.

KEY
CA   APPROXIMATELY                STEL  SHORT TERM EXPOSURE LEVEL (15 MINUTES)
NA   NOT APPLICABLE               TLV   THRESHOLD LIMIT VALUE
C    CEILING                      TWA   TIME WEIGHTED AVERAGE
                                  BUAC  BUTYL ACETATE
CERCLA  COMPREHENSIVE ENVIRONMENTAL RESPONSE, COMPENSATION AND LIABILITY
        ACT CF  1980.
NSC     NATIONAL SAFETY COUNCIL ('FUNDAMENTALS OF INDUSTRIAL HYGIENE,'
        3RD ED., 1988).

BURDICK & JACKSON'S DISCLAIMER:  THE INFORMATION AND RECOMMENDATIONS
PRESENTED IN THIS MATERIAL SAFETY DATA SHEET ARE BASED ON SOURCES BELIEVED TO
BE RELIABLE ON THE DATE HEREOF.  BURDICK & JACKSON MAKES NO REPRESENTATION ON
ITS COMPLETENESS OR ACCURACY.  IT IS THE USER'S RESPONSIBILITY TO DETERMINE THE
PRODUCT'S SUITABILITY FOR ITS INTENDED USE, THE PRODUCT'S SAFE USE, AND THE
PRODUCT'S PROPER DISPOSAL.  NO REPRESENTATIONS OR WARRANTIES, EITHER EXPRESS
OR IMPLIED, OF MERCHANTABILITY OR FITNESS FOR A PARTICULAR PURPOSE OR OF ANY
OTHER NATURE ARE MADE WITH RESPECT TO THE INFORMATION PROVIDED IN THIS
MATERIAL SAFETY DATA SHEET OR TO THE PRODUCT TO WHICH SUCH INFORMATION
REFERS.  BURDICK & JACKSON NEITHER ASSUMES NOR AUTHORIZES ANY OTHER PERSON
TO ASSUME FOR IT, ANY OTHER OR ADDITIONAL LIABILITY OR RESPONSIBILITY RESULTING
FROM THE USE OF, OR RELIANCE UPON, THIS INFORMATION.
```

Figure S7-1 *(Continued)*

MSDS Section 2—Ingredients and Hazards

Absolute clarity in describing all ingredients of a material and their hazardous components is essential; however, experience indicates that this information does not always appear in the MSDS. Most of the 11 reviewed MSDSs will address pure substances or aqueous dilutions, with the notable exception of that for gasoline. For example, when discussing chlorine and its hazards, an MSDS preparer would assume chlorine to be the pure chemical in the gaseous form; however, we are more likely to encounter chlorine as a solid (HTH—commonly used in swimming pools) or as commercial bleaches (a liquid that is fairly dilute). Most commercial bleaches for domestic use contain from 30,000 to 50,000 parts per million (ppm) sodium hypochlorite as a source of chlorine.

Upon reviewing the ingredients and hazards of anhydrous ammonia and ammonium hydroxide, we see that anhydrous ammonia is a colorless gas with an extremely pungent odor and that ammonium hydroxide is a clear, colorless liquid. Although their forms are different and their ability to impinge on exposures when released is different, the hazard is the same. Ammonia is intensely corrosive to human tissue, whether it is inhaled, contacts the skin, or is ingested. OSHA regulates workplace exposures of ammonia at 50 ppm (permissible exposure limit, PEL) while the American Conference of Governmental Industrial Hygienists (ACGIH) recommends a level of 25 ppm (threshold limit value, TLV). Additionally, OSHA regulations state that at concentrations of 300 ppm in air, the material becomes immediately dangerous to life and health (IDLH).

The OSHA system is designed to provide working conditions for reasonably healthy adult humans for 8-hour exposures for 40 hours per week for 40 years. The data are not directly applicable to general populations. Obviously, anyone with preexisting respiratory ailments would be expected to be more affected by irritants and by those chemicals that affect the central nervous system (CNS). The limits are not applicable to children, especially those in the first year of life, since their metabolism and nervous system responses are significantly different from those of adults or older children. *Emergency Response Planning Guidelines* prepared by the American Industrial Hygiene Association provide additional exposure guidelines for use when determining concentrations of concern for released chemicals.

All of the OSHA limits are for airborne concentrations and vary widely among the substances listed. It is important to note that the ratio of exposure limit to IDLH concentration also varies widely. The greater the range between these two numbers, the greater the safety factor for an exposed person to avoid permanent harm or death.

One important area of information not available from this section is how the liquids and the solid on the preceding list become airborne concentrations and how fast this occurs. For this information, we will have to look elsewhere on the MSDS.

MSDS Section 3—Physical Data

In the process of hazard assessment, the ability to evaluate physical data combined with health hazard data is essential. The common physical properties provided on the reviewed MSDS include boiling point, freezing point, specific gravity, vapor pressure, vapor density, solubility, and appearance. Other parameters may be provided at the discretion of the company completing the sheets.

1. *Boiling point.* The temperature at which a liquid turns to a vapor. Since the ambient temperature of this planet ranges from around –20°C to 50°C (–10°F to 120°F), any chemical with a boiling point below the ambient temperature will rapidly become a gas when released from its container. This is certainly the case for chlorine and anhydrous ammonia. Other materials with boiling points only slightly above normal ambient temperature will, if confined in a container, rapidly expand and pressurize that container with the potential for a rapid release if heated even slightly. Other materials, such as PCBs and sodium hydroxide pellets, will be unaffected by the heat of normal structural fires but could be affected by the application of water to that fire. Sodium hydroxide pellets, for example, will dissolve in water to form a corrosive liquid.

2. *Freezing point.* Temperature at which the liquid form of a chemical will turn into the solid form.

3. *Melting point.* Temperature at which the solid form of a chemical will turn into the liquid form. The preceding two physical parameters may be of limited use to response personnel for most chemicals. There are several chemicals for which control measures such as freezing are effective and where dry ice, for example, may be used to mitigate a release. Similarly, there are some chemicals where the property changes under structural fire temperatures may be significant and may seriously alter the hazard to response personnel. Exposure of low melting point solids and most liquids to fire temperatures may result in production of toxic materials in the smoke plume.

4. *Specific gravity.* Density of a chemical compared to the density of water. If the specific gravity is less than one, the chemical will float on water. If the specific gravity is greater than one, the chemical will sink. In either case, it is important for response personnel to consider the property of solubility concurrently with specific gravity. These properties for the 11 chemicals are listed in Table S7-1.

Toluene, gasoline, and methyl alcohol are all flammable or combustible liquids with similar TLV levels. A glance at their respective solubilities, however, shows that mitigation techniques would have to be substantially different due to their solubility. That is, methyl alcohol is completely miscible in water, whereas the others are relatively insoluble. Not only would firefighting methods differ, but additional attention would

Table S7-1 Exposure Limits for Common Chemicals

Chemical Name	Physical State (Ambient Temperatures)	Inhalation Exposure Limit	IDLH
Ammonium hydroxide	Liquid	25 ppm (NIOSH) 50 ppm (OSHA)	300 ppm
Anhydrous ammonia	Gas	25 ppm (NIOSH) 50 ppm (OSHA)	300 ppm
Chlorine	Gas	C 0.5 ppm (NIOSH)	10 ppm
Gasoline	Liquid	300 ppm (ACGIH) 500 ppm (OSHA) 10 ppm benzene	
Hydrochloric acid	Liquid	C 5 ppm	50 ppm
Methyl alcohol	Liquid	200 ppm (NIOSH)	6000 ppm
Nitric acid (<70%)	Liquid	2 ppm (NIOSH/OSHA)	25 ppm
PCBs	Liquid	0.5 mg/m^3 (ACGIH)	
Sodium hydroxide	Solid	2 mg/m^3	200 mg/m^3
Sulfuric acid (93%)	Liquid	1 mg/m^3	80 mg/m^3
Toluene	Liquid	100 ppm (NIOSH) 200 ppm (OSHA)	500 ppm

have to be paid to the solubility when environmental damage is possible. Many chemicals that are listed as only slightly soluble can still cause significant environmental toxicity to plants or aquatic life. Because the toxicity of methyl alcohol is 250 ppm and toluene 1180 ppm, for example, each presents a serious environmental hazard if significant runoff is allowed to occur.

Most MSDSs do not provide environmental risk information; therefore, this information will have to be sought from other sources. One excellent source for environmental risk information for many common chemicals is the EPA's OHM-TADS (Oil & Hazardous Materials—Technical Assistance Data System). Access to this system can be gained through any EPA regional office.

5. *Vapor density.* Density of a gas compared to the density of air. If the vapor density is less than one, the material will rise in still air and dissipate. If the vapor density is greater than one, the vapor will attempt to sink in still air and potentially collect in low spots and valleys.

6. *Vapor pressure.* Pressure exerted by vapors against the sides of the container. Vapor pressure is very temperature dependent. The lower the boiling point of the liquid, the greater the vapor pressure it will exert at a given temperature. In more common terms, the higher the vapor pressure, the more rapidly the material will change from the liquid form to a vapor when released to the environment and the higher the equilibrium concentration with air will be.

The data contained in Table S7-2 were found on MSDSs reviewed by the author. However, it is apparent that errors do creep into the MSDS listings (as shown in the sulfuric acid listing presented here). Also, MSDS listings vary in the depth of detail provided—from rough estimates or general statements for some materials to multiple listings for others.

If you can picture a room in which a release occurs from its container, and then look at the range of vapor pressures for the most commonly released substances, it will be apparent that both chlorine and anhydrous ammonia will present an almost instantaneous vapor (inhalation) hazard. Since both of these chemicals are soluble to some extent, a fog line may be helpful in suppression of volatilization or reduction of concentrations, even when the release is continuous. However, when the intent is to reduce vapor production, the water from the hose lines should not enter pooled materials like ammonia or chlorine. For materials like sodium hydroxide and PCBs, a vapor hazard is not likely to exist under most real-world conditions.

The physical properties of a chemical will help personnel determine how the chemical will behave when released from its container.

MSDS Section 4—Fire and Explosion Data

Most of the MSDSs reviewed contain specific information for the fire fighter on the physical characteristics of the chemicals when involved in a fire. These characteristics, as summarized in Table S7-3, should be made familiar to most fire personnel.

In addition to these normal fire characteristics, the chemicals have other fire-related hazards, some of which are reported in the fire and explosion section. The following examples are:

1. Chlorine and anhydrous ammonia are generally stored in pressure containers, and the violent rupture of these containers represents a significant hazard, in addition to their toxicity.

Table S7-2 Examples of Physical Data Found on MSDSs

Chemical	Boiling Point (°C)	Specific Gravity	Solubility	Vapor Pressure (@ 20°C)	Vapor Density
Ammonium hydroxide	36	0.9	Infinite	115 mmHg	1.2
Anhydrous ammonia	–33	0.68	Soluble	23 atm	0.6
Chlorine	–34	2.4	0.7%	4800 mmHg	2.49
Gasoline	38–204	0.7–0.8	Insoluble	—	3–4
Hydrochloric acid	53	1.18	Infinite	190 mmHg	1.27
Methyl alcohol	64.5	0.8	Miscible	97 mmHg	1.1
Nitric acid (68%)	122	1.41	Complete	62 mmHg	2.3
PCBs	360–390	1.5	0.01 ppm	<1 mmHg	—
Sodium hydroxide	1390	2.13	111 gm/100 gm	—	—
Sulfuric acid (93%)	**310**	**1.84**	**Infinite**	**<0.3 mmHg @ 25°C**	**3.4**
Toluene	232	0.86	0.05 gm/100 gm	22 mmHg	3.14

Table S7-3 Examples of Fire and Explosion Data

Chemical	Flash Point	Autoignition Temperature	Flammable Range	Extinguishing Media
Ammonium hydroxide	—	—	—	—
Anhydrous ammonia	NA	651°C	16–27%	Shut off gas
Chlorine	NA	NA	NA	NA
Gasoline	–45°F	536–853°F	1.5–7.6%	Dry chemical, water spray
Hydrochloric acid	NA	NA	NA	NA
Methyl alcohol	52°F	385°F	6–36.5%	Water spray
Nitric acid	NA	NA	NA	NA
PCBs	NA	NA	NA	NA
Sodium hydroxide	NA	NA	NA	NA
Sulfuric acid	NA	NA	NA	NA
Toluene	40°F	480°F	1.3–7.1%	Dry chemical

2. Many of the chemicals listed generate toxic vapors or mists when involved in a fire, thus representing an additional hazard.
3. Hydrochloric acid, nitric acid, sodium hydroxide, and sulfuric acid are such vigorous oxidizers or reducers that, although they are not flammable hazards themselves, they react with metals to produce hydrogen gas, which is extremely flammable.

MSDS Section 5—Health Hazard Information

This section of the MSDS presents information on the routes of exposure (inhalation, ingestion, dermal) and, in some cases, the severity of these risks (low, moderate, high). This information is essential for the selection of appropriate personal protective equipment and safety procedures for response actions at incidents. Some of the MSDSs reviewed highlighted the major hazards in Section 1 on the sheets, while others give a more detailed formal listing of the hazards in this section. Some sheets list the NFPA 704 rating for the specific chemical (use of the 704 system by local industry should be encouraged, as it provides local emergency response personnel a basis for quick judgments about the severity of personal exposure). A brief summary of the hazards for each chemical as contained in the M 44SDSs reviewed is listed in Table S7-4. *More than one source should always be used to clearly identify all of the hazards associated with the chemical of concern.*

The most common hazard of the chemicals listed is their corrosive effect on nearly every part of the human body. The effects of chlorine and sulfuric acid are very similar. What makes chlorine a greater risk is the volatility of the liquid when released compared to the acid, which is already a liquid at ambient temperatures and volatilizes very slowly.

MSDS Section 6—Reactivity Data

Generally, four areas of information are presented in this section, and all are potentially useful to those responding to a hazardous chemical emergency.

1. *Stability.* Is the material stable at ambient temperature and pressure or at normal storage conditions? Most of the chemicals reviewed are stable and not liable to undergo spontaneous changes.

Table S7-4 Examples of Hazards Listed on MSDSs

Chemical	Hazards as Listed in the MSDSs
Ammonium hydroxide	Corrosive, severe eye and skin irritant
Anhydrous ammonia	Corrosive, severe eye and skin irritant
Chlorine	Corrosive, life threatening toxic effects possible at concentrations of 25 ppm on short exposures
Gasoline	Flammable, irritant, CNS effects, some evidence of carcinogenicity, also numerous chronic effects
Hydrochloric acid	Corrosive, may be fatal if ingested
Methyl alcohol	Flammable, may be fatal if ingested
Nitric acid (68%)	Corrosive, strong oxidizer at higher concentrations
PCBs	Very long lasting material, some evidence of liver damage, carcinogenic risk, adverse reproductive effects
Sodium hydroxide	Corrosive, may be fatal if swallowed, causing severe burns
Sulfuric acid (93%)	Corrosive, causes sever burns, may be fatal if swallowed, harmful if inhaled
Toluene	Flammable, chronic skin irritant, various systematic effects on CNS, liver, kidneys

2. *Polymerization.* Will the chemical change through polymerization at normal conditions of storage and temperature? For chemicals that spontaneously polymerize, this frequently leads to generation of heat and potential container failure.

3. *Decomposition.* What new chemicals and what hazards will be created by the thermal decomposition of the chemical? Important information is included in this section for officials concerned about the exposures of response personnel and general population if the chemical is exposed to fire. For example, formaldehyde may be formed from fire involving methyl alcohol, oxides of nitrogen from anhydrous ammonia, and from most of the other chemicals, oxides of carbon that may increase the hazards from simple asphyxiation.

4. *Incompatibles.* What materials may cause violent reactions with the chemical? Note especially the MSDS for gasoline.

Predicting the potential violent reactions of the estimated 6 million chemicals in the world requires some idea of the likelihood of any of these chemicals coming in contact with each other. Many of the chemicals reviewed are potent acids or bases, and they will certainly be incompatible with chemicals of widely differing pH. For example, the sheet for sulfuric acid lists water as being incompatible. The mixing of sulfuric acid (96 percent) with water (at pH of 7) releases enough heat to cause a violent reaction.

MSDS Section 7—Spill or Leak Procedures

This section contains suggested steps for handling releases of the chemical in question. The information provided is usually similar to the 1996 DOT *North American Emergency Response Guide*. It is important to note the order in which the material is presented. If the material is extremely flammable, but not particularly toxic, initial advice will usually be to control ignition sources. If the material is extremely toxic, initial advice will generally be to evacuate.

MSDS Section 8—Special Protection Information

On many MSDSs now in use, this section is not very specific. Hopefully, improvements will be made that recommend specific respiratory and clothing information. It is important to know that none of the impervious clothing is suitable for all chemicals. For example, polyethylene protective clothing is not recommended for concentrated sulfuric acid but is suitable for more dilute solutions.

Special problems may be created for first responders by those materials that adversely affect normal fire fighter protective clothing. These materials (i.e., chlorobenzene, methyl iodide, etc.), for which breakthrough times are less than one tank of air, may not offer any useful protection to the responder. Once a hazard analysis is completed and response organizations are at the point of their contingency planning where they are selecting response equipment, it is suggested that they obtain copies of the various protective clothing vendors' performance information, especially for the multilayer garments, and also talk with other responders about the selection and use of specific protective clothing ensembles.

MSDS Section 9—Special Precautions

Many MSDSs do not contain any information in this area. In some cases, for extremely flammable materials there is an additional warning about sparks and radiant heat; for chlorine, there is a warning about igniting other combustible materials on contact; and for many other chemicals there is a reiteration of standard storage and handling procedures.

One important area that may be covered on some MSDSs is the hazard of the chemical to animal or aquatic life. This information is frequently based on scientific testing of the compound or chemical in controlled laboratory settings. The information from this testing is presented in terminology different from the regulatory TLV and PEL information and will require additional effort before the responder can evaluate the information.

Depending on the potential use of the chemical, a series of tests may be conducted over a period of time in a manner that resembles successive elimination. Tests are run for a variety of acute and chronic effects as well as exotic effects on more and more complex animals. Initial screening is done on bacteria, which allows the testing of large numbers of individuals and numerous generations in small spaces and in a short time. Subsequent tests may be conducted with any of a wide variety of rodents, pigs, dogs, and, sometimes, primates. The sequence of the tests is shown in Figure S7-2.

Tests are done to evaluate the physical/chemical properties of the substance, note routes of entry into the organisms being tested, and document exposure variables. The tests are used to evaluate the biological fate of the chemicals and develop a dose/response curve for the specific effects being evaluated. Hypothetical dose/response curves are shown in Figure S7-3. The most common expression of the results of these tests is the dose or concentration at which 50 percent are affected, known as the TD50. Toxicologists exhibit their skills by the accuracy with which they can extrapolate animal data to predict effects on man. In general, TD50 data are commonly given for pesticides and other chemicals developed for pest and weed control. An example of interpreting these data for responders is shown in Table S7-5.

Early

- Acute toxicity—handling hazards
- 1st level screen—mutagen/carcinogen
- Subchronic toxicity—target organ, toxic dose—rodent
- Birth defects—teratology
- 2nd level screen—mutagen/carcinogen
- Absorption/distribution/metabolism/excretion—lab animals (metabolism/pharmacokinetics)
- Subchronic toxicology—non-rodent species
- Reproduction study
- Behavioral tests
- Synergism/potentiation
- Residue evaluation
- Long-term studies—carcinogenesis—rodents
- Definitive test for mutagenesis—rodents
- Metabolism/pharmacokinetics—humans
- Epidemiology

Late

Figure S7-2 *Chronology of testing.*

Dose/response curves deal with acute exposures, but it is important to also consider the potential for repetitive exposures at lower doses, which may accumulate in the body. This situation is called chronic exposure and is shown diagrammed in Figure S7-3. The two toluene sheets discussed earlier provide chronic exposure data indicating the potential for brain cell damage from long-term inhalation of toluene vapor.

SUMMARY

Local government emergency response personnel can avoid much confusion if they concentrate on utilizing MSDSs in pre-emergency planning. That is, they should identify in advance the buildings or processes that store or utilize extremely toxic materials, then make basic decisions regarding "no attack" before an emergency occurs. There is a recent major effort by a new NFPA committee to develop standard recommended practices for pre-incident planning responses. This document, NFPA 1620, is still in the draft stage but could be obtained for review by contacting the Committee Members or the NFPA Standards Administration Staff Assistant.

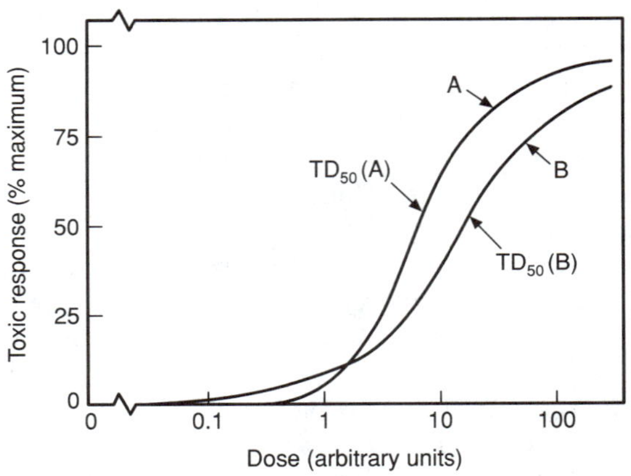

Figure S7-3 *Hypothetical dose/response curve of two chemicals, A and B.*

Once response community personnel have completed the hazard analysis and have evaluated the collected MSDS in the manner discussed here, numerous additional questions need to be answered to complete the contingency planning portion of the work. Some of the questions that the hazard analysis and contingency planning process will help answer include the following:

1. What risks will be encountered by first responders?
2. What protective equipment (respiratory and clothing) will be needed by the responders?
3. What type of support resources are likely to be necessary for mitigation supplies or medical assistance?

One useful way to clarify these questions and to provide practical guidance for the response community is to use the highest risk situation from the hazard analysis as a scenario for a hands-on drill/exercise for the participating members of the response community.

Reference

1. *Acute Hazardous Events*, Data Base Industrial Economics, Inc., Cambridge, MA 02140, December 1985.

Table S7-5 Relative Index of Toxicology

Toxicity Rating	Probable Oral Dose	Lethal Dose for Average Adult Human
Practically nontoxic	>15 g/kg	More than a quart
Slightly toxic	5–150 g/kg	Between pint and quart
Moderately toxic	0.5–5 g/kg	Between ounce and pint
Very toxic	50–500 mg/kg	Between teaspoon and ounce
Extremely toxic	5–50 mg/kg	7 drops to teaspoonful
Supertoxic	<5 mg/kg	A taste (less than 7 drops)

SUPPLEMENT 8

NY Fire Department Hazardous Materials Emergency Response Plan: An Overview

Eddie McDonald, Battalion Commander, Safety Battalion FDNY, Retired

Editor's Note: The New York City FD Haz Mat Response Plan has been widely available as a training and planning resource for many years. Here, Eddie McDonald, one of the authors of the original New York City FD plan (with Tom Fitzpatrick), describes how the plan was developed.(For a complete copy of the New York City Haz Mat Response Plan, please contact Tom Fitzpatrick, Executive Assistant to the Fire Commissioner, FDNY, 250 Livingston Street, Brooklyn, NY 11201.) The Haz Mat Plan in Action, written by Haz Mat Captain Peter Stuebe and appearing in this supplement, describes how a recent chemical spill in New York was handled with the plan in place. Retired Commander McDonald is now with Inter-Fire, an international fire consulting company based in Mattituck, New York. Both Fitzpatrick and Stuebe continue to serve on the FDNY.

BACKGROUND OF ORIGIN AND DEVELOPMENT

During the late 1970s, the threat of hazardous materials biological and radiological incidents, with their potential harm to health and contamination to the environment, became real in this country and around the world. These incidents proved that a disaster could be deadly, could cause extensive personal injury and property damage, and could occur in one's backyard.

In order to carry out the responsibilities delineated in the New York City Hazardous Materials Contingency Plan (Mayor's Office of Emergency Management) and to comply with standards established by federal legislation, the New York City Fire Department's Hazardous Material's Emergency Response Plan was established.

This plan development included extensive research of federal, state, and local regulations. Regulations, 29 *CFR* 1910.120 and EPA 311, require each employer, whether governmental or private, to develop specific response plans and/or utilize the plans required by SARA Title III. The regulations contained in 29 *CFR* 1910.120, paragraph q(1) require emergency response agencies to develop emergency response plans. The plan must include hazardous materials response standard operating procedures.

To be effective, the New York City Fire Department's Hazardous Materials Emergency Response Plan is also integrated into the Local Emergency Planning Commission Plan (LEPC).

The regulations further mandate that an Incident Command System (ICS) be the operating management system for all response personnel. That includes fire, emergency medical, police, and other agencies that might be expected to respond. The person in charge, the incident commander (IC), is responsible for the success of the entire operation and the safety of all personnel involved.

In the event of a significant accident or other incident involving a toxic or hazardous material where, because of fire, explosion, radioactive toxic air release, or chemical reaction there exists a danger to the health and safety of the general public, and/or emergency response personnel, the senior fire department officer will be the incident commander at the scene and will implement the Fire Department Hazardous Materials Emergency Response Plan.

The plan is built on the fundamental organization and strategy of the FDNY Incident Command System (ICS) ensuring maximum safety and efficiency of the operating personnel while fulfilling responsibility to the public. The plan includes policy statements that describe the following:

- Operational objectives
- Resource accounting
- Command interfaces
- Organizational positions
- Assessment of response hazards
- Levels of response
- Basic staffing
- Training

Implementing the plan will facilitate the coordination and control of all tasks. The incident commander will manage the command and control of all mitigation activities and functions. When the Mayor's Office of Emergency Management's on-scene coordinator is present, the IC will coordinate activities with that person.

All mitigation operations will be managed by the Operations Chief, who will be from the fire department. The specific tactical objectives will be managed by branch directors and/or sector/group supervisors; other needs will be met by staffing the necessary ICS positions.

Hazardous materials incidents represent potentially dangerous situations. Chemicals, along with biological and radioactive materials, can affect the general public or the environments as well as emergency responders. Although the response activities needed at each incident are unique, there are similarities. One common element is that every response requires protecting the health and safety of the responders.

This plan identifies the functions needed to control and mitigate a hazardous materials incident. It also describes the lines of authority, responsibility, and communication between and among various responders. *(See Figures S8-1, S8-2, and S8-3.)* It defines the interface of the fire department with other agencies. Finally, it specifies the authority of each responder in directing specific operations.

The plan will provide direction on how to accomplish tasks in a safe manner. In concept and principle,

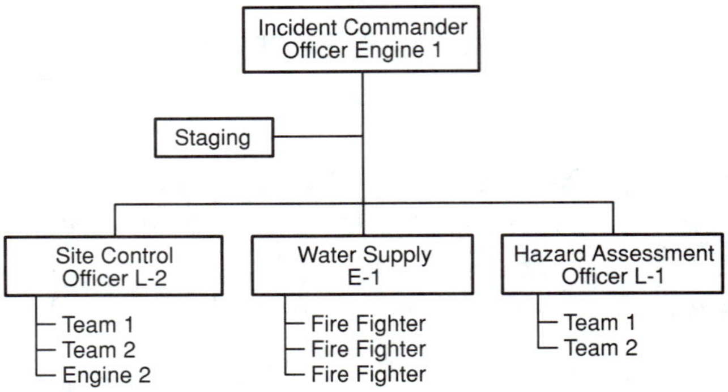

Figure S8-1 *Command structure for the initial response to a hazardous materials incident.*

standard operating safety guidelines are independent of the incident type. Their applicability at a particular incident must be determined and necessary modifications made to match the situation. However, in the case of hazardous materials operations, the specific requirements of training, equipment, and competence preclude the generalized statements that might apply to other types of emergency work.

The plan will provide guidance for the fire department responders in areas of site control, entry, decontamination, and mitigation of hazardous materials incidents. The guidance is not meant to be a comprehensive treatment of each of the subjects discussed. Formal training in these areas will complement this document; specific training will provide more information for the technical, administrative, and management-oriented skills needed to fulfill our mission. The plan will provide standard operating guides to develop more specific procedures.

MAYOR'S OFFICE OF EMERGENCY MANAGEMENT—AGENCY COORDINATION OF THE PLAN

The Mayor's Office of Emergency Management has developed the New York City Hazardous Materials Contingency Plan. The concept of the plan is to provide an organized response to what may generally be perceived as a chaotic and unmanageable situation. The focus of the Hazardous Materials Contingency Plan (HMCP) is to establish the city's policy for preparedness for, mitigation of, response to, and recovery from hazardous materials incidents. All city agencies involved in the plan comply with the provisions of the plan as well as all pertinent city, state, and federal laws and regulations. It is imperative that involved agencies know, understand, and comply with these laws and regulations.

Hazardous materials events require extensive coordination within a logical command structure to en-

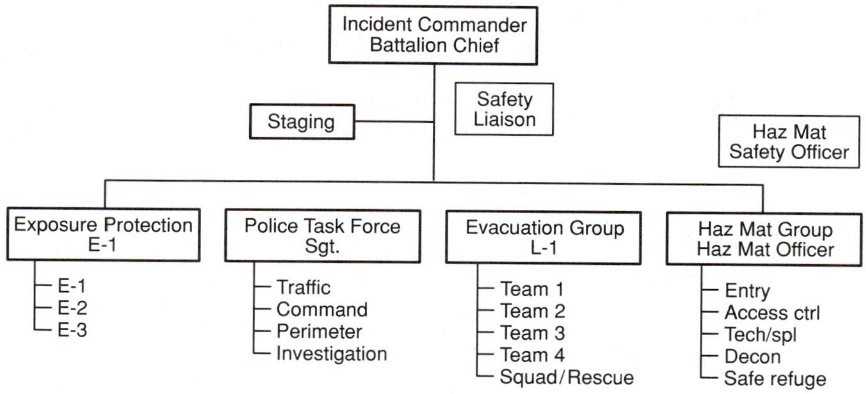

Figure S8-2 *Command structure for a reinforced response to a hazardous materials incident.*

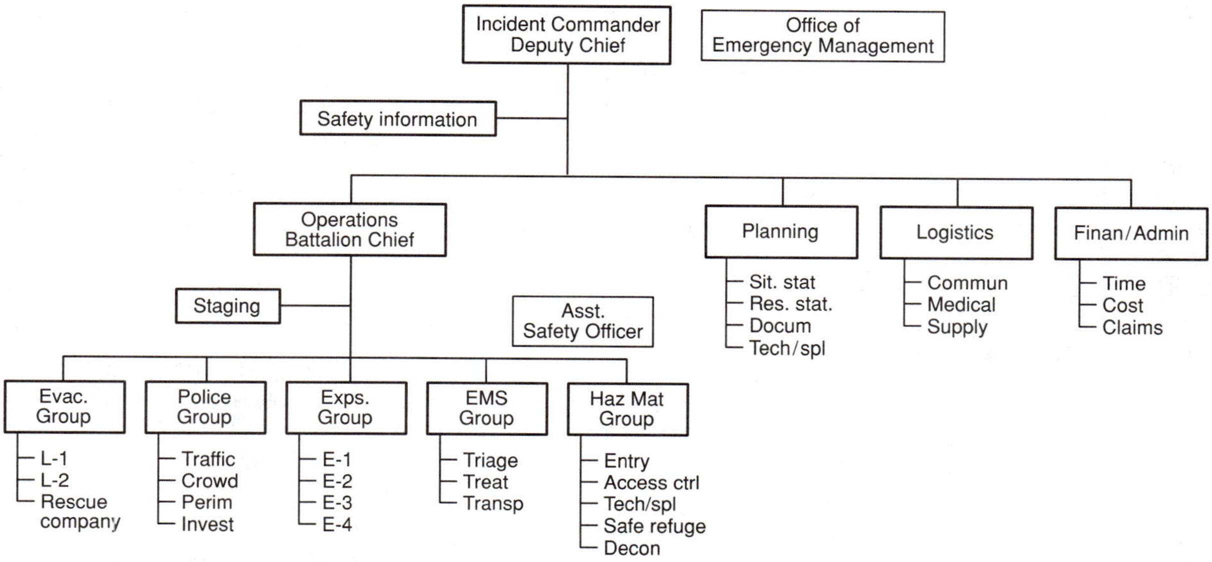

Figure S8-3 *Command structure for responding to a major hazardous materials incident.*

sure a safe and efficient response. Within the city's plan, the incident commander for a hazardous materials incident is now the fire department, with the Mayor's Office of Emergency Management serving as the on-scene coordinator.

The HMCP articulates the hazardous material response from the various city agencies that would be involved in an incident of this type. The purpose is to ensure a safe, coordinated response to a release or potential release of a hazardous material. It defines the roles and responsibilities for agencies responding to and operating at a hazardous materials incident.

Upon arrival at the scene of a release or suspected release of a hazardous material, the responding agency must follow the procedures set out in the HMCP. This includes the New York City fire and police departments, the city Department of Environmental Protection (DEP), and the Mayor's Office of Emergency Management.

The incident will be managed under the Incident Command System. The senior fire department officer at the scene will be the incident commander. The Mayor's Office of Emergency Management will be the on-scene coordinator and establish the Interagency Command Post (IACP) to assist the incident commander with interagency activities. The on-scene coordinator acts as a resource supplier to the incident commander. He or she will procure the necessary resources requested by the incident commander to contain, control, and remediate the incident.

Upon his or her arrival at the scene, the ranking official from each agency reports to the command post and establishes a liaison with the incident commander and the Mayor's Office of Emergency Management. At the scene of a hazardous materials incident the agencies will have the following responsibilities:

- OEM. This office assumes the role of on-scene coordinator with responsibility to ensure coordination of the activities of all responding agencies.
- FDNY. The senior officer will be the incident commander. This department has authority and responsibility for the strategic and tactical planning and implementation of rescue, containment, and mitigation of the incident as well as decontamination, triage, and treatment of victims and responders. It will establish control zones, identify areas of evacuation, and ensure that operations are coordinated and performed by properly equipped and trained personnel.
- NYPD. This department reports to the IACP and maintains a liaison with the incident commander and the on-scene coordinator. Its responsibilities include scene security and assistance with evacuation as determined by and under the direction of the incident commander. The NYPD establishes a traffic plan for emergency response vehicles. It assumes the role of incident commander from the senior fire department officer when it has determined the incident has reached a solely investigative stage.
- DEP. The DEP reports to IACP, maintains a liaison with the incident commander and the on-scene coordinator, and confers with them relative to proper course of action to prevent spread of product and appropriate steps to safeguard potential victims and responders. Once the hazard is rendered harmless, the DEP is responsible for managing removal and disposal as well as site redemption. If the site is a crime scene, DEP will work with NYPD to coordinate the redemption effort and the investigation.
- DOH. The Department of Health reports to IACP, assesses the nature and extent of the contamination, advises the incident commander of the health effects, and determines the appropriate actions for incidents involving radiological or biological materials.

The preceding list outlines the basic concepts of the city's Hazardous Materials Contingency Plan and is the policy for the interagency response to hazardous materials incidents. The New York City Fire Department's Hazardous Materials Emergency Response Plan fulfills the identified responsibilities.

The following are the objectives of the Fire Department's Hazardous Materials Emergency Response Plan:

1. Save lives and protect the environment and property
2. Describe the department's response organization
3. Identify the responsibilities of the responders
4. Establish lines of authority and coordination for the incident
5. Facilitate communication between elements of the organization
6. Describe the framework for the liaison with emergency responders and the private sector
7. State guidelines for the strategic and tactical operations at the incident

General Incident Procedures and Site Safety Operations

This part of the plan describes the concept of operations and an overview of resource utilization for the operational aspects at a hazardous materials incident. It does not provide specifics on individual topics. This is a brief discussion of the items, which are then explained in depth during the training program. This section is intended to provide background so interaction within the organization is accomplished effectively and safely. The activities and tasks performed in this section require a thorough understanding of the topics as it relates to the city and safety of the responders, public, and environment.

Roles and Responsibilities

Under the authority outlined in the Mayor's Office of Emergency Management—City of New York Hazardous Materials Contingency Plan, the senior fire officer is designated as the incident commander for all hazardous materials incidents within the city. The fire department's Bureau of Training provides an incident commanders' course that covers their responsibilities.

The following list includes objectives for the incident commander of a hazardous materials incident and specific responsibilities identified in 29 *CFR* 1910.120.

- Direct and coordinate all aspects of the incident from initial response through stabilization using the departments Incident Command System [29 *CFR* 1910.120 (1) (3) (I)]
- Operate within the scope of the Mayor's Office of Emergency Management's integrated management plan
- Coordinate on-scene operations by all agencies engaged in incident operations
- Direct all resources with assigned tasks and on-scene activities based on their capability
- Ensure appropriate resources are requested and assigned in a timely manner
- Provide management overview, technical overview, and logistical support to other agency personnel

- Provide contact point for information to Mayor's Office of Emergency Management, the media, and the public
- Provide public warning in coordination with the Mayor's Office of Emergency Management
- Make initial assessment of public and environmental hazards [29 *CFR* 1910.120 (q) (3)(11)]
- Provide protective measures for responders, the public, and the environment [29 *CFR* 1910.120 (q)(3) (III) and 29 *CFR* 1910.120(Q) (3) (IV)]
- Coordinate the logistical aspects of recovery, including site cleanup and disposal of hazardous waste
- Coordinate perimeter security
- Establish documentation of hazardous materials incidents
- Transfer of command to the appropriate post-emergency agency
- Conduct critique of incident with all involved agencies
- Limit the number of personnel within the hot and warm zone to those actively performing operations [29 *CFR* 1910.120(q) (3) (V)]
- Provide EMT support personnel [29 *CFR* 1910.120(q) (3) (vi)]
- Designate Haz Mat Safety Officer [29 *CFR* 1910.120 (q) (3) (vii)]
- Implement appropriate decontamination procedures [29 *CFR* 1910.120 (q) (3) (IX)]

Incident Commander's Goals for a Hazardous Material Incident

The incident commander is also responsible for determining the strategic goals for the incident, the broad general statements of what is to be accomplished. There are generally nine accepted strategic goals for a hazardous materials incident and the incident commander uses these to guide his or her goal setting.

1. Isolation
   - Perimeter
   - Staging
   - Initial Evacuation
   - Site Access Control Points (hot zone, warm zone, cold zone, area of refuge)
2. Notification
   - EMS
   - Police
   - Office of Emergency Management
   - Department of Environmental Protection
   - Department of Health
3. Identification
   - Placards (I.D. numbers, shipping papers, name, phone number)
   - Pre-plan
   - Facility plan
   - Responsible party
4. Protective actions
   - Evacuation
   - In-place protection
   - Rescue
   - Decontamination
5. Spill control
   - Type (gas/air, liquid/surface, liquid/water, solid/surface)
   - Disperse
   - Divert
   - Adsorb/Absorb
   - Blanket
   - Dike
   - Retain
   - Dam
   - Boom
6. Leak control
   - Plug
   - Patch
   - Overpack
   - Displace
   - Product transfer
   - Remote shutoff
   - Pressure reduction
7. Fire control
   - Exposure protection
   - Fire suppression
   - Vapor suppression
8. Recovery
   - Equipment decontamination
   - Personnel decontamination
   - Cleanup oversight
9. Termination
   - Debrief
   - Incident critique
   - Fire prevention
   - After-action report

Isolation is to secure and/or gain control of the entire incident scene. This would include denying entry, setting up initial zones, and so on. *Notification* would address the mayor's directive for notification to other city agencies, and state and federal agencies as well. The list can be extensive.

Identification addresses the attempt to identify the product involved, its properties, name, hazards, container type, and possible impacts on responders, the public, and the environment. *Protective actions* addresses the responders, the public, and the environment. It is accomplished with the use of protective clothing, evacuation, in-place protection, and zones.

Spill control is the process by which the spread of the product is minimized, or stopped. *Leak control* is the technical process of dealing with breach or failure of the container. *Fire control* includes all the methods used to minimize the impact of a fire that involves or threatens to involve the product.

Recovery deals with the post-emergency activities to return the site to as close to normal conditions as possible. *Termination* includes the documenting of information relative to the incident. It also includes review of the plan and a critique of the incident operations to see what worked and what didn't work completely right.

The order in which the strategic goals are listed is not necessarily their priority order. Often the goals are met out of order, or concurrently, and sometimes not every one is required; that is, there may not be a leak and/or fire. Usually several of these goals are pursued simultaneously based on the incident action plan. However, certain goals will have to be achieved before others can be addressed. This is why the incident action plan must be clearly thought out. Following the procedures used for assigning specific units tactical objectives in fire fighting, specific tasks for hazardous materials incidents have also been assigned.

However, unlike other emergency incidents, a hazardous materials incident is often complicated by the lack of easily definable impact on responders, the environment, and property. The mishandling of the incident can result in long-term health and environmental consequences. The plan takes a defensive approach by the initial response until adequate information is obtained and a clearly defined incident action plan is developed. The initial strategy and actions consist of isolating the scene and denying entry while assessing the characteristics of the product(s). This defensive position is appropriate when the responders' further actions are not clearly understood. At a time when the risks and consequences of abating the incident are known and understood, and the necessary resources are on-scene, an offensive action by properly trained and equipped responders can be appropriate.

The purpose of the procedures in the plan is to reduce mishaps, injuries, illnesses, and deaths during the incident. They will also prevent exposures to hazardous materials and minimize future health problems and disabilities that could affect the responders and the general public.

First Responder Operational Objectives

The plan is designed with a system of interconnected elements to achieve given objectives by performing specific functions. Individual responsibilities are designated to provide an organization that will accomplish the necessary tactical activities and provide the proper supervision and control at the incident. It is important that *command, control, coordination*, and *communication* be established immediately on arrival.

The specific assignments to be given to the initial response team are designed to isolate the incident, notify incoming resources of potential hazards, gather preliminary information on the site and the product, and ensure protective measures are taken for responders, the public, and the environment. The specific assignments for units are further broken down to tasks assigned to individual teams within the company. A key point is the establishment of a buddy system. Members of a company are formed into teams of two, each equipped with a communications system (radio). This allows assistance to a partner if he or she becomes in trouble. Each can observe the partner for signs of exposure and notify the command post if emergency help is needed. The buddy system also permits periodic checking of the integrity of a partner's protective clothing and equipment.

The *communications system* is necessary for the accountability and safety of members and to coordinate all actions of responders. It provides for initial and additional information transfer to the incident commander. It allows safety information discovered during survey activities to be passed along. These procedures provide a greater degree of safety and reduce the possibility of spreading contaminants.

The *first arriving ladder company* is responsible for initial identification of hazards and assessment of the 1996 *North American Emergency Response Guidebook* (NAERG) for isolation, evacuation, and protective clothing requirements. The second ladder company is assigned to isolate the incident scene by establishing site access control. This company establishes the initial isolation zone using physical barriers. It confirms the information gathered by the first arriving ladder company for appropriate isolation, evacuation recommendations, and the correct NAERG guide number based on placards, visible markings, chemical names, or preplanning information.

The *first arriving engine company* is assigned water supply. The second arriving engine company is responsible for assisting and coordinating with the second ladder company to control site access. All other units remain together as a unit unless ordered by their officer as directed by the incident commander to perform specific objectives.

These procedures are designed to control the activities of the initial responders, minimize exposures, isolate the contaminants, and establish initial information. The assignments begin to address the first four previously listed strategic goals of the incident commander (isolation, notification, identification, and protective actions).

While the initial response of the NYFD is larger than many others, these initial tasks are required at all haz mat incidents. Other departments must seek and find individual resources and develop procedures to utilize the concepts and apply them to their initial assignment.

As response capabilities are developed, planners need to consider several things: the resources available, what is expected of them, and what level of training is required. All potential responders should be included in the training and plan development. A response will be more effective if you train and drill together. If you familiarize the individuals and agencies in your community with each other and develop procedures through simulations, responding effectively to an incident will be easier.

Safe Work Practices

To ensure a strong safety awareness and enforce safe procedures at an incident, a list of general procedures as well as specific functions within the control zones were developed. The procedures identify the practices that must always be followed and those that must never occur in contaminated areas of the incident. Separate procedures should be developed for the *exclusion area* (hot zone) and the *contamination reduction area* (warm zone). The members of the hazardous materials team contribute to the development of these procedures as the overall plan is developed.

Hazardous Materials Unit

The hazardous materials unit responds to releases or potential releases for the purpose of stopping or controlling them. They are trained to assume an offensive, more aggressive role than the initial response units; they will approach the point of release. Their duties require a more direct technical knowledge of the various substances they may be called on to contain. Their training includes knowledge of procedures for the use of chemical protective clothing, survey equipment, and procedures for containing a chemical, biological, or radiological hazard and decontamination.

Upon arrival at the incident, the hazardous materials unit reports to the incident commander and is briefed on the actions taken by the initial responders and the information that is available. They review this data and recommend the necessary modifications to the initial isolation area. At this point an integrated incident action plan (IAP) is formulated. It is a step-by-step plan used to implement the necessary activities to control the incident. The incident action plan will contain the following:

1. Strategic goals
2. Tactical and control objectives
3. Assignments
4. General safety precautions
5. Weather conditions
6. Site diagram
7. Communications and medical plan

The IAP is developed based on the incident commander's strategic goals. It gives all responders direction and provides the guidelines to accomplish assigned missions in the safest, most efficient manner possible. It describes the activities to be performed by all responders. As with all plans, however, IAPs must constantly be evaluated and modified if necessary.

The hazardous materials unit develops a site safety plan, conducts monitoring, and will establish the control zones, decontamination, and access control points. The operations of the hazardous materials unit is incorporated into the department's Incident Command System. Their functions include maintaining a safety perimeter around the hazard utilizing zones, entry into the hot zone, and decontamination in the warm zone. Specific responsibilities are assigned to individuals who make up the team. They are supervised by the hazardous materials group supervisor.

The hazardous materials unit develops the hazardous materials portion of the IAP and has input into other portions of the action plan. The functions assigned to the hazardous materials team expand on the activities on the initial response units, and address spill control, leak control, and fire control (previously listed strategic goals) as required.

Again, the purpose is to minimize potential contamination of responders, the public, and the environment. The functions performed control the activities and movement of people at an incident. The degree of control necessary depends on site characteristics, site size, and the surrounding area.

Decontamination

At every incident involving hazardous materials there is the possibility that response personnel and equipment may become contaminated. A contaminant poses a threat not only to the person contaminated but to other personnel who may come in contact with that individual or subsequent contact with contaminated equipment. Procedures have been established to limit cross-contamination and to properly dispose of contaminated materials. Decontamination procedures were put in place and are established upon arrival at the incident. A decontamination unit was established and personnel trained in decontamination procedures.

To address the situation, whenever contamination is suspected the procedures are implemented. Initially the incident commander and the hazardous materials unit establish a decontamination zone. The decontamination unit is called and department EMS personnel also respond to provide medical evaluation. The Department of Environmental Protection provides technical information and analysis of samples. The potential contaminated clothing and equipment are impounded and isolated. Members who may have suffered a possible exposure shower receive a medical evaluation at the scene.

Clothing and equipment potentially contaminated are transported to a departmental facility for decontamination and cleaning. This procedure was established for the health and safety of members and their families. It has proven very cost effective.

Recovery and Termination

Recovery is the goal of utilizing the necessary resources to return the site to the safest condition possible. There are times when it may not be possible to return it to the condition of safety that existed prior to the incident. To accomplish this may require a large amount of resources depending on the incident size and complexity. There may be a need for representatives from shippers, contractors, and chemical companies as well as state, local, and federal officials. The efforts of all these individuals and organizations will have to be controlled and monitored. This is where the on-scene coordinator from the Mayor's Office of Emergency Management will assist the incident commander in overseeing the activities required. At the termination phase of the incident an analysis of the incident will be conducted. A critique is conducted including a review of the actions taken, and an after-action report is completed with recommendations.

Incident Critique

The critique uses the plan as a benchmark for review; it focuses on reinforcing the most appropriate and effective actions at the incident while identifying any inappropriate, expedient, or impulsive activities. What is learned from the critique is then plugged back into the plan to improve the response to the next incident. In short, planning, response, and critique form a feedback loop. Lessons learned contribute to long-range planning; they strengthen the plan and are incorporated into it after they are reviewed for compliance with laws and regulations, applicability, and consequences. Conversely, similar lessons learned from mistakes at other operations should be a warning sign that training or reinforcement is necessary.

Too often, plans and post-operations critiques turn out to be (most times, unconsciously) post hoc defenses or justifications for actions taken, rather than a candid assessment of any and all problems or mistakes made. Closer analysis may reveal valuable information and identify flaws in the plan that can be fixed, before injuries or exposures take place.

Program Support and Services

The department developed a training and certification program to ensure effectiveness of the plan. The training program objectives for the Emergency Response Plan are referenced from 29 *CFR* 1910.120.(q) (6), and NFPA 472, *Standard for Professional Competence of Responders to Hazardous Materials Incidents*. The department has added specifics to these functions where necessary to address local concerns. The following are the minimum levels of training for personnel of the department.

First responder—Awareness level:
  Fire prevention personnel and fire dispatchers

First responder—Operational level:
  Engine and ladder company, EMT personnel, and chiefs

Haz mat technicians:
  Haz mat response team

Haz mat specialist:
  Haz mat team officer

On-scene incident commander:
  Chief officers

All emergency responders receive initial training of 24 hours on the department's emergency response plan. They receive annual refresher training of sufficient content and duration to maintain their competencies, or shall demonstrate competency at least yearly. The training or competency for each responder is recorded, along with the methodology used to demonstrate competency [29 *CFR* 1910.120 (q) (8) (II)].

A medical surveillance program in accordance with 29 *CFR* 1910.120 (q) (9) is provided to members of the haz mat team and any other personnel who exhibit signs or symptoms that may have resulted from exposures to hazardous materials during the course of an incident.

The department has instituted a written personnel protective equipment program that complies with 29 *CFR* 1910.120 (q)(10), dictating when chemical protective clothing will be used by the haz mat team members. It includes the policy procedures and guidelines for their use.

The department also participates yearly in exercising the city's Hazardous Materials Contingency Plan. This also provides the department with an opportunity to test the Emergency Response Plan under simulated situations and make improvements from any lessons learned.

THE HAZ MAT PLAN IN ACTION: A BROMINE SPILL IN BROOKLYN

By Captain Peter Stuebe, Hazardous Materials Unit, FDNY

The true test of any plan is not how well it looks on paper, but how well it works when actually implemented at an incident. A recent chemical spill in New York City demonstrated that the Fire Department Emergency Response Plan (ERP) does indeed make the transition from a document that works on paper to a plan that works in practice. At this particular incident, which occurred in Brooklyn, an alarm was initially transmitted for a reported chemical spill on the sixth floor of a factory building, with reports of people overcome.

A normal first alarm assignment consisting of two engines, two ladders, and a battalion chief was assigned, and the Bureau of Emergency Medical Services (EMS) was also dispatched. Hazardous Materials Company 1 was also assigned, at the discretion of the Brooklyn supervising dispatcher, due to the reported chemical nature of the incident.

Upon arrival, the first-due engine took its designated position at a hydrant, to supply water if called for. As fire fighters were hooking up, several employees from the sixth floor approached them, coughing and complaining of irritated, burning eyes. The information obtained from the employees confirmed some type of a chemical spill. The engine officer then transmitted the radio code signal 10-80 Code 2, thus notifying all other responding units of a hazardous materials release. (Additionally, on the 10-80 Code 2 signal a deputy chief, the Safety Operating Battalion, and the Field Communications Unit were assigned.) The exposed civilians were initially isolated and given treatment by flushing eyes with water, which is standard treatment for an eye exposure.

The first-due truck company donned bunker gear and SCBA and proceeded to the reported location on the sixth floor. The ERP calls for the first-due truck to break up into two radio-equipped teams, with the first team assigned to attempt to identify the material, using all available information and clues. The information from both the exposed employees outside and those still in the building indicated that the spilled material was bromine. The facility employees reported that two boxes, each containing four one-gallon bottles of liquid bromine, had fallen and some bottles had broken, although nobody knew how many had broken. They also stated that as per facility procedures, they had covered the spilled material with soda ash, in an attempt to neutralize the spill. This information was then communicated to the first truck's second team.

The second team accessed the 1996 *North American Emergency Response Guidebook* which is carried in every apparatus. The NAERG listed toxicity as the major hazard of bromine. Other information contained in the NAERG warned that bromine is an inhalation and skin-contact hazard; it does not burn but may act as oxidizer; and since structural fire-fighting clothing is not effective for bromine releases, specific chemical protective clothing is necessary. Additionally, the entry is highlighted, meaning that the user must go the "Table of Initial Isolation and Protective Action Distances" because the vapors may be toxic/poisonous by inhalation. This information was verified by the second-due truck's team, who used the NAERG to crosscheck the findings of the first truck's second team, as per the ERP.

Based on this information, the IC ordered the evacuation of the entire building, with the two truck companies performing primary and secondary searches. While there was a risk to personnel entering the building without chemical protective clothing, the IC decided that the potential benefit was worth the risk. The building was fully occupied, except for the those people who had self-evacuated from the sixth floor. The remaining life hazard made the risk justifiable, with the fire fighters getting a great deal of protection from their SCBA.

After the evacuation was completed and all personnel accounted for, access to the building was controlled and no one permitted to enter the building. The police department was utilized to control building access and to control street traffic.

EMS paramedics were able to give advanced treatment to the exposed civilians, once the identity of the product was confirmed. Because of the severity of his symptoms, one person was subsequently transported to a hospital.

Initially, a command post had been established in front of the building, but the heavier-than-air bromine vapors descended through the building and could be felt at the doorway to the building. It was quickly relocated across the street. This location was under the elevated section of the Brooklyn-Queens Expressway, which afforded a good view of the entire building, and would provide protection from an impending rainstorm. Representatives from all other responding agencies reported in here, which included EMS, the Department of Environmental Protection, the Police Department, and the Mayor's Office of Emergency Operations.

At this point, while there was still a real threat to property and the environment from the released bromine, all occupants had been removed and accounted for. The injured civilians were being treated, the building had been evacuated, and all FD personnel removed from the building. Since the information contained in the ERG stated that structural fire-fighting clothing would not provide effective protection and that chemical protective clothing was necessary, there would be no further benefit from risking exposure to first responders. The first responders had completed their duties, the first four of the IC's eight strategic goals (isolation, notification, identification, and protective actions). The situation had stabilized, and the decision was made to wait for Haz Mat 1, which had an estimated response time of twenty minutes.

Upon arrival of Haz Mat 1, a briefing was held with the incident commander, all officers on the scene, the members of Haz Mat 1, representatives of other city agencies, and facility personnel. It was determined that Haz Mat 1 personnel would have to make an entry to determine the situation on the sixth floor and what mitigation procedures would be necessary.

After checking chemical clothing compatibility, setting up decontamination, and monitoring vital signs, the first entry was made. It was discovered that only two gallons of bromine had broken, but being an oxidizer, it caused the corrugated cartons to begin burning. The heat of the fire had melted the plastic caps off two more bottles. Once the situation was known, another discussion was held to determine what needed to be done.

After deciding on their tactics, Haz Mat 1 personnel then made several more entries to place the bromine and soda ash mixture into overpack drums. These entries were all performed wearing gas/vapor-tight suits. When the overpacking was completed, the drums were brought down to the street. They were not sealed, because the reacting bromine and soda ash continued to give off heat and carbon dioxide, and the resultant pressure could cause a failure of the drum.

At this point, the mitigation was complete, and the incident passed from an emergency situation to a final cleanup operation. Jurisdiction was then transferred to the Department of Environmental Protection, as called for by the ERP, to oversee the return of the site to its previous condition. For the fire department, this meant the recovery and termination phase of the operation. Units then began the process of repacking gear and "taking up."

At this particular incident involving a bromine spill, the first arriving units responded to the scene and demonstrated a solid understanding of their roles in the plan by carrying out their pre-designated tasks and working together under the incident commander's direction.

Because of this, a potentially life-threatening release was mitigated with no exposures sustained by fire department personnel. The civilian injuries that did occur were prior to FD arrival, with no additional civilian injuries occurring once the FD arrived and took control.

Looking Back—Lessons Learned

One of the reasons for the success of this operation was the effective execution of prior training received by the responding companies. All line units in the New York City fire department have been trained to the operations level in haz mat response. This includes training on the Emergency Response Plan, focusing on the specific functions of each member of each responding company.

The ERP designates specific functions based on the assignment of each person. For example, the first-due engine officer and chauffeur are responsible for establishing a water supply, while two members of the first-due truck are responsible for product identification. No matter which position a member is assigned each tour, he or she is trained in the responsibilities involved with each position. The only factors that will vary involve which position one is assigned and whether the unit arrives first- or second-due at an incident. Part of the training also includes getting responders to realize that a haz mat incident is not "business as usual." A cautious mindset will prevent responders from operating beyond the limits of their training and personal protective equipment, allowing them to accomplish their functions safely. Training in the ERP also helps to prevent "free-lancing," which should not occur during an incident that is managed with an effective incident command system.

SUPPLEMENT 9

City of Sacramento/Sacramento Fire Department Hazardous Materials Emergency Response Plan, 1997

Editor's Note: The following plan is presented as one example of a metropolitan haz mat plan with an emphasis on mutual aid to surrounding communities. This plan meets the requirements established in NFPA 471, 472, and 473 as presented in this handbook. However, as presented here the plan has been edited for length and applicability for areas outside of California alone. The section numbers found in the original plan were removed from the version presented here to avoid confusion with the various sections of the NFPA documents in this handbook. For a complete copy of the plan, please contact the Sacramento Fire Department, Hazardous Materials Division, 1231 I Street, Room 401, Sacramento, CA 95814.

PLANNING BASIS

Purpose

To establish an organization to mitigate hazardous materials incidents within the City Limits of Sacramento and on mutual aid hazardous materials incidents outside the City Limits of Sacramento.

Objectives

1. To describe operational concepts, organization, and support systems required to implement the plan
2. To identify authority, responsibility, and actions of federal, state, local, private industry, and utility agencies necessary to minimize damage to human health, natural systems, property, and to aid in the mitigation of the hazard
3. To establish an operational structure that has the ability to function not only within the City of Sacramento, but also on any mutual aid call where Sacramento City Fire Department equipment responds to a hazardous materials incident outside of the City Limits of Sacramento
4. To define responsibilities and authorities of Sacramento Fire Department Hazardous Materials Response Team officers who have been trained to handle hazardous materials incidents
5. To establish lines of authority and management for any hazardous material incident in any jurisdiction having authority
6. To establish and provide an overall response plan that adheres to and addresses the provisions of California Code of Regulations (CCR), Section 5192 (which is identical to Title 29 CFR Section 1910.120), that affect the operations and functions of the fire service and hazardous materials response teams who will or might be engaged in various mitigation activities at the scene of a hazardous materials incident

ADMINISTRATION

Scope

Geographical Factors. This plan applies to all hazardous materials incidents which occur within the jurisdictional boundaries of the Sacramento Fire Department; any incident occurring within response contract jurisdictional boundaries; and any mutual aid request to any location or agency outside the jurisdictional boundaries of the Sacramento Fire Department, response contract jurisdictional boundaries, and the County of Sacramento.

The Hazards Factor. Includes actual or the threat of fires, spills, leaks, ruptures, container stress or failure, contamination, pollution, or any other threat to life safety, property, or the environment involving hazardous materials.

The Hazardous Materials Factor. The hazardous material itself may include but not be limited to: explosives, flammables, combustibles, compressed gases, cryogenics, poisons, toxics, inhalation hazards, irritants, reactive and oxidizing agents, radioactive materials, corrosives, carcinogenics, etiological and biological agents, ORMs, hazardous substance, hazardous waste, or any combination thereof, or any material that may pose a hazard to health and/or the environment in the opinion of the Incident Commander and/or Officer of the Hazardous Materials Response Team.

The Circumstances Factor. This plan applies to any hazardous material incident associated with any mode of transportation, any industrial process, storage or storage sites, any waste disposal procedure, manufacturing, or usage, abandonment, and any illegal usage and/or inappropriate discharge or disposal.

Authority

1. Charter of the City of Sacramento
2. Sacramento City Code, Chapter 15, Article 2
3. Uniform Fire Code: Articles 1 through 10; Article 79; Article 80
4. California Government Code: Chapter 7, Division 1, Title 2
5. California Health and Safety Code: Sections 25115 and 2517, and Sections 2560 through 25610
6. California Vehicle Code
7. California State Office of Emergency Services Fire and Rescue Mutual Aid Plan

References

1. California State Hazardous Materials Incident Contingency Plan
2. California State Oil Spill Contingency Plan
3. California State Radiological Emergency Assistance Plan
4. California Code of Regulations, Section 5192
5. Federal Response Plan
6. Sacramento County Hazardous Materials Emergency Response Plan
7. Sacramento City/Sacramento County Hazardous Materials Response Contract

HAZARDOUS MATERIALS INCIDENT CLASSIFICATION (LEVELS)

There are three (3) levels of hazardous materials incident classification. The five elements below are the basis used for the establishment of the concept of classifying hazardous materials incidents into the appropriate levels. These criteria include:

(a) Level of *technical expertise* required to abate the incident
(b) Extent of local, state, and federal government, and private industry *involvement required* to assist in abating the hazard
(c) Extent of *evacuation* of civilians
(d) Extent of *injuries and/or deaths* related to the hazardous materials incident
(e) Extent and involvement of *decontamination* procedures required

Level I Incident (Known as a Level I HMI)

Spills, leaks, ruptures, damaged containers and/or fires involving hazardous materials which can be contained, extinguished, and/or abated utilizing equipment, supplies, and resources immediately available to the first responders (FRO) of the fire department having jurisdiction; and

The incident can properly be handled by fire department personnel whose qualifications are limited to and do not exceed the scope of training explained in CCR Section 5192(q) with reference to *First Responder*, and as a minimum are trained to *First Responder Operational* (FRO) in accordance with NFPA 472 (National Fire Protection Association standard); and

Hazardous materials incident which may require the removal and evacuation of civilians within the perimeter of incident scene isolation; and

Hazardous materials incident which does not exceed the necessity to utilize standard structural/flammable liquid protective equipment immediately available to the first responder.

Level II Incident (Known as a Level II HMI)

A hazardous materials incident which may require the use of any kind of specialized protective equipment, tool, or knowledge not available to and beyond the scope of the first responder of the agency having jurisdiction; and/or

A hazardous materials incident which can only be identified, tested, sampled, contained, extinguished, and/or abated utilizing the expertise and resources of the Sacramento Fire Department Hazardous Materials Response Team; and/or

A hazardous materials incident which may require the removal and evacuation of civilians within the area of the fire department having jurisdiction which may encompass several buildings; and/or

Fires involving hazardous materials that, due to the complexities of the chemical involved, are permitted to burn for a controlled period of time or are allowed to consume themselves, or which may require special extinguishing techniques and objectives; and/or

The incident can only be properly handled by fire department personnel whose qualifications meet or exceed the scope of training explained in CCR Section 5192(q) with reference to *Hazardous Materials Specialist*, and as a minimum are trained to *Hazardous Materials Technician/Specialist* (HMT/HMS) in accordance with NFPA 472.

Level III Incident (Known as a Level III HMI)

Hazardous materials incident which, in the opinion of the Incident Commander of the agency having jurisdiction, or the Officer of the Sacramento Fire Department Hazardous Materials Response Team, requires at least two Sacramento Fire Department Hazardous Materials Response Teams on scene; and/or

The Sacramento Fire Department De-Con Team is required on scene for HMRT incident support, and/or civilians or personnel have become contaminated; and/or

Hazardous materials incident can only be contained and/or abated only by utilizing the highly specialized equipment, services, or supplies available from special municipal, environmental, and industrial response personnel who are in support of the activities of the HMRT. Such equipment, techniques, and qualified personnel are in excess of or are in addition to those available from the on-scene HMRT; and/or

Fires involving hazardous materials that are allowed to burn due to the ineffectiveness or dangers of the use of any kind of extinguishing agent, or the unavailability of the proper extinguishing agent, or the material is highly reactive, water-reactive or may be prone to sudden polymerization; and/or there is a real threat of large container failure or an explosion, detonation, BLEVE or container failure has already occurred; and/or

Hazardous materials incident which requires evacuation of civilians from a large geographical area, or evacuation has extended across jurisdictional boundaries; and/or there are serious civilian injuries and/or deaths as a result of the hazardous material incident; and/or

The hazardous materials incident has become one of a multi-agency involvement.

DISPATCH PROCEDURES FOR HAZ MAT INCIDENTS

Within Jurisdiction of Sacramento Fire Department

Dispatch of equipment to a reported hazardous materials incident shall be as follows:

Level I HMI (First Responder Operational capability)

Initial dispatch: One Engine Co.
(as a First Responder)

Level II HMI (HMRT is required to the HMT/HMS Training Level)

Initial dispatch: One Engine Co.
(if not already on scene)
One HMRT
One BC
One investigator

Upgrade of a Level I HMI to a Level II HMI (if engine is already on scene)

Upgrade dispatch: One HMRT
One BC
One investigator

Level III HMI (Multiple HMRT or De-Con is required on scene)

Upgrade of a Level II HMI to a Level III HMI (Level II response is already on scene)

Upgrade dispatch: One additional HMRT
One De-Con Team
One additional BC

Within Response Contract Jurisdictions

(County of Sacramento and West Sacramento Fire Department)

Level I HMI (Handled by fire department having jurisdiction on a first responder level)

Initial dispatch: One engine co. (of the fire department having jurisdiction, as first responder)

Level II HMI (Request for HMRT from outside agency already on scene)

Initial dispatch: One HMRT (From City of Sacramento)
One BC (Or Command Unit) (From fire department having jurisdiction)

Level III HMI (Multiple HMRT or De-Con is required on scene, request from outside agency or HMRT already on scene)

Upgrade dispatch: One Additional HMRT (From City of Sacramento)
One De-Con Team (From City of Sacramento)
One BC (From City of Sacramento)
Additional units from fire department having jurisdiction to meet their protocols

INCIDENT COMMAND AND SCENE MANAGEMENT

Scene Management

Scene management (as provided by the agency having incident command responsibility) shall include identification of incident resources and needs, the procurement of these resources, and the coordination of the resources so as to abate the incident and protect life, property, and the environment.

Scene management shall not include being responsible for the detailed direction of technical or specialized procedures, but instead shall ensure that these procedures are followed and implemented when suggested.

Scene management shall include a communications function to assure all decisions are made with respect given to technical expertise, training capability, and real practical experience. All decisions made with regard to intervention criteria must be approved by the HMRT.

Good scene management decisions cannot and shall not interfere with intervention criteria and protocols suggested by the HMRT.

Incident Commander

The position of incident commander shall be instituted at all Level II and Level III hazardous materials incidents.

The *incident commander* (IC) shall be responsible to provide all management and operational support directed toward the containment and mitigation of the hazards at the scene of a hazardous materials incident.

The IC shall coordinate and direct within its jurisdiction and responsibility all activities in support of rescue, first aid, product identification, scene stabilization, overall scene management, agency notification, scene isolation, personnel protection, safety, decontamination, investigation, and all enforcement of all applicable laws, regulations, fire department procedures, and Sacramento Fire Department HMRT protocols.

The IC shall assure that the captain of the HMRT will be provided with liaison to the incident commander, and will support the establishment of the Haz Mat Group portion of the incident command system within which the HMRT functions and coordinates.

Unified Incident Command

The policy of *unified incident command*, as prescribed by FIRESCOPE ICS HM-120 / 1996, will be practiced and shall be adopted at the scene of each hazardous materials incident by the IC of the agency having jurisdiction, and by the Sacramento Fire Department Hazardous Materials Response Team.

Unified incident command shall consist of and include the following designated agencies at all hazardous materials incidents:

(a) Law enforcement agency having jurisdiction
(b) Fire department having jurisdiction
(c) County health agency representative having jurisdiction

Provision of Incident Command

The position of incident commander shall be provided by the agency having incident command responsibilities for hazardous materials incidents.

City of Sacramento

(a) Surface Streets, and Private Property—*Sacramento Fire Department*
(b) Freeways, State Roads, State Property—*California Highway Patrol*

County of Sacramento

(a) Private Property—*Sacramento County Sheriff*
(b) Freeways, State Roads, County Roads, State Property—*California Highway Patrol*

City of West Sacramento

(a) Surface Streets, and Private Property—*West Sacramento Fire Department*
(b) Freeways, State Roads, State Property—*California Highway Patrol*

Jurisdictions Beyond County of Sacramento

(a) Surface Streets, and Private Property—It will be presumed by the HMRT that the *Sheriff's Office having jurisdiction* shall be functioning as the IC unless indicated otherwise upon arrival.
(b) Freeways, State Roads, State Property—*California Highway Patrol*

INCIDENT COMMAND OPERATIONAL FLOW CHARTS

Level I Hazardous Materials Incident

Typical incident command structure for a first responder–managed hazardous materials incident. *(See Figure S9-1.)*

Level II Hazardous Materials Incident

Typical incident command structure beyond a first responder–managed hazardous materials incident, and must include at least one HMRT response. *(See Figure S9-2.)* Shown in Figure S9-2 are the most used positions of the FIRESCOPE Unified Incident Command System, for a typical Level II hazardous materials incident.

Level III Hazardous Materials Incident

Typical incident command structure beyond a first responder–managed hazardous materials incident, and beyond a Level II incident, and must include at least one additional HMRT and a De-Con response. *(See Figure S9-3.)*

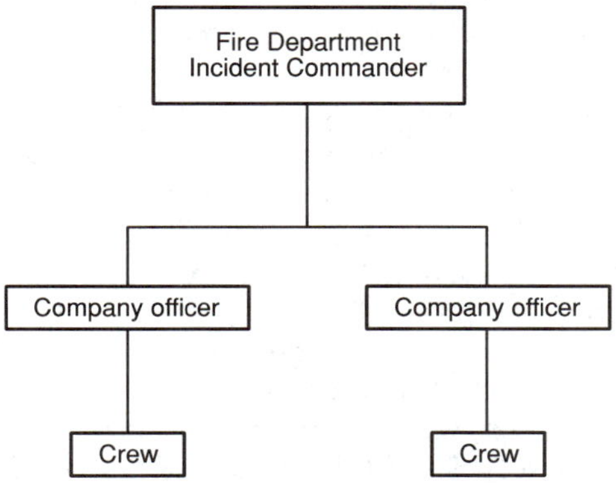

Figure S9-1 *Incident command structure for Level I hazardous materials incident.*

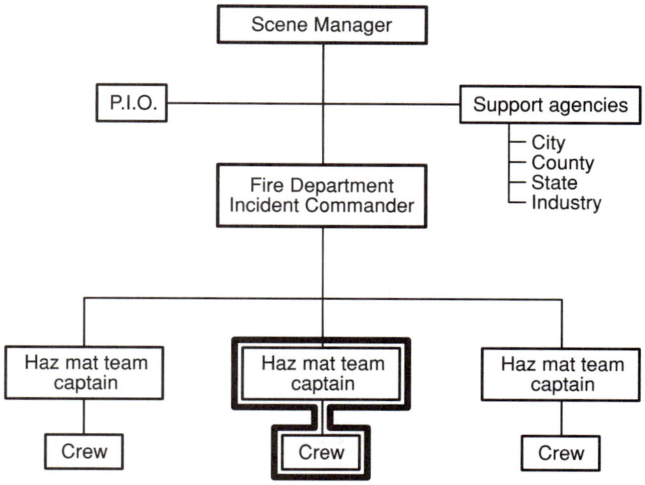

Figure S9-2 *Incident command structure for Level II hazardous materials incident.*

HAZARDOUS MATERIALS RESPONSE TEAM (HMRT) EMERGENCY RESPONSE PROGRAM

The Sacramento Fire Department Hazardous Materials Response Program consists of:

(a) Three (3) specially trained and equipped "four member" haz mat teams, referred in this document as HMRT
(b) One specially trained and equipped decontamination team, referred in this document as De-Con
(c) One Division Chief of Hazardous Materials
(d) One Captain, Hazardous Materials Coordinator

Response Discipline

Standard Response Service. The HMRT provides emergency response service to the City of Sacramento and the jurisdiction of the Sacramento Fire Department, which encompasses 134 square miles.

Contract Response Service. The HMRT provides emergency response service to the County of Sacramento, a geographical area which encompasses 1,000 square miles, in accordance with the Sacramento County Hazardous Materials Response Contract. Response into the County of Sacramento is at no cost to the respective county fire districts.

The HMRT provides emergency response service to the City of West Sacramento, a geographical area which encompasses 21 square miles, in accordance with the West Sacramento City Hazardous Materials Response Contract.

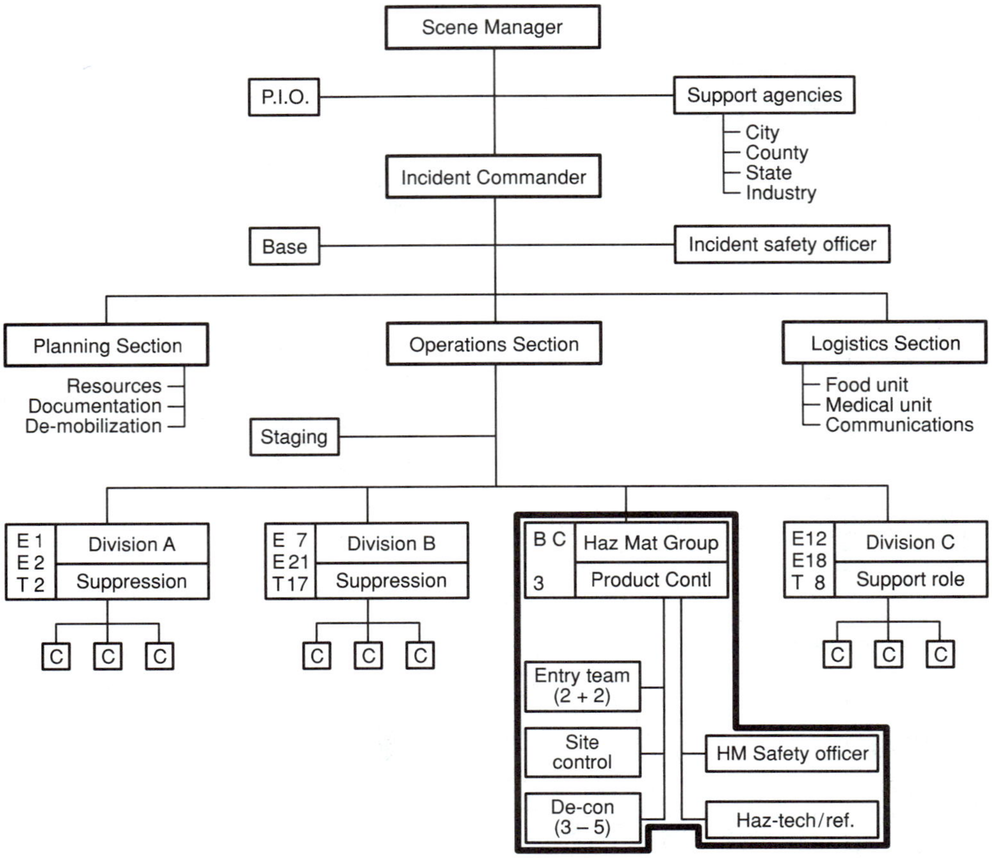

NOTE: The module highlighted by a border is that portion of the incident command system that the hazardous materials response team shall always implement. This portion of the incident command structure shall be implemented by and shall function with Sacramento fire department hazardous materials members only.

Figure S9-3 *Incident command structure for Level III hazardous materials incident.*

Non-Contract Response Service Within 50-Mile Radius. The Sacramento Fire Department HMRT is available to respond to any other county to a pre-approved distance by the City Council not to exceed 50-mile radius on *"Mutual Aid."* This distance is measured from the interchange of I-80 / HWY 99 / HWY 50. This response into any county other than the County of Sacramento will be based on a current fee structure chargeable to the agency requesting assistance.

Request for this mutual aid is made in standard fashion through the Sacramento Fire Dispatch Center.

Recovery costs of response and time on scene will be based on prevailing cost of departmental operation on an hourly rate. It will be the policy of the Sacramento Fire Department to bill the requesting agency for services rendered; however, the ultimate responsible party is that who directly contributed to the cause of the hazardous materials incident. (See the section entitled Financial Responsibility.)

Non-Contract Response Service Exceeding 50-Mile Radius. The Sacramento Fire Department HMRT is available to respond to any distance exceeding 50 miles when requested by an outside agency on *"Mutual Aid"* (for example, by OES or CHP).

This response must be requested utilizing the standard California Office of Emergency Services Mutual Aid System. Request may be made by contacting the OES IV Coordinator and requesting said response. Following this, contact with the Sacramento Fire Department Duty Chief must be achieved. This response will be based on a current fee structure chargeable to the agency requesting assistance.

Mutual Aid response request can also be requested from California Office of Emergency Services, Fire and Rescue Division, when such a request is for movement of an HMT/HMS TYPE I Haz Mat Response Team to any part of California, such as during a disaster situation.

Equipment Discipline

All equipment, instruments, protective clothing, tools, and kits assigned to an HMRT *are not for use* by any other individual or agency. They are not to be loaned to or used by any other fire fighter, fire department, civilian or agency without the express consent of the HMRT Captain on scene.

Decision to allow usage by an individual from an outside agency shall be based on the individual's qualification training and certification, and said certification to be authenticated on scene only by the Captain of the HMRT or the Chief Officer of the Haz Mat Group.

All equipment, instruments, protective clothing, tools, and kits used and which are damaged, including that which might have to be discarded or destroyed at a hazardous materials incident, will be inventoried and documented for the purpose of cost recovery. This will be a concern for every hazardous materials incident.

Basic Incident Discipline

When appropriate it shall be the responsibility of the HMRT Captain to initiate and place into position at all hazardous materials incidents the following actions:

(a) Upon arrival, identify themselves as the Officer of the HMRT to all other agencies on scene including the Incident Commander

(b) Immediately arrange for a briefing with the key lead agency representatives on scene

(c) Function within the FIRESCOPE HM-120 Incident Command System, and establish when necessary the Haz Mat Group

(d) Modify as necessary the boundaries for the Warm Zone (Limited Access Zone), or identify and mark if not yet established

(e) Identify and mark as necessary the boundaries for the Hot Zone (Restricted Zone)

(f) Determine if a Level III HMI is required to provide appropriate staffing to function within the guidelines of FIRESCOPE HM-120, and CCR Section 5192(q), and initiate a Level III dispatch

1. Request for a Level III HMI upgrade can be made enroute by the Captain of the responding HMRT to any Level II hazardous materials incident
2. Request for a Level III HMI upgrade can be made by the on-scene Incident Commander or a member of the Unified Incident Command. This includes the on-scene First Responder Officer of the fire department having jurisdiction, the California Highway Patrol, the Sacramento County Sheriff, or the Sacramento County Health Representative

(g) Assign a "Recorder" to maintain a written log of all pertinent on-scene activities and decisions. It is preferable that this person be obtained from an on-scene engine company so as not to deplete the staffing of the on-scene HMRT

(h) Establish and assign a Site Access Control Leader as necessary in accordance with FIRESCOPE HM-120 ICS

(i) Establish and assign an Entry Team and Leader as necessary in accordance with FIRESCOPE HM-120 ICS

(j) Establish and assign a De-Con Team and Leader as necessary in accordance with FIRESCOPE HM-120 ICS

Initially, upon arrival the HMRT Captain shall work with, and be subordinate to, the Incident Commander. If it becomes necessary to establish the position within the incident command system known as the Hazardous Materials Group, the HMRT Captain will work with the IC to determine who would be qualified to function in that position. Later, when another individual can be assigned to this position (i.e., another Command Chief Officer appropriately trained), the HMRT Captain shall work with, and be subordinate to, the Hazardous Materials Group Supervisor.

Agency Notification Responsibilities of HMRT

The HMRT shall determine what governmental, industrial, utility, or other outside agency(s) need to be *notified* of the incident. The exact number and type of agencies that require *notification only* shall be dependent upon the nature and magnitude of the incident, and the jurisdictional location of the incident.

Note: An "outside agency" is any agency other than the fire department having jurisdiction.

A listing of all agencies that require *notified only* shall be compiled by the HMRT Captain for each incident. This list shall be made available to the Incident Commander and the Hazardous Materials Group Supervisor so that contact of these agencies is coordinated. It should be suggested by the Captain of the HMRT that permission be given by the IC on scene to allow the HMRT to have the authority to initiate these contacts.

Note: The HMRT may be in need of specific and technical information from various sources and contacts. It is prudent to allow the HMRT to establish the required contacts, as they will be in the best position to explain the circumstances of the incident, and to ask the necessary technical questions.

The HMRT *must contact* the Office of Emergency Services (OES) for every Level II and Level III HMI that involved some sort of intervention, sample taking, or testing. The OES must be briefed on the incident, and shall issue a "CHMIR" code number to the HMRT.

Notification of all state and federal agencies can be accomplished by making one call to the California Office of Emergency Services. Requests to have representatives of various state or federal agencies return contacts to the HMRT shall be done at this time.

Ensure that the Office of Emergency Services is always notified of the following regarding each hazardous materials incident:

(a) *Any* incident involving spillage of a suspected or known hazardous material that has *contacted the ground*
(b) *Any* incident involving leakage or venting of a flammable, toxic, corrosive, or reactive substance into the atmosphere
(c) *Any* incident involving radioactive or etiological materials with or without package or container failure
(d) *Any* incident that involves civilians that have, or suspected to have, been *injured or contaminated* due to the nature of the incident
(e) *Any* incident that involves a *wildlife kill* or the eminent threat of a wildlife kill.

Determine what governmental, industrial, utility or outside agencies need to be *summoned to the scene* of the incident. The specific agencies that need to be summoned to the scene shall be dependent upon the nature and magnitude of the incident, the jurisdictional responsibilities, and the legal ramifications that exist or that may become likely.

A listing of all agencies that should be *summoned to the scene* shall be compiled by the HMRT Captain for each hazardous materials incident. This list shall be made available to the Incident Commander and the Hazardous Materials Group Supervisor so that contact of these agencies be coordinated.

Intervention Discipline

Who May Enter Hot Zone During Intervention

1. The Sacramento Fire Department Hazardous Materials Response Team shall have final say as to who will be allowed into a Hot Zone during any intervention activities.

2. When permission has been granted for a specialist to accompany the HMRT entry team into the Hot Zone, these individuals will not be allowed to directly involve themselves in the intervention activity. Decisions as to who may accompany the HMRT into the Hot Zone shall be based on:

(a) Training with regard to hazardous materials, intervention techniques, and chemical protective clothing
(b) Certification with regard to HMT, HMS, or equal training
(c) Expertise and familiarity with regard to systems, plant or device plumbing, emergency procedures, override or bypass functions, off-loading, tank righting, stabilization, neutralization, or any procedure where the trained and certified individual will be acting as a consultant and guide to the members of the HMRT entry team

Who May Assist HMRT in Intervention. Individuals who may be allowed to function as part of the HMRT entry team for the purposes of intervention must themselves be a member of a bonafide hazardous materials emergency response team, meet the criteria in the Intervention Section (Discipline), and be fully familiar with the technical and specialized hazardous materials tools, equipment and protective clothing that comprises a Type I haz mat team.

Who May Enter Hot Zone After Intervention. Specialists may be allowed to enter the Hot Zone only when the existing or potential danger(s) within a Hot Zone have been reduced significantly by the entry team so as to allow for additional activities to proceed that will aid in the total mitigation of the incident and elimination of the dangers.

These activities are specialized to the extent that they are not the function and responsibility of the HMRT, and permission may be given, accompanied by appropriate planning, for individuals who are trained and certified in accordance with the Intervention Section (Discipline) to enter the hot zone for the purpose of effecting and applying activities that will abate the situation.

DECONTAMINATION TEAM (DE-CON)

Response Discipline

The Sacramento Fire Department shall maintain one (1) specially trained and equipped "four member" Decontamination Team *(De-Con Team).*

Response shall be the same as explained in *the dispatch procedures* of this plan.

The De-Con Team shall respond to all Level III hazardous materials incidents.

The De-Con Team shall provide all decontamination support at all Level III HMI incidents. The Captain of the De-Con Team shall assume the ICS position of Decontamination Team Leader, and shall select, designate, and set up the appropriate decontamination corridor based on information provided by the HMRT on scene.

Equipment Discipline

The De-Con Team can provide expertise and special equipment especially prepared for the purpose of decontaminating equipment, tools, personnel, and civilians. This includes a portable "De-Con Trailer" that will respond as part of the De-Con Team at all times.

First Responders, trained to the operational level (FRO), or trained in "First Responder Decontamination," may assist the De-Con Team. This includes setting up the decontamination corridor, placing of the equipment as directed, and assisting with decontamination commensurate with their level of training.

Most FRO have been trained to institute and apply De-Con, which would not involve using any specialized protective clothing beyond their own turnout safety gear.

FRO may participate in FRO level of De-Con and may assist the De-Con team only if the De-Con team leader has ascertained and verified that the suspect contaminant is not a threat to the level of protective clothing worn by the FRO.

FRO trained to "First Responder Decontamination" may assist the De-Con team in instituting and applying a De-Con procedure which would involve using "Splash Protective Clothing," as supplied by the De-Con Team, only if the De-Con Team Leader has ascertained and verified that the suspect contaminant is not a threat to the level of protective clothing worn by the FRO.

Basic Incident Discipline

When appropriate, it shall be the responsibility of the De-Con Captain to initiate and place into position at all hazardous materials incidents the following actions:

(a) Upon arrival, immediately arrange for a briefing with the HMRT Captain
(b) Locate the De-Con Trailer in a safe location and place it into operation as necessary
(c) Be responsible for identifying the location of the De-Con corridor, then getting it set up
(d) Function as the De-Con team for the duration of the incident in accordance with FIRESCOPE HM-120 incident command
(e) Inform the HMRT Captain as to the best recommended method(s) of decontamination suitable for the incident, and the reasons for these recommendations
(f) Inform the HMRT Captain, and the IC, of those items that cannot or should not be decontaminated, and the reasons

Work with, and be subordinate to, the first arriving HMRT Captain, and thereafter the Haz Mat Group supervisor.

CONTROL ZONES

Warm Zone (Limited Access Zone, Yellow Zone)

The *Warm Zone* shall be a designated area to define where some potential or real danger exists with respect to safety and health to the public and harm to the environment.

Identification of the Warm Zone shall be done by the first arriving fire department company officer. Yellow "banner" tape shall be used to identify the boundaries of the Warm Zone.

Access into the Warm Zone shall be controlled as necessary by the Site Access Control Leader. Access shall be limited to only those members of agencies on scene who are appropriately protected and are directly engaged in incident ground activities at the direction of the incident commander, the Hazardous Materials Group supervisor, or the HMRT Captain.

Hot Zone (Restricted Zone, Red Zone)

The *Hot Zone* shall be designated as necessary by the HMRT Captain, and shall be utilized to identify and define an area of exceptional danger or potential danger, including extreme danger to life safety.

Identification of the boundaries of the Hot Zone shall be with the use of red "banner tape" and will be positioned by the HMRT.

Access into the Hot Zone shall be controlled by the Site Access Control Leader. Access shall be allowed only by permission of the HMRT Captain or Entry Team Leader. Only properly protected and equipped members of the HMRT and other designated workers will be allowed to enter the Hot Zone.

An "Entry Point" into the Hot Zone shall be identified by the Site Access Control Team. All entry into the Hot Zone shall be made only at this designated location.

Exiting from the Hot Zone shall be controlled and supervised by the De-Con Team. The De-Con Corridor may become part of the exiting from the Hot Zone.

A log shall be maintained by the Site Access Control Team of all personnel who are allowed to enter the

Hot Zone, including times of entry and inspection of protective clothing.

Decontamination Corridor

The *De-Con Corridor* shall be designated as necessary to establish a controlled environment to decontaminate personnel, civilians, equipment, and tools in an effort to reduce or stop the spread of suspected contamination.

Workers entering into the De-Con Corridor to assist in procedures shall do so only as directed by the De-Con Captain, and only when properly equipped and protected.

Decontamination procedures shall be implemented and executed only by trained members of a Hazardous Materials Response Team or by the De-Con Team, in keeping with the requirements of NFPA Standard 472, Section 4.

ACTIVATION

Activation and application of this Hazardous Materials Emergency Response Plan will occur each time the Sacramento Fire Department receives notification of any Level II or Level III HMI.

Notification and Dispatch Response

For a Level II HMI or a Level III HMI dispatch, the Sacramento Communications Center (Comm Center) shall dispatch the appropriate response according to the dispatch procedures of this document.

The Comm Center shall dispatch the closest available HMRT and Battalion Chief to all Level II HMI.

Response shall be "Code 3" unless specified otherwise during dispatch, or as revised after dispatch.

Location of the teams are as follows:

- HMRT 5 consists of Truck 5 and LP 5, in Battalion One.
- HMRT 7 consists of Truck 7 and LP 7, in Battalion Two.
- HMRT 20 consists of Truck 20 and LP 20, in Battalion Three.
- De-Con 19 consists of Engine 19 and De-Con Trailer 19, in Battalion Three.

Notification of Administrative Officers

Level II HMI: The Comm Center is required to notify:

(a) Haz Mat Coordinator, for all calls
(b) Haz Mat Division Chief, for all calls
(c) The Duty Chief for incidents within the City or County of Sacramento
(d) Alert next up HMRT
(e) Alert Poison Control Center
(f) Sacramento County Health, Environmental Management Division

Level III HMI: The Comm Center shall additionally notify:

(a) Dr. Steve Tharratt
(b) City Fire OEP
(c) County OEP if in Sacramento County
(d) Sacramento County District Attorney's Office
(e) Sacramento County Sheriff's Office, if in Sacramento County
(f) Cal/EPA via California OES, specifically for Kelvin Yamada
(g) Sacramento City Safety Officer
(h) Environmental Crimes Task Force Officer

For Special Call Notification: The Comm Center shall additionally notify, as appropriate for the nature of the call:

(a) Sacramento Area Explosive Ordinance Disposal Team
(b) Sacramento City Police/Sacramento County Sheriff/State of California Department of Justice Drug Lab Task Force
(c) Sacramento County Water Quality Division Chlorine Team

The Comm Center shall advise on the nature of the incident, the type, the magnitude, the location, and the units responding.

Agency Call Lists

The Comm Center shall maintain current telephone contact numbers for all appropriate local and state government agencies.

The Comm Center shall maintain a file of private industry contacts and telephone numbers. These contacts should represent a resource of expertise and abilities beyond the normal scope of public agencies, and can be notified and summoned to the scene to assist in the containment, control, transfer, and removal of the hazardous material.

Upgrade of a Hazardous Materials Incident

In keeping with this plan, the Sacramento County Hazardous Materials Plan, and the FIRESCOPE HM-120 Incident Command system adopted by the Sacramento Fire Department Hazardous Materials Response Team, the following must be administered in order to ensure proper haz mat team dispatch:

The lead officer functioning in the capacity of Incident Commander of the fire department having jurisdiction can upgrade an incident to a Level II HMI and to a Level III HMI.

The lead officer functioning in the capacity of Incident Commander of the law enforcement agency having jurisdiction can upgrade an incident to a Level II HMI and a Level III HMI.

The lead officer representing the Sacramento County Health, Environmental Management Division, can upgrade an incident to a Level II HMI.

IMMEDIATE ON-SCENE ACTIONS

Fire Department First on Scene

Identification. The first fire department unit on scene will usually be a "First Responder" (FRO engine or truck company). They shall determine if hazardous materials are involved in the incident. If confirmed, the company captain must, in a safe manner, attempt to identify:

(a) The type of material involved
(b) The quantity of material involved
(c) The possibility of contamination
(d) The immediate exposure problem
(e) The threat to life safety

This information is to be broadcast via radio to the Comm Center immediately.

If the captain of the first arriving unit determines that hazardous materials are indeed involved, but the incident is a Level I HMI that is within the capabilities of a "First Responder" to handle correctly, they shall:

(a) Inform the Comm Center that the unit on scene can and will handle it
(b) Proceed to handle the incident and mitigate the problem

Scene Isolation. If the captain of the first arriving unit determines that the incident is beyond the capabilities of a "First Responder," the incident shall be upgraded to a Level II HMI. This will initiate the dispatch of a HMRT.

The captain shall also do the following:

(a) Isolate the scene, deny entry
(b) Secure and identify scene using yellow "banner" tape to mark boundaries of the Warm Zone
(c) Assure that crew assignments are within the expertise and limitations of their equipment, protective gear, and training
(d) Begin gathering information regarding the incident and the product
(e) Initiate containment techniques within the scope of their capabilities
(f) Initiate procedures to protect or remove civilians from the immediate area
(g) Identify a Staging Area when appropriate

In all cases, the captain of the first arriving unit shall inform all incoming companies of the situation and the actions being initiated. The captain shall advise the responding HMRT and battalion chief of which access routes they should use when approaching the incident.

In addition to the Level II HMI response, the captain shall determine what other assistance would be necessary to call to the scene, such as:

(a) Additional fire units for staffing and support
(b) Law enforcement units for traffic control, street blockage, civilian control
(c) Sand from the Corporation Yard (or from Cal/Trans if incident is on state highway)
(d) EMS assistance (ambulance) for injured

It is *not advisable* to call for "Life Flight" or other helicopters at a hazardous materials incident because:

(a) High possibility of chemicals or fire being spread over a wide area by the strong backwash of the rotor blades
(b) Unavailability of suitable landing location
(c) Possibility of contamination to helicopter interior, especially when considering transportation of injured

Advantage and Reasons for a Level II HMI. In addition to scrutinizing an incident to determine if intervention may go beyond the capability of the responding FRO, it is important to note what other reasons are also legitimate arguments for elevating an incident to a Level II HMI, even if some intervention can be done at the FRO level:

(a) The need for identifying a suspected unknown to determine or verify its identity
(b) The need to take samples for documentation. Only the HMRT will take samples associated to a haz mat response call (Level I HMI). If samples are contemplated, then the incident should be elevated to a Level II HMI. A separate call for "Fish & Game" or "Sacramento County EMD" without elevating an incident to a Level II HMI circumvents the system, and these agencies rely on HMRT on scene to take samples, and start the "chain of evidence."
(c) The need to determine migration of substance, including sizable quantities of known chemicals (gasoline), through drainage systems, and the protocols of notifying all of the appropriate responsible and regulatory agencies associated with such a case
(d) The need to establish photo documentation by the HMRT. It is possible that what appears to be a

borderline haz mat incident in one part of the city/county actually may be tied to others that have been occurring and for which there is documentation and an investigation is in progress.

Command Post and Battalion Chief. The battalion chief, upon arrival, shall establish a command post location in the most strategically desirable and safe location.

The location of the command post shall be indicated via radio broadcast to the Comm Center.

The battalion chief shall assume the position of incident commander upon arrival at the scene. As necessary, the battalion chief shall also institute other portions of the Incident Command System for the incident, which may include some or all of the following:

(a) Divisions
(b) Groups, including Hazardous Materials Group and Medical Group
(c) Public Information Officer
(d) Incident Safety Officer
(e) *Hazardous Materials Safety Officer* **
(f) *Entry Team and Leader* **
(g) *Site Access Control Team and Leader* **
(h) *De-Con Team and Leader* **

Note: Items marked (**) above, and in *italics*, are positions that must be assigned to HMT/ HMS personnel only.

Staging. The location of *staging location* shall be established as necessary outside of the anticipated hazard area and outside of the Warm Zone. This area and its resources shall be coordinated by assigned personnel.

The staging location is to be transmitted to the Comm Center as soon as possible, and all responding units dispatched to this incident shall report to staging unless otherwise directed during response.

Fire Department Not First on Scene

When another agency is first on scene of a hazardous materials incident (usually law enforcement or County Health Officer) prior to the arrival of the fire department, it will be incumbent upon the first arriving fire department officer to establish contact and communications with that agency.

The first fire department officer on scene shall ascertain, if possible, what level the incident is. If it is a Level II HMI, the fire officer shall call for the proper dispatch. The fire department officer shall then proceed to gather as much information as possible about the incident to relay and pass on to other responding units.

Until a higher ranking chief officer of the fire department having jurisdiction arrives, the fire department officer on the scene shall initiate a Unified Incident Command, and will establish the necessary incident command structure to deal with the hazardous materials incident.

A Level III HMI shall follow the same operational procedures as outlined in this plan for a Level II HMI. It should be understood that a Level III HMI will by its nature involve a large number of outside agencies.

Mutual Aid and Automatic Aid

The Sacramento Fire Department has a special written agreement with the County of Sacramento to provide hazardous materials emergency response to any area within the boundaries of the County of Sacramento.

Activation of emergency response of the Sacramento Fire Department Hazardous Materials Response Team is initiated by a call from the Sacramento Fire Dispatch Center requesting a Level II HMI response. A standard Level II HMI dispatch according to the Administrative chapter of this plan will be initiated.

Other features and guidelines explaining the policy regarding mutual aid and automatic aid dispatch of the HMRT are explained in the Haz Mat Discipline chapter of this plan.

FINANCIAL RESPONSIBILITY

Primary Responsible Party

The *Primary Responsible Party* for the assumption of all costs for the cleanup and disposal of any hazardous materials incident shall be in the following order:

The person, persons, or agency whose neglect, action, inaction, or willful or deliberate act caused or allowed to perpetuate said incident;

The person, persons, or agency who owned or had custody or control of the transportation vehicle that was used to move the hazardous material and its containers at the time the incident occurred or was discovered and reported;

The person, persons, or agency who owned or had custody or control of the hazardous material and its containers at the time the incident occurred or was discovered and reported;

The person, persons, or agency who owns the property or who has immediate financial and tax liability to the property on which the incident occurred.

Determining Responsible Party. All agencies represented by Unified Command, and the captain of the HMRT shall work together to identify the Primary Responsible for every hazardous materials incident. The person, persons, or agency identified as the Primary Responsible shall be liable for all costs associated to control, identification, and clean up.

In the event that the Primary Responsible is known but cannot be located or is incapable of assuming total financial responsibility, or is unknown, then procedures must be initiated to ascertain what city, county, or state governmental agency is to assume financial responsibility.

City Property—Spiller Is Not City of Sacramento. If the incident is on City property (street, curb, city parking lot, sidewalk, parks, etc.) and the spiller is unknown, or is known but is unable to assume financial liability, the responsibility for assuming all costs associated to control, identification and cleanup may be the City of Sacramento. The specific city division or department shall be determined based on exact location of the incident, and that division or department shall be liable for all costs associated to the incident.

For incidents occurring on city streets, parking lots, sidewalks, city owned property, city landfill, water systems, waste water systems, sewer facilities, flood control facilities, storm drainage systems, the financial liability for all costs will be the Sacramento City Public Works Department.

For incidents occurring in city parks, museums, cemeteries, community centers, city swimming pool facilities, ball parks, city zoo, city marinas, the financial liability for all costs will be the Sacramento City Parks and Recreation.

For incidents occurring on Convention Center property, the financial liability for all costs will be the Convention Center.

For incidents occurring on Fire Department property, the financial liability for all costs will be the Fire Department.

For incidents occurring on Police Department property, the financial liability for all costs will be the Police Department.

In the event a spiller is known for the circumstances described in the section on the primary responsible party, they will be the Primary Responsible and the City of Sacramento may elect to pursue total cost recovery from the Primary Responsible by civil action, court action, property lien, pursuant to the provisions of the City Charter.

City Property—Spiller Is City of Sacramento. The specific *city* division or department shall be determined based on exact location of the incident and what division or department caused the incident.

For incidents caused by city equipment (i.e., hydraulic failure), regardless as to where it occurred, the financial liability for all costs will be the division or department that is responsible for the piece of equipment that caused the incident.

For incidents caused by city employees (i.e., accidents, traffic or industrial), regardless as to where it occurred, the financial liability for all costs will be the division or department that employs the employee.

Private Property. If the incident occurred on private property within the City Limits of Sacramento, then the Primary Responsible for all financial liability shall be that as outlined in the section on the primary responsible party of this plan.

In the event that the Primary Responsible is known but is unable to assume financial liability, or is unknown, then the following shall apply with regard to ascertaining who will initiate procedures for cleanup and cost recovery:

If the Primary Responsible has been identified and is known, but is unavailable or unable to assume immediate financial liability for the costs incurred for the hazardous materials incident, including cleanup, the Sacramento Fire Department shall assume these costs and initiate appropriate procedures to abate the incident in as timely a manner as is deemed necessary. The Sacramento Fire Department may elect to pursue total cost recovery from the "primary responsible" in accordance with the section entitled "Cleanup, Repacking, Disposal" of this plan.

If the Primary Responsible cannot be identified at the time of the incident, the Sacramento Fire Department shall assume all costs associated to clean up and abate the incident. If and when it becomes known to the Sacramento Fire Department at a later date that a Primary Responsible has been located, the Sacramento Fire Department may elect to pursue total cost recovery from the Primary Responsible in accordance with Section 14 of this plan entitled "Cost Recovery."

Special Case—Drug Lab/Crime-Related Dumping. Clandestine hazardous materials incidents include those associated with drug labs, drug lab chemicals and precursors, drug lab waste products, glassware, hardware, paraphernalia, and abandoned chemicals, and all associated containers. It is imperative that the HMRT work closely with the law enforcement agency having jurisdiction on scene to determine if there is sufficient evidence to connect or declare the hazardous materials incident scene a *Crime Related Drug Lab* incident. If in the opinion of the law enforcement agencies on scene that it is crime related, then the total cost associated to the incident regarding control, identification, and cleanup shall be assumed by the lead law enforcement agency having jurisdiction on scene.

(a) All sampling will only be done as necessary by law enforcement task force, most likely DEA or DOJ.

(b) Authority and control of all evidence, including chemicals and hazardous materials, is now the responsibility of the law enforcement task force. The HMRT may assist as necessary only to the extent of removal of chemicals to a safe location for sample taking, and stabilization of certain situations to allow law enforcement personnel to proceed with their investigation.

(c) Notification of a reputable cleanup agency shall be done by the lead law enforcement agency having jurisdiction on scene, and that agency shall bear all associated costs of cleanup and abatement. This is often associated to activation of the "Drug Lab Super Fund," which may be accessed by the lead law enforcement agency on scene to assist in funding the cost of cleanup of these types of incidents.

If in the opinion of the law enforcement agency on scene that the hazardous materials incident is *NOT crime related*, or that there is insufficient evidence to allow the law enforcement agency to follow through with a crime-related scene, thereby absolving law enforcement of any relationship to the scene, then the following shall be followed in the order listed for cost recovery:

(a) Individual or agency who caused the spill/incident
(b) Lessee or property owner of the property/building/lot
(c) Owner of the materials
(d) Sacramento Fire Department

State Property. For hazardous materials incidents that occur on state roads or state freeways, the agency that shall be responsible for the abatement of the incident is Cal/Trans (California Department of Transportation). Cal/Trans shall make the necessary arrangements for contact with a licensed hazardous waste hauler.

For hazardous materials incidents that occur on all other state property and in state buildings, the agency that shall be responsible for the abatement of these incidents is California Highway Patrol (formerly California State Police). California Highway Patrol shall make all of the necessary arrangements for contact with a licensed hazardous waste hauler.

Sacramento County. If the incident occurs on private property in the County of Sacramento, then the Primary Responsible for all financial liability shall be that as outlined in the Hazardous Materials book of this plan entitled "Primary Responsible Party."

In the event that the Primary Responsible is known but is unable to assume financial liability, or is unknown, then arrangements will be made by the Sacramento County Sheriff (functioning as Scene Manager) to contact the Sacramento County Public Works Department and request for financial assistance to abate the incident.

Access State "Superfund"

If all avenues for determining responsible party have failed, or a responsible is known but is unable to fund the immediate removal of a hazardous material, and the hazardous materials are declared by the captain of the haz mat team or the representative of Sacramento County Environmental to pose an immediate health threat, the following procedure may be appropriate:

By haz-catting, determine degree of: flammability; corrosiveness (pH); and toxicity.

If any or all of the chemicals meet the specific minimum declared levels of hazard as applied by the California Department of Toxic Substance Control (DTSC) for flammability, corrosiveness, and toxicity, this may qualify for possible removal by authorization by DTSC.

If declared levels are met, notification of DTSC will be attempted by the HMRT or Sacramento County EMD, by going through California OES Warning Center, and contacting the DTSC "on call" specialist. The results of the haz-catting will be discussed. His decision to grant release of "Superfund" moneys is based on these results, and is final.

Authority to Abate a Hazard

Within the City Limits of Sacramento. The Sacramento Fire Department has the authority to order the immediate cleanup, removal, and total abatement of any hazardous materials incident.

When the Sacramento Fire Department is to assume the financial liability for abatement costs, the Captain of the HMRT shall make the appropriate arrangements by contacting the appropriate Duty Chief. Only Duty Chief can grant final approval to release city treasury moneys for this purpose.

COST RECOVERY

Initiate Action

In the event that the Sacramento Fire Department ultimately must pay for cleanup and abatement costs of a hazardous materials incident, and when the HMRT and the De-Con teams suffer loss and damage of equipment, the Sacramento Fire Department may pursue all appropriate legal avenues to initiate action, including civil action and liens against property, against all parties stated in the Financial Responsibility Section of this plan, "Primary Responsible Party" and "City Property—Spiller Is Not the City of Sacramento," in order to recover all costs.

The agency acting in the capacity of incident commander, when it is not the Sacramento Fire Department, shall assist the Sacramento Fire Department in initiating all actions necessary to recover all costs incurred in the handling and abatement of the hazardous materials incident.

CLEANUP, REPACKING, DISPOSAL

Policy

It shall not be the responsibility nor the policy of the Sacramento Fire Department HMRT to engage fire department personnel in the cleanup and/or removal of hazardous materials incident when such actions circumvent the responsibilities of a licensed hazardous waste hauler and circumvent existing state and federal law regarding cleanup and abatement requirements.

The HMRT may elect to abate certain small spills when within the capabilities of the team, and when within the constraints of law and outside agency policy guidelines.

The HMRT may elect to assist as a matter of safety a hazardous waste hauler as is deemed prudent and necessary by the HMRT captain.

DEFINITIONS

This listing of definitions is for the purpose of defining words or terms used in this document that need further explanation due to their specific application or meaning. All other words or terms not listed and used in this document shall be defined and accepted in accordance with any typical word dictionary. Other specialty words or terms unique to hazardous materials response may have definitions found in the "Glossary of Standardized Terms," *California Hazardous Material Incident Contingency Plan, 1992.*

Editor's Note: References that applied only to the state of California and that would not add significantly to the reader's understanding of the plan, as well as items already defined in Section 1 of the various standards presented in this handbook, have been deleted due to space limitations.

BC. Acronym for *Battalion Chief*, a supervisorial position of upper-level management within a fire department having command responsibilities at an emergency.

Captain. A supervisory position of middle management within a fire department having initial command responsibilities at an emergency and being the manager of a fire company.

CHP. Acronym for *California Highway Patrol*, the state agency with primary responsibility for traffic supervision and control on all State highways and all County roads, and has Incident Commander responsibility within these jurisdictions.

Code 3. To respond to an incident with siren and red lights operating.

Cost Recovery. A procedure that allows for the agency having jurisdiction to pursue reimbursement for all costs associated with a hazardous materials incident.

CP. Acronym for *Command Post.*

De-Con. Abbreviation for *decontamination*, the physical and/or chemical process of reducing and preventing the spread of contamination from persons and equipment used at a hazardous materials incident.

De-Con Team. Abbreviation for *decontamination team*, a designated group of appropriately trained employees and resources operating within a decontamination corridor

FIRESCOPE. The Incident Command System developed by the California Department of Forestry and adopted by all state and local emergency response agencies in the State of California.

FRO. Acronym for *First Responder Operational*, an employee or group of employees that have been given a level of certified hazardous materials training consisting of an initial 24 hours and a yearly refresher of 8 hours to maintain certification.

Haz Mat. Acronym for *Hazardous Materials.*

Haz Mat Group. The organizational position of *Group* within the FIRESCOPE ICS with a specific "hazardous materials" functional responsibility. *[Editor's Note: Also called a Branch in NFPA 472.]*

HMI. Acronym for *Hazardous Materials Incident*, used during dispatching to designate a "level" of an incident, such as "Level III HMI."

HMRT. Acronym for *Hazardous Materials Response Team.*

HMT. Acronym for *Hazardous Materials Technician.*

Hot Zone. An area immediately surrounding a hazardous materials incident, which extends far enough to prevent adverse effects from hazardous materials releases to personnel outside of this zone. The *hot zone* is also referred to as the "restricted zone," the "red zone," and the "exclusion zone" in other documents.

ICS. Acronym for *Incident Command System*, an organized system of roles, responsibilities, and standard operating procedures used to manage and direct emergency operations.

Incident Command. A disciplined method of management established for the specific purpose of control and direction of resources and personnel.

OEP. Acronym for Sacramento City Fire Department *Office of Emergency Planning*.

OES. Acronym for California *Office of Emergency Services*, is responsible for the notification and coordination of all state agencies that may become involved in a hazardous materials incident through its "State Warning Center."

Unified Incident Command. Lead representative individuals of the three specific agencies (fire, law, and public health) having intervention, investigative, and regulatory responsibility within a specific jurisdictional area at a hazardous materials incident functioning together and jointly determining objectives, strategy and priorities.

Warm Zone. The area where personnel and equipment, decontamination, and hot zone support takes place. It includes control points for the access into and exit from the hot zone. This is also referred to as the "decontamination," the "contamination reduction," the "yellow zone," and the "support zone" in other documents.

SUPPLEMENT 10

Guidelines for Decontamination of Fire Fighters and Their Equipment Following Hazardous Materials Incidents

Editor's Note: The following supplement is a reprint of a document published by the Canadian Association of Fire Chiefs. It includes guidelines for decontaminating fire fighters and their equipment after exposure to hazardous materials and for planning decontamination procedures before an incident occurs. We are grateful for the opportunity to include this detailed, practical guide in the Hazardous Materials Response Handbook.

NOTE TO READERS

The contents of this decontamination guide are based on information and advice believed to be accurate and reliable. The Canadian Association of Fire Chiefs Inc., its officers, and members, jointly and severally, make no guarantee and assume no liability in connection with this booklet. Moreover, it should not be assumed that every acceptable procedure is included or that special circumstances may not warrant modified or additional procedures.

The user should be aware that changing technology or regulations may require a change in the recommended procedures contained herein. Appropriate steps should be taken that the information is current when used.

The suggested procedures should not be confused with any federal, provincial, state, municipal, or insurance requirements, or with national safety codes.

INTRODUCTION

The number of hazardous materials incidents to which the fire service is called increases year by year. At each of these incidents, there is a good chance that the responding fire fighters may become contaminated with the hazardous material. Frequently, however, the matter of decontamination is never thought of, or is only performed cursorily.

The Dangerous Goods Sub-Committee of the Canadian Association of Fire Chiefs, in 1986–87, undertook the preparation of a series of guidelines for decontamination, to be adopted by any fire department that wishes to do so, either as printed here or with local variations due to their own circumstances. Note that these are indeed *guidelines, not standards*.

The procedures listed are designed so they can be carried out by any department, rural or urban, volunteer or full-time, with a minimum of investment in special equipment.

BACKGROUND OF THE STUDY AND RATIONALE FOR ITS CONCLUSIONS

In 1986 the Dangerous Goods Sub-Committee carried out an extensive study of fire services across the world to investigate the different approaches to decontamination of fire fighters following hazardous materials incidents.

Procedures were reviewed in detail from North America (Phoenix, San Francisco, Colorado, Metropolitan Toronto area) and England (Hampshire, Cambridgeshire, Greater Manchester, London, and the Home Office Guidelines). In addition, information was requested from Hong Kong, New Zealand, Australia, the People's Republic of China, France, Germany, Switzerland, Italy, Sweden, and the Netherlands. From these latter countries no formal replies were received, however, and indications are that decontamination procedures are either limited or absent. Japanese fire officials wrote back to indicate that they were studying various options but had not yet finalized any procedures.

Many magazine articles from the various periodicals published for the European and North American fire service market were reviewed. Furthermore, members consulted with chemical manufacturers, nuclear medicine physicists, hazardous waste disposal companies, industrial hygienists, toxicologists, and various jurisdictional agencies such as the Atomic Energy Control Board and provincial and federal Ministries of Health, Labour, and Environment.

All this research led to the conclusion that there were three basic philosophies in existence:

1. Wet and dry procedures
2. Dispose or retain runoff
3. Severity and type of the material

The idea of a dry procedure made sense because of easier containment and no reaction with water. A single wet procedure, however, was not deemed to be sufficiently comprehensive; on the other hand some wet procedures called for making up solutions of a variety of chemicals, and these were deemed to be too complicated for use by every fire department.

The dispose or retain philosophy is usually considered a wet procedure; however, to base one's procedures solely on the concern about run-off appeared to be overly simplistic. Note, however, that concerns about run-off are addressed later in this document.

The third philosophy was examined in more detail. The methods of determining the severity and type of material were defined by various fire departments along the following lines:

1. By UN class
2. By effects on the environment
3. By chemical characteristics
4. By physiological effects on people
5. By broad groups

The first alternative was deemed unsuitable because there are too many variables within a class (e.g., some flammable liquids are highly toxic, others are not). The second alternative was deemed to be of secondary importance to fire fighter safety (see the section on Environmental Considerations later in this document). It was found that alternatives three and four could in fact be used to arrive at alternative five, and this was the route taken to define the procedures in this document.

The procedures that were developed are therefore broken down as follows:

- Three general procedures for light, medium, and extreme hazards
- Two specific procedures for substances that do not fit into the three general groups above (although they share many common factors)
- One initial routine performed in some cases prior to the start of one of the other procedures

The authors realize that if the procedures listed here are to be completed thoroughly, a number of decontamination operatives and a Decontamination Officer to oversee them are needed. Typically, this will require the services of at least one fire-fighting company. Attention to detail and careful execution of all steps should lead to successful and safe completion of fire fighter decontamination.

DECONTAMINATION—GENERAL OBSERVATIONS

Six levels of decontamination are outlined. The incident commander will determine which level is applicable for the substance involved, using any reference sources that may state the applicable level. In the absence of such sources, advice should be sought from experts such as toxicologists, chemical company representatives, CANUTEC, CHEMTREC, and so on.

The levels are:

A—for light hazards
B—for medium hazards
C—for extreme hazards
D—dry contamination for water-reactive and certain dry substances
E—for etiologic agents and certain dry pesticides and poisons
R—for radioactive materials

Note that A-level decontamination, the most common, need only be done at the station. However, other levels need to be started at the incident scene as well as being continued on return to the station.

The most stringent level for the most toxic substances, C-level decontamination, may involve the destruction of all clothes worn.

In a few cases, scrubbing of clothes must be done while wearing SCBA as vapors released during cleaning may be harmful.

D-level decontamination is almost always followed by one of the other levels of decontamination, which will be dependent on the substance involved.

The procedures should be initiated if personnel are known or suspected to have been directly exposed to the chemical or its vapors, products of combustion, etc.

Officers should be aware of any cuts, wounds, lesions, or abrasions that their crews may have. If the apparatus is sent to an incident involving hazardous materials, such personnel should wherever possible exercise special care to avoid the chance of contamination through such wounds. Chemicals absorbed through the skin will be absorbed much faster if the skin is cut or abraded, thereby presenting a serious health hazard.

Adequate awareness is necessary to realize when decontamination will be required, so that early action can be taken to bring to the scene the equipment and manpower resources needed to set up and staff the decontamination area.

DECONTAMINATION PROCEDURES

Level A for Light Hazards

On Return to Station

1. Wash down all protective clothing with a mild (1 percent to 2 percent) trisodium phosphate solution. Rinse with water.
2. Wash down SCBA cylinders and harnesses with a mild trisodium phosphate solution. Take care to wipe, not scrub, around regulator assembly. Rinse with clean water. If damage is suspected to any part of the unit, ensure it is sent for service.
3. Scrub hands and face with soap and water.

Note: Where the scrubbing of the protective clothing may release harmful vapors caught in the fibers, it may be necessary to wear breathing apparatus while washing down protective clothing. In these cases, monitor the atmosphere around the washing area. Release of vapors may indicate commercial cleaning is required.

Level B for Medium Hazards

At the Scene

1. Do not remove SCBA facepiece. Place helmet on back of neck.
2. Assistant to flush fire fighter downwards from head to toe with copious amounts of low-pressure water. Include inside and outside of helmet, mask, harness, and inside of coat-wrists to the cuff.
3. Do not smoke, eat, drink, or touch face.

On Return to Station

4. Place apparatus temporarily out of service.
5. Remove all protective clothing and accessories. If possible, remove liner from helmet. Scrub all items, including the helmet liner, inside and out with a mild (1 to 2%) trisodium phosphate solution. Then flush with water.

Note: Where the scrubbing of the protective clothing may release harmful vapors caught in the fibers, it may be necessary to wear breathing apparatus while washing down protective clothing. In these cases, monitor the atmosphere around the washing area. Release of vapors may indicate commercial cleaning is required.

6. Scrub all other protective gear such as gloves and breathing apparatus items likewise. Be sure to flush out gloves with water. If SCBA is stored in its case while returning from incident, scrub the case also.
7. Remove all clothing worn at the scene, including underwear, and place in garbage bag for laundering and/or dry cleaning (preferably the latter). Take all garbage bags with contaminated clothing to a place where they can be cleaned separately from other garments.
8. Shower, scrubbing all of the body with soap and water, with particular emphasis on areas around the mouth and nostrils and under fingernails. Shampoo hair and thoroughly clean mustache if you have one.
9. Do not smoke, drink, eat, touch face, or void until Step 8 is completed.
10. Put on clean clothes.
11. Do not put apparatus back in service until clean-up completed.

To Change SCBA Cylinders at the Scene. Flush empty cylinder and surrounding area of fire fighter's back with copious amounts of low-pressure water. Also flush facepiece and breathing tube to prevent inhalation of harmful materials when regulator is disconnected.

Wear gauntlet-type rubber gloves, such as those used by linemen, when changing cylinders. Flush gloves after use before removing them.

Level C for Extreme Hazards

At the Scene

1. Do not remove SCBA facepiece. Place helmet on back of neck.

2. Assistant, wearing protective clothing and SCBA (plus disposable chemical suit wherever possible), to flush fire fighter downwards from head to toe with copious amounts of low-pressure water. Include inside and outside of helmet, mask, harness, and inside of coat-wrists to the cuff.

3. Do not smoke, eat, drink, or touch face.

4. Put SCBA, used cylinders, and any equipment (including hoses and tarps) suspected or known to be contaminated in garbage bags. Seal bags and return them to the station. Where circumstances permit, remove and bag protective clothing also.

On Return to Station

5. Put bags returned from incident scene in exterior or cordoned-off area away from public access. Place apparatus out of service.

6. Strip completely. Place all clothing (protective clothing and personal clothing) in plastic garbage bags. Place portable radios in a separate bag. Seal bags; place in exterior cordoned-off area.

7. Arrange for the supply of a number of steel drums. Upon their arrival, seal garbage bags with contaminated items into drums. Mark drums and place in exterior cordoned-off area, minimum 5-meter radius.

8. Arrange for the drums to be picked up and the contents analyzed. Some or all items may be destroyed; some may be able to be decontaminated and returned.

9. Shower, scrubbing all of the body with soap and water, with particular emphasis on areas around the mouth and nostrils and under fingernails. Shampoo hair. Thoroughly clean mustache if you have one.

Special Attention for Radioactive Incidents. After showering, scan entire body with a radiation contamination monitor, paying special attention to hair, hands, and fingernails. Hold monitor approximately 3 cm from body. If any reading beyond normal background level is detected, the fire fighter should shower again, scrubbing with more soap than before.

10. Do not smoke, drink, eat, touch face, or void until Step 9 is completed.

11. Put on clean clothes.

12. Report to hospital for medical examination. Inform physician which hazardous material was involved.

To Change SCBA Cylinders at the Scene. Flush empty cylinder and surrounding area of fire fighter's back with copious amounts of low-pressure water. Also flush facepiece and breathing tube to prevent inhalation of harmful material when regulator is disconnected.

Wear gauntlet-type rubber gloves, such as those used by linemen, when changing cylinders. Flush gloves after use before removing them.

Place empty cylinder in black plastic garbage bag and seal for subsequent decontamination.

The person doing the flushing and cylinder-changing must wear protective clothing and SCBA, plus a disposable chemical suit if available.

Special Note. Where circumstances, local climate, and available resources permit, the performance of *all* steps at the scene (instead of performing Steps 5–11 at the station) is preferable. The procedure is outlined as shown, however, in recognition of the fact that for many departments this will usually be impossible to achieve.

Level D for Water-Reactive Hazards

At the Scene

1. Set up a suitable vacuum cleaner with power supply. Provide a dry brush and a containment capture method for materials falling off the contaminated personnel. Assistants to don full protective clothing and SCBA, plus disposable chemical suits if available and appropriate.

2. If this is a radiation incident: The fire fighters suspected of being contaminated will be scanned carefully with a radiation monitor suitable for detecting surface contamination. All parts of their clothing and personal equipment will be scanned, including the soles of the boots. If no readings are found, the personnel that have been checked can leave the decontamination area.

3. If not a radiation incident, or if the fire fighter was found to be radioactively contaminated: Stand fire fighter in center of containment area, clean helmet and place on back of neck, then clean inside of helmet.

4. Commence cleaning from head downwards. Include all external areas. Slacken SCBA harness to allow cleaning behind straps and backplate. Likewise, loosen the hose-key belt and clean behind it.

5. When fire fighters have been fully vacuumed or brushed off, they will step out of the containment area. As they do so, their boots, including the soles, must be cleaned off so any contaminant will remain within the containment area.

6. Procedures will then continue as follows:

- Radioactive incident—go to Level "R" routine.
- Etiological or dry pesticide incident—go to Level "E" routine. Other incidents—go to Level "B" routine (unless advice is received that Level "C" is more appropriate).

7. All used filters and collected waste are to be placed in a garbage bag, sealed and tagged, and disposed of in a manner acceptable to the agency having jurisdiction.

Level E for Etiologic Hazards

Special Equipment Required. A presentation spray can (such as used for pesticide spraying), biological neutralizing substance (such as bleach, commercial sterilizing agent, etc.), orange garbage bags, black garbage bags, sterilization bags as used by hospital laundries, and a box of surgical masks.

At the Scene

1. If using bleach, make up a 5 percent to 6 percent bleach solution in the spray can. Take note of the bleach concentrate percentage when calculating the make-up of the solution. Many brands as purchased in the store are already 6 percent.

If using a commercial sterilizer, follow the manufacturer's directions.

2. Flush the fire fighter downwards from head to toe with low-pressure *water*. SCBA facepiece can now be removed. Place helmets in black plastic garbage bag(s) and seal. Place surgical mask on fire fighter.

3. If using bleach, spray the fire fighters' boots (but not their bunker gear) and any tools, hoses, and other equipment used (except for portable radios) with the *bleach* solution in the spray can. Leave for 10 minutes, then flush with water.

If using a commercial sterilizer, follow the manufacturer's instructions.

4. Remove SCBA. Place in black plastic garbage bag and seal. Remove fire fighters' protective clothing (except boots) and gloves. Place in orange plastic garbage bag and seal. Remove any portable radio worn. Place in black plastic garbage bag and seal. Discard surgical masks.

5. Do not smoke, eat, drink, or touch face.

6. Before leaving the scene, a fire fighter wearing SCBA should attempt to spray as much of the ground exposed to the material and the wash-down water as possible with bleach solution. Then flush the outside of the spray can with clean water.

7. Before leaving the scene, seal the orange garbage bags into the sterilization bags.

On Return to Station

8. Place apparatus temporarily out of service.

9. One fire fighter should dress in protective clothing and SCBA, and in an outside area perform the following tasks:

- Open the black plastic garbage bags, wipe all helmets, portable radios, SCBA sets, and used cylinders with a rag lightly dampened with a 6 percent bleach solution. After 10 minutes, wipe these items again with a rag dampened with clean water. If using a commercial sterilizer, follow the manufacturer's directions.
- Seal all used black garbage bags and rags into another bag and put out for normal garbage pickup. If using bleach, empty the spray can and flush out to remove bleach residue.

10. Remove all clothing worn at the scene, including underwear, and place in garbage bag for laundering and/or dry cleaning (preferably the latter). Take all garbage bags with contaminated clothing to a place where they can be cleaned separately from other garments.

11. All personnel should shower, scrubbing all of the body with soap and water, with particular emphasis on areas around the mouth and nostrils and under fingernails. Shampoo hair and thoroughly clean mustache if you have one.

12. Do not smoke, eat, drink, touch face, or void until Step 11 is completed.

13. Put on clean clothes. Place apparatus back in service when decontamination is completed.

14. Have cleaned firehose and SCBA checked by competent personnel before placing it back in service.

15. Arrange for the sterilization bags to be taken to a hospital laundry facility for cleaning and sterilization of the protective clothing, gloves, and any other garments sent in.

Reminder. Black garbage bags are to be used for items retained at the station. Orange bags are for items sent away for sterilization.

To Change SCBA Cylinders at the Scene. Flush empty cylinder and surrounding area of fire fighter's back with copious amounts of low-pressure water. Also flush facepiece and breathing tube to prevent inhalation of harmful material when regulator is disconnected.

Wear gauntlet-type rubber gloves, such as those used by linemen, when changing cylinders. Flush gloves after use before removing them.

Place empty cylinder in black plastic garbage bag and seal for subsequent decontamination.

The person doing the flushing and cylinder-changing must wear protective clothing and SCBA.

Level R for Radioactive Hazards

At the Scene

1. Preparation

(a) Mark off a decontamination area with two parts.
(b) Make up a solution of detergent and water. Obtain scrub brushes.
(c) Set out a reserve air supply, preferably with a workline unit or otherwise with a spare SCBA.
(d) In the first part of the decontamination area, set up a runoff capturing method, either with wading pools or through the use of tarpaulins.

(e) If appropriate, a "walkway" of polyethylene sheeting (weighted down if necessary) can be placed from the exit from the incident scene to the decontamination area, to prevent possible contamination of the ground.

2. The decontamination crew will don SCBA and, where available, disposable chemical suits.

3. The fire fighters suspected of being contaminated will be scanned carefully with a radiation monitor suitable for detecting surface contamination. All parts of their protective clothing and personal equipment will be scanned, including the soles of the boots. If no readings are found, the personnel that have been checked can leave the decontamination area.

4. Personnel found to be contaminated will be scrubbed down thoroughly with the detergent solution by the decontamination crew. This is followed by a flushing off using low-pressure water. Efforts should be made to capture the runoff.

5. The fire fighters will then move to the second part of the decontamination area, where they will be scanned again with the radiation monitor. If any readings are found, they will return to the first part of the decontamination area and Step 4 will be repeated.

6. When all personnel have been cleaned of contamination, the decontamination crew themselves will be hosed down. The matter of the captured runoff water will be discussed with environmental authorities and disposal arranged in a manner acceptable to them.

7. In the event fire fighters being decontaminated run out of breathing air, the reserve supply set out in Step 1 will be passed to them. They should hold their breath while changing facepieces.

8. In the event that, despite repeated scrubbing, any fire fighters cannot be decontaminated, they will remove as much of their clothing as possible in the second part of the decontamination area, and don clean or spare clothing. The clothing that has been taken off will be sealed into garbage bags and returned to the station. This evolution must be executed in such a manner as not to contaminate the clean clothing.

9. Any equipment suspected or known to be contaminated will be sealed into garbage bags and returned to the station.

On Return to Station. Follow the Level "C" procedure Steps 5 to 12 for those fire fighters who were found to be contaminated in Step 3, and for any contaminated equipment.

To Change SCBA Cylinders at the Scene. Personnel emerging from the incident to have their breathing apparatus cylinder changed will be scanned with a radiation contamination monitor in a manner identical to Step 3.

If no readings are found, the fire fighter can proceed to the SCBA cylinder change area and may then return to the incident with a fresh cylinder.

Personnel found to be contaminated may not return to the incident. They will be put through the full Level "R" decontamination procedure, and other fire fighters will be sent in to the incident to replace the fire fighters withdrawn.

Before the replacement fire fighters go in, they should attempt to obtain information as to where the other personnel might have received their contamination, in order to allow them to take the necessary caution when approaching that area.

Note: Steps 1 and 2 of the Level "R" procedure must be in place by the time the first fire fighter emerges from the incident. If circumstances permit, these preparations should be made before personnel even enter the incident area for the first time.

Decontamination—Specific Observations

Pre-Incident Planning. Review the procedures and, if they are suitable for your location, assemble the equipment necessary into an easily transported container. Some departments, for instance, have all the special items needed for etiologic decontamination carried in a "Level E Decontamination Kit."

Many departments will have infrequent need to use these procedures. To prevent skill decay, and to prevent certain critical steps in the procedures being accidentally left out, it is suggested that a copy of the procedures be available at the scene and that regular training in the procedures take place. Executing these procedures accurately is not as easy as it would seem.

The time when you have twenty garbage bags with contaminated clothing sitting on your apparatus floor is not the time to start looking for a laundry that will clean them. Most commercial cleaning companies will not be interested in handling contaminated clothing.

Furthermore, it should be recognized that at some incidents the nature or extent of the contamination may be such that full decontamination is beyond the resources of the fire department (especially with Levels C, E, and R) and will require specialist treatment. With these three levels, consideration should be given to the destruction of all permeable items in case of serious exposure. You should therefore make prior arrangements for the following:

- Obtaining steel drums at any time of the day or night. The drums must be clean and must have a removable lid—not just a bung and vent-hole.

- Analysis and expert decontamination of equipment and clothing contaminated by severely hazardous substances. This is needed for Level C and Level R, although different companies are likely to be needed for the two levels.
- Acceptable methods of disposal for items that cannot be cleaned, or that would be uneconomical to attempt to clean, for Level C, E, and R contaminants.
- The use of a hospital laundry service to perform Level E decontamination on protective clothing. This laundry should be approached for the loan of a number of sterilization bags, which are typically used in the hospitals to put dirty laundry in for shipment to the laundry service. Check that the hospital laundry service can take bunker coats—in some cases the buckles may bash the inside of their machines too much.
- Check the availability of replacement protective clothing and equipment that can be used while the original items are out being decontaminated under Levels C, E, or R.

You may want to establish a policy regarding personal items such as rings, wallets, watches, etc. Many of these, especially leather items, cannot be decontaminated and may have to be destroyed. Fire fighters should be aware of their department's policy with regard to recompense or replacement.

One further item of preplanning will always stand you in good stead: Note the names and contact numbers of any local experts who could assist and advise you during the incident and its subsequent decontamination.

Plastic Bags. Notwithstanding the fact that throughout the preceding procedures "black" garbage bags have been mentioned, there is a distinct advantage to using clear, plastic bags. These will permit the contents to be identified without opening them.

They should be at least 6 mil gauge and should be large enough that they can also be used as drum-liner bags.

Decontamination Area Layout

When choosing the location of the decontamination area, consider the following:

- Prevailing weather conditions (temperature, precipitation, etc.)
- Wind direction
- Slope of the ground
- Surface material and porosity (grass, gravel, asphalt, etc.)
- Availability of water
- Availability of power and lighting
- Proximity of the incident
- Location of drains, sewers, and watercourses

When setting up the area, provide the following features:

- Containment of wash-down water if that is necessary
- Spare supply of breathing air (extra SCBA, extra cylinders, or workline units)
- A supply of industrial-strength garbage bags, double- or triple-bagged if necessary
- Clearly marked boundaries, not just a rope lying on the ground
- Clearly marked entry and exit points with the exit upwind, away from the incident and its contaminated area
- A waiting location at the entry point where contaminated personnel can await their turn without spreading contamination further
- Access to triage and other medical aid upon exit if necessary
- Protection of personnel from adverse weather conditions
- Security and control from the setting up of the area to final clean-up of the site

Environmental Considerations

One fundamental concept forms the basis for these decontamination procedures: "The human being comes before the environment."

Notwithstanding the above, where containment of runoff is called for, genuine attempts must be made if only to avoid possible legal consequences. Examples of containment basins are:

- Children's wading pools
- Portable tanks (as used in rural fire fighting)
- Tarps laid over a square formed by hard suction hose or small ground ladders
- Diking with earth, sandbags, etc. covered with tarps

Fire fighters stepping out of a containment basin should lift one foot, have it rinsed off so the water falls inside the basin, step out with that foot, and repeat for the other foot.

When the containment basin is full, it should be able to be siphoned or pumped off into drums or into a vacuum truck for controlled disposal in a manner acceptable to the authority having jurisdiction.

Any runoff that is not contained will eventually enter sewers and water-courses, or if it sinks into the ground will ultimately reach the water-table. The

Department of Mechanical and Fluid Engineering at Leeds (U.K.) University has determined that provided a chemical is diluted with water at the rate of approximately 2000:1, pollution of water-courses will be significantly reduced.

There is also a change in attitude coming with the environmental authorities, whereby they recognize that the small amount of chemical likely to be washed off contaminated fire fighters with adequate dilution will result in minimum damage to the environment, especially when compared to the results of the spill that generally led to the personnel contamination in the first place.

Any substances that enter sewers and water-courses should be reported to environmental authorities and to the sewage treatment plant likely to receive it. If necessary, advise water authorities downstream from the decontamination area of actual or potential pollution.

The most appropriate decontamination for materials that have a severe effect on the environment will usually be to use minimal amounts of water, with run-off containment. Other substances should be deluged off personnel with the 2000:1 factor as a minimum guideline.

Weather

If decontamination is done indoors because of bad weather, ensure that the drains go into a holding tank and not directly into the sewers.

If the hazardous material involved requires Level D decontamination, and it is raining or snowing, protect fire fighters from the precipitation until they have been processed.

Take care when using instruments in wet weather. Extreme cold may affect the operating effectiveness of instruments, especially delicate ones originally designed for use in laboratory environments.

Under extreme weather conditions (heat or cold), decontamination personnel must be rotated more frequently.

These decontamination procedures should be reviewed in light of your local climate and adapted if necessary where your area's weather conditions dictate.

Fluid Replacement

At hazardous materials incidents, especially when chemical suits are worn, serious dehydration can occur in fire fighters. Replacement of fluids should only be permitted if at least gross decontamination is performed—a washdown especially around the head and upper body.

The preferable method of consuming liquids is by means of drinking boxes with straws (the straw inserted by someone with uncontaminated hands), or by means of a squeeze bottle with an attached drinking tube as used by athletes.

The above should form part of comprehensive rehabilitation procedures which should be developed in consultation with your EMS providers.

Chemical Suit Decontamination

When a chemical suit is taken off its wearer, a suitably protected assistant should roll it in on itself in order to keep the outside of the suit from coming into contact with the wearer.

Because of the inherent smoothness and impermeability of chemical suits, it is usually only required that the on-scene washdown part of fire fighter decontamination is performed. Upon return to the station, instead of doing the steps listed in the appropriate procedure, fire fighters should wash and rinse the chemical suits and examine them carefully for damage caused at the incident. Zippers should be lubricated with their special lubricant.

Follow-up communication with the suit manufacturer as to the exposure, as well as follow-up from the exposing chemical's manufacturer, is useful in determining long-term effect of exposure to chemical-protective ensembles. Any questionable or unusual findings anywhere in the decontamination or testing process should be immediately referred to the manufacturers; the clothing should be placed out of service until it can be repaired or reevaluated. If a limited-use (disposable) suit becomes contaminated, after gross decontamination it should be bagged and disposed of in a manner acceptable to the authority having jurisdiction.

Vacuum Cleaners for Level D

When selecting a vacuum cleaner, the following points should be taken into consideration:

- Can it operate off a generator, or is it unforgiving so far as voltage fluctuations are concerned?
- Will it operate safely in an area where it might get wet?
- How effective are the filters?
- Can the unit be safely cleaned out itself?
- Are replacement hoses easy to come by?

Although you won't want to operate your vacuum cleaner under water, it might accidentally get splashed so some basic water protection will be of benefit.

The degree of filtering achieved is important. Most wet/dry industrial type vacuums will achieve a reasonable effectiveness. Some specialized cleaners, equipped with HEPA (High Efficiency Particulate Air) filters will go down to 0.3 micron but they are expensive. The small, cigarette-lighter plug powered car interior cleaners are not suitable as they filter very little, instead blowing most particulate they pick up back out through their exhaust ports.

Easy removal of contaminated filters will help, as will good access to the machine's insides for its own decontamination. You will usually find that it is impossible to guarantee the effectiveness of cleaning of the accordion-style hose, and you should consider replacing these if they become contaminated.

Remember not to operate a vacuum cleaner in a flammable or explosive atmosphere, unless yours is intrinsically safe.

Bleach

Bleach, as shown on the bottle's label, is corrosive. Do not spray bleach on fire fighters' skin—it hurts! It is also reactive—do not let it come in contact with fuels and solvents, as a heat-generating reaction (and possible fire) will result.

Do not spray bleach on protective clothing, as it deteriorates and discolors the garment. It also impairs its fire retardancy.

Regular bleach containers are often made of a hard plastic and are liable to crack or leak around the cap when carried on a vehicle. Consider transferring the bleach to a container such as a new, unused plastic gasoline can, which is far sturdier, but then be sure to label the gas can as containing bleach. Never put bleach in a metal container, as it will react.

At room temperature, bleach shielded from sunlight will degrade about 1 percent per year, i.e., from 6 percent to 5 percent (faster in warmer temperatures, slower at colder temperatures). You should therefore replace the bleach at the appropriate time with a fresh supply, as its strength will have decreased with time.

It is recommended that, if possible, nonchlorinated bleach be used in case the bleach accidentally contacts the protective clothing.

Record Keeping

A member of the crew responsible for performing the decontamination should maintain written records of the following:

- Fire fighter's name, material involved, length of exposure
- Level of decontamination performed
- Any ill effects observed
- Where fire fighter went, i.e., returned to station, sent to rest area, removed to hospital, reassigned to other duties at the scene, etc.

At the station, entries should be made on the fire fighters' medical records of the incident date, material involved, and decontamination performed, where exposure is known or suspected. This will assist both in tracing future sickness through synergistic effects of chemicals in the body and with support of any later injury or sickness claims.

If appropriate, records should also be kept of the length of time each chemical suit was exposed, and what substance it was exposed to. This will permit the tracking of cumulative degradation of the suit material due to exposure to a variety of chemicals or due to repeated exposure to one particular substance.

Contamination of Vehicles

Any vehicle driven through a contaminated area must be washed down, including the undercarriage, chassis, and cab. Air filters on vehicle (and, where appropriate, generator) engines must be replaced. Porous items such as wooden hose beds, wooden equipment handles, seats, and cotton jacketed hose may be difficult to clean completely and may have to be discarded.

It is therefore better to take the "uphill and upwind" approach and keep vehicles at a suitable distance from incidents.

Precautionary Decontamination

There are occasions when an apparently normal alarm response turns into a hazardous materials incident. Frequently, most of the initial assignment crews will have gone into the incident area, and have the potential of being contaminated.

It is essential that all members so involved remove themselves from the area at once, call for decon capability, and stay together in one location. They must not wander around, climb on and off apparatus, and mix with other personnel since there is a potential for them to be contaminated.

Fire fighters so exposed should be given "gross decontamination" (a simple on-scene washdown) as a precautionary measure. Knowledgeable haz mat personnel such as the decontamination sector officer, in conjunction with the incident commander, should determine whether any further, more definitive decontamination is necessary.

Remember, the primary objective of decontamination must be to avoid contaminating anyone or anything beyond the hot zone. When in doubt about contamination, decon all affected personnel, equipment, and apparatus.

One Final Observation

The entire foregoing contents of this document have probably made you realize by now that it is much more desirable to handle hazardous materials incidents with chemical suits than with regular fire fighting turnouts. The cost of disposable suits is relatively cheap; even for a small department, throwing away a few hundred dollars' worth of disposable suits after one use will be cheaper than replacing fire fighting clothing or paying for commercial cleaning. In many jurisdictions, the fire service is permitted to recover the cost of destroyed equipment from the party responsible for the incident's occurrence, and the cost of disposable chemical suits can thus be recovered.

Always remember: If the emergency response crew is not equipped with gear suitable for entry into a hazardous or toxic atmosphere, then the option of "no go" should be considered the most appropriate tactic.

Speed—A Case for Exception?

Decontamination should emphasize thoroughness, not speed. Under noncritical conditions certain commonsense actions should be taken, such as decontaminating the fire fighter with the lowest air reserve first.

Speed is only important where a victim is involved and even then decontamination should be as thorough as is practicable.

Circumstances may dictate that emergency decontamination becomes necessary, examples of such situations being where a protective suit has become split or damaged, or when a fire fighter is injured. Emergency decontamination may also be applicable when contaminated civilians or other emergency workers (police, ambulance, etc.) are involved.

Emergency Decontamination Procedure

Paragraphs 1 to 6 below, although arranged in a basic chronological order, do not necessarily have to be undertaken in the exact sequence outlined. The officer-in-charge should act in the most expedient manner appropriate without worsening the situation.

The procedure outlined should be carried out as quickly as possible.

To protect the ambulance crew and hospital staff as well as the victim, every attempt must be made to perform at least this emergency procedure prior to transporting the victim to the hospital.

1. Remove the victim from the contaminated area into the decontamination zone and provide a supply of uncontaminated air or oxygen.
2. Remove fire helmet if worn and immediately wash with flooding quantities of water any exposed parts of the body that may have been contaminated.
3. If the victim is wearing SCBA, release the harness and remove the set leaving the face mask in position.
4. Remove all contaminated clothing (if necessary by cutting it off the victim) ensuring where practicable that the victim does not come into further contact with any contaminant. Maintain the washing of the victim while the clothing removal is taking place.
5. Remove the victim to a clean area. Render first aid as required, but do not apply mouth-to-mouth resuscitation. Send victim for medical treatment as soon as this emergency decontamination procedure has been completed.
6. Ensure hospital/ambulance personnel are informed of the contaminant involved.

SUPPLEMENT 11

EMS Sector Standard Operating Procedures

Editor's Note: This supplement contains standard operating procedures for a hazardous materials incident EMS sector developed by the Montgomery County, Maryland, Department of Fire and Rescue Services along with sample medical protocols developed by the state of Maryland. Thanks to Chief Mary Beth Michos of Prince William County, Virginia, previously the Deputy Chief of the Montgomery County Department of Fire and Rescue Services, for sharing this plan with us.

MONTGOMERY COUNTY, MARYLAND, STANDARD OPERATING PROCEDURES

General Information

On all hazardous materials incidents requiring levels A or B protective clothing or specialized protective clothing, an EMS sector officer (designated Haz Mat EMS) shall be assigned by the Haz Mat sector officer.

Where possible, the EMS sector officer should be trained to a minimum of the EMT-P level.

At the discretion of the Haz Mat sector officer, an EMS sector officer may be assigned on other incidents where conditions may subject personnel to severe stress.

Haz Mat EMS shall assume responsibility for the medical care of all Haz Mat response personnel and advise the EMS control officer (FRC ICS) on the care of other emergency services personnel and civilian victims.

Haz Mat EMS Functions

The Haz Mat EMS sector shall be conducted in accordance with the following:

1. The health and emergency care of all Haz Mat personnel shall be the prime mission of the Haz Mat EMS sector.
2. At least one Advanced Life Support (ALS) unit shall remain committed to provide advanced care whenever Haz Mat personnel are engaged in entry operations.
3. The Haz Mat EMS officer shall assign ALS personnel to perform pre-entry and post-entry medical evaluations of entry team personnel in accordance with the sections Personnel Medical Evaluations and Physical Signs of this procedure.
4. The Haz Mat EMS officer shall have the authority to deny entry to any Haz Mat personnel for medical reasons, after evaluation. The Haz Mat EMS officer shall also retain the authority to order any Haz Mat personnel to undergo medical evaluation and transport to a hospital for further evaluation and/or treatment.

5. The Haz Mat EMS officer will coordinate with the research officer on the acute, delayed, and chronic effects of exposure and treatment for each hazardous material. The Haz Mat EMS officer shall ensure that such information is provided to the EMS control officer and any receiving hospitals.

6. The Haz Mat EMS officer shall ensure that a complete and accurate log is maintained of all EMS functions including pre- and post-entry evaluations, treatment of personnel, and communications with the EMS control officer.

7. The Haz Mat EMS officer shall complete the Hazardous Materials EMS Checklist, as appropriate, on the following pages.

Haz Mat EMS Resources

- Hazardous Materials EMS Checklist
- ALS unit immediately available
- BLS equipment, monitor and drug kit from Haz Mat 7
- Haz Mat medical evaluation forms
- HIRT Internal Communications Capability
- Note pad and pencil

Incident Operations Structure

The Haz Mat EMS officers shall be responsible for maintaining the following lines of communications with other sectors. This directive shall not preclude direct communications with other sector officers where necessary. *(See Figure S11-1.)*

Personnel Medical Evaluations

Medical evaluations of physical condition are to be conducted on all personnel prior to suiting up and engaging in activities while wearing chemical protective clothing.

Assessment of the following physical signs shall be conducted and recorded for a pre-entry baseline. The pre-entry baseline should be compared to the medical data carried on board Haz Mat 7. Any significant deviations may, in the opinion of the Haz Mat EMS officer, preclude an individual from operating as part of an entry team.

An assessment of the same physical signs shall be conducted and recorded for all personnel immediately upon leaving decon. Any significant changes from the pre-entry baseline may, in the opinion of the Haz Mat EMS officer, preclude an individual from participating in another entry.

If, in the opinion of the Haz Mat EMS officer, personnel require further evaluation at a medical facility, personnel shall be transported without delay and shall not deny transport.

Physical Signs

1. *Blood Pressure.* Entry shall be denied to personnel with a blood pressure exceeding 150 systolic or 100 diastolic where there is 20 or more points deviation from their normal resting pressure.

2. *Pulse.* Entry shall be denied to personnel with a pulse greater than 110 or irregular without prior history.

3. *Respirations.* Entry shall be denied to personnel with a respiratory rate greater than 24.

4. *Temperature.* Entry shall be denied to personnel with an oral temperature greater than 99.2°.

5. *EKG.* All personnel shall have a minimum 10 second rhythm strip obtained.

6. *Weight.* Re-entry shall be denied personnel who show a loss of more than 2 percent pre-hydration weight.

Prior to entry, all personnel are to hydrate with AT LEAST 1 PINT of water. Weight should be taken prior to hydration to prevent false fluid loss readings.

(See Figures S11-2 through S 11-7.)

MARYLAND MEDICAL PROTOCOLS FOR HAZARDOUS MATERIALS EXPOSURE

This protocol assumes that the ambulance is the first and only unit to arrive on the scene. Should there already be other units on the scene, the Incident Commander's instructions should be strictly adhered to in conjunction with this protocol.

En Route to and Approaching the Incident Scene

If hazardous material involved in the incident is known while responding to the scene, begin to research the hazardous material using appropriate reference material [e.g., manufacturer safety data sheets (MSDS), *North American Emergency Response Guidebook*, pre-incident plans]. Become familiar with the following:

1. Potential health hazards
2. Proper level of personal protection equipment indicated by the hazardous material

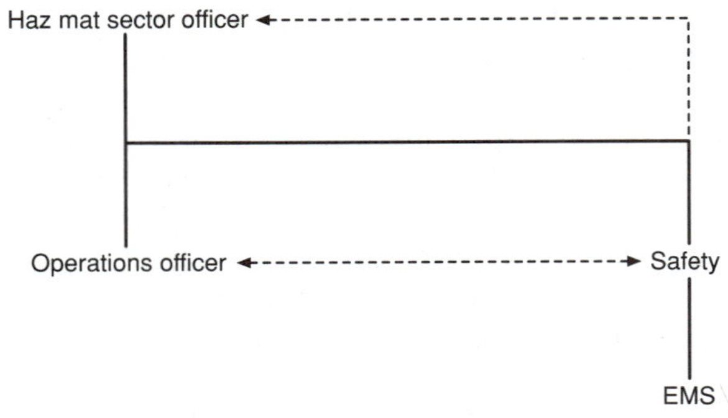

Figure S11-1 *Incident operations structure.*

EMS Sector Officer Checklist

Nature of incident: ______________________________

____

Location: ______________________________

EMS sector officer: ______________________________

____

- ❑ EMS sector officer identified by EMS vest
- ❑ EMS sector personnel / assignments:
  1. ____________ / ____________
  2. ____________ / ____________
  3. ____________ / ____________
  4. ____________ / ____________

Command

Haz mat sector officer: ______________________________

Haz mat safety officer: ______________________________

Haz mat operations officer: ______________________________

Decon officer: ______________________________

EMS control officer: ______________________________

Command post location: ______________________________

Figure S11-2 EMS sector officer checklist.

Site Set-up

❑ **Treatment and Triage Site Set-up** *(patients)*
Location (describe area, should be close to decon): ____________

____

❑ **Medical Evaluation Site Set-up** *(pre- and post-entry evaluations)*
Location (describe area, should be close to haz mat units):

____

❑ **Command, Entry, Safety, and Decon Officers Notified of Location**

❑ **Medical Evaluation and Treatment Supplies and Equipment Available**

❑ **Transport Vehicle Available** *(one must be an ALS unit)*

- ❑ Unit number ________ ❑ ALS [ ]
- ❑ Unit number ________ ❑ ALS [ ] ❑ BLS [ ]
- ❑ Unit number ________ ❑ ALS [ ] ❑ BLS [ ]
- ❑ Unit number ________ ❑ ALS [ ] ❑ BLS [ ]

Other (bus, helicopter, etc.) ______________________________

____

❑ **Protective Clothing for EMS Personnel Determined**
Level of protection: __________ Type of clothing: __________

❑ **Primary Receiving Hospital Defined**
(Check with EMS control officer.)

❑ **Receiving Hospital Notified of Decontamination Procedures**
(Consult decon officer for recommendations.)

Figure S11-3 Site set-up form.

3. Other potential hazards
4. "Safe distance" (the distance from the incident that is considered to be free from hazards)

If at all possible, approach the incident from uphill and upwind

While nearing the scene, be observant for environmental clues (e.g., the lean of the trees may indicate wind direction; unusual odors or vapor clouds may indicate a hazardous condition).

Begin to don the proper level of protective clothing and equipment if available and trained in its use.

Arrival at the Incident Scene

Position the ambulance vehicle outside the "hot" zone at a safe distance.

Immediately establish a "hot" zone and deny access by anyone into that area. Upon arrival of additional units, stage as necessary and establish "warm" and "cold" zones as appropriate.

Evaluate the magnitude of the incident and gather as much specific information as possible on the hazardous material involved without endangering personnel.

Call for appropriate assistance.

Coordinate closely with other responding units and/or agencies. Confirm hazardous material involved, advise best route of travel, etc.

Advise potential receiving hospitals of hazardous material involved and possible number of patients involved.

Contact appropriate poison control center to receive detailed health implications of hazardous material involved and product-specific treatment protocols. The following may be required when calling the designated poison control center:

- The chemical name of the hazardous material
- Length of exposure
- State (i.e., gas, solid, or liquid) of hazardous material
- Route of introduction

Complete the donning of personal protective clothing and equipment if available and trained in its use.

Gain Access to the Patient(s)

When dealing with *ambulatory patients* (persons able to remove themselves from the "hot" zone), *assume that*

Chemical Information

❑ **Name(s) of Chemicals Involved** *(obtained from research)*

1. ______
2. ______
3. ______
4. ______
5. ______
6. ______

❑ **Signs/Symptoms of Exposure and Onset**

Chem ❑ Acute ❑ Delayed . . . . . Time: ______

1.		
2.		
3.		
4.		
5.		
6.		

❑ **Additional Chemicals Listed in Notes Section**

Figure S11-4 *Chemical information form.*

Medical Treatment

❑ **Exposure Treatment** ❑ Protocol ❑ By case

❑ Physician contacted Who: ______ Time: ______

1. ______
2. ______
3. ______
4. ______

❑ **Antidotes**

1. ______ 3. ______
2. ______ 4. ______

Contraindications

1. ______ 3. ______
2. ______ 4. ______

❑ **Facility Contacted for Treatment/Antidote Information**

❑ Poison control center ❑ Phone number: ______

❑ Other:

Facility: ______ Phone number: ______

Contact person: ______

Facility: ______ Phone number: ______

Contact person: ______

❑ **Availability of Drugs/Antidotes Established**

Locations: ______

______

______

Figure S11-5 *Medical treatment form.*

anyone leaving the "hot" zone is contaminated. They should be treated as such until properly assessed and decontaminated.

1. Move these patients to, and contain them in, a controlled area at the perimeter of the "hot" zone.
2. Do not make physical contact with these persons until the proper level of personal protective clothing and equipment has been donned.
3. Move these personnel to the decontamination area in an organized fashion.

When dealing with *non-ambulatory patients* proceed as follows.

1. Attempt to remove these patients from the "hot" zone if the proper level of personal protection and personnel trained in their use are available.
2. Treatment in the "hot" zone should be limited to gross airway management, cervical spine immobilization, and control of obvious hemorrhage. No invasive procedures should be performed, as this would provide a direct route of introduction of the hazardous material into the patient.
3. Move patient to the decontaminated area.

Decontamination Procedures

1. Remove gross contaminants.
2. Remove all the contaminated clothing. Articles that remain on the patient and cannot be removed should be isolated from the environment.
3. Further decontamination should be completed based upon the patient's condition, environmental conditions, and resources available.
4. Take care not to introduce contaminants into open wounds.
5. Contain all runoff from decontamination procedures for proper disposal.
6. Isolate patient from the environment to prevent the spread of any remaining contaminants.
7. Transfer patient to a "clean, protected" crew for transport if resources are available.

Assessment of Patient(s)

1. Complete primary and secondary surveys as conditions allow. Bear in mind the product-specific information received from the designated poison control center.

Entry Team Safety

- ❑ **Entry Team Briefed on Effects of Chemical(s)**
- ❑ **Safety Officer Briefed on Effects of Chemical(s)**
- ❑ **EMS Personnel Briefed:**
  - ❑ on effects of chemical(s)
  - ❑ treatment procedures
  - ❑ medical monitoring procedures review procedures sheet
- ❑ **Pre-entry Physicals Conducted** *(see attached sheet)*
- ❑ **Protective Clothing for EMS Determined**
- ❑ **Level of Protection** ❑ A ❑ B ❑ C ❑ D
- ❑ **Post-entry Physicals Conducted** *(see attached sheet)*
- ❑ **Post-transport Decon Required for:**
  - ❑ Rescuers ❑ Vehicles ❑ Equipment
- ❑ **Receiving Hospital Notified of Decon Requirements and Procedures:**
  - ❑ Personnel ❑ isolated area required?
  - ❑ Equipment ❑ isolated area required?

Notes:

(Include significant observations such as time in suit, inappropriate behaviors, intuitive feelings, etc.)

Figure S11-6 *Entry team safety form.*

Medical Evaluation Form — Entry Team No. ________

Pre-entry Evaluation

Name	B/P	Pulse	Resp.	Temp.	Weight	EKG

Post-entry Evaluation

Name	B/P	Pulse	Resp.	Temp.	Weight	EKG

5 Minutes Post-entry

Name	B/P	Pulse	Resp.	Temp.	Weight	EKG

Figure S11-7 *Medical evaluation form.*

2. In multiple patient situations, begin proper triage procedures.

Treatment Procedures

1. Treat presenting signs and symptoms as appropriate and when conditions allow.
2. Administer orders of "on-line" medical direction.
3. IV therapy should be administered only with physician direction.
4. Invasive procedures should be performed only in fully decontaminated areas where conditions permit. These procedures may create a direct route for introduction of the hazardous material into the patient.
5. Reassess the patient frequently, as many hazardous materials have latent physiological effects.

Transport to Hospital

1. Recontact receiving hospital.
2. Update on treatment provided and any other information received from appropriate poison control center.
3. Obtain specific instructions regarding entering the hospital.
4. Transport patient.
   (a) Land transport—Protect vehicle and equipment from contaminants.
   (b) Air transport—Is inappropriate for contaminated patients.

Transferring Responsibility for Patient to Hospital Personnel

1. Await direction from hospital personnel before entering hospital.
2. Assist hospital personnel with patient decontamination and treatment as requested.
3. Arrange for personal decontamination.

Decontamination Procedures

Arrange for decontamination of the following in accordance with information received from expert resources.

- Personnel
- Emergency care equipment
- Vehicles

Medical Follow-up of Personnel

All public safety personnel who came into close contact with the hazardous material should receive an appropriate medical examination, post incident, based upon information from the designated poison control center. This should be completed within 48 hours of the incident and compared with the findings of any recent, pre-incident examination. Personnel who routinely respond to hazardous materials emergencies should have periodic pre-incident examinations. Personnel should be advised of possible latent symptoms at the time of their exam.

MARYLAND MEDICAL TOXIC GAS (SMOKE INHALATION) FIELD PROTOCOL

A specialty referral program for carbon monoxide/cyanide inhalation has been developed by the MIEMSS Department of Hyperbaric Medicine. Exposure to these gases may be related to a fire scene and smoke inhalation or inhalation of exhaust fumes or some paint solvents.

It is not feasible to list the absolute triage for every possible toxic gas inhalation patient, nor to define on a statewide basis which patients should go directly from the field to the department of hyperbaric medicine at MIEMSS or to go first to a closer facility. Time, distance, weather, and proximity to MIEMSS are all factors that must be considered in making an individual patient decision based upon the patient assessment and mechanism of exposure.

The following guidelines are intended to aid in the decision making, with the understanding that appropriate consultation should be obtained if there is any question regarding appropriate referral, treatment, and/or transport. Consultation is particularly important if the nature of the toxic gas is known, e.g., carbon monoxide (CO), general smoke inhalation, cyanide gas, hydrogen sulfide (H_2S), or methylene chloride (CH_2C_{12}-dichloromethane), because exposure to these substances can be treated with hyperbaric oxygen therapy.

Candidates for Hyperbaric Medicine Referral

- Toxic gas inhalation only
- Unconscious patients
- Incoherent, does not follow verbal commands
- Combative, does not follow verbal commands*
- Burn patients with toxic gas inhalation

**Note:* All combative patients are to be transported via ambulance.

Adult:

(a) Patient 50 years of age or less who is unconscious, combative, and/or incoherent and who does not follow verbal commands with:

1. 20 percent BSA burns or less (second and third degree)
2. Above 20 percent BSA burns (second and third degree) should be referred to the appropriate burn center

(b) Patients over 50 years of age with burns (second and third degree) over greater than 10 percent BSA should also be referred to the appropriate burn center

Pediatric:

(a) Patient unconscious, combative, and/or incoherent, who does not follow verbal commands with:

1. 10 percent BSA burns or less (second and third degree) if 10 years of age or younger
2. 20 percent BSA burns or less (second and third degree) if over 10 years of age

(b) All other patients should be referred to the appropriate facility after consultation with the appropriate pediatric trauma center and the appropriate burn center.

Clinical Data and Referral

Prior to obtaining consultation, have as much of the following data as possible collected:

1. Age, race, and sex of the patient
2. Vital signs: pulse, BP, respiration, and breath sounds
3. Nature of the injury: toxic gas inhalation or toxic gas inhalation with burns and/or other associated injuries
4. Specifics to the exposure
   (a) Type of fire, namely the combustible involved, e.g., PVC, acrylics, styrofoams, urethanes, wood, petroleum products
   (b) In cases other than fire-related, the type of gas involved
   (c) Type of occupancy (e.g., dwelling, vehicle)
   (d) Duration of exposure, when possible
   (e) Level of consciousness (utilize Glasgow coma scale) with clinical signs and symptoms
   (f) Prehospital care rendered

Note: Once as much of the above information as possible has been obtained, radio contact with MIEMSS systems communication (SYSCOM) or other appropriate facility should be made and the information passed on. A copy of the ambulance report form should be transported with the patient if at all possible.

Advanced Life Support (ALS) Unit Responses

1. An ALS unit should be dispatched to all suspected toxic gas inhalation incidents and immediately requested when not dispatched initially.

2. Upon arrival of the ALS unit, blood samples are to be collected via closed vacutainer technique prior to starting the IV.

3. For conscious patients, informed consent must be obtained prior to drawing blood samples. In the case of unconscious patients, blood samples may be obtained at the time the IV infusion is started.

4. The blood sample will be placed in one 5-ml purple-top tube to be transported with the patient. The tube containing the blood sample should also contain the patient's name along with the date and time the sample was obtained.

5. SYSCOM will be notified whenever any unconscious toxic gas inhalation patient is taken to a facility other than the MIEMSS Department of Hyperbaric Medicine.

Note: Some concern has been expressed regarding the type of tube in which to place the blood sample. The main concern of blood analyzing facilities is that the blood remain uncoagulated. Therefore, if purple-top tubes are not immediately available, any tube (e.g., gray tops) containing an anticoagulant would suffice.

Treatment

Toxic gas inhalation only.

1. Remove patient from toxic environment
2. Obtain vital signs every 5 minutes
3. Administer oxygen, 50–100 percent
4. Initiate cardiac monitoring
5. IV
   (a) For symptomatic or unconscious adult patients, D5W KVO (20–30 ml/hr).
   (b) For pediatric patients, if an IV is indicated, the infusion should be lactated Ringer's solution titrated to a systolic BP of 80 mmHg.
   (c) For adult patients with burns or associated trauma, the IV should be lactated Ringer's solution titrated to a systolic BP of 100 mmHg.
   (d) For pediatric patients with burns, the IV solution shall be lactated Ringer's solution KVO unless medical direction specifies otherwise.
6. MAST as indicated

Note: Patients with respiratory burns should not have an esophageal airway inserted.

Due to the extreme toxicity and cumulative effects of certain by-products of combustion and/or incomplete combustion, any person suspected of toxic gas exposure who refuses treatment shall be advised of the possible consequences and advised against returning to the toxic environment. The necessary signature on the ambulance report form shall be obtained.

SUPPLEMENT 12

Preparing for a Hazardous Materials Accident: The Hospital Perspective

Lawrence Ferazani, Captain, Cambridge Fire Department, Chair, LEPC; Anthony Fucaloro, Executive Director, South Middlesex EMS; Nancy Hays, R.N., Nursing Ambulatory Specialist; and William Schroeder, CHPA Director, Protection Services and Safety, Mount Auburn Hospital

Editor's Note: The standard incident plan for EMS presented elsewhere in this handbook addresses the treatment of patients at the scene. In this supplement, the authors describe the hospital experience and outline the procedures established at this Harvard Medical School teaching hospital in 1994 to increase the haz mat preparedness of the Emergency Department staff. Based on this initial experience, the plan is now under revision. According to William Schroeder, one of the authors and the CHPA Director, Protection Services and Safety, Mount Auburn Hospital, since its inception, the Mount Auburn ED has handled two hazardous materials contamination cases in its special receiving area—the only one of its kind in the state.

INTRODUCTION

In 1984, a chemical manufacturing plant in Bhopal, India, accidentally released over 50 thousand tons of methyl isocyanate into the atmosphere. Methyl isocyanate, one of many toxic and deadly chemicals used to create the pesticide Seven, caused over 8000 deaths and 300,000 injuries.

In the aftermath of the tragedy, U.S. government officials expressed concerns about the possibility of a similar occurrence in the United States. In many communities, more than 100 of the 366 chemicals labeled by the federal government as "extremely hazardous" are found in amounts greater than 10,000 pounds. Many of these chemicals are so dangerous that a few pounds released into the atmosphere have the potential to kill hundreds of people.

Superfund Established

Due to the enormity of this issue, the federal government created the Superfund Amendments and Reauthorization Act of 1986, which includes the Emergency Planning and Community Right to Know Act, known as Title III. The law mandates that each state establish a State Emergency Response Commission (SERC) and each local government, a Local Emergency Planning Committee (LEPC). These entities give state and local governments responsibility for emergency planning, emergency release reporting, and hazardous chemical reporting. It also requires the creation of an emissions inventory.

Cambridge Recognizes a Need

Cambridge, Massachusetts, ranks third on the EPA's list of priority planning areas that have a comparative likelihood of chemical accidents. The ranking is based on the following EPA criteria:

- Population density
- Density of highway and railway transportation routes

- Number of industries in the area
- Number of hazardous material spills in the area over a specified range of time

In the first stages of any hazardous material accidental release, local public safety agencies act independently. Because of this, the city of Cambridge recognized the need to maintain a continuous state of preparedness. Industry, public safety agencies, healthcare organizations, and interested citizens began planning for chemical accidents in order to reduce the risk to the public from toxic chemicals released into the environment.

As a first step, in the mid 1980s, the Cambridge Fire Department developed and staffed its own hazardous materials response team (this team has since been incorporated into the state-run regional response system as part of District 3). The team members are highly trained experts equipped with the latest technology to respond to any hazardous materials release in the community.

Captain Lawrence Ferazani of the Cambridge Fire Department was appointed to chair the Local Emergency Planning Committee (LEPC). He organized the community's response to hazardous materials incidents by creating subcommittees made up of representatives from the city departments, such as the fire department, the public works department, the water department, and law enforcement, as well as representatives from local industry and healthcare organizations. The subcommittees included Assessment, Medical and Health, Law Enforcement, Public Information, Resource Management, Low Level Radiation, Warning Evacuation and Communication, American Red Cross, and University Planning (Harvard and MIT).

Training for an Emergency

Each subcommittee chairperson participated in a training program sponsored by the EPA that qualified them as hazardous materials technicians. Fire fighters and police were already offered first responder training through their training academies. Emergency medical personnel had, thus far, been left out of the training loop.

In an attempt to resolve this problem, Captain Ferazani and Anthony Fucaloro, Executive Director of the South Middlesex Emergency Medical Services, developed a regional program targeting emergency medical personnel throughout Middlesex County. Using the national standard curriculum as a foundation, they developed a training program for both pre-hospital and hospital. The program satisfies the state and federal mandates for EMS personnel and contains pertinent information specifically for these personnel. The program was also sanctioned by the State Emergency Response Commission (SERC) and was designed to comply with local emergency planning committees.

Mount Auburn Hospital Responds

Once program development was complete, training began. Mount Auburn hospital took the lead in developing a response to a hazardous material incident by hosting 12 of the 24 programs offered in the county: training of their entire Emergency and Protection Services Departments, as well as members of its Environmental Services Department and Safety Committee.

The objective of the eight-hour training program was to prepare personnel to respond to incidents that involve hazardous materials, be it chemical, radioactive, or biological. *(See Figure S12-1.)* At the end of the course, each participant had an understanding of the following:

- Hazard recognition
- Effects of individual exposure to hazardous materials
- Decontamination procedures
- Personal protective equipment required to manage patients contaminated with chemicals

An integrated practical exercise followed the course, which included personnel from Emergency Medical Services and the following hospital areas: Emergency, Protection Services, Community Relations, and Decontamination.

Construction of a Special Receiving Area

While training commenced, the hospital commissioned a contractor to build a decontamination room in an area adjacent to the Emergency Department and the ambulance bay. The site includes a "clean area" and a "dirty area." The clean area contains all required supplies, such as protective suits, respirators, and emergency equipment. The dirty area is equipped with heat, electricity, water, suction, oxygen, stretchers with a water containing system, and a shower with a self-contained water disposal system (*see Figure S12-2*).

The Hospital's Protection Services Department Plays a Vital Role

The Mount Auburn Hospital Protection Services Department plays a vital role in the plan due to its extensive involvement with the hospital's Safety Program and the availability of officers 24 hours a day. Officers are trained to do the following:

- Assist and back up Emergency Department staff in the decontamination room
- Obtain appropriate chemical information by in-house material safety data sheets or by the CAMEO database
- Secure the area from vehicle and pedestrian traffic

Introduction
Program Purpose
Goals
Objectives

Historical Perspective
Standards and Regulations
Levels of Training
Myths Surrounding Disasters
Large Disasters vs. Mini-Disasters in the U.S.
Emergency Medical Care Prior to the Last Decade

Emergency Medical Care Today
Disaster Preparedness in the U.S. Today
CBS Video
The Disaster Plan
Preplanning
Levels of Disaster
EMS Response to a Hazardous Material Incident
External Preplanning

Hazard Recognition
Occupancy and Location
Container Shape
Markings and Colors
Placards and Labels
Shipping Papers
Senses
Summary

Exposure to Hazardous Chemicals
Goal
Health Effects
Adverse Effects
Immediate Injuries
Localized Toxic Effects vs. Damage to Skin
Routes of Exposure
Factors Specific to Exposed Patients
Effects Produced by Toxic Compound
Effects on Humans vs. Animals
Exposure Limits

Chemistry of Hazardous Materials
Basic Knowledge
Analytical Activities
Objectives
Common Chemistry Terms
Flammable Liquids
Pressurized Gases
Liquefied Gases
Cryogenics
Flammable Solids
Combustible Metals

Toxic Effects
The Cardiovascular System
Blood and Blood-Forming Organs
The Gastrointestinal System
Urinary Track
The Reproductive System
Response to the Skin
Central Nervous System
Peripheral Nervous System
Toxicity of Specific Hazard Classes

Personal Protective Equipment
Personal Protection and Safety Principles
Personal Protective Equipment
Two Objectives
Levels of Protection
Chemical Protective Clothing
Respiratory Protection

Patient Management and Decontamination
En Route to a Hazardous Material Incident
Appropriate Care
Arrival at the Scene
Things You Should Not Do
Assessment Decontamination and Initial Treatment
External Decontamination
Patient Treatment
Patient Transport
Patient Arrival at the Hospital
Team Member Decontamination

Incident Command Guides and References/ Practical Exercise
Area Haz Mat Commander's Presentation
Material Safety Data Sheet
National Institute for Occupational Safety and Health
DOT Emergency Response Guidebook
Practical Exercise

Figure S12-1 *Mount Auburn Hospital haz mat training program*

- Inform press representatives of appropriate staff contacts
- Assist with the implementation of the hospital's Internal Disaster Plan, if needed
- Notify the infectious waste hauler for haz mat decontamination disposal

According to the plan, after each incident, a critique will take place that includes all participating parties. All incidents are then reviewed by the Mount Auburn Hospital Safety Committee to evaluate the overall coordination effort.

Testing the Plan

On November 17, 1994, a tabletop and functional exercise tested the coordination of agencies and personnel. All designated personnel in the city of Cambridge—fire, police, emergency medical services, public works, traffic, water, city administration, Mount Auburn Hospital, and universities—participated in a simulated hazardous materials incident. All systems were tested with a community critique following. This team approach to responding to hazardous materials proved successful, with Mount Auburn Hospital as the last vital link to the citywide effort.

Needs Identified

The exercise was not without its minor pitfalls. During the critique, some needs were identified, along with corrective actions to be taken. For instance, the team found a need to develop a system to bill the company with the hazardous exposure for the cost of equipment and supplies. They also discovered a need for early notification of the waste hauler, so that contaminated water and equipment could be removed and the area could be readily available for the next incident. Finally, they found a need to separate valuables from clothes and decontaminate valuables for the client, if appropriate.

A Path-Breaking Approach

Title III represents a path-breaking approach to environmental protection. It assumes that the more citizens know about chemical hazards in their communities, the better equipped they will be to make decisions and take action. The Cambridge team proved that the level of safety provided by our communities depends on the level of local involvement by police, fire, industry, and healthcare personnel and that the success of any major incident relies on the preplanning that this comprehensive team provides.

As a result of the initial experience and lessons learned from two contamination cases handled through the Emergency Department, Mount Auburn Hospital is currently revising its haz mat plan to include new experience and information available since 1994. The hospital also plans to provide expanded training opportunities for the new challenges in hazardous materials planning. A draft of the current accident plan is

Figure S12-2 This freestanding decontamination receiving area at Mount Auburn Hospital in Cambridge, Massachusetts, is designed for easy containment and decontamination without risk of exposure to the main Emergency Department. Once assessed and fully decontaminated, a patient can be treated in the main hospital building.

presented here as a tool for hospitals in similar plan revision situations. A final plan is expected to be adopted sometime in late 1997 or early 1998.

4-F-2 HAZARDOUS MATERIALS ACCIDENT PLAN (EXTERNAL)

The execution of a successful Hazardous Materials (Haz Mat) Accident Plan depends on each employee knowing what is expected of him or her. The purpose of this document is to explain in detail to each employee what he or she is to do if involved in dealing with a hazardous materials accident.

Accident Procedure (External)

1. Obtain the following information from CMED, EMTs, and so forth:

- Type and nature of incident
- Caller's telephone number
- Number of patients
- Signs/symptoms being experienced by the patients
- Nature of injuries
- Name of chemical(s) involved
- Extent of patient decontamination in the field
- Estimated time of arrival

2. Contact poison control center, ATSDR (Agency for Toxic Substances and Disease Registry—404-639-0615), or CHEMTREC (Chemical Transportation Emergency Center—800-424-9300) for information regarding definitive care procedures, which should include decontamination methods that need to be performed. Protection services has a CAMEO data base with access to material safety data sheets for many substances. Determine the appropriate personal protective clothing for whatever level described as appropriate for the substance(s) involved, as well as any special treatment. This may be determined by consulting reference guidebooks, data base networks, or telephone hotlines as above. Communications should be kept open with on-site response personnel to obtain as much advance information as possible. Protection services has a CAMEO data base and may be able to get you MSDS info.

3. If incident notification comes from other than usual emergency communication channels, the call should be verified before a hazardous materials response plan is initiated. Ambulance personnel should be advised *not* to bring the patient into the Emergency Department until the patient has been assessed and accepted by the Emergency Department.

4. If a patient contaminated by hazardous materials is brought into the Emergency Department unannounced or not through regular EMS channels, call the fire department to advise them of the situation and for help in setting up a decontamination *area* outside the hospital. In any event, *these patients should be isolated from other patients and assessed and decontaminated as soon as possible.*

5. Unless only a very few patients are involved, you should probably initiate the hospital disaster plan. If you feel comfortable not using the hospital disaster plan, then notify the nursing supervisor and ask her or him to notify the administrator on call: the hospital operator should be instructed to notify Protection Services and Community Relations.

6. Notify the Emergency Department Chairman and the Associate Chairman (Dr. Setnik and Dr. Patrick). Designate the Emergency Department decontamination team; this should ordinarily include the attending physician, a nurse, a clinical assistant, and

someone to act as scribe/ messenger. Make sure the Emergency Department is adequately staffed for the team's absence. Protection Services personnel have been haz mat trained and can assist.

7. The nurse on the team should check the decontamination supplies to make sure they are adequately stocked. The nurse and clinical assistant should prepare the decontamination room, ready the special decontamination stretcher, and lay out the personal protective equipment (PPE) appropriate for the substance(s) involved for three individuals on the "clean" side of the room. No person should wear and use specialized PPE, especially respiratory protective gear, without prior training. To prevent unnecessary contamination, all nonessential and nondisposable equipment should be removed from the decontamination area.

All door knobs, cabinet handles, light switches, and other areas that have contact with hands should be taped, and the floors should be covered with plastic or paper sheeting to prevent contamination. The floor coverings should be securely taped to prevent slippage and the entrance to the room marked with a wide strip of colored tape to indicate a contaminated area. A "clean" member of the staff (usually from Protection Services) should stand on the clean side of the entrance to hand in supplies and receive medical specimens.

8. Since any victim of a hazardous materials incident must be considered to be contaminated until demonstrated otherwise, the route from the emergency entrance to the decontamination area may also become contaminated. All persons along that route should be removed by Protection Services personnel. Ideally, this area should be protected with plastic or paper sheeting. This barrier should be taped securely to the floor/ pavement, and care should be taken while walking on it because plastic can be very slippery when wet.

9. Protection Services personnel should be stationed at the main entrance of the Emergency Department close to the decontamination area to prevent unauthorized entry, to control the entrance of the contaminated patient into the department, and to direct the vehicle transporting the patient to the appropriate area. A reception area should be set up just inside the ambulance bay, where arriving contaminated patients can be screened for adequate decontamination before entering the department.

10. Once the first patient arrives in the area, personnel should not enter the "dirty" area unless properly protected, and no personnel or equipment should leave the area until properly decontaminated!

11. The emergency physician-in-charge or an Emergency Department nurse should meet the ambulance upon arrival and assess the condition of the patients as well as the degree of contamination. Personnel should keep in mind that the actual contamination may be (or become) a life-threatening condition. Triage procedures should also be initiated at this point, if necessary. During initial patient survey and stabilization, contamination reduction should simultaneously be performed. This consists of cutting away or otherwise removing all suspected contaminated clothing, including jewelry and watches, and brushing or wiping off any contamination. Care should be taken to protect any open wounds from contamination. If not severely injured or ill, the patient may be able to remove his or her own contaminated clothing, place it in a double bag, and do his or her own soap and water decontamination. Emergency Department personnel should make every effort to avoid contact with any potentially hazardous substance.

12. Contaminated clothing should be double bagged in plastic bags, sealed, and labeled. If practical, valuables should be separately double bagged in plastic bags, sealed, and labeled. The decontamination team should bring the prepared stretcher to the ambulance, transfer the patient, and take him or her directly to the decontamination area along the predesignated route.

13. Priority should be given to the ABCs (airway, breathing, and circulation) and simultaneous contamination reduction. Once life-threatening matters have been addressed, Emergency Department personnel can then direct attention to thorough decontamination and secondary patient assessment. Identification of hazardous materials involved can be simultaneously performed by other personnel. It is important to remember that appropriate personal protective clothing must be worn until personnel are no longer in danger. Therefore, the sooner the patient becomes decontaminated, the sooner personnel may reduce protective measures.

14. Effective decontamination consists of making the patient as clean as possible. This means that the contamination has been reduced to a level that is no longer a threat to the patient or the responder. The recorder notes on a diagram of the body the areas found by the physician to be contaminated. The basic purpose of decontamination is to reduce external contamination, contain the contamination present, and prevent the further spread of potentially dangerous substances. In other words, remove what you can and contain what you cannot. With a few exceptions, intact skin is more resistant to hazardous materials than injured flesh, mucous membranes, or eyes. Therefore, decontamination should begin at the head of the patient and proceed downward, with initial attention to contaminated eyes and open wounds. Once wounds have

been cleaned, care should be exercised so that the wounds are not recontaminated. This can be aided by covering the wounds with a waterproof dressing. For some chemicals, such as strong alkali, it may be necessary to flush exposed skin and eyes with water or normal saline for an extended period of time.

15. External decontamination should be performed using the least aggressive layer methods. Mechanical or chemical irritation to the skin should be limited to prevent damage to the epidermal layer, which would result in increased permeability. Contaminated areas should be gently washed under a spray of water, with a sponge and a mild soap. Warm, never hot, tap water should be used. Care should be taken so that contaminants are not introduced into open wounds. All run-off from decontamination procedures should be collected for proper disposal.

16. The first priority in the process of decontamination should be contaminated open wounds. These areas allow for rapid absorption of hazardous materials. Wounds should be irrigated with copious amounts of normal saline, and deep debridement and excision should be performed only when particles or pieces of material have been embedded in the tissues. Decontamination of eyes should also have high priority. Gentle irrigation of the eyes should be performed with the stream of normal saline diverted away from the medial canthus so that it does not force material into the lachrymal duct. Contaminated nasal and ear canals should also be gently irrigated with frequent suction to prevent any material being forced deeper into those cavities. Washing with soap and tepid water is usually all that is needed to remove contamination. Hot water, stiff brushes, or vigorous scrubbing should never be used because they cause vasodilatation and abrasion. This increases the chances for absorption of hazardous materials through the skin.

17. The sooner the patient becomes decontaminated, the sooner personnel may reduce protective measures or downgrade the level of protection. Primary and secondary surveys should be completed as conditions allow. In treating patients, personnel should consider the chemical-specific information received from the hazardous materials response resources. In multiple patient situations, proper triage procedures should be implemented. Presenting signs and symptoms should be treated appropriately if and when conditions allow. The sooner a patient has been decontaminated, the sooner he or she can be treated like a "normal" patient. Orders of the designated poison control center and attending physician should be administered.

Invasive procedures, such as IVs or intubation, should be performed only for life-threatening conditions, until decontamination is performed. These procedures may create a direct route for introducing the hazardous material into the patient. The patient should be frequently reassessed because many hazardous materials have latent physiological effects.

18. After the patient has been decontaminated, he or she should be discharged home or admitted to the hospital, depending on the patient's clinical condition. Place a clean piece of plastic on the floor for the patient and staff to use when exiting the clean area. If the patient is not ambulatory, a clean stretcher or wheelchair should be brought to the doorway by an individual who has not been exposed. After the patient is transferred to the clean area, a new physician can perform the physical examination and initiate routine patient management. *Note:* Remember that since exposure to some substances can result in serious delayed effects, sustained observation and monitoring are often required.

19. *Decontamination of Personnel.* Personnel should remove protective clothing in the following sequence:

- Remove tape securing gloves to suit.
- Remove outer gloves, turning them inside out as they are removed.
- Remove suit, turning it inside out and avoiding shaking it.
- Remove plastic shoe cover from one foot and step over "clean line." Remove other shoe cover and put that foot over the line.
- Remove mask. The last staff member removing his or her mask may want to wash all masks with soapy water before removing suit and gloves. Place masks in plastic bag and hand over the clean line, and place in second bag held by another member of the staff. Send for decontamination.
- Remove inner gloves and discard in drum inside dirty area.
- Close off dirty area until level of contamination is established and the area is properly cleaned.
- Personnel should then move to a shower area, remove scrub suit, and place it in a plastic bag.
- Shower and redress in normal working attire.

Note: Double bag clothing and valuables and label appropriately.

20. As soon as possible after each incident, all participating units should send knowledgeable representatives to review the measures that were taken by each unit or agency. The purpose of this review is to examine which activities succeeded and which did not and to evaluate the overall coordination effort.

21. Protection Services will notify Receiving, who will contract to decontaminate the "dirty" side of the haz mat room and remove all contaminated equipment

and supplies. Receiving will notify Materials Management, which will in turn bill the company responsible for the costs incurred.

22. Information needed for an incident might include the following:

- Chemical name of substance involved
- Form of material (solid, liquid, gas)
- Length of exposure
- Routes of exposure
- Possible adverse health effects
- Treatment/antidote therapy
- PPE required
- Decontamination procedures

The importance of finding out as much as possible, as soon as possible, about an unknown substance cannot be emphasized enough. Based on experience, however, NIOSH and EPA recommend that Level B protection is the minimum level to be worn when entering an area containing unknown substances.

However, if the substance in question is suspected to involve the skin as a route of exposure or is otherwise noted to be dangerous by absorption, corrosion, and the like, Level A protection should be worn because it provides additional skin protection.

Summary of Protection Levels

- *Level A* protection should be worn when the highest level of respiratory, skin, eye, and mucous membrane protection is needed. It consists of a fully encapsulating chemical-resistant suit and self-contained breathing apparatus (SCBA).
- *Level B* protection should be selected when the highest level of respiratory protection is needed but a lesser level of skin and eye protection is sufficient. It differs from Level A only in that it provides splash protection by use of chemical-resistant clothing (overalls, long sleeves, jacket, and SCBA).
- *Level C* protection should be selected when the type of airborne substances is known, concentration is measured, criteria for using air-purifying respirators are met, and skin and eye exposures are unlikely. This involves a full facepiece, air-purifying, canister-equipped respirator and chemical-resistant clothing. It provides the same level of skin protection as Level B but a lower level of respiratory protection.
- *Level D* is primarily a work uniform. It should not be worn on any site where respiratory or skin hazards exist. It provides no respiratory protection and minimal skin protection.

Appropriate Dress for the Decontamination Team

- A scrub suit
- Plastic shoe covers
- Disposable CPC with hood and booties built in; tape hood at neck
- Poly vinyl chloride (PVC) gloves taped to sleeves
- Respiratory protection as appropriate
- Multiple layers of surgical gloves, neoprene or disposable nitrile gloves; change whenever torn; tape bottom layer
- Protective eye wear
- A 2-inch-wide piece of masking tape with the team member's name placed on the back of the protective suits—will often assist employee in communicating

SUPPLEMENT 13

Grounding and Bonding Applications for Emergency Responders

Bobby Clark, Hazardous Materials Officer
Commonwealth of Virginia Department of Emergency Services

Editor's Note: The NFPA Hazardous Materials Response Personnel Committee directed that a supplement on grounding and bonding be added to this handbook to help increase the safety level for personnel operating at flammable liquids spills. These personnel need to safely apply these techniques. We are grateful to Bobby Clark for his assistance in preparing this supplement and to Robert Benedetti for his review and advice.

INTRODUCTION

Static electricity is everywhere, and it is definitely present at the scene of a flammable liquids spill; therefore, emergency responders need to be concerned with proper grounding and bonding. Flammable and/or combustible liquids are one of the more common major types of chemical spills that emergency responders are called on to mitigate.

To effectively and safely mitigate an emergency involving flammable products, emergency responders need to know how to properly perform grounding and bonding. Knowing the proper procedure for grounding and bonding is also of utmost importance for monitoring a cleanup contractor or trucking company that may be performing emergency transfer operations, in order to ensure that operations are carried out in a safe and appropriate manner.

Grounding and bonding applications are necessary to effectively control the generation or conduction of static electricity. Static electricity occurs as an electric charge in the body of an insulator (glass, rubber, plastic, etc.) or on the outer surface of a conductive body (insulated metal). It is generated (meaning made free to act) through the expenditure of mechanical work such as occurs when liquids are pumped through pipes or hoselines, agitated, or fall freely through the air. The generation of static electricity cannot be prevented absolutely, because it is present everywhere. For static to be a source of ignition, four conditions must be fulfilled.[1]

1. There must first be an effective means of static generation.
2. There must be a means of accumulating the separate charges and maintaining a suitable difference of electrical potential.
3. There must be a spark discharge of adequate energy.
4. The spark must occur in an ignitable mixture.

Proper grounding and bonding applications must be accomplished before product removal and transfer operations begin. This is necessary for any container that contains flammable or combustible products (flammable/combustible liquids, gases, solids, and

1. Ground Nurse (Damaged or Leaking tank)
   (a) Place grounding rod. Place as far away as possible but within the reach of the cable.
   (b) Test ground resistance. With tester calibrated, test ground resistance. The reading should be 25 ohms or less.
   (c) Place single-point clamp. When placed properly, tanker is grounded.
   (d) Test resistance. Set ohm meter correctly, test connection after making. The reading should be 0 ohms or less.
   (e) Attach alligator clamp to grounding rod. Place low to be in foam.
   (f) Test resistance. Test connection after making. The reading should be 0 ohms or less.
2. Ground Calf (Good tank to which product is to be transferred)
   (a) Place grounding rod. Place as far away as possible but within reach of the cable.
   (b) Test ground resistance. With tester calibrated, test ground resistance. The reading should be 25 ohms or less.
   (c) Place single-point clamp. When placed properly, tanker is grounded.
   (d) Test resistance. Test connection after making. The reading should be 25 ohms or less.
   (e) Attach alligator clamp to grounding rod. Place low so as to be in foam, if foaming is necessary.
   (f) Test resistance. Test connection after making. The reading should be 25 ohms or less.
3. Bond between Nurse and Calf
   (a) Place single-point clamp to Nurse. Make good contact between nurse and clamp.
   (b) Test resistance. Test connection after making. The reading should be 25 ohms or less.
   (c) Place single-point clamp to Calf. Make good contact between calf and clamp.
   (d) Test resistance. Test connection after making. The reading should be 25 ohms or less.
4. Delay before performing any work and bonding of other equipment used.
   (a) After grounding and bonding are in place, there should be a 5-minute delay before any work begins in order to allow for any static charge to be dissipated.
   (b) Any other equipment such as stingers or pumps to be used in transfer operations must also be properly grounded and/or bonded. Nothing should be introduced into a tank until it has been properly bonded and the charge allowed to dissipate.
5. After the transfer has been completed, the grounding and bonding equipment should be the last equipment to be removed. All domes and hoses should be closed or removed before disconnecting the grounding and bonding equipment.

Figure S13-1 *The step-by-step grounding and bonding procedure.*

dusts). This would also be necessary for products that are not normally flammable but may give off flammable gases when contaminated, such as sulfuric acid. Sulfuric acid will give off hydrogen gas when contaminated with certain metals. Proper grounding and bonding, along with other proper control measures, will greatly minimize the hazards of a flash fire or explosion during any incident mitigation operations.

DEFINITIONS

Bonding. The process of connecting various pieces of conductive equipment together to keep them at the same electrical potential, eliminating or minimizing the change of static sparking.

Grounding. A special form of bonding in which conductive equipment is connected to the earth through an "earthing electrode" or ground. This minimizes potential differences between objects and the ground.

Ground Resistance Tester. A device that measures the earth resistance to a ground rod.

Ohmmeter. A device used to measure resistance and to determine continuity of a circuit.

Resistance. The difficulty an electrical current encounters in passing through a material. Resistance is measured with an ohmmeter. In hydraulics, the resistance to water passing through a pipe or hoseline is called friction loss and is measured in pounds lost in pressure over the length of the pipe or hoseline. In electricity, resistance can be measured in terms of voltage drop over a part of the circuit but usually is measured in terms of ohms.

EQUIPMENT

The routine care and inspection of the equipment needed for proper grounding and bonding must be performed regularly. Inspection should include checking for wear and defects in the cable (broken strands, kinks, etc.), that there is a solid connection between the clamp and the cable, that the points of the clamp are in good condition, and that sufficient stiffness remains in the clamp spring.

PROCEDURE

Prior to performing any grounding and bonding procedures, detection and monitoring must be done to determine whether the atmosphere is above the lower explosive limits (LEL). If the atmosphere is above the action level (currently 25 percent of the LEL), then personnel should not be allowed to enter the area until vapor suppression is carried out by the application of the proper type of foam. Detection and monitoring must be continued throughout the course of the incident.

The resistance of the cables to be utilized should be tested prior to use. To test the resistance, connect the ohmmeter cables to each clamp of the grounding or bonding cable. The reading should be 0 ohms. After conducting this test, then proceed with the steps shown here as Figure S13-1 (the same procedure applies for tank trucks, rail cars, or drums).

Reference

1. NFPA 77, *Recommended Practice on Static Electricity*, National Fire Protection Association, Quincy, MA, 1993.

SUPPLEMENT 14

Emergency Response to Incidents Involving Chemical and Biological Warfare Agents

Lt. Col. John Medici, U.S. Army Chemical Corps, retired, Hazardous Materials Officer for Prince William County, Virginia; and Steve Patrick, Hazardous Materials Officer, Virginia Department of Emergency Services.

Editor's Note: There are many similarities between handling a hazardous materials incident and an incident involving chemical and biological agents. The real difference occurs during the identification phase. Keep in mind as you read this supplement that the person(s) responsible for creating the hazard through criminal or terrorist activity has aimed at injury or destruction and does not want you or the public to detect or identify the chemical or biological agent at the scene. This is truly a worst-case scenario.

INTRODUCTION

International terrorism has been a global issue and threat for many years. These events, for the most part, have occurred in other countries. Recently, two terrorist acts in the United States—the World Trade Center and Oklahoma City Federal Building bombings—have heightened awareness of this threat within our borders.

Terrorist acts may be carried out by either groups or individuals but the patterns of terrorism are rapidly changing. Emerging alliances of extremist and radical elements transcend the customary national, political, religious, and ethnic boundaries that formerly marked these activities. The frequency of terrorist attacks fluctuates annually, and, for a while, the number of incidents seemed to decrease. However, even as the number of incidents in a year has dwindled, there has been an unsettling trend toward ever increasing viciousness in the nature of the attacks and the resultant loss of human life and property damage. This recent trend has manifested itself terribly in the United States. Had the desired damage been inflicted on the World Trade Center, the carnage would have been horrendous. It is also not easy to forget the pictures of those killed and injured in Oklahoma City.

Along with the increasing trend toward more spectacular and destructive terrorist acts, an even more disturbing element has emerged. The recent terrorist use of a deadly chemical agent by the extremist group in Japan poses a formidable challenge that has far reaching implications for emergency responders. The use of a military chemical agent in Japan signifies the introduction of weapons of mass destruction into the terrorists' arsenals. The March 1995 nerve agent release in the Tokyo subway resulted in over 5000 casualties. There are reports that many of the most seriously injured were emergency responders who were unaware of the dangers they were facing.

The use of weapons of mass destruction has prompted emergency response agencies worldwide to reevaluate current plans and capabilities. It is essential to expand the scope of knowledge of all emergency responders concerning chemical and biological agents in order to be prepared to operate safely and effectively should the need arise.

In addition to the challenges posed by the possible use of chemical and biological agents by extremists, emergency responders in other countries have found themselves to be targets as part of an individual's or organization's attempt to carry out a terrorist act. Although security issues are beyond the scope of this manual, all emergency responders are advised to consider the ramifications of becoming targets and to exercise extreme caution when reacting to a real or suspected terrorist act.

This supplement is intended as a chemical and biological primer. It integrates technical information regarding chemical and biological agents into existing hazardous materials response incident management, training, operations, and planning principles.

CHEMICAL AND BIOLOGICAL AGENTS: AN OVERVIEW

Chemical and biological agents are classes of hazardous materials that are unique to military arsenals and are usually classified as secret or top secret. As such, the characteristics of these agents are difficult to recognize, identify, and treat and are unfamiliar to most emergency responders. These agents can be lethal in extraordinarily small concentrations and can be released on a target or into the environment by various surreptitious and relatively unsophisticated methods.

At an incident site, acquiring necessary information about these agents may be much more difficult than it is to obtain data about other hazardous materials. This document is a compilation of the unclassified technical information needed to fill that void. This information, once understood and integrated into local jurisdictions' training programs, will provide a foundation upon which an effective response to such exposures can be planned, organized, and implemented.

History of Chemical Agents

Even though there are more than 100 known types of chemical warfare agents, only a small number of these have actually been used in warfare. In fact, World War I represents the only large-scale use of chemical agents. After that war, development of chemical agents continued but major battlefield use did not. Indeed, significant efforts have been underway to ratify banning the use of chemical weapons.

The first chemical warfare agent used in World War I against the Allies by the Germans was *chlorine,* followed later by *phosgene.* Initially, the chemicals used as agents on the battlefield were common industrial chemicals. Chlorine, especially, is still in widespread use. These first agents were indeed true gases when released. Consequently, the term *poison gas* was used to describe them. However, the continued use of the term *gas* is a misnomer. Most common agents in chemical warfare arsenals are actually liquids.

Later in World War I, the Germans introduced the *mustard agents.* The mustard agents caused the majority of the chemical casualties in the war. Prior to World War II, Germany began development of *nerve agents.* Even today these agents are regarded as the most toxic of the chemical warfare agents.

The German development and use of mustard agents, followed by the development of the nerve agents, demonstrated the military value of programs designed to synthesize, test, produce, and stockpile chemicals expressly to be used as weapons. After the war, both the United States and the Soviet Union, building on captured German agent technology, embarked on extensive research and development programs that resulted in the production and stockpiling of thousands of tons of chemical agents and munitions. Other nations also continued research and development programs and acquired chemical weapons.

During the 1960s, 1970s, and 1980s, chemical agents once again emerged as a very real threat. Egyptians used mustard agent in Yemen. In Vietnam, the United States used irritating agents and defoliant chemicals. In the Iran–Iraq war the Iraqis used both mustard gas and nerve agents.

Early in the 1990s, the threat of Iraq's chemical and biological weapons was a major concern during the Gulf War. Just recently, admissions by former Iraqi military officials regarding the possession and readiness of nerve and biological weapons have been reported in the media.

However, the 1995 incident in the Tokyo subway system involving the release of nerve agent sarin by an extremist group is the first time a chemical agent has been used for terrorism in a major metropolitan area. In Japan, a small nerve gas release incident reported in June 1994 killed 7 people. In the second, more widely publicized attack in March 1995, 12 deaths and over 5000 casualties were reported.

The Role of the Emergency Responder

Before emergency response personnel can hope to be effective at the scene of a chemical agent incident, they must be aware of the nature and characteristics of chemical agents. This awareness is essential for self-protection; it also provides the capability to render aid and assistance to those affected.

While not generally considered lethal, a few incidents involving military irritating agents happen every year. In 1992 a CS tear canister was discharged inside a high school in Spostylvania County, Virginia, causing injuries to students as well as responding fire fighters. In 1995, CS from a military training exercise in Caroline County, Virginia, traveled to a state roadway injuring motorists as well as responding fire fighters.

In addition to the use of chemical agents in battle and in deliberate terrorist acts, numerous sites have been identified as containing or are suspected to contain buried chemical agents and munitions. Discovery and remediation activities at these sites have resulted in evacuations as well as extensive excavations. In 1994, residents in the Spring Valley development in Washington, D.C., were evacuated when such a site was discovered.

Awareness Equals Readiness

All emergency responders should recognize the proximity of a potential terrorist target within their community (such as military installations, federal and state offices, etc.), but these should not be considered the only threatened locations. Chemical and biological agents must be produced, packaged, and delivered to the intended place of use. Emergency responders should not be complacent because there are no obvious terrorist targets in their first-due area. The Japanese agent was produced in a chemical plant expressly designed and built to produce agents. The agents were then transported and used first in Masumoto and months later in Tokyo with reported testing along the way in a remote location in Australia. The materials for the bombs that were detonated in New York City and Oklahoma City were collected, stored, and finally fabricated at distant locations and the resulting bombs were transported to the targets along heavily congested roads through densely populated areas.

Consequently, emergency responders should be sensitive to the possibility of discovering a clandestine laboratory that is making something other than designer drugs, a storage locker filled with unusual chemicals, or an unplacarded vehicle containing an unexpected cargo.

Another ominous possibility results from the current availability of chemical agent information from underground publishers, as well as on the computer networks that comprise the growing information superhighway. The potential of a botched experiment with recipes obtained from books or the Internet should not be considered unlikely.

CHEMICAL AGENTS

Today, the most common chemical agents are those chemicals expressly selected and produced because of their ability to cause injury or incapacitation. Chemical warfare agents are generally classified into broad categories based on their intended use.

- Lethal agents
- Incapacitating agents
- Harassing agents

Another more recognizable categorization based on physiologic effects includes nerve agents, blister agents, blood agents, choking agents, and irritating agents.

Nerve Agents

Nerve agents are specific organophosphorus compounds that are considered to be the most dangerous of the chemical warfare agents. Similar physiological effects are produced by carbonates and other organophosphate based pesticides. However, nerve agents are 100–500 times more potent than these other compounds.

There are two major classes of nerve agents. Most chemical agents are commonly designated by one- or two-letter symbols. The first letter represents the type, group, or the developer, and the second letter represents a specific agent within the type or group. Common nerve agents are basically the same compounds originally synthesized in the 1930s by the Germans. Accordingly, the nerve agents are designated GA, GB, GD, and VX. The G stands for German and the A, B, and D signify the specific chemical. The common names for the G-agents sarin, soman, and tabun are from part of the name of the scientist that developed each type. Another class of nerve agents is represented by the letter V. The most common agent in this group is VX, the V standing for venom and the X originating from a series of chemicals originally synthesized to be used as insecticides. VX has no common name.

The common nerve agents are listed in the Table S14-1. Nerve agents are liquids at ambient conditions. They are clear, colorless, and tasteless. The G-agents are reported to have a slightly fruity odor; the V-agents are said to be odorless.

Although GA, GB, and GD are all volatile compounds, GB is the most volatile. All of these agents present a vapor hazard under temperate conditions. VX is oily with little volatility; however, a large surface area or widely dispersed droplets can, especially under high-temperature conditions, present a vapor hazard. All nerve agents penetrate the skin rapidly and well. Inhalation of vapors or aerosols is especially dangerous.

Exposure to these agents causes a disruption of nerve impulse transmissions by reacting with the enzyme acetylcholinesterase. Exposure to even minute quantities may be rapidly fatal.

Symptoms of exposure may occur within minutes or hours, depending on the dose and mode of entry into the body. Symptoms include the following:

- *Eyes.* Pinpoint pupils, blurred and dimming vision, pain in and above the eyes aggravated by bright light
- *Skin.* Excessive sweating and fine tremors of the muscles under the skin
- *Muscles.* Involuntary twitching and contractions of various muscles of the body
- *Respiratory System.* Runny nose and nasal congestion, chest pressure, cough, and difficulty breathing
- *Digestive System.* Excessive salivation, abdominal pain, nausea, vomiting, involuntary urination and defecation
- *Nervous System.* Giddiness, anxiety, difficulty in thinking, difficulty in sleeping, and nightmares

Detection clues for nerve agents are limited because these agents may resemble water or light oil without any characteristic odor.

Large inventories of these materials are usually found only at secure military laboratories or ammunition depots. However, there are a few private laboratories that conduct chemical agent testing for the government in the United States. Awareness of the location of such a facility in the area is essential. Consequently, any incident in or around a known facility should be suspect. Transportation of nerve agents in bulk in the United States has been very limited and such transports are accompanied by members of the U.S. Army Technical Escort Unit. Table S14-2 lists the ID numbers and DOT Hazard classes and other transport information that can alert emergency responders to a potentially dangerous transport-related release in the community.

Clandestine activities that may involve nerve agent production may be evident by the presence of unusual chemicals, laboratory glassware as well as underground "cookbooks," military manuals, or chemical textbooks. Discovery of a clandestine laboratory or storage site containing unusual chemicals in an unexpected or unlikely place may be indicative of an intention to synthesize chemical agents. Chemicals used to synthesize other chemicals are called precursors. The precursors for nerve agents are not generally found in bulk in commercial shipments nor are they usually associated with clandestine drug laboratories. Possible nerve agent precursors are listed in Table S14-3.

Outward Warning Signs. Outward warning signs will generally be the first clue of a release of nerve agent. The most significant sign will be the rapid onset of similar symptoms in a large group of people. Pinpointed pupils (miosis) are the best symptomatic indication of nerve agent use. Because the nerve agents are so lethal, mass fatalities without other signs of trauma may also be present. The following are other outward warning signs of a nerve agent release:

- Explosions that dispense liquids, mists, or gases
- Explosions that seem only to destroy a package or bomb device
- Unscheduled and unusual spray being disseminated
- Abandoned spray devices
- Numerous dead animals, fish, and birds
- Lack of insect life
- Mass casualties without obvious trauma

Table S14-1 Common Nerve Agents

Common Name	NFPA 704 Labeling	Military Abbreviation	PEL/TWA mg/m^3	LD_{50} ($mg\ min/m^3$)
Sarin	411	GB	0.0001	100
Soman	411	GD	none estab.	100
Tabun	421	GA	0.0001	400
V-agent	411	VX	0.00001	1–100

Table S14-2 Nerve Agents

Chemical Agent	UN ID#	DOT Hazard Class	Pkg. Group	Zone
Tabun (GA)	2810	6.1	I	A
Sarin (GB)	2810	6.1	I	B
Soman (GD)	2810	6.1	I	B
V-agent (VX)	2810	6.1	I	A

Table S14-3 Chemical Precursors and Resulting Nerve Agents

Chemical Precursors	Nerve Agent
Ammonium bifluoride	Sarin (GB), soman (GD)
Diethyl ethylphosphonate	Ethyl sarin (GE)
Diethyl N,N-dimethyl phosphoramidate	Tabun (GA)
Diethylphosphite	Sarin, soman
Diisopropylamine	V-agent (VX)
Dimethylamine	Tabun
Dimethyl ethylphosphonate	Ethyl sarin
Dimethyl methylphosphonate	Sarin, soman
Ethylphosphonous dichloride	Ethyl sarin
Ethylphosphonous difluoride	Ethyl sarin, V-agent
Ethylphosphonyl dichloride	Ethyl sarin
Ethylphosphonyl difluoride	Ethyl sarin
Hydrogen fluoride	Sarin, soman
Methylphosphonyl dichloride	Sarin, soman, V-agent
Methylphosphonyl difluoride	Sarin, soman
N,N-Diisopropyl-aminoethanethiol	V-agent
N,N-Diisopropyl-(beta)- aminoethanol	V-agent
N,N-Diisopropyl-(beta)- aminoethyl	V-agent chloride
Phosphorus oxychloride	Tabun
Phosphorus pentachloride	Tabun
Phosphorus trichloride	Tabun, sarin
Pinacolone	Soman
Pinacolyl alcohol	Soman
Potassium bifluoride	Sarin, soman
Potassium cyanide	Tabun
Potassium fluoride	Sarin, soman
Sodium cyanide	Tabun
Sodium fluoride	Sarin, soman
Thionyl chloride	Sarin

- Definite pattern of casualties and common symptoms
- Civilian panic in potential target areas (government buildings, public assemblies, subway system, etc.)

Blister Agents

Blister agents were used against the British at Ypres during World War I. The British called it mustard due to its characteristic smell. The French named it Yperite after the locality where it was first used. The terms *blister* and *vesicant agent,* which are also used, refer to the physiologic effect. The term *mustard agent* is the most commonly used.

Blister agents are heavy oily liquids. In the pure state, they are colorless and nearly odorless, but in the impure state they are dark-colored and have an odor strongly suggesting mustard, onion, or garlic. Blister agents cause severe burns to the skin, eyes, and tissue in the respiratory tract. In addition, if a large area of skin is involved, significant amounts of agent can be absorbed into the bloodstream and cause severe systemic poisoning. These agents have a very high propensity for penetration and easily penetrate layers of clothing before being quickly absorbed through the skin. The common blister agents are listed in Table S14-4, and Table S14-5 lists the U.S. Department of Transportation information for each material.

These agents are extremely toxic, although they are far less lethal than nerve agents. A few drops of mustard on the skin can cause severe injury, and 3 grams absorbed through the skin can be fatal. Symptoms of exposure may not appear for minutes, hours, or days. Symptoms include the following:

- *Eyes.* Exposure time until symptoms appear ½ to 12 hours. Reddening, congestion, tears, burning

Table S14-4 Common Blister Agents

Common Name	NFPA 704 Label Information	Military Abbreviation	PEL/TWA mg/m^3	LD_{50} (mg min/m^3)
Mustard	411	H, HD	0.003	1500
Lewisite	411	L	0.003	1000–1500

Table S14-5 DOT Information on Blister Agents

Chemical Agent	Symbol	UN ID#	DOT Hazard Class	Pkg. Group
Mustard	H	2810	6.1	I
Distilled mustard	HD	2810	6.1	I
Nitrogen mustard	HN	2810	6.1	I
Lewisite	L	2810	6.1	I

and gritty feeling in the eyes. In more severe cases, marked swelling of the eyelids, severe pain and spasm of the eyelids.

- *Skin.* Exposure time until symptoms appear 1 to 12 hours. Initially mild itching only followed by redness, tenderness, and burning pain in the affected area. Later, burns appear, some with large fluid-filled blisters. The blisters appear particularly in the groin and armpit where the skin is warm and moist.
- *Respiratory System.* Exposure time until symptoms appear 2 to 12 hours. Burning sensation in the throat and nose, hoarseness, profusely runny nose, severe cough, severe shortness of breath.
- *Digestive System.* Exposure time until symptoms appear 2 to 3 hours. Abdominal pain, nausea, blood-stained vomiting, and bloody diarrhea.

Detection clues for blister agents are limited. These materials usually are found only at secure military installations, and any incident in or around this type of facility may be suspect. Generally, these materials are not transported except in very small amounts. The presence of unusual chemicals, in unlikely places, underground "cookbooks," military or chemical books, and even a clandestine laboratory may also be clues. The chemicals used to prepare blister agents may be discovered in storage, shipment, or in a clandestine laboratory. The chemical precursors for mustard agent are as follows:

- Thiodiglycol
- Thionyl chloride
- 2-Chloroethanol
- Arsenic trichloride
- Trethanolamine
- Sodium sulfide
- Hydrochloric acid

Outward Warning Signs. Outward warning signs will generally be the first clue of a release of blister agents. Signs may not be evident immediately as would be the case for nerve agents. Blisters take hours to days to form. Complaints of eye and respiratory irritation along with the reports of the characteristic garlic-like odor would be the initial signs. Similar symptoms experienced by a large number of people as well as the following may indicate a blister agent release:

- Explosions that dispense liquids, mists, or gases
- Explosions that seem only to destroy a package or bomb device
- Unscheduled and unusual spray being disseminated
- Abandoned spray devices
- Mass casualties without obvious trauma
- Definite pattern of casualties and common symptoms
- Civilian panic in potential target areas (government buildings, public assemblies, subway system, etc.)

Blood Agents

Blood agents produce casualties by interfering with the blood's ability to transfer oxygen to the cells, which can lead to death by asphyxiation. Signs and symptoms of blood agent poisoning include rapid death if exposed to high concentrations. Small concentrations cause respiratory distress, vomiting, diarrhea, vertigo, and headache. Large numbers of casualties displaying these common symptoms and reports of peach blossom or bitter almond odors indicate a possible blood agent release.

Blood agents are liquids under pressure. The discovery of lecture bottles and gas cylinders is a possible clue to their presence. Most blood agents are derivatives of cyanide compounds. The discovery of packages of cyanide salts and acids that are precursors for blood agents may also be considered clues. Table S14-6 shows the DOT information for these agents, which are common industrial chemicals. Information on these agents should be readily available from most technical reference sources.

Choking Agents

Choking agents produce casualties by severely stressing respiratory system tissues. This distress produces copious fluids, which can result in death by asphyxiation.

Signs and symptoms that choking agents were released include severe irritation of the respiratory tract and eyes, as well as coughing and choking. Reports of

Table S14-6 Blood Agents

Chemical Name	NFPA 704	UN ID #	DOT Hazard Class	DOT ERG
Hydrogen cyanide AC	442	1051	6.1 PG I	117
Cyanogen chloride CK	442	1589	2.3	125

a strong, irritating chemical odor would be characteristic. Most people recognize chlorine, and phosgene has an odor like newly cut hay.

These agents are liquid when stored under pressure. The discovery of lecture bottles or gas cylinders are possible clues to their presence. Table S14-7 shows the DOT information for these agents, which are common industrial chemicals. Information on them should be readily available from most technical reference sources.

Irritating Agents

Irritating agents are also known as riot control agents or tear gas. They cause respiratory distress and copious tearing that incapacitates a victim. These agents are generally nonlethal, but under certain conditions they can act as an asphyxiant.

Another common compound that produces effects similar to tear gas is pepper spray. The active ingredient in pepper spray is capsicum, a natural organic compound extracted from hot peppers. The frequency of incidents involving these agents appears to be on the increase in schools and fast-food restaurants, as "key-chain" personal defense devices have become available at retail stores almost everywhere.

Several manufacturers market these products as either a single agent or a mixture. Some devices contain dyes to visually mark a sprayed assailant. The common irritating agents are listed in Table S14-8.

Outward Warning Signs. Outward warning signs will generally be the first clue of a release of irritating agents. Signs will include casualties complaining of burning and irritation of the eyes and throat. In severe exposures or when direct contact with the liquid occurs, complaints of burning skin as well as abdominal pain may also be present. Exposure to these agents is accompanied by tearing, coughing, choking, difficulty breathing, nausea, and vomiting. Additional signs and symptoms may include the following:

- A characteristic peppery odor in the area of the event
- A characteristic peppery odor on the clothing of persons exposed
- Reports of tear gas–like odor from those exposed
- Identification of tear gas munitions used by either military or police
- Identification of discharged personal protection devices
- Brownish colored stains on objects near the site of the suspected release
- Dye stains near the site of the suspected release

The effects of these agents are temporary, although casualties must be monitored should the irritant trigger a secondary medical problem such as an asthma attack or other respiratory problem. Infants and the elderly will usually exhibit the most severe symptoms and secondary medical problems.

Detection clues for the irritating agents are usually the characteristic odors reported by those exhibiting symptoms and recognition of the dispensing devices. Irritating agents are dispensed from burning or bursting grenades in the form of micropulverized powders. Personal defense devices are low concentrations of agent dispensed in a carrier solution from a small spray device.

Summary

Many common hazardous materials used in industry pose the same threat to emergency responders as the chemicals used and classified by the military as nerve,

Table S14-7 Choking Agent DOT Information

Chemical Name	NFPA 704	UN ID #	DOT Hazard Class	DOT ERG
Chlorine	300 ox	1017	2.3	124
Phosgene	400	1076	2.3	125

Table S14-8 Common Irritating Agents

Name	Military Abbreviation	PEL/TWA	IDLH
Chloropicrin	none	0.1 ppm	4 ppm
MACE™	CN	0.05 ppm	100 mg/m^3
Tear gas	CS	0.05 ppm	2 mg/m^3
Capsicum/pepper spray	none		

blister, blood, and choking agents. Some examples are shown in Table S14-9.

Standard haz mat emergency response equipment and procedures provide adequate protection when dealing with these chemicals. Ample reference materials are readily available from multiple sources regarding these materials, and industrial facility personnel are also a valuable source of information and assistance.

BIOLOGICAL WEAPONS

To provide a more comprehensive technical reference for dealing with weapons of mass destruction, information concerning biological agents has been included in this supplement. Although the use of biological agents by terrorist groups and national extremists has, thankfully, been limited, the prospect of biological terrorism is chilling.

It makes sense to cover these agents concurrently with chemical agents, as the large-scale effects and emergency response considerations for incidents involving both agents are closely related.

Biological warfare agents are living organisms or the materials derived from them (endotoxins or exotoxins) that cause harm to or disease in humans. A biological agent has a latency period of days to weeks between infection and onset of disease, depending on the microorganism. Toxins are an example of very quick-acting biological agents, with death resulting in minutes or hours. Biological agents that cause disease have a longer period from exposure to onset of symptoms. They typically have no characteristic signature because biological agents are usually odorless and tasteless.

Biological agents have not been used in warfare to any great extent. The United States destroyed its offensive stockpile in the late 1960s. Other countries have not necessarily followed suit. There have been scattered reports of alleged use of biological agents by the Japanese during World War II in Asia as well as a suspected accident in the former Soviet Union involving anthrax.

Table S14-9 Common Hazardous Materials Used in Industry with Toxic Effects Resembling Chemical Weapons

Common Chemical	Agent Its Effects Resemble
Organophosphate insecticide	Nerve agent
Dimethyl sulfate (DMS)	Blister agent
Methyl isocyanate (MIC)	Blood agent
Anhydrous ammonia	Choking agent

Biological agents pose a significant threat because their use is even more difficult to recognize than the use of chemical agents. The presence of symptoms may well be confused with a naturally occurring case or outbreak of disease. Many of the initial symptoms may be common to several other types of disease, which further complicates recognition, identification, and treatment.

The ease with which people can travel throughout the world today presents a situation in which an individual can become infected in one part of the world and then carry the infection home before becoming symptomatic. The recent outbreak of the plague in India and the Ebola Virus in Zaire are examples of opportunities for a dangerous disease to spread. Fortunately, the diseases remained confined to the local area. Table S14-10 offers a list of potential biological agents.

The biological agents that produce disease are living microorganisms. Once released into the environment or host, these organisms can mutate and may become even more deadly and resistant to available drugs. Such organisms can be obtained from secretions or tissues from sick or dead individuals and animals, and many of them can be cultured, or grown, relatively

Table S14-10 Possible Biological Agents

Disease	Days/Latency	Fatal*	Other Possible Toxins
Anthrax	1–5	Yes	Enterotoxin B
Tularemia	1–10	Yes	Alpha toxin
Cholera	2–5	Yes	Ricin
Encephalitis	2–5	Yes	Saxitoxin
Plague	1–3	Yes	Tetrodotoxin
Botulism**	2–3	Yes	Tricothene mycotoxin

*The degree of mortality associated with any of these agents is determined by many factors, such as the health status of the individual before infection, when treatment is started, how appropriate the drugs are for the particular agent as well as the variation in individual response to the treatment. Pulmonary anthrax has a mortality rate as high as 99 percent for untreated persons. To be most effective, treatment must begin early with the most appropriate drugs. To be early enough, treatment may have to begin even before symptoms appear. Selection of the most appropriate drugs may be delayed until the causative agent is positively identified. A further complication results from the potential unavailability of the most appropriate drugs because of the large number of casualties.

**Botulism does not produce a disease. The causative agent is the exotoxin produced by the microorganism. Many other microorganisms produce toxins that poison the body. Toxins are especially quick-acting and are extremely difficult to treat effectively once symptoms appear. Both the toxin itself and the organism that produces it can be used to cause casualties.

easily. Controls on biological materials are not as stringent as those for chemical agents, and small quantities can easily be transported undetected. In 1995 the Federal Bureau of Investigation confiscated samples of plague that had been obtained by a member of the Aryan Army.

Figure S14-1 lists the steps that should be included in an effective preplan for both chemical and biological release incidents.

INCIDENT MANAGEMENT

Management of an incident involving chemical and biological warfare agents can be conducted in a manner similar to managing a conventional hazardous materials incident. Unique challenges may be present such as a lack of specific information, mass casualties, multiple fatalities, large-scale crime scene, or a direct attack on public safety facilities or personnel. Incidents of this type will usually necessitate the response of multiple agencies from all levels of government. Aside from the immediate public safety concerns, parallel operations may be underway in the interests of national security and law enforcement. A unified command is necessary to ensure the safety and effectiveness of all response actions.

Under the unified command system, the agency or individual designated as the incident commander should be selected based on preexisting emergency operations plans and specific incident priorities. Agency commanders should work in a unified manner to contribute to the incident plan and integrated operations.

The incident commander should always be guided by the SEE principle.

According to this principle, incident operations should be *safe* (no one gets hurt); *effective* (everyone works towards stated objectives); and *efficient* (all resources are utilized to maximum benefit). Management of the incident is based on three steps.

1. Establishing and updating incident priorities:
   - Life safety
   - Incident stabilization
   - Property and environmental conversation
   - Investigation of cause and origin
2. Continuing to size up the incident:
   - Present situation
   - Predicted behavior
3. Establishing and updating incident action plan:
   - Strategic goals (what needs to be done)
   - Tactical objectives (how will it be done)
   - Task operations (who and when)

Incident Size-Up

Incident size-up is the continual process of determining the types and degree of hazards and the damage that may be caused to life, critical systems, property, and the environment. This process is generally conducted in a rapid fashion early in an incident and is studied in more detail as the incident progresses. The goal is to answer three questions.

1. Coordinate efforts in your community addressing deliberate releases. Include all public safety, health, and law enforcement agencies. Involve and educate public information specialists.
2. Assess the likelihood of a deliberate release and potential vulnerable locations (water treatment plants, transportation systems, public buildings, etc.).
3. Ensure that your plan:
   (a) Requires training on a broad range of incidents, including deliberate releases, discovery of stockpiles, clandestine production facilities, transport vehicles, treatment of contaminated patients, recognition of booby traps and protection of responders against personal attack
   (b) Identifies and practices "Unified" or "Integrated" command operations including communication with all critical agencies
   (c) Includes rapid notification procedures to federal, state, and local authorities

   National Response Center: 1-800-424-8802

   State Emergency Operations Center (number varies by state)

   Federal Bureau of Investigation (number varies by state)

   (d) Includes rapid notification procedures to medical care facilities as well as health care providers in the affected area
   (e) Addresses rapid public warning without causing undue alarm
   (f) Addresses personal protection for non-fire service personnel including law enforcement, EMS, and medical facility staff
   (g) Addresses decontamination and contamination control procedures for mass casualty chemical incidents
   (h) Provides for special security procedures for access to key facilities
   (i) Allows for unified public information briefings
   (j) Highlights personnel and procedures for access control, rumor control, isolation-in-place, and evacuation control
   (k) Provides for communications with nearby sites and facilities that may also be targets of deliberate releases
   (l) Identifies access to advice and procedures concerning tactical operations involving chemical and biological warfare agents:

   CHEMTREC: 1-800-424-9300

   U.S. Public Health Service: 1-800-USA-NDMS

   U.S. Army Operations Center: 1-703-697-0218/0219

   Defense Logistics Agency: 1-800-851-8061

   (m) Provides for securing and treating the incident site as a crime scene

Figure S14-1 *Preplanning for chemical and biological incidents.*

1. What is the present situation?
2. What is the predicted behavior?
3. How has this affected the incident priorities?

There are many ways to conduct an incident size-up. The method generally used in a hazardous materials incident is to attempt to answer the following questions:

1. What is causing the problem?
2. What are the physical properties, health hazards, fire hazards, reactivity hazards, and environmental hazards?
3. What are the container type, release, and impingement area?
4. What are the incident conditions (weather, terrain, time)?
5. What has already been damaged?
   - Life (injuries, fatalities)
   - Systems (utilities, transportation)
   - Property
   - Environment
6. What are the current exposures to life, systems, property, and the environment?
7. What are the estimated type and degree of harm?

Life	*Systems*
severe	severe
moderate	moderate
minor	minor
Environment	*Property*
severe	severe
moderate	moderate
minor	minor

Incident Action Plan

Developing an incident action plan is based on local, state, and federal response plans in conjunction with available resources. The plan should define goals and objectives to achieve a favorable outcome. Developing and implementing the plan is based on three principles: strategy, tactics, and task operations.

Strategy. Determine the response objectives. Ask, "What needs to be done?" Consider two basic principles when using this approach: that you cannot influence events that have already happened, and that the earlier the event sequence can be interrupted the more acceptable the loss. Estimate exposures that can be saved. Focus on changing the actions of the stressors, container and/or the material.

Tactics. Determine response options. Ask, "How will it be done?" Evaluate potential response options and estimate how each option will affect the outcome. Prioritize the response options based on their effects on the outcome.

Task Operations. Select response options. Ask, "Who will do it and when?" Determine resources required for each option. Inventory available resources and determine how to obtain the resources. Select response options consistent with available resources and the time factor to have them deployed and operational.

As the action plan is developed and deployed, provide unified command and control of all emergency operations. Ensure the incident is run safely, effectively, and efficiently to achieve a favorable outcome. Figure S14-2 offers a list of considerations for the incident commander to keep in mind in case a chemical or biological exposure incident is suspected.

Incident Considerations for Chemical Incidents

Nerve Agents. Detection of nerve agents for first responders requires individuals to be acutely alert for signs, symptoms, detection clues, and outward warning signs. This is the most practical means for first responders to identify a potential chemical agent release. Various devices for detection are available, including colorimetric tubes, the "Improved Chemical Agent Monitor-Detector" (ICAM-D), the M18A2 Chemical Agent Detector Kit, U.S. Army M 256A1 Chemical Agent Detector Kit, and various detection papers such as U.S. Army M8 and M9 and enzyme tickets.

Treat any suspicious incident as an unknown. Employ the highest level of personal protection available. The primary objective must be to protect yourself. The following guide should be kept available for quick reference.

Nerve Agent Response Guide

North American ERG Guide #:
153—Physical State: Liquid

UN ID#: 2810—Poisonous Liquid, N.O.S.

GA, GB, GD, VX—Inhalation Hazard Zone A

Personal protection—Hot Zone: SCBA with Level A protection. Compatible materials for chemical-protective clothing, gloves, and overboots include butyl rubber and various trade name materials.

Decontamination: Chemical-protective clothing and equipment should be decontaminated using 5 percent (household) bleach, then washed with soapy water. Plan on using at least one gallon of bleach per suit. Skin can be decontaminated with 0.5 percent bleach solution (a 10:1 dilution).

1. Be alert for outward warning signs.
2. Be alert for detection clues.
3. Be alert for booby traps and explosive devices.
4. Resist rushing in; approach incident from upwind; stay clear of all spills, vapors, fumes, and smoke. Be extremely mindful of enclosed or confined spaces.
5. Implement the Incident Command System:
   - Activate your emergency operations plan and call for resources.
   - Notify state and federal agencies.
   - Anticipate unified command operations.
6. Establish clear incident priorities.
7. Conduct incident size-up.
8. Establish incident action plan.
9. Implement protective actions:
   - Isolate the immediate area, 1500 feet in all directions.
   - Establish decontamination operations.
   - Evacuate the immediate area.
   - Protect people downwind.
   - Consider in-place protection.
10. Remember these considerations for nerve and blister agents (see the Guides in this supplement).
11. Establish strict site control.
12. Ensure very early notification of medical agencies and establish triage operations.
13. Monitor the progress of meeting incident priorities.
14. Continuously conduct incident size-up and update your plan as needed.
15. Anticipate the implications of clean-up and disposal of contaminated materials:
   - Expect a mass fatality situation to result from a chemical agent incident. Unique problems will be confronted when planning and conducting mortuary related activities. Postmortem examination, identification, and preparation for burial will be complicated by the presence of contamination.
   - The insidious nature of nerve and blister agents necessitates the consideration of disposing of all contaminated protective equipment used during the response. The difficulty in decontaminating suits, gloves, and footwear is such that residual contamination may result in off-gassing that can cause injury long after the incident is resolved. A decision must be made immediately regarding disposal so that replacement actions can be initiated quickly.
   - The extent and level of decontamination that may be required will be beyond the capabilities of even the most well-equipped haz mat team. Specialized federal teams from EPA, FEMA, Public Health Service, and the Department of Defense with their equipment and materials will most probably be required to assist.

Figure S14-2 *Response considerations for chemical agents.*

Blister Agents. Detection of blister agents for first responders requires individuals to be acutely alert for signs, symptoms, detection clues, and outward warning signs. This is the most practical means for first responders to identify a potential chemical agent release.

Various devices for detection are available, including colorimetric tubes, the "Improved Chemical Agent Monitor-Detector" (ICAM-D), the M18A2 Chemical Agent Detector Kit, U.S. Army M256A1 Chemical Agent Detector Kit, and various detection papers such as U.S. Army M8. The following guide should be kept available for quick reference.

Blister Agent Response Guide

North American ERG Guide #:
153—Physical State: Liquid

UN ID#: 2810—Poisonous Liquids, N.O.S.

H, HD, L—Inhalation Hazard Zone A

Personal protection—Hot Zone: SCBA with Level A protection. Compatible materials for chemical-protective clothing, gloves and overboots include butyl rubber and various trade name materials.

Decontamination: Chemical-protective clothing and equipment should be decontaminated using 5 percent (household) bleach, then washed with soapy water. Plan on using at least one gallon of bleach per suit. Skin can be decontaminated with 0.5 percent bleach solution (a 10:1 dilution).

Note: Decontamination and compatible materials listed are intended only as a guide. Additional research for the specific material and situation will be necessary.

Irritant Agents. Detection of this agent with most commonly used Haz Mat team air monitoring devices is virtually impossible. Identification of irritating agents must be done with a combination of recognition of the presenting outward warning signs and detection clues. The following guide should be kept available for quick reference.

Irritant Agent Response Guide

North American ERG GUIDE #:
159—Physical State: Liquid or powdery solid

UN ID#: 1700

CN, CS, MACE™, Pepper Spray

Personal Protection—Hot Zone: SCBA; cover exposed skin by wearing gloves, rolling down sleeves; coveralls such as Saran Coated Tyvek™ will keep turnout gear from becoming contaminated. Air filtering respirators are effective as long as the material has been identified and an IDLH atmosphere is not present.

Decontamination: Brush powder off clothing and skin. Wash with cool water and soap.

Response Considerations for Biological Incidents

A biological agent release, unless identified as such at the time of release by the person or group involved, will evidence itself only as a large number of people begin to exhibit symptoms of a disease not normally seen in the area. The nature of the biological agent may leave one or more areas contaminated with organisms or toxin. However, the people infected will probably appear across a large geographic area as they disperse and begin to seek treatment at emergency rooms, at urgent care centers, or from private physicians.

The key to dealing with a biological incident is to identify the event. When an event is identified as a biological incident, it is imperative to take steps to limit the spread of the disease by attempting to control the movement of persons that may have been exposed. Both strict site control and quarantine of suspected exposures is essential. Site control will limit the spread of the material and contamination. Quarantine of possible exposures will limit the spread of a disease that may be communicable.

Imposing quarantine requires action by a state health commissioner or designee. Notifying health officials as soon as a biological incident is suspected is critical. Quarantine must be imposed if the disease produced by a biological agent is communicable. Generally, transporting a few exposed persons away from the scene for treatment may be reasonable. The facility to which casualties are transported must be alerted and the facility should be capable of isolating the patients when they arrive. When large numbers of exposures are involved, it may be both more useful as well as necessary to impose quarantine at or near the incident site to begin treatment.

When a biological agent incident is suspected, all exposed persons should be considered to be contagious and treated as such until competent medical authority can evaluate the situation and circumstances and provide specific information and guidance. The medical authority may advise prophylactic treatment for any person, including emergency responders, involved in activities at or near the incident site.

Traditionally, non-disaster haz mat operations have focused on providing a "clean" patient to the medical care provider. An infected person may be contagious. This prospect results in the potential for spreading disease. Be aware of the fact that decontamination as it applies to chemical exposure may not be equally effective for biological agent casualties.

REFERENCES

Note: All documents used in preparation of this supplement are unclassified.

1. *CDC Recommendations for Civilian Communities Near Chemical Weapon Depots: Guidelines for Medical Preparedness,* Federal Register, June 27, 1995, Department of Health and Human Services, Centers for Disease Control and Prevention.
2. *Hazard Communication; Final Rule - 29 CFR Part 1910, et al.,* Federal Register, February 9, 1994, Department of Labor, Occupational Safety and Health Administration.
3. *Planning Guidance for the Chemical Stockpile Emergency Preparedness Program,* 1992, Federal Emergency Management Agency and the Department of the Army.
4. *Chemical/Biological Incident Handbook, June 1995,* The Director of Central Intelligence, Interagency Intelligence Committee on Terrorism, Community Counterterrorism Board.
5. *Chemical Warfare, A Family Defense Manual,* 1990, Ilan Yeshua, Center for Education Technology, Israel.
6. *Emergency Care and Transportation of the Sick and Injured, fifth edition,* 1993, American Academy of Orthopaedic Surgeons.
7. *Emergency Room Procedures in Chemical Hazard Emergencies,* U.S. Department of Health and Human Services, CDC, Public Health Service.
8. *Commonwealth of Virginia Emergency Operations Plan,* Virginia Department of Emergency Services.
9. *Hazardous Materials Incident Management,* course manual, 1995, Virginia Department of Emergency Services.
10. *Guidelines for the Cleanup of Clandestine Drug Laboratories,* March 1990, Joint Federal Task Force DEA, EPA and USCG.
11. *USAMRICD Technical Memorandums 90-1, 90-2, 90-3,* 1990, U.S. Army Medical Research Institute of Chemical Defense, Aberdeen Proving Ground, Maryland.
12. *"Draft" report on Chemical Warfare Agents,* 1995, Jack Sawicki, Geomet Technologies, Inc.
13. *Material safety data sheets for GA, GB, VX, GD, CS, Lewisite, and HD,* prepared by U.S. Army Edgewood Research, Development and Engineering Center.
14. *Responding to the Consequences of Chemical and Biological Terrorism,* July 1995, Workshop presented by the U.S. Public Health Service, Office of Emergency Preparedness, Rockville, Maryland.
15. *Emergency Response Guidebook,* 1996, U.S. Department of Transportation, Washington, D.C.
16. *The Poor Man's James Bond,* 1972, Kurt Saxon.
17. *Disruptive Terrorism,* 1984, Victor Santoro.
18. *Silent Death,* 1989, Uncle Fester.
19. *Medicine Chest Explosives,* 1995, Don McLean.
20. *Patterns of Global Terrorism,* 1994, U.S. Department of State Publication 10239, Office of the Secretary of State.
21. *Terrorism in the United States,* 1994, Terrorist Research and Analytical Center, National Security Division.
22. *The Federal Response Plan,* 1992, For Public Law 93-288, as amended, Federal Emergency Management Agency.

DEFINITIONS

Acetylcholinesterase—An enzyme that hydrolyzes the neurotransmitter acetylcholine. The action of this enzyme is inhibited by nerve agents.

Aerosol—Fine liquid or solid particles suspended in air, for example, fog or smoke.

Antibiotic—A substance that inhibits the growth of or kills microorganisms.

Antisera—The liquid part of blood containing antibodies.

Atropine—A medication used as an antidote for nerve agents.

Bacteria—Single-celled organisms that multiply by cell division and that can cause disease in humans, plants, or animals.

BDO—battle dress overgarment—Multipiece suit used by the military for protection against chemical warfare agents.

Biochemicals—The chemicals that make up or are produced by living things.

Biological warfare—The intentional use of biological agents as weapons to kill or injure humans, animals, or plants, or to damage equipment.

Biological warfare agents—Living organisms or the materials derived from them that cause harm to or disease in humans, animals, or plants, or cause deterioration of material. Biological agents may be used as liquid droplets, aerosols, or dry powders.

Bioregulators—Biochemicals that regulate bodily functions. Bioregulators that are produced by the body are termed "endogenous." Some of these same bioregulators can be chemically synthesized.

Blister agents—Substances that cause blistering of the skin. Exposure is through liquid or vapor contact with any exposed skin (eyes, skin, lungs). For example, mustard gas.

Blood agents—Substances that injure a person by interfering with cell respiration (the exchange of oxygen and carbon dioxide between blood and tissues).

Casualty (toxic) agents—Substances that produce incapacitation, serious injury, or death and include the choking, blister, nerve, and blood agents.

Causative agent—The organism or toxin that is responsible for causing a specific disease or harmful effect.

Chemical agent—A chemical substance that is intended for use in military operations to kill, seriously injure, or incapacitate people through its physiological effects. Excluded from consideration are riot control agents and smoke and flame materials. The agent may appear as a vapor, aerosol, or liquid; it can be either a casualty/toxic agent or an incapacitating agent.

Choking agents—Substances that cause physical injury to the lungs. Exposure is through inhalation. In extreme cases, membranes swell and lungs become filled with liquid. Death results from lack of oxygen; hence the victim is "choked."

CNS—Pertaining to the central nervous system.

CNS depressants—Compounds that have the predominant effect of depressing or blocking the activity of the central nervous system. The primary mental effects include the disruption of the ability to think, sedation, and lack of motivation.

CNS stimulants—Compounds that have the predominant effect of flooding the brain with too much information. The primary mental effect is loss of concentration, causing indecisiveness and an inability to act in a sustained, purposeful manner.

Contagious—Capable of being transmitted from one person to another.

Culture—A population of microorganisms grown in a medium.

Cutaneous—Pertaining to the skin.

CWA—chemical warfare agents—One of three types of nonconventional warfare (see N.B.C).

Decontamination—The process of making any person, object, or area safe by absorbing, destroying, neutralizing, making harmless, or removing the hazardous material.

Fungi—Any group of plants mainly characterized by the absence of chlorophyll, the green-colored compound found in other plants. Fungi range from microscopic single-celled plants (such as mold and mildews) to large plants (such as mushrooms).

G-series nerve agents—Chemical agents of moderate to high toxicity developed in the 1930s. Examples are tabun (GA), sarin (GB), and soman (GD).

Host—An animal or plant that harbors or nourishes another organism.

IDLH—Concentrations immediately dangerous to life and health.

Incapacitating agents—Substances that produce temporary physiological and/or mental effects via action on the central nervous system. Effects may persist for hours or days, but victims usually do not require medical treatment. However, such treatment does speed recovery.

Industrial agents—Chemicals developed or manufactured for use in industrial operations or research by industry, government, or academia. These chemicals are not primarily manufactured for the specific purpose of producing human casualties or rendering equipment, facilities, or areas dangerous for use by man. Hydrogen cyanide, cyanogen chloride, phosgene, chloropicrin and many herbicides and pesticides are industrial chemicals that also can be chemical agents.

Infectious agents—Biological agents capable of reproducing in an infected host.

Infectivity— (1) The ability of an organism to spread. (2) The number of organisms required to cause an infection to secondary hosts. (3) The capability of an organism to spread out from the site of infection and cause disease in the host organism. Infectivity also can be viewed as the number of organisms required to cause an infection.

Level A protection—The level of protective equipment in situations where the hazardous material is considered acutely vapor toxic to the skin or hazards are unknown. Full encapsulation, airtight chemical suit with SCBA or SABA.

Level B protection—The level of protective equipment in situations where the environment is not considered acutely vapor toxic to skin but may cause respiratory effects. Chemical splash suit or full coverage non-airtight chemical suit with SCBA or SABA.

Level C protection—The level of protective equipment required to prevent respiratory exposure but not to exclude possible skin contact. Chemical splash suit with cartridge respirator.

Level D protection—The level of protective equipment required when the atmosphere contains no known hazard, when splashes, immersions, inhalation, or contact with hazardous levels of any chemical is precluded. Work uniform such as coveralls, boots, leather gloves, and hard hat.

Liquid agent—A chemical agent that appears to be an oily film or droplets. The color ranges from clear to brownish amber.

Mycotoxin—A toxin produced by fungi.

Microorganism—Any organism, such as bacteria, viruses, and some fungi, that can be seen only with a microscope.

Mustard (vesicants) agents—See Casualty agents.

N.B.C. nuclear, biological, and chemical—the three forms of nonconventional warfare.

Nerve agents—Substances that interfere with the central nervous system. Exposure is primarily through contact with the liquid (skin and eyes) and secondarily through inhalation of the vapor. Three distinct symptoms associated with nerve agents are pinpoint pupils, an extreme headache, and severe tightness in the chest. (See also Casualty agents.)

Nonpersistent agent—An agent that upon release loses its ability to cause casualties after 10 to 15 minutes. It has a high evaporation rate and is lighter than air and will disperse rapidly. It is considered to be a short-term hazard. However, in small unventilated areas, the agent will be more persistent.

Organism—Any individual living thing, whether animal or plant.

Organophosphorus compound—A compound, containing the elements phosphorus and carbon, whose physiological effects include inhibitation of acetylcholinesterase. Many pesticides (malathion and parathion) and virtually all nerve agents are organophosphorus compounds.

Parasite—Any organism that lives in or on another organism without providing benefit in return.

Pathogen—Any organism (usually living) capable of producing serious disease or death, such as bacteria, fungi, and viruses.

Pathogenic agents—Biological agents capable of causing serious diseases.

PEL—Permissible exposure limit. An occupational health term used to describe exposure limits for employees. Usually described in time weighted averages (TWA) or short-term exposure limits (STEL).

Percutaneous agent—Substance that is able to be absorbed through the skin.

Persistent agent—An agent that upon release retains its casualty-producing effects for an extended period of time, usually anywhere from 30 minutes to several days. A persistent agent usually has a low evaporation rate and its vapor is heavier than air. Therefore, its vapor cloud tends to hug the ground. It's considered to be a long-term hazard. Although inhalation hazards are still a concern, extreme caution should be taken to avoid skin contact as well.

Precursor—A chemical substance required for the manufacture of chemical agent.

SABA— Supplied air breathing apparatus.

SCBA—Self-contained breathing apparatus.

Spore—A reproductive form some microorganisms can take to become resistant to environmental conditions, such as extreme heat or cold, while in a "resting phase."

Tear agents—Substances that produce irritating or disabling effects that rapidly disappear within minutes after exposure.

Terrorism—The unlawful use of force or violence against people or property to intimidate or coerce a government, the civilian population, or any segment thereof, in furtherance of political or social objectives. Domestic terrorism involves groups or individuals whose terrorist activities are directed at elements of the U.S. government or population without foreign direction. International terrorism involves terrorist activity committed by groups or individuals who are foreign-based and/or directed by countries or groups outside the United States or whose activity transcends national boundaries.

Toxicity—A measure of the harmful effect produced by a given amount of toxin on a living organism. The relative toxicity of an agent can be expressed in milligrams of toxin needed per kilogram of body weight to kill experimental animals.

Triage—A sorting technique of establishing rescue, decontamination, treatment, and transportation priorities in any event where the number of casualties overwhelm the resources of the emergency response organizations.

V-series nerve agents—Chemical agents of the moderate to high toxicity developed in the 1950s. They are generally persistent.

Vaccine—A preparation of killed or weakened microorganism products used to artificially induce immunity against a disease.

Vapor agent—A gaseous form of a chemical agent. If heavier than air, the cloud will be close to the ground; if lighter than air, the cloud will rise and disperse more quickly.

Virus—An infectious microorganism that exists as a particle rather than as a complete cell. Particle sizes range from 200 to 400 nanometers (one-billionth of a meter). Viruses are not capable of reproducing outside of a host cell.

Volatility—A measure of how readily a substance will vaporize.

Vomiting agents—Substances that produce nausea and vomiting effects; can also cause coughing, sneezing, pain in the nose and throat, nasal discharge, and tears.

Index

-Q-

-R-

NFPA 473

Standard for Competencies for EMS Personnel Responding to Hazardous Materials Incidents

1997 Edition

Reference: Chapters 2 and 3, F-3 (New)
TIA 97-1 (NFPA 473)

Pursuant to Section 5 of the NFPA Regulations Governing Committee Projects, the National Fire Protection Association has issued the following Tentative Interim Amendment to NFPA 473, *Standard for Competencies for EMS Personnel Responding to Hazardous Materials Incidents,* 1997 edition. The TIA was processed by the Hazardous Materials Response Personnel Committee, and was issued by the Standards Council on July 16, 1998, with an effective date of August 5, 1998.

A Tentative Interim Amendment is tentative because it has not been processed through the entire standards-making procedures. It is interim because it is effective only between editions of the standard. A TIA automatically becomes a proposal of the proponent for the next edition of the standard; as such, it then is subject to all of the procedures of the standards-making process.

1. Add the following new paragraphs to read:

2-2.3* Given a description of a typical community, the Level I responder shall identify at least four types of locations that could become targets for criminal or terrorist activity using hazardous materials.

A-2-2.3 The following are some examples of potential criminal or terrorist targets:

(a) Public assembly
(b) Public buildings
(c) Mass transit systems
(d) Places with high economic impact
(e) Telecommunications facilities
(f) Places with historical or symbolic significance
(g) Military installations
(h) Airports
(i) Industrial facilities

2-2.4* Given an emergency scenario involving potential criminal or terrorist activity, the Level I responder shall describe the difference between a chemical and a biological incident.

A-2-2.4 A chemical incident is characterized by a rapid onset of medical symptoms (minutes to hours) and can have observed signatures such as colored residue, dead foliage, pungent odor, and dead insect and animal life.

With biological incidents, the onset of symptoms usually requires days to weeks and there are typically no characteristic signatures because biological agents are usually odorless and colorless. The area affected can be greater due to the migration of infected individuals because of the delayed onset of symptoms. An infected person might transmit the disease to another person.

2-2.5* Given an emergency hazardous materials scenario, the Level I responder shall identify at least four indicators of possible criminal or terrorist activity involving chemical agents.

A-2-2.5 The following are some examples of indicators of possible criminal or terrorist activity involving chemical agents:

(a) The presence of hazardous materials or laboratory equipment that is not relevant to the occupancy.

(b) Intentional release of hazardous materials.

(c) Unexplained patterns of sudden onset of similar, nontraumatic illnesses or deaths. The pattern might be geographic, by employer, or associated with agent dissemination methods.

(d) Unexplained odors or tastes that are out of character with the surroundings.

(e) Multiple individuals exhibiting unexplained signs of skin, eye, or airway irritation.

(f) Unexplained bomb/munitions-like material, especially if it contains a liquid.

(g) Unexplained vapor clouds, mists, and plumes.

(h) Multiple individuals exhibiting unexplained health problems such as nausea, vomiting, twitching, tightness in chest, sweating, pin-point pupils (miosis), runny nose (rhinorrhea), disorientation, difficulty breathing, convulsions, or death.

(i) Trees, shrubs, bushes, food crops, and/or lawns that are dead, discolored, abnormal in appearance, or withered. (No current drought or not just a patch of dead weeds.)

(j) Surfaces exhibiting oily droplets/films. Unexplained oily film on water surfaces.

(k) An abnormal number of sick or dead birds, animals, and/or fish.

(l) Unusual security, locks, bars on windows, covered windows, and barbed wire.

2-2.6* Given an emergency hazardous materials scenario, the Level I responder shall identify four indicators of possible criminal or terrorist activity involving biological agents.

A-2-2.6 The following are some examples of indicators of possible criminal or terrorist activity involving biological agents:

(a) Unusual number of sick or dying people or animals. Any number of symptoms might occur. The time required before symptoms are observed is dependent on the agent used, but usually requires days to weeks.

(b) Health care facilities reporting multiple casualties with similar signs or symptoms.

(c) Unscheduled or unusual spray being disseminated, especially if outdoors during period of darkness.

(d) Abandoned spray devices. Devices will have no distinct odors.

2-4.4*Given an emergency hazardous materials scenario, the Level I responder shall identify four specific actions necessary when an incident is suspected to involve criminal or terrorist activity.

A-2-4.4 The following are some examples of actions required to be taken:

(a) Take the appropriate actions to protect yourself and other responders.

(b) Communicate the suspicion during the notification process.

(c) Isolate potentially exposed people.

(d) Document the initial observation.

(e) Attempt to preserve evidence while performing operational duties.

(f) Be alert for booby traps and/or explosive devices.

(g) Establish control zones and access control points.

2-4.5 Given either a facility or transportation scenario of hazardous materials, with or without criminal or terrorist activities, the Level I EMS/HM responder shall identify the appropriate initial notifications to be made and how to make them, consistent with the local emergency response plan or the organization's standard operating procedures.

2-4.6 Given an incident involving the suspicion of a biological warfare agent, the Level I responder shall identify each of the following:

(a) The correct body substance isolation procedures to be followed.

(b) The proper decontamination procedures in accordance with their standard operating procedures or guidelines.

(c)* The necessary post-exposure reporting.

A-2-4.6(c) This is important to facilitate post-exposure prophylaxis when available.

3-2.3 Given an emergency scenario involving potential criminal or terrorist activity, the Level II responder shall identify the basic tools for identification of the substance, detection devices appropriate to the substance, and where these detection devices are available locally.

3-2.4 Given an emergency scenario involving potential criminal or terrorist activity, the Level II responder shall describe procedures, such as those listed in the local emergency response plan or the organization's standard operating procedures, to preserve evidence at hazardous materials incidents involving suspected criminal or terrorist acts.

2. Revise paragraph 2-4.2 to read as follows:

2-4.2 Given a patient from a hazardous materials incident, the Level I responder shall provide patient care consistent with the planned response and the organization's standard operating procedures. The Level I responder shall be able to:

(a) Describe how chemical contamination alters the assessment and care of the hazardous materials patient

(b) List the common signs and symptoms and describe the EMS treatment protocols for exposure to the following:

(1) Corrosives (e.g., acid, alkali)
(2) Pesticides (e.g., organophosphates, carbamates)
(3) Chemical asphyxiants (e.g., cyanide, carbon monoxide)
(4) Hydrocarbon solvents (e.g., xylene, methylene chloride)
(5) Nerve agents (e.g., tabun, sarin, soman, V agent)
(6) Vesicants (blister agents, e.g., mustard, distilled mustard)
(7) Blood agents (e.g., hydrogen cyanide, cyanogen chloride)
(8) Choking agents (pulmonary agents, e.g., ammonia, chlorine, diphosgene, phosgene)
(9) Irritants (riot control agents, e.g., CS (orthochorobenzalmalononitrile), CN (chloroacetophone), CR (dibenzoxazcpine), MACE (phenylchloromethylketone)
(10) Biological agents and toxins (e.g., anthrax, mycotoxin, plague, tularemia)
(11) Incapacitating agents (e.g., BZ, LSD)

(c) Identify the potential risk for patients exposed to hazardous materials from the use of invasive medical procedures.

(d) Demonstrate the following EMS functions within the incident management system during incidents involving multiple patients exposed to hazardous materials:

(1) EMS control
(2) Triage
(3) Treatment
(4) Disposition and transportation

3. Add a new F-3 item to read as follows:

F-3 The following references can be useful regarding criminal or terrorist activities.

Chemical Casualty Care Office: *Medical Management of Chemical Casualties Handbook*, 2nd Edition, Medical Research Institute of Chemical Defense, Aberdeen Proving Ground, MD 21010, Sept, 1995 also available @ http://www.nbc-med.org/

U.S. Army Medical Research Institute of Infectious Diseases: *Medical Management of Biological Casualties*, 2nd Edition, Fort Detrick, Frederick MD, Aug. 1996 also available @ http://www.nbc-med.org/

Sidell, Frederick R.: *Management of Chemical Warfare Agent Casualties: A Handbook for Emergency Medical Services*, 1995. HB Publishing P.O. Box 902, Bel Air, MD, 21014.

Carder, Thomas A.: *Handling of Radiation Accident Patients by Paramedical and Hospital Personnel.* CRC Press Inc., Boca Raton, FL

National Fire Academy: Emergency Response to Terrorism, Self-Study Course, 1997 also available at http://www.usfa.fema.gov/nfa/tr_ertss.htm

US Army Chemical and Biological Defense Command